Letts

Revise AS

Biology

John Parker

Contents

Chapter 5 Transport

Chapter 6 The genetic code

Chapter 7 Continuity of life

Chapter 8 Energy and ecosystems

Chapter 9 Human health and disease

Specification lists

AQA A Biology

MODULE	SPECIFICATION TOPIC	CHAPTER REFERENCE	STUDIED IN CLASS	REVISED	PRACTICE QUESTIONS
Module 1 (M1)	*Biological molecules*	1.1, 1.2, 1.3, 1.4			
	Biochemical tests	1.5			
	Microscopy	2.2			
	Cell ultrastructure	2.1			
	Cell fractionation	2.2			
	Transport across cell membranes	4.1, 4.2			
	Enzymes	3.1			
	Inhibitors	3.2			
	Tissues and organs	2.3			
	Heart and circulation	5.3, 5.4			
	Effects of exercise	9.1			
Module 2 (M2)	*Enzyme applications*	3.4			
	Cell division	6.2			
	DNA	6.1, 6.2			
	Protein synthesis	6.1			
	Gene technology	6.3			
	Immunology	9.3			
	Electrophoresis	6.3			
	Genetic fingerprinting	6.3			
	Isolating genes	6.3			
	Ethical issues	6.4			
	Adaptations to environment	4.3, 5.6			
	Commercial crops	8.2			
	Fertilisers and pesticides	8.2			

Examination analysis

The specification comprises three compulsory modules. In modular tests 1 and 2, all questions are compulsory; they consist of structured questions and questions requiring extended answers.

Module 1	1 hour 30 minutes examination	35%
Module 2	1 hour 30 minutes examination	35%
Module 3	Centre-assessed coursework	30%

Note: the Centre-assessed coursework tests 10 different skills. Each may be assessed several times during the course Only the best mark in each of the ten skills counts. Marks awarded by your teacher are subject to change by an external moderator.

AQA B Biology

MODULE	SPECIFICATION TOPIC	CHAPTER REFERENCE	STUDIED IN CLASS	REVISED	PRACTICE QUESTIONS
Module 1 (M1)	*Biological molecules*	*1.1, 1.2, 1.3, 1.4, 1.6*			
	Biochemical tests	*1.5*			
	Chromatography	*1.5*			
	Cell ultrastructure	*2.1*			
	Cell fractionation	*2.2*			
	Microscopy	*2.2*			
	Tissues and organs	*2.3*			
	Transport across cell membranes	*1.3, 4.2*			
	Exchange with environment	*4.1*			
	Enzymes	*3.1, 3.4*			
	Inhibitors	*3.2*			
	Digestion	*3.3*			
Module 2 (M2)	*Genes and DNA*	*6.1*			
	The genetic code	*6.1*			
	Protein synthesis	*6.1*			
	Mutation	*6.1*			
	Cell division	*6.2, 7.1*			
	Gene technology	*6.3*			
	Industrial fermenters	*6.3*			
	Genetically modified organisms	*6.4*			
Module 3(a) (M3)	*Ethical issues*	*6.4*			
	Mass transport	*5.1*			
	Heart and circulation	*5.2, 5.3, 5.4*			
	Oxygen transport	*5.4*			
	Ventilation	*4.3*			
	Nervous control of heart	*5.2*			
	Transport in plants	*5.5*			
	Xylem and phloem	*5.5, 5.6*			
	Transpiration	*5.6*			
	Xerophytes	*5.6*			
	Translocation	*5.6*			

Examination analysis

The specification comprises three compulsory modules. In modular tests 1, 2 and 3(a) all questions are compulsory; they consist of structured questions and questions requiring extended answers.

Module 1	*1 hour 15 minutes examination*	*30%*
Module 2	*1 hour 15 minutes examination*	*30%*
Module 3(a)	*1 hour 15 minutes examination*	*25%*
Module 3(b)	*Centre-assessed coursework*	*15%*

OCR Biology

MODULE	SPECIFICATION TOPIC	CHAPTER REFERENCE	STUDIED IN CLASS	REVISED	PRACTICE QUESTIONS
Module 2801 (M1)	Cell ultrastructure	2.1			
	Microscopy	2.2			
	Tissues and organs	2.3			
	Biological molecules	1.1, 1.2, 1.3, 1.4			
	Biochemical tests	1.5			
	Enzymes	3.1			
	Inhibitors	3.2			
	Cell membranes	4.1, 4.2, 4.3			
	Transport across cell membranes	1.3, 4.2			
	DNA	6.1			
	Protein synthesis	6.1			
	Cell division	6.2			
	Ecosystems	8.1			
	Energy transfer	8.2			
	Nitrogen cycle	8.3			
Module 2802 (M2)	Diet	9.1			
	Gaseous exchange in lungs	4.3			
	Effects of exercise	9.1			
	Smoking and disease	9.1			
	Infectious disease	9.2			
	Immunity	9.3			
	Disease control	9.3			
Module 2803 (M3)	Transport in mammals	5.4			
	Blood	5,4, 9.3			
	Heart and circulation	5.2, 5.3, 5.4			
	Nervous control of heart	5.2			
	Transport in plants	5.5			
	Xylem and phloem	5.5, 5.6			
	Water potential	4.2			
	Translocation	5.6			
	Transpiration	5.6			
	Xerophytes	5.6			

Examination analysis

The specification comprises three compulsory modules. In module tests all questions are compulsory; they consist of structured questions and questions requiring extended answers.

Module 2801	1 hour 30 minutes examination	30%
Module 2802	1 hour 30 minutes examination	30%
Module 2803	1 hour examination	20%
	Centre-assessed coursework **or**	20%
	1 hour 30 minute practical examination	20%

Edexcel Biology

MODULE	SPECIFICATION TOPIC	CHAPTER REFERENCE	STUDIED IN CLASS	REVISED	PRACTICE QUESTIONS
Unit 1 (M1)	*Biological molecules*	*1.1, 1.2, 1.3, 1.4*			
	DNA	*6.1, 6.2*			
	The genetic code	*6.1*			
	Protein synthesis	*6.1*			
	Enzymes	*3.1*			
	Immobilised enzymes	*3.4*			
	Enzyme applications	*3.4*			
	Cell ultrastructure	*2.1*			
	Microscopy	*2.2*			
	Transport across cell membranes	*1.3, 4.2*			
	Water potential	*4.2*			
	Tissues and organs	*2.3*			
	Cell division	*6.2*			
Unit 2B (M2)	*Exchange surfaces in plants and animals*	*4.1, 4.2, 4.3*			
	Gaseous exchange in lungs	*4.3*			
	Digestion and absorption	*3.3*			
	Transport in animals	*5.2, 5.3, 5.4*			
	Transport in plants	*5.5*			
	Xylem and phloem	*5.5, 5.6*			
	Transpiration	*5.6*			
	Translocation	*5.6*			
	Heart and circulation	*5.2, 5.3, 5.4*			
	Nervous control of heart	*5.2*			
	Blood	*5.4, 9.3*			
	Haemoglobin; dissociation curves	*5.4*			
	Adaptations to environment	*4.3, 5.6*			
	Sexual reproduction in plants	*7.2*			
	Sexual reproduction in humans	*7.3*			
	Oogenesis and spermatogenesis	*7.3*			
	Menstrual cycle	*7.3*			
	Birth and lactation	*7.3*			
Unit 3 part (a) (M3)	*Energy flow though an ecosystem*	*8.1*			
	Food chains and webs	*8.1*			
	The nitrogen cycle	*8.3*			
	The carbon cycle	*8.3*			
	Effects of human activities on the environment	*8.5*			

Examination analysis

The specification comprises three compulsory modules. In module tests all questions are compulsory; they consist of structured questions and questions requiring extended answers.

Unit 1	*1 hour 30 minutes examination*	*33.3%*
Unit 2B	*1 hour 30 minutes examination*	*33.3%*
Unit 3 part (a)	*1 hour examination*	*18.1%*
Unit 3 part (a)	*Centre-assessed coursework*	*15.2%*

WJEC Biology

MODULE	SPECIFICATION TOPIC	CHAPTER REFERENCE	STUDIED IN CLASS	REVISED	PRACTICE QUESTIONS
Unit 1 (M1)	*Biological molecules*	*1.1, 1.2, 1.3, 1.4*			
	Biochemical tests	*1.5*			
	Cell ultrastructure	*2.1*			
	Microscopy	*2.2*			
	Transport across cell membranes	*4.1, 4.2*			
	DNA	*6.1, 6.2*			
	Protein synthesis	*6.1*			
	Cell division	*6.2*			
	Enzymes	*3.1*			
	Inhibitors	*3.2*			
	Immobilised enzymes	*3.4*			
	Enzyme applications	*3.4*			
Unit 2 (M2)	*Blood*	*5.4, 9.3*			
	Haemoglobin; dissociation curves	*5.4*			
	Ecosystems and energy transfer	*8.1*			
	Food chains and webs	*8.1*			
	Predators and prey	*8.1*			
	Colonisation and succession	*8.4*			
	Effects of human activities on the environment	*8.5*			
	Pest control	*8.2*			
	Heart and circulation	*5.2, 5.3, 5.4*			
	Mass transport	*5.1*			
	Exchange with environment	*4.2, 4.3*			
	Root structure and function	*5.5*			
	Transpiration	*5.6*			
	Xerophytes	*5.6*			
	Translocation	*5.6*			
	Nutrient cycles	*8.3*			

Examination analysis

The specification comprises three compulsory modules. In module tests all questions are compulsory; they consist of structured questions and questions requiring extended answers.

Unit 1	*1 hour 40 minutes examination*	*35%*
Unit 2	*1 hour 40 minutes examination*	*35%*
Unit 3	*3 hours 45 minutes of practical work in centres, assessed by external assessor*	*30%*

NICCEA Biology

MODULE	SPECIFICATION TOPIC	CHAPTER REFERENCE	STUDIED IN CLASS	REVISED	PRACTICE QUESTIONS
Module 1 (M1)	*Biological molecules*	*1.1, 1.2, 1.3, 1.4*			
	DNA	*6.1, 6.2*			
	Protein synthesis	*6.1*			
	The genetic code	*6.1*			
	Gene technology	*6.3*			
	Enzymes	*3.1*			
	Immobilised enzymes	*3.4*			
	Enzyme applications	*3.4*			
	Cell ultrastructure	*2.1*			
	Microscopy	*2.2*			
	Transport across cell membranes	*4.1, 4.2*			
	Water potential	*4.2*			
	Tissues and organs	*2.3*			
Module 2 (M2)	*Photosynthesis*				
	Energy flow through an ecosystem	*8.1*			
	Food chains and webs	*8.3*			
	The nitrogen cycle	*8.3*			
	The carbon cycle	*8.5*			
	Effects of human activities on the environment	*8.5*			
	Cell division	*6.2*			

Examination analysis

The specification comprises three compulsory modules. In module tests all questions are compulsory; they consist of structured questions and questions requiring extended answers.

Module 1	*1 hour 30 minutes examination*	*40%*
Module 2	*1 hour 30 minutes examination*	*40%*
	Centre-assessed coursework	*20%*

AS/A2 Level Biology courses

AS and A2

All Biology A Level courses being studied from September 2000 are in two parts, with a number of separate modules or units in each part. Most students will start by studying the AS (Advanced Subsidiary) course. Some will go on to study the second part of the A Level course, called A2. It is also possible to study the full A Level course in either order. Advanced Subsidiary is assessed at the standard expected halfway through an A Level course i.e. between GCSE and A Level. This means that the new AS and A2 courses are designed so that difficulty steadily increases:

- AS Biology builds from GCSE Science/Biology
- A2 Biology builds from AS Biology.

How will you be tested?

Assessment units

AS Biology comprises three units or modules. The first two units are assessed by examinations. The third component usually involves some method of practical assessment (this is dependent on the Examination Group). Examination Groups use ***either*** centre-assessed coursework ***or*** a practical examination.

Centre-based coursework involves practical skills marked by your teacher. The marks can be adjusted by moderators appointed by the awarding body.

If a practical examination is an option, it is based on identical skills to the Centre-assessed option. Some groups also include another part to the third component. This is a short examination of further content.

For AS Biology, you will be tested by three assessment units. For the full A Level in Biology, you will take a further three units. AS Biology forms 50% of the assessment weighting for the full A Level.

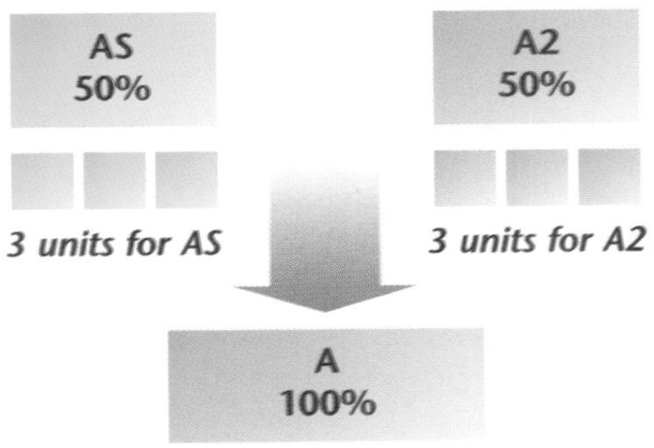

Tests are taken at two specific times of the year, January and June. It can be an advantage to you to take a unit test at the earlier optional time because you can re-sit the test, **(only once!)**. The best mark from the two will be credited and the lower mark ignored.

Each unit can normally be taken in either January or June. Alternatively, you can study the whole course before taking any of the unit tests. There is a lot of flexibility about when exams can be taken and the diagram below shows just some of the ways that the assessment units may be taken for AS and A Level Biology.

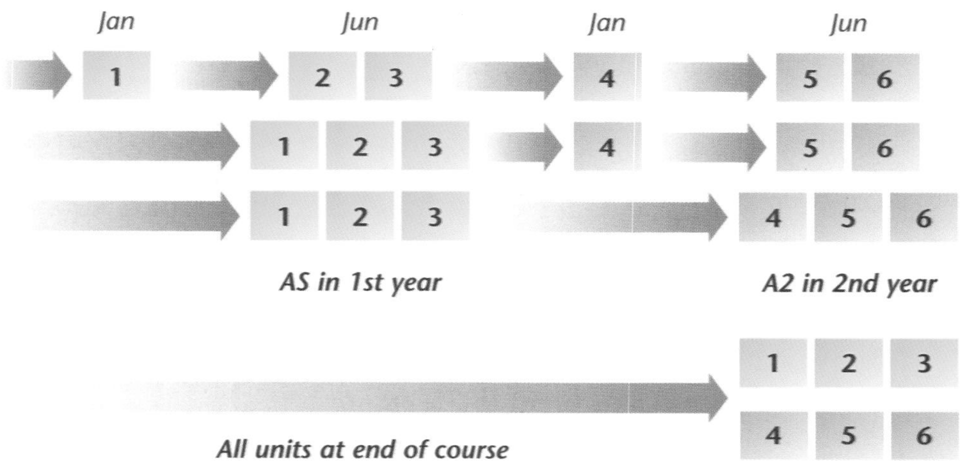

If you are disappointed with a module result, you can resit each module once. You will need to be very careful about when you take up a resit opportunity because you will have only one chance to improve your mark. The higher mark counts.

A2 and synoptic assessment

Many students who have studied at AS Level may decide to go on to study A2. There are three further units or modules to be studied. Some units are optional, so it is the choice of the Centre e.g. a biotechnology unit may be chosen, or one of an ecological nature. Every A Level specification includes a 'synoptic' assessment at the end of A2. Synoptic questions make use of concepts from earlier units, bringing them together in holistic contexts. Examiners will test your ability to inter-relate topics through the complete course from AS to A2.

Coursework

Coursework may form part of your A Level Biology course, depending on which specification you study. Where students have to undertake coursework, it is usually for the assessment of practical skills but this is not always the case.

Key skills

These are new! Your work in Biology AS and A2 can be used to gain a further award, the key skills qualification. This helps you to develop important skills that are needed, whatever you do beyond A Level. The key skills include: Application of number, Communication and Information technology. There are three levels of award (1–3). Biology AS and A2 students have opportunities to study one or more of the key skills. You must collect evidence together in a portfolio to show your level of competence. The awarding body specification will show opportunities of appropriate topics which can also be used to develop key skills. Additionally, the QCA publication 'Introduction to Key Skills' will be helpful.

Other subjects may be used to develop your key skills as well as AS and A2 Biology.

Remember that key skills are in demand by Further Education institutions and by employers.

What skills will I need?

For AS Biology, you will be tested by assessment objectives: these are the skills and abilities that you should have acquired by studying the course. The assessment objectives for AS Biology are shown below.

Knowledge with understanding

- recall of facts, terminology and relationships
- understanding of principles and concepts
- drawing on existing knowledge to show understanding of the responsible use of biological applications in society
- selecting, organising and presenting information clearly and logically

Application of knowledge and understanding, analysis and evaluation

- explaining and interpreting principles and concepts
- interpreting and translating, from one to another, data presented as continuous prose or in tables, diagrams and graphs
- carrying out relevant calculations
- applying knowledge and understanding to familiar and unfamiliar situations
- assessing the validity of biological information, experiments, inferences and statements

You must also present arguments and ideas clearly and logically, using specialist vocabulary where appropriate. Remember to balance your argument!

Experimental and investigative skills

Biology is a practical subject and part of the assessment of AS Biology will test your practical skills. This may be done during your lessons or may be tested in a more formal practical examination. You will be tested on four main skills:

- planning
- implementing
- analysing evidence and drawing conclusions
- evaluating evidence and procedures.

The skills may be assessed in the context of separate practical exercises, although more than one skill may be assessed in any one exercise. They may also be assessed all together in the context of a 'whole investigation'. An investigation may be set by your teacher or you may be able to pursue an investigation of your own choice.

You will receive guidance about how your practical skills will be assessed from your teacher. This study guide concentrates on preparing you for the written examinations testing the subject content of AS Biology.

Different types of questions in AS examinations

In AS Biology examinations different types of questions are used to assess your abilities and skills. Unit tests mainly use structured questions requiring both short-answers and more extended answers.

Short-answer questions

A question will normally begin with a brief amount of stimulus material. This may be in the form of a diagram, data or graph. A short-answer question may begin by testing recall. Usually this is followed up by questions which test understanding. Often you will be required to analyse data.

Short-answer questions normally have a space for your responses on the printed paper. The number of lines is a guide as to the amount of words you will need to answer the question. The number of marks indicated on the right side of the paper shows the number of marks you can score for each question part.

Here are some examples. (The answers are shown in blue)

The diagram shows part of a DNA molecule.

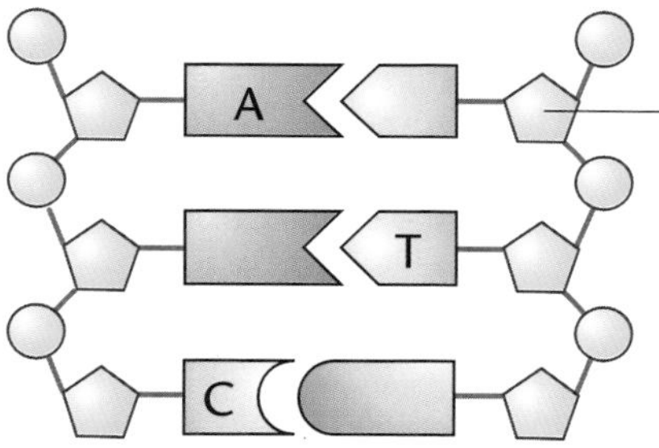

(a) Label part X. [1]

(b) Complete the diagram by writing a letter for each missing organic base in each empty box. [1]

(b) How do two strands of DNA join to each other?
The organic bases ✓ link the strands by hydrogen bonds ✓ [2]

Structured questions

Structured questions are in several parts. The parts are usually about a common context and they often progress in difficulty as you work through each of the parts. They may start with simple recall, then test understanding of a familiar or unfamiliar situation. If the context seems unfamiliar the material will still be centred around concepts and skills from the Biology specification. (If a student can answer questions about unfamiliar situations then they display understanding rather than simple recall.)

The most difficult part of a structured question is usually at the end. Ascending in difficulty, a question allows a candidate to build in confidence. Right at the end technological and social applications of biological principles give a more demanding challenge. Most of the questions in this book are structured questions. This is the main type of question used in the assessment of AS Biology.

When answering structured questions, do not feel that you have to complete a question before starting the next. Answering a part that you are sure of will build your confidence. If you run out of ideas go on to the next question. This will be more profitable than staying with a very difficult question which slows down progress. Return at the end when you have more time.

Here is an example of a structured question which becomes progressively more demanding.

Question

The diagram shows the molecules of a cell surface membrane.

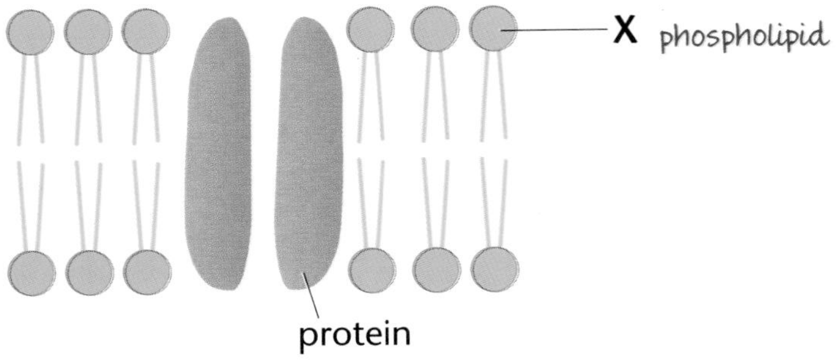

(a) (i) Label molecule X. [1]

(ii) The part of molecule X facing the outside of a cell is hydrophilic. What does this mean?

water loving/water attracting [1]

(iii) Describe **one** feature of the part of molecule X which faces inwards.

Hydrophobic/ water hating fatty acid residues [1]

(b) Explain how the protein shown in the diagram can actively transport the glucose molecule into the cell.

Energy is released from mitochondria near the channel protein the channel protein opens [3]

Note the help given in diagrams. The labelling of the protein molecule may trigger the memory so that the candidate has to make a small step to link the 'channel' function to this diagram. Examiners give clues! Expect more clues at AS Level than at A2 Level.

Extended answers

In AS Biology, questions requiring more extended answers will usually form part of structured questions. They will normally appear at the end of a structured question and will typically have a value of three to six marks. Longer answers are allocated more lines, so you can use this as a guide as to the extent of your answer. The mark allocation is a guide as to how many points you need to make in your response. Often for an answer worth six marks the mark scheme could have eight creditable answers. You are awarded up to the maximum, six in this instance.

Depending on the awarding body, longer extended questions may be set. These are often open response questions. These questions may be worth up to ten marks for full credit. Extended answers are used to allocate marks for the **quality of written communication**.

Candidates are assessed on their ability to use a suitable style of writing, and organise relevant material, both logically and clearly. The use of specialist biological words in context is also assessed. Spelling, punctuation and grammar are also taken into consideration. Here is a longer extended response question.

Question

Give an account of the effects of sewage entry into a river and explain the possible consequences to organisms downstream.

The sewage enters the river and is decomposed by bacteria.✓ These bacteria are saprobiotic ✓ they produce nitrates which act as a fertiliser.✓ Algae form a blanket on the surface ✓ light cannot reach plants under the algae so these plants die.✓ Bacteria decompose the dead plants ✓ the bacteria use oxygen/bacteria are aerobic ✓ fish die due to lack of oxygen ✓ Tubifex worms or bloodworms increase near sewage entry ✓ mayfly larvae cannot live close to sewage entry/mayfly larvae appear a distance downstream where oxygen levels return.✓

10 marking points → [7]

Remember that mark schemes for extended questions often exceed the question total, but you can only be awarded credit up to a maximum. Examiners sometimes build in a hurdle, e.g. in the above responses, references to one organism which increases in population is worthy of a mark, and another which decreases in population is worth another. Continually referring to different species which repeat a growth pattern will not gain further credit.

Exam technique

Links from GCSE

AS Biology builds from grade C in GCSE Science Double Award or the equivalent in Science: Biology. This study guide has been written so that you will be able to tackle AS Biology from a GCSE Science background.

You should not need to search for important Biology from GCSE science because this has been included where needed in each chapter. If you have not studied Science for some time, you should still be able to learn AS Biology using this text alone.

What are examiners looking for?

Whatever type of question you are answering, it is important to respond in a suitable way. Examiners use instructions to help you to decide the length and depth of your answer. The most common words used are given below, together with a brief description of what each word is asking for.

Define

This requires a formal statement. Some definitions are easy to recall.

Define the term active transport.

This is the movement of molecules from where they are in lower concentration to where they are in higher concentration. The process requires energy.

Other definitions are more complex. Where you have problems it is helpful to give an example.

Define the term endemic.

This means that a disease is found regularly in a group of people, district or country. Use of an example clarifies the meaning. Indicating that malaria is invariably found everywhere in a country, confirms understanding.

Explain

This requires a reason. The amount of detail needed is shown by the number of marks allocated.

Explain the difference between resolution and magnification.

Resolution is the ability to be able to distinguish between two points whereas magnification is the number of times an image is bigger than an object itself.

State

This requires a brief answer without any reason.

State one role of blood plasma in a mammal.

Transport of hormones to their target organs.

List

This requires a sequence of points with no explanation.

List the abiotic factors which can affect the rate of photosynthesis in pond weed.

carbon dioxide concentration; amount of light; temperature; pH of water

Describe

This requires a piece of prose which gives key points. Diagrams should be used where possible.

Describe the nervous control of heart rate.

The medulla oblongata ✓ of the brain connects to the sino atrial node in the right atrium, wall ✓ via the vagus nerve and the sympathetic nerve ✓ the sympathetic nerve speeds up the rate ✓ the vagus nerve slows it down.✓

Discuss

This requires points both for and against, together with a criticism of each point. (**Compare** is a similar command word.)

Discuss the advantages and disadvantages of using systemic insecticides in agriculture.

Advantages are that the insecticides kill the pests which reduce yield ✓ they enter the sap of the plants so insects which consume sap die ✓ the insecticide lasts longer than a contact insecticide, 2 weeks is not uncommon ✓

Disadvantages are that insecticide may remain in the product and harm a consumer e.g. humans ✓ it may destroy organisms other than the target ✓ no insecticide is 100% effective and develops resistant pests. ✓

Suggest

This means that there is no single correct answer. Often you are given an unfamiliar situation to analyse. The examiners hope for logical deductions from the data given and that, usually, you apply your knowledge of biological concepts and principles.

The graph shows that the population of lynx decreased in 1980. Suggest reasons for this.

Weather conditions prevented plant growth ✓ so the snowshoe hares could not get enough food and their population remained low ✓ so the lynx did not have enough hares(prey) to predate upon. ✓ The lynx could have had a disease which reduced numbers. ✓

Calculate

This requires that you work out a numerical answer. Remember to give the units and to show your working, marks are usually available for a partially correct answer. If you work everything out in stages write down the sequence. Otherwise if you merely give the answer and it is wrong, then the working marks are not available to you.

Calculate the Rf value of spot X. (X is 25 mm from start and solvent front is 100 mm)

$$Rf = \frac{\text{distance moved by spot}}{\text{distance moved by the solvent front}}$$

$$= \frac{25\text{ mm}}{100\text{ mm}}$$

$$= 0.25$$

Outline

This requires that you give only the main points. The marks allocated will guide you on the number of points which you need to make.

Outline the use of restriction endonuclease in genetic engineering.

The enzyme is used to cut the DNA of the donor cell. ✓

It cuts the DNA up like this AT|GCCGAT = AT + GCCGAT ✓
TACGGC|TA TACGGC TA

The DNA in a bacterial plasmid is cut with the same restriction endonuclease. ✓

The donor DNA will fit onto the sticky ends of the broken plasmid. ✓

If a question does not seem to make sense, you may have mis-read it. Read it again!

Some dos and don'ts

Dos

***Do** answer the question*

No credit can be given for good Biology that is irrelevant to the question.

***Do** use the mark allocation to guide how much you write*

Two marks are awarded for two valid points – writing more will rarely gain more credit and could mean wasted time or even contradicting earlier valid points.

***Do** use diagrams, equations and tables in your responses*

Even in 'essay style' questions, these offer an excellent way of communicating biology.

***Do** write legibly*

An examiner cannot give marks if the answer cannot be read.

***Do** write using correct spelling and grammar. Structure longer essays carefully*

Marks are now awarded for the quality of your language in exams.

Don'ts

***Don't** fill up any blank space on a paper*

In structured questions, the number of dotted lines should guide the length of your answer.

If you write too much, you waste time and may not finish the exam paper. You also risk contradicting yourself.

***Don't** write out the question again*

This wastes time. The marks are for the answer!

***Don't** contradict yourself*

The examiner cannot be expected to choose which answer is intended. You could lose a hard-earned mark.

***Don't** spend too much time on a part that you find difficult*

You may not have enough time to complete the exam. You can always return to a difficult calculation if you have time at the end of the exam.

What grade do you want?

Everyone would like to improve their grades but you will only manage this with a lot of hard work and determination. You should have a fair idea of your natural ability and likely grade in biology and the hints below offer advice on improving that grade.

For a Grade A

You will need to be a very good all-rounder.

- You must go into every exam knowing the work extremely well.
- You must be able to apply your knowledge to new, unfamiliar situations.
- You need to have practised many, many exam questions so that you are ready for the type of question that will appear.

The exams test all areas of the syllabus and any weaknesses in your biology will be found out. There must be no holes in your knowledge and understanding. For a Grade A, you must be competent in all areas.

For a Grade C

You must have a reasonable grasp of biology but you may have weaknesses in several areas and you will be unsure of some of the reasons for the biology.

- Many Grade C candidates are just as good at answering questions as the Grade A students but holes and weaknesses often show up in just some topics.
- To improve, you will need to master your weaknesses and you must prepare thoroughly for the exam. You must become a better all-rounder.

For a Grade E

You cannot afford to miss the easy marks. Even if you find biology difficult to understand and would be happy with a Grade E, there are plenty of questions in which you can gain marks.

- You must memorise all definitions.
- You must practise exam questions to give yourself confidence that you do know some biology. In exams, answer the parts of questions that you know first. You must not waste time on the difficult parts. You can always go back to these later.
- The areas of biology that you find most difficult are going to be hard to score on in exams. Even in the difficult questions, there are still marks to be gained. Show your working in calculations because credit is given for a sound method. You can always gain some marks if you get part of the way towards the solution.

What marks do you need?

The table below shows how your average mark is transferred into a grade.

average	*80%*	*70%*	*60%*	*50%*	*40%*
grade	*A*	*B*	*C*	*D*	*E*

Four steps to successful revision

Step 1: Understand

- Study the topic to be learned slowly. Make sure you understand the logic or important concepts.
- Mark up the text if necessary – underline, highlight and make notes.
- Re-read each paragraph slowly.

GO TO STEP 2

Step 2: Summarise

- Now make your own revision note summary:
  What is the main idea, theme or concept to be learned?
  What are the main points? How does the logic develop?
  Ask questions: Why? How? What next?
- Use bullet points, mind maps, patterned notes.
- Link ideas with mnemonics, mind maps, crazy stories.
- Note the title and date of the revision notes
  (e.g. Biology: Cells, 3rd March).
- Organise your notes carefully and keep them in a file.

This is now in **short term memory**. You will forget 80% of it if you do not go to Step 3.
GO TO STEP 3, but first take a 10 minute break.

Step 3: Memorise

- Take 25 minute learning 'bites' with 5 minute breaks.
- After each 5 minute break test yourself:
  Cover the original revision note summary.
  Write down the main points.
  Speak out loud (record on tape).
  Tell someone else.
  Repeat many times.

The material is well on its way to **long term memory**.
You will forget 40% if you do not do step 4. **GO TO STEP 4**

Step 4: Track/Review

- Create a Revision Diary (one A4 page per day).
- Make a revision plan for the topic, e.g. 1 day later, 1 week later, 1 month later.
- Record your revision in your Revision Diary, e.g.
  Biology: Cells, 3rd March 25 minutes
  Biology: Cells, 5th March 15 minutes
  Biology: Cells, 3rd April 15 minutes
  ... and then at monthly intervals.

Chapter 1

Biological molecules

The following topics are covered in this chapter:

- Essential substances
- Carbohydrates
- Lipids
- Proteins
- Biochemical tests and chromatography
- The importance of water to life

1.1 Essential substances

After studying this section you should be able to:

- recall the number of elements essential for life
- recall the four major elements and how they are linked to form biological molecules

LEARNING SUMMARY

Substances required for living processes

AQA A M1
AQA B M1
EDEXCEL M1
OCR M1
WJEC M1
NICCEA M1

Element	percentage (approximate)
Carbon	9.5
Hydrogen	63.0
Oxygen	25.5
Nitrogen	1.4
Calcium	0.32
Potassium	0.06
Phosphorus	0.20
Chlorine	0.03
Sulphur	0.05
Sodium	0.03

Living things are based on a total of 16 elements out of the 92 which exist on Earth. Over 99% of the biomass of organisms is composed of just 4 key elements, **carbon**, **hydrogen**, **oxygen**, and **nitrogen**.

Carbon is the most important element because of its following properties:

- carbon atoms bond with each other in long chains
- the chains can be branched or even joined up as rings
- the carbon atoms bond with other important elements like hydrogen, oxygen, nitrogen, sulphur, calcium and phosphorus.

The linking of carbon to carbon in long chains forms the backbone of important structural molecules. Electrons not used in the bonding of carbon to carbon are shared with other elements, like hydrogen, oxygen and nitrogen. All the essential elements together have incredible properties contributing to the diversity of life forms on Earth.

The table in the margin shows a range of elements found in the human body.

Some important elements

The molecules of every organism consist of a number of elements which bond together, and are vital to life. The properties of these inter-linking elements contribute to both structure and life processes.

Sodium atoms and chlorine atoms would be very destructive to life! Their properties would kill cells. However, in the form of ions they are vital to the survival of an organism. Inorganic ions are needed by organisms for a range of functions.

Ion	*example in animals*	*examples in plants*
Iron (Fe^{2+})	haemoglobin – transports oxygen efficiently; cytochromes – energy release	chlorophyll synthesis; energy release
Magnesium (Mg^{2+})	muscle and nerve function; bone formation	major constituent of chlorophyll
Potassium (K^{+})	transmission of nerve impulses and muscle function; formation and disease resistance	chlorophyll formation
Calcium (Ca^{2+})	formation of bones and teeth; clotting of blood; muscle function	cell wall constituent; cell division

1.2 Carbohydrates

After studying this section you should be able to:

- *recall the main elements found in carbohydrates*
- *recall the structure of glucose, starch, galactose and maltose*
- *recall the role of glucose, starch, cellulose and pectin*

LEARNING SUMMARY

Structure of carbohydrates

AQA A	M1
AQA B	M1
EDEXCEL	M1
OCR	M1
WJEC	M1
NICCEA	M1

Monosaccharides

All carbohydrates are formed from the elements carbon (C), hydrogen (H) and oxygen (O). The formula of a carbohydrate is always $(CH_2O)_n$. The n represents the number of times the basic CH_2O unit is repeated, e.g. where n = 6 the molecular formula is $C_6H_{12}O_6$. This is the formula shared by glucose and other simple sugars like fructose. These simple sugars are known as **monosaccharides**.

The molecular formula, $C_6H_{12}O_6$, does not indicate how the atoms bond together. Bonded to the carbon atoms are a number of –H and –OH groups. Different positions of these groups on the carbon chain are responsible for different properties of the molecules. The structural formulae of α and β glucose are shown below.

These molecules are mirror images of each other. When molecules have the same molecular formula but different structural formulae, they are known as **isomers**. Isomers have different properties to each other.

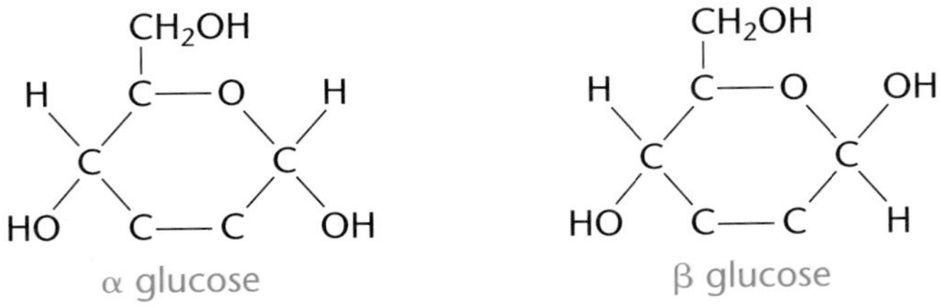

Glucose is so small that it can pass through the villi and capillaries into our bloodstream. The molecules subsequently release energy as a result of respiration. Simple glucose molecules are capable of so much more. They can combine with others to form bigger molecules.

Disaccharides

Each glucose unit is known as a **monomer** and is capable of linking others. This diagram shows two molecules of α glucose forming a disaccharide.

In your examinations look for different monosaccharides being given, like fructose or β glucose. You may be asked to show how they bond together. The principle will be exactly the same.

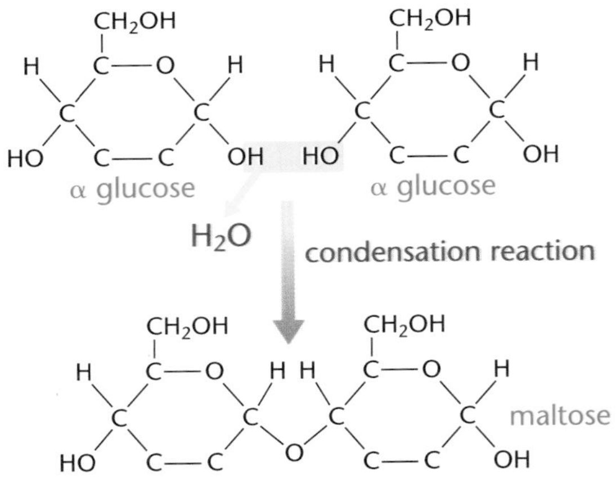

A **condensation** reaction means that as two carbohydrate molecules bond together a water molecule is produced. The link formed between the two glucose molecules is known as a **glycosidic bond**.

A glycosidic bond can also be broken down to release separate monomer units. This is the opposite of the reaction shown above. Instead of water being given off, a water molecule is needed to break each glycosidic bond. This is called hydrolysis because water is needed to split up the bigger molecule.

'**Lysis**' literally means '**splitting**'. In hydrolysis water is needed in the reaction to break down the molecule.

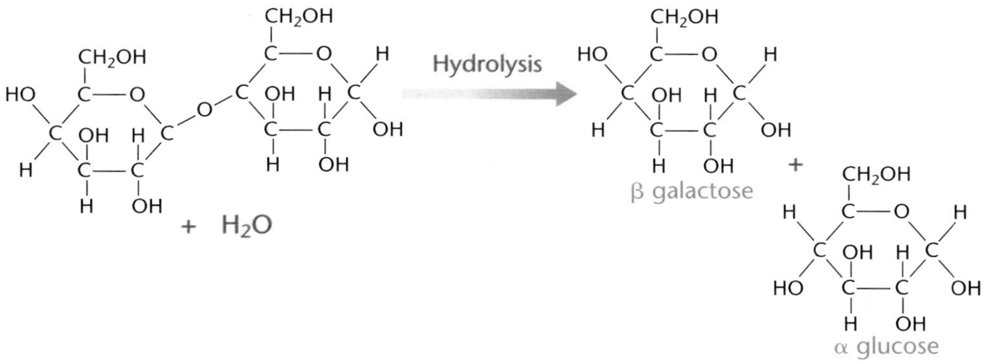

Polysaccharides

Like disaccharides, they consist of monomer units linked by the glycosidic bond. However, instead of just two monomer units they can have many. Chains of these 'sugar' units are known as polymers. These larger molecules have important structural and storage roles.

Starch is a polymer of the sugar, glucose. The diagram below shows part of a starch molecule.

Notice the five glycosidic bonds on just a small part of a starch molecule.

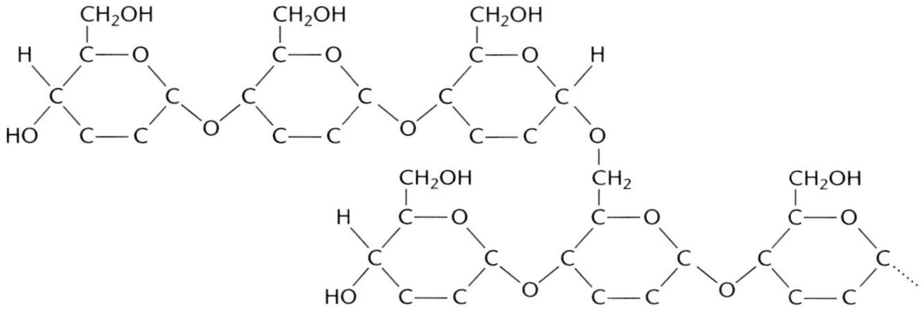

part of a branched section of a starch molecule

The table classifies carbohydrates.

Remember that each individual sugar unit is a monomer.

Monosaccharide (one sugar unit)	*Disaccharide (two sugar units)*	*Polysaccharide (many sugar units)*
glucose	maltose	starch
fructose	sucrose	glycogen
galactose	lactose	cellulose
		pectins

How useful are polysaccharides?

- Starch is stored in organisms as a future energy source, e.g. potato has a high starch content to supply energy for the buds to grow at a later stage.
- Glycogen is stored in the liver, which releases glucose for energy in times of low blood sugar.

Both starch and glycogen are insoluble which enables them to remain inside cells.

- Cellulose has long chains and branches which help form a tough protective layer around plant cells, the cell wall.
- Pectins are used alongside cellulose in the cell wall. They are polysaccharides which are bound together by calcium pectate.

Pectins help cells to bind together.

Together the cellulose and pectins give exceptional mechanical strength. The cell wall is also permeable to a wide range of substances.

1.3 Lipids

After studying this section you should be able to:

- *recall the main elements found in lipids*
- *recall the structure of lipids*
- *distinguish between saturated and unsaturated fats*
- *recall the role of lipids*

LEARNING SUMMARY

What are lipids?

AQA A	M1
AQA B	M1
EDEXCEL	M1
OCR	M1
WJEC	M1
NICCEA	M1

These are the **oils**, **fats** and **waxes**. They consist of exactly the same elements as carbohydrates, i.e. carbon (C), hydrogen (H) and oxygen (O) but their proportion is different. There is always a high proportion of carbon and hydrogen, with a small proportion of oxygen. The diagram below shows the structural formula of a typical fat.

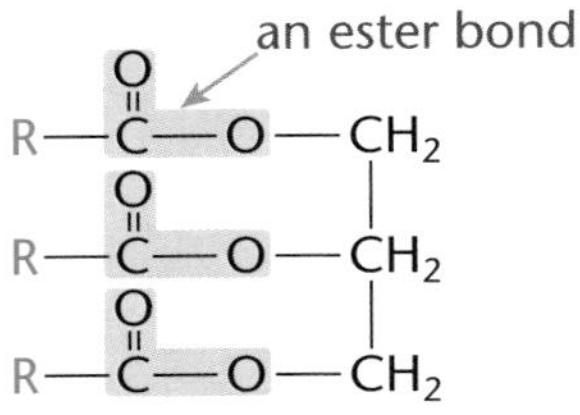

R represents groups such as CH_3 or C_2H_5

a **triglyceride** fat

Fats and oils are formed when fatty acids react with glycerol. During this reaction water is produced, a further example of a condensation reaction. The essential bond is the **ester bond**.

Note that water is produced during triglyceride formation. This is another example of a condensation reaction. Different triglyceride fats are formed from different fatty acids.

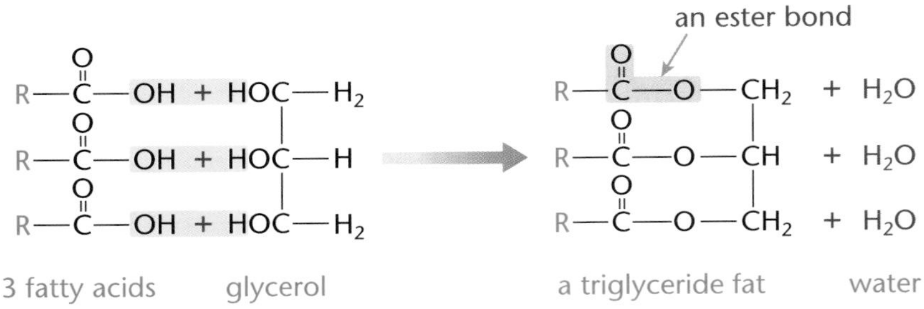

Fats and oils can be changed back into the original fatty acids and glycerol. Enzymes (see page 46) are needed for this transformation together with water molecules. An enzyme reaction which requires water to break up a molecule is known as **hydrolysis**.

The hydrocarbon chains are so long that they are often represented by the acid group (–COOH) and a zig-zag line.

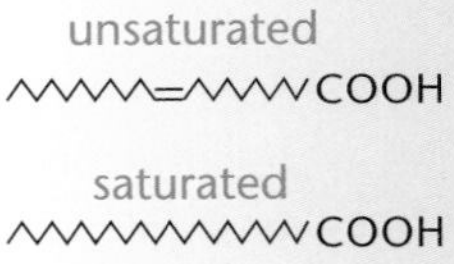

What are saturated and unsaturated fats?

The answer lies in the types of fatty acid used to produce them.

stearic acid

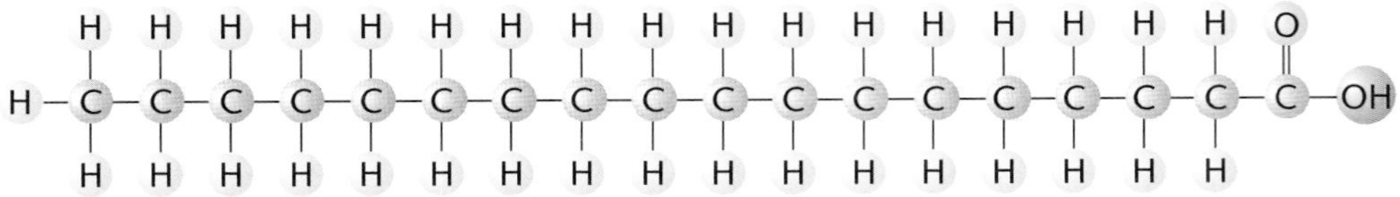

a **saturated** fatty acid

Saturated fats lead to cholesterol build up in the blood vessels so many people try to avoid them in their diet. Blocked vessels cause heart attacks.

oleic acid

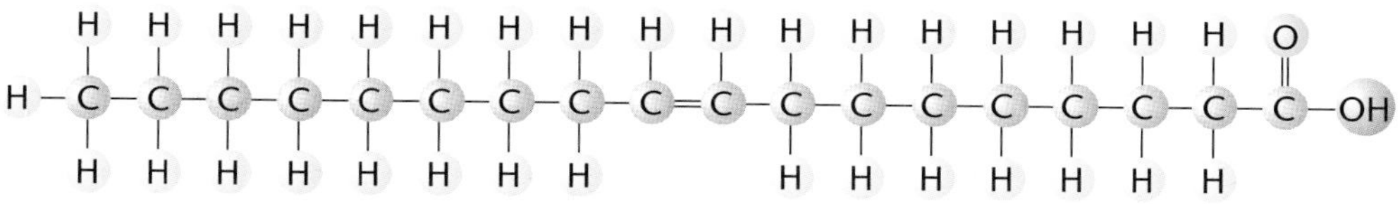

an **unsaturated** fatty acid

Note that when saturated fatty acids react with glycerol they make saturated fats. Conversely, unsaturated fatty acids make unsaturated fats.

KEY POINT

Saturated fatty acids have no C=C (double bonds) in their hydrocarbon chain, but unsaturated fatty acids do. This is the difference.

How useful are lipids?

Like carbohydrates, they are used as an **energy** supply, but a given amount of lipid release more energy than the same amount of carbohydrate. Due to their **insolubility** in water and **compact** structure, lipids have long-term **storage** qualities. Adipose cells beneath our skin contain large quantities of fat which **insulate** us and help to maintain body temperature. Fat gives **mechanical** support around our soft organs and even gives **electrical insulation** around our nerve axons.

Never give an ambiguous answer like this; 'fats keep an animal warm'. The examiner does not know whether you are referring to energy release by mitochondria or the insulation property. Be specific, otherwise you will not be credited.

An aquatic organism such as a dolphin has a large fat layer which:

- is an energy store
- a thermal insulator
- helps the animal remain buoyant.

The most important role of lipids is their function in cell membranes. To fulfil these functions a triglyceride fat is first converted into a **phospholipid**.

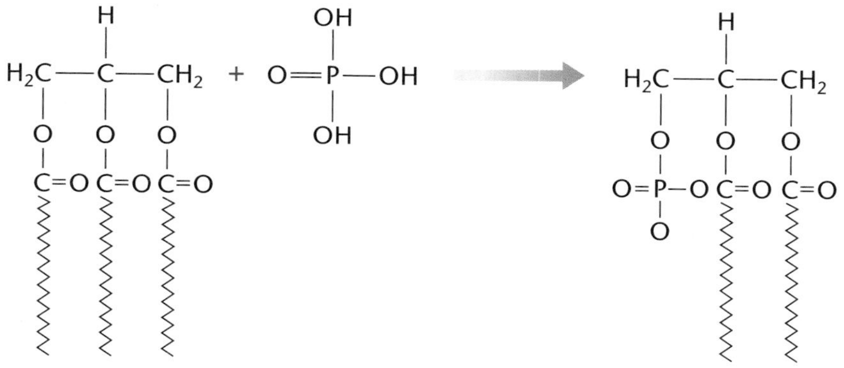

triglyceride — phosphoric acid — phospholipid

Phosphoric acid replaces one of the fatty acids of the triglyceride. The new molecule, the phospholipid, is a major component of cell membranes. The diagram below represents a phospholipid.

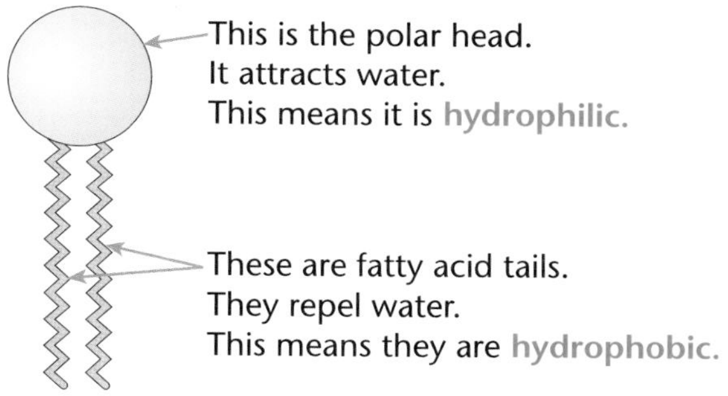

a phospholipid

Remember this simplified diagram when you learn about the cell membrane.

This is the polar head.
It attracts water.
This means it is hydrophilic.
These are fatty acid tails.
They repel water.
This means they are hydrophobic.

1.4 Proteins

After studying this section you should be able to:

- *recall the main elements found in proteins*
- *recall how proteins are constructed*
- *recall the structure of proteins*
- *recall the major functions of proteins*

LEARNING SUMMARY

The building blocks of proteins

AQA A M1
AQA B M1
EDEXCEL M1
OCR M1
WJEC M1
NICCEA M1

Like carbohydrates and lipids, proteins contain the elements carbon (C), hydrogen (H) and oxygen (O), but in addition they also **always** contain **nitrogen** (N).

Sulphur is often present as well as iron and phosphorus. Before understanding how proteins are constructed, the structure of **amino acids** should be noted. The diagram below shows the general structure of an amino acid.

Just like the earlier carbohydrate and lipid molecules '**R**' represents groups such as $-CH_3$ and $-C_2H_5$. There are about 20 commonly found amino acids but you will not need to know them all. Instead, learn the basic structure shown opposite.

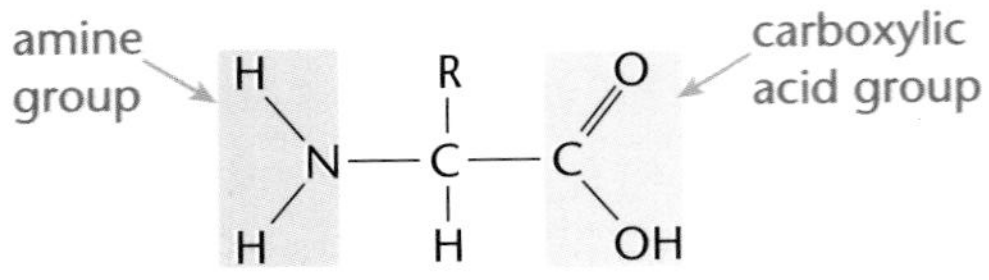

an amino acid

How is a protein constructed?

The process begins by amino acids bonding together. The diagram shows two amino acids being joined together by a **peptide bond**.

This is another example of a condensation reaction as water is produced as the dipeptide molecule is assembled.

Note that the peptide bonds can be broken down by a hydrolysis reaction.

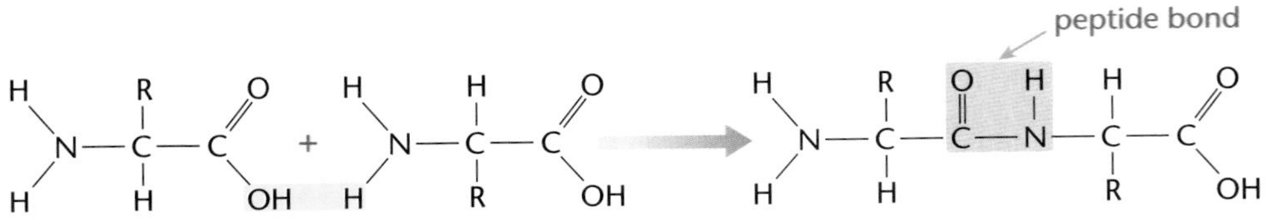

amino acid   amino acid   a dipeptide + H_2O

When many amino acids join together a long-chain **polypeptide** is produced. The linking of amino acids in this way takes place during protein synthesis (see page 83). There are around 20 different amino acids. Organisms join amino acids in different linear sequences to form a variety of polypeptides, then build these polypeptides into complex molecules, the **proteins**. Humans need eight essential amino acids as adults and ten as children, all the others can be made inside the cells.

The sequence of amino acids along a polypeptide is controlled by another complex molecule, DNA (see the genetic code, page 82).

The structure of proteins

AQA A M1
AQA B M1
EDEXCEL M1
OCR M1
WJEC M1
NICCEA M1

Primary protein structure

This is the **linear sequence** of amino acids.

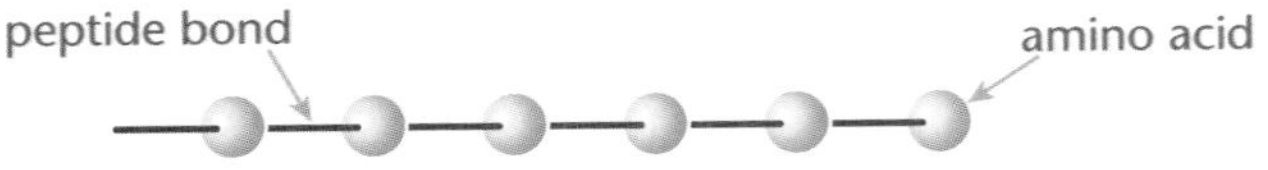

primary structure

Secondary protein structure

Polypeptides become twisted or coiled. These shapes are known as the secondary structure. There are two common secondary structures; the α-helix and the β-pleated sheet.

Both secondary structures give additional strength to proteins. The α-helix helps make tough fibres like the protein in your nails, e.g. keratin. The β-pleated sheet helps make the strength-giving protein in silk, fibroin. Many proteins are made from both α-helix and β-pleated sheet.

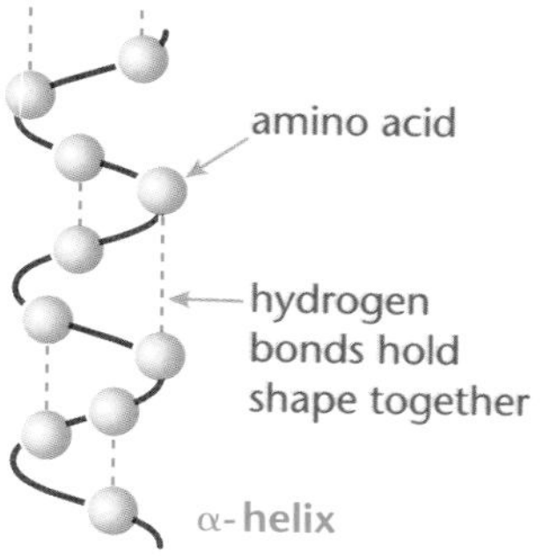

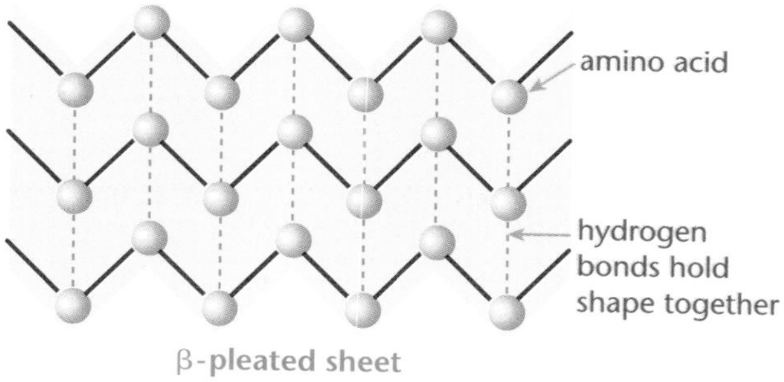

The polypeptides are held in position by hydrogen bonds. In both α-helices and β-pleated sheets the C = O of one amino acid bonds to the H–N of an adjacent amino acid, like this, C = O - - - H–N.

hydrogen bonds

An α-helix is a tight, twisted strand; a β-pleated sheet is where a zig-zag line of amino acids bonds with the next, and so on. This forms a sheet or ribbon shape.

The protein shown, only achieves a secondary structure as the simple α–helix polypeptides do not undergo further folding.

This is the structure of a fibrous protein. It is made of three α–helix polypeptides twisted together.

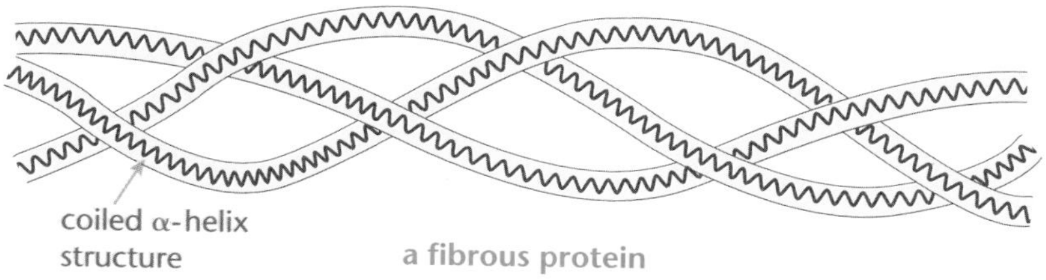

Tertiary protein structure

Note that the specific contours of proteins have extremely significant roles in life processes. (See enzymes page 46 and immunity page 134.)

This is when a polypeptide is folded into a precise shape. The polypeptide is held in 'bends' and 'tucks' in a permanent shape by a range of bonds including:

- disulphide bridges (sulphur–sulphur bonds)
- hydrogen bonds
- ionic bonds.

This is the structure of a **globular** protein. It is made of an α-helix and a β-pleated sheet. Precise shapes are formed with specific contours.

Quaternary protein structure

Some proteins consist of different polypeptides bonded together to form extremely intricate shapes. A haemoglobin molecule is formed from four separate polypeptide chains. It also has a haem group, which contains iron. This inorganic group is known as a prosthetic group and in this instance aids oxygen transport.

Note that some proteins do not have a quaternary structure. If they consist of just one folded polypeptide then they are classified as having tertiary structure. If they are simple fibres of α-helices or β-pleated sheets then they have only secondary protein structure.

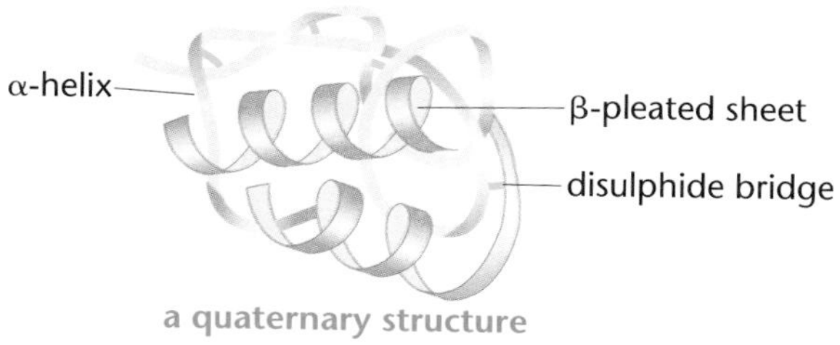

How useful are proteins?

AQA A	M1
AQA B	M1
EDEXCEL	M1
OCR	M1
WJEC	M1
NICCEA	M1

Just as carbohydrates and lipids can release energy, proteins are just as beneficial. Broken down into their component amino acids, these also liberate energy during respiration. The list below shows **important** uses of proteins:

- **cell-membrane proteins** transport substances across the membrane for processes such as facilitated diffusion and active transport
- **enzymes** catalyse biochemical reactions, e.g. pepsin breaks down protein into polypeptides
- **hormones** are passed through the blood and trigger reactions in other parts of the body, e.g. insulin regulates blood sugar
- **immuno-proteins**, e.g. antibodies are made by lymphocytes and act against antigenic sites on microbes
- **structural proteins** give strength to organs, e.g. collagen makes tendons tough
- **transport proteins**, e.g. haemoglobin transports oxygen in the blood
- **contractile proteins**, e.g. actin and myosin help muscles shorten during contraction
- **storage proteins**, e.g. aleurone in seeds helps germination, and casein in milk helps supply valuable protein to babies
- **buffer proteins**, e.g. blood proteins, due to their charge, help maintain the pH of plasma.

Progress check

1 List the sequence of structures in a globular protein such as haemoglobin.

2 The following statements refer to proteins used for different functions in the body. The list gives the name of different types of protein. Link the name of each type of protein with the correct statement.

(i) transport proteins
(ii) immuno-proteins
(iii) storage proteins
(iv) buffer proteins
(v) cell-membrane proteins
(vi) contractile proteins
(vii) enzymes
(viii) structural proteins
(ix) hormones

A used to transport substances across the membrane for processes such as facilitated diffusion.

B used to catalyse biochemical reactions, e.g. amylase breaks down starch into maltose.

C passed through blood, used to trigger reactions in other parts of the body, e.g. FSH stimulates a primary follicle.

D antibodies made by lymphocytes against antigens.

E used to give strength to organs, e.g. collagen makes tendons tough.

F haemoglobin is used to transport oxygen in blood.

G actin and myosin help muscles shorten during contraction.

H aleurone in seeds is a source of amino acids as it is broken down during germination.

I blood proteins, due to their charge, help maintain the pH of plasma.

1 primary structure: amino acids linked in a linear sequence; secondary structure: α-helix or β-pleated sheet; tertiary structure: further folding of polypeptide held by disulphide bridges, ionic bonds, and hydrogen bonds; quaternary structure: two or more polypeptides bonded together.

2 A (v), B (vii), C (ix), D (ii), E (viii), F (i), G (vi), H (iii), I (iv).

1.5 Biochemical tests and chromatography

After studying this section you should be able to:

- *describe biochemical tests for carbohydrates, proteins and lipids*
- *describe the separation and identification of molecules by chromatography*

LEARNING SUMMARY

Biochemical tests

AQA A M1
AQA B M1
EDEXCEL M1
OCR M1
WJEC M1
NICCEA M1

Tests for carbohydrates in the laboratory

Benedict's test used to identify reducing sugars (monosaccharides and some disaccharides)

- Add Benedict's solution to the chemical sample and heat.
- The solution changes from blue to brick-red or yellow if a reducing sugar is present.

Non-reducing sugar test used to test for non-reducing sugars, e.g. the disaccharide, sucrose

- First a Benedict's test is performed.
- If the Benedict's test is negative, the sample is hydrolysed by heating with hydrochloric acid, then neutralised with sodium hydrogen carbonate.
- This breaks the glycosidic bond of the disaccharide, releasing the monomers.
- A second Benedict's test is performed which will be positive because the monomers are now free.

All the biochemical tests need to be learned. This work is good value because they are regularly tested in 2 or 3 mark question components.

Starch test

- Add iodine solution to the sample.
- If starch is present the colour changes to blue-black.

Tests for lipids in the laboratory

Emulsion test used to identify fats and oils

- Add ethanol to the sample, shake, then pour the mixture into water.
- If fats or oils are present then a white emulsion appears at the surface.

Tests for proteins in the laboratory

Biuret test used to identify any protein

- Add dilute sodium hydroxide and dilute copper sulphate to the sample.
- A violet colour appears if a protein is present.

Chromatography

AQA A M1
AQA B M1
NICCEA M1

This technique is used to separate out the components in a mixture. It is used to separate out the components of substances such as chlorophyll, and can be used to help identify substances. The method is outlined below:

- a spot of the substance is placed on chromatography paper and left to dry
- the paper is suspended in a solvent such as propanone
- as the solvent molecules move through the paper the components begin to move up the paper, big molecules move slower than small ones
- the small solvent molecules move through the paper faster than any of the components of the substance
- the substance separates out into different spots or bands.

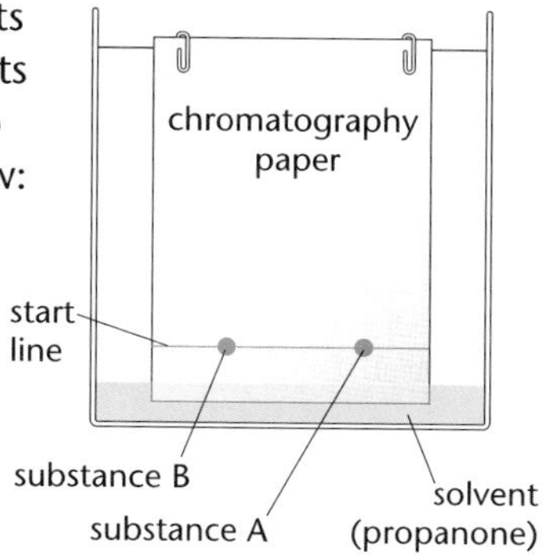

paper chromatography (before separation)

You need to remember that this technique separates substances in terms of the relative size of the molecules.

The longer the chromatogram is left after the start, the higher the spots or bands ascend. For this reason every compound has its R_f value calculated. However long the chromatogram is left, the R_f value is the same when using the same solvent.

R_f value of a substance

This is calculated after the distances moved by compounds and solvent up the chromatogram have been measured. The distance moved by the solvent is called the solvent front.

$$R_f \text{ value} = \frac{\text{distance moved by substance}}{\text{distance moved by solvent front}}$$

Different compounds show up as different coloured bands. The technique shows the number of compounds in the mixture. When this method is used on chlorophyll, five colours separate out.

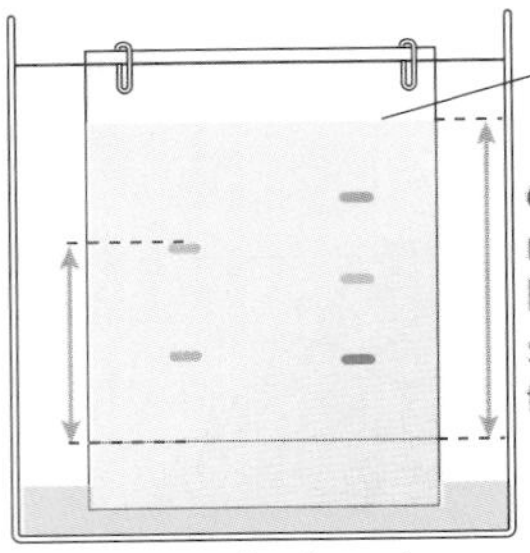

paper chromatography (after separation)

Progress check

A chromatogram was prepared for substance X. Five different spots were noted on the chromatogram.

1 What does this indicate?

2 What is the equation used to calculate the R_f value of a spot?

1 Substance X consisted of 5 different substances.

2 R_f value = $\frac{\text{distance moved by substance}}{\text{distance moved by solvent front}}$

1.6 The importance of water to life

LEARNING SUMMARY

After studying this section you should be able to:

- *recall the properties of water*
- *recall the functions of water*

Properties and uses of water

AQA A	M1
AQA B	M1
EDEXCEL	M1
OCR	M1
WJEC	M1
NICCEA	M1

Try to learn all of the functions of water molecules given in the list. Water is used in so many ways that the chance of being questioned on the topic is high.

Water is essential to living organisms. The list below shows some of its properties and uses.

- **Hydrogen bonds** are formed between the oxygen of one water molecule and the hydrogen of another. As a result of this water molecules have an attraction for each other known as **cohesion**.
- **Cohesion** is responsible for surface tension which enables aquatic insects like pond skaters to walk on a pond surface. It also aids capillarity, the way in which water moves through xylem in plants.
- Water is a **dipolar** molecule, which means that the oxygen has a slight negative charge at one end of the molecule, and each hydrogen a slight positive charge at the other end.
- Other **polar** molecules dissolve in water. The different charges on these molecules enable them to fit into water's hydrogen bond structure. Ions in solution can be transported or can take part in reactions. Polar substances which dissolve are **hydrophilic** and non-polar, which cannot dissolve in water, **hydrophobic**.
- Water is used in **photosynthesis**, so it is responsible for the production of glucose. This in turn is used in the synthesis of many chemicals.
- Water helps in the **temperature regulation** of many organisms. It enables the cooling down of some organisms. Owing to a high **latent heat of vaporisation**, large amounts of body heat are needed to evaporate a small quantity of water. Organisms like humans cool down effectively but lose only a small amount of water in doing so.

- A relatively high level of heat is needed to raise the temperature of water by a small amount due to its **high specific heat capacity**. This enables organisms to control their body temperature more effectively.
- Water is a solvent for ionic compounds. A number of the essential elements required by organisms are obtained in ionic form, e.g.:
  (a) plants absorb nitrate ions (NO_3^-) and phosphate ions (PO_4^-) in solution
  (b) animals intake sodium ions (Na^+) and chloride ions (Cl^-).

Sample questions and model answers

1 Below are the structures of two glucose molecules.

(a) Complete the equation to show how the molecules react to form a glycosidic bond and the molecule produced.

Remember that you will be given molecule structures. These stimulate your memory which helps you work out the answer.

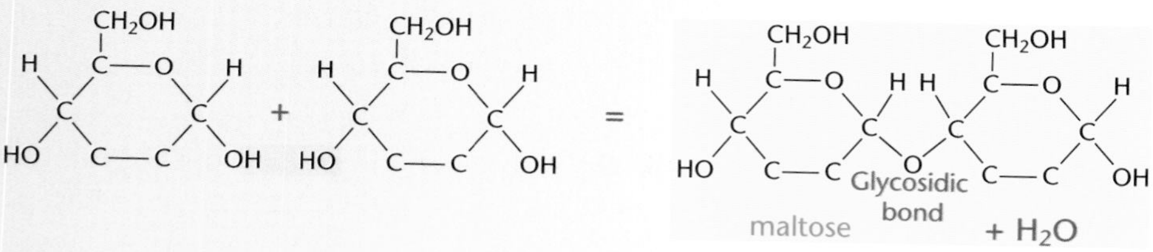

(b) Which form of glucose molecules is shown?
Give a reason for your answer. [2]

α glucose, because the –OH groups on carbon atom 1 are down

The correct answer here is condensation. A regular error in questions like this is to give the wrong reaction, i.e. hydrolysis. Revise carefully then you will make the correct choice.

(c) State the type of reaction which takes place when the two molecules shown above react together. [2]

Condensation.

2 The diagram below shows a globular protein consisting of four polypeptide chains.

Look out for similar structures in your examinations. The proteins given may be different, but the principles remain the same.

(a) Use your own knowledge and the information given to explain how this protein shows primary, secondary, tertiary and quaternary structure. [5]

Primary structure: it is formed from chains of amino acids; it has polypeptides made of a linear sequence of amino acids.

Secondary structure: it has an α-helix, it has a β-pleated sheet.

Tertiary structure: the polypeptides are folded, the folds are held in position by disulphide bridges.

Quaternary structure: there are four polypeptides in this protein. Two or more are bonded together to give a quaternary structure.

(b) Name and describe a test which would show that haemoglobin is a protein. [3]

The Biuret test.

Take a sample of haemoglobin and add water, sodium hydroxide and copper sulphate.

Most examinations include at least one biochemical test.

The colour of the mixture shows as violet or mauve if the sample is a protein.

Practice examination questions

Try all of the questions and check your answers with the mark scheme on page 139.

1 The chromatogram below shows a substance which has been separated into its component compounds.

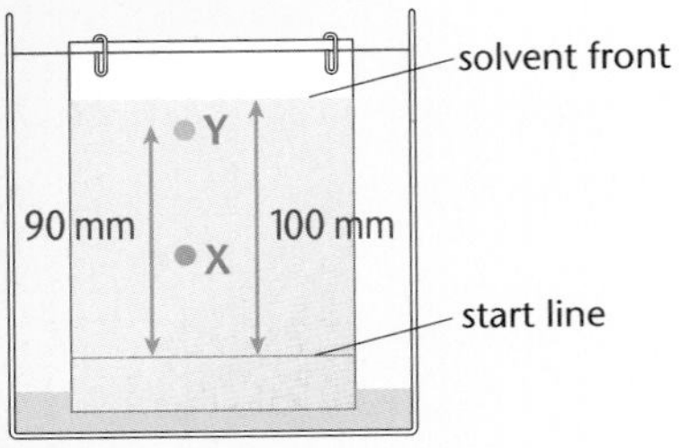

(a) Calculate the R_f value of spot Y. [2]

(b) Which spot contains the biggest molecules? [1]

(c) The chromatogram had been left for six hours after a drop was put on the start line. Why was it important to take the measurement for the calculation of the R_f value of Y before another hour had past? [1]

2 (a) Complete the equation below to show the breakdown of a triglyceride fat into fatty acids and glycerol. [2]

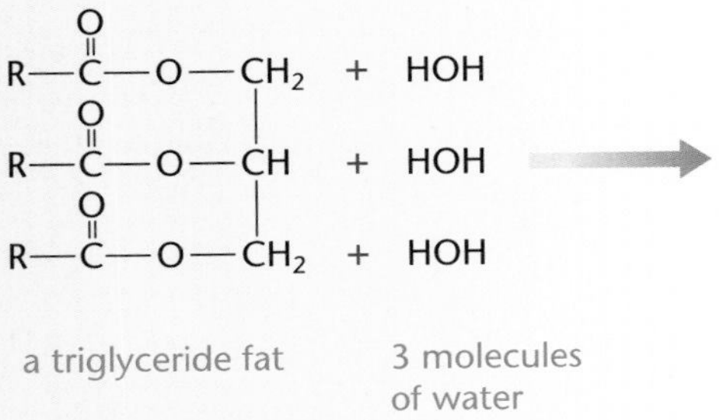

(b) Describe a biochemical test which would show that a sample was a fat. [3]

3 The diagram below shows a polypeptide consisting of 15 amino acids.

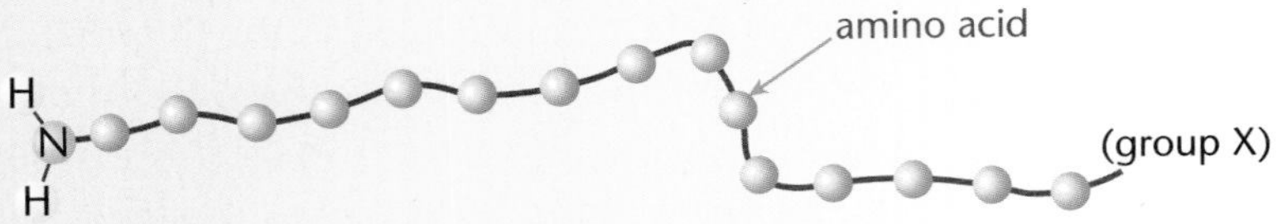

(a) Name the bond between each pair of amino acids in this polypeptide. [1]

(b) What is group X? [1]

(c) Which level of protein structure is shown by this polypeptide? Give a reason for your answer. [2]

4 Explain how the following properties of water are useful to living organisms:

(a) a large latent heat of evaporation [2]

(b) a high specific heat capacity [2]

(c) the cohesive attraction of water molecules for each other. [2]

Chapter 2

Cells

The following topics are covered in this chapter:

- *The ultra-structure of cells*
- *Isolation of cell organelles*
- *Specialisation of cells*

2.1 The ultra-structure of cells

After studying this section you should be able to:

- *identify cell organelles and understand their roles*
- *recall the differences between prokaryotic and eukaryotic cells*

LEARNING SUMMARY

Cell organelles

AQA A	M1
AQA B	M1
EDEXCEL	M1
OCR	M1
WJEC	M1
NICCEA	M1

The cell is the basic functioning unit of organisms in which chemical reactions take place. These reactions involve energy release needed to support life and build structures. Organisms consist of one or more cells. The amoeba is composed of one cell, whereas millions of cells make up a human.

> Every cell possesses internal coded instructions to control cell activities and development (see the genetic code page 82). Cells also have the ability to continue life by some form of cell division.
>
> KEY POINT

Organelles are best seen with the aid of an electron microscope.

The ultra-structure of a cell can be seen using an electron microscope. Sub-cellular units called **organelles** become visible. Each organelle has been researched to help us understand more about the processes of life.

The animal cell and its organelles

The diagram below shows the organelles found in a typical animal cell.

A plant cell has all of the same structures plus:

- a cellulose cell wall
- chloroplasts (some cells)
- a sap vacuole with tonoplast.

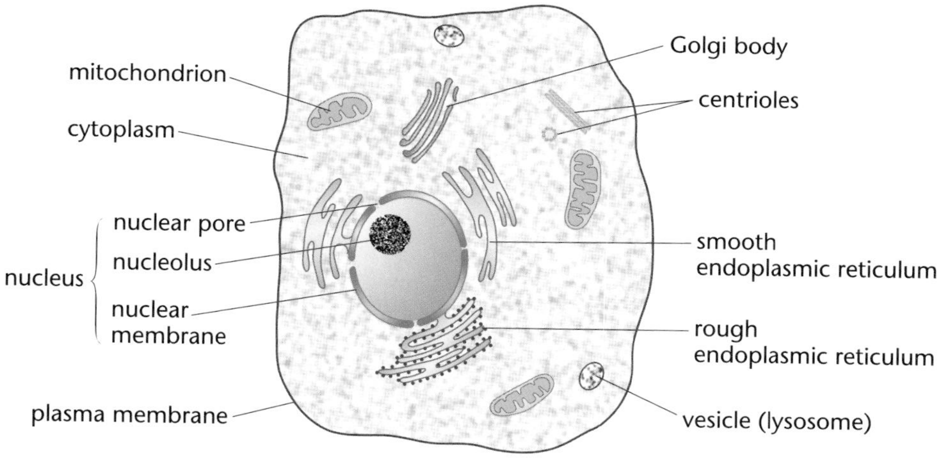

Cell surface (plasma) membrane

This covers the outside of a cell and consists of a **double** layered sheet of lipid molecules interspersed with proteins. It separates the cell from the outside environment, gives physical protection and allows the import and export of **selected** chemicals.

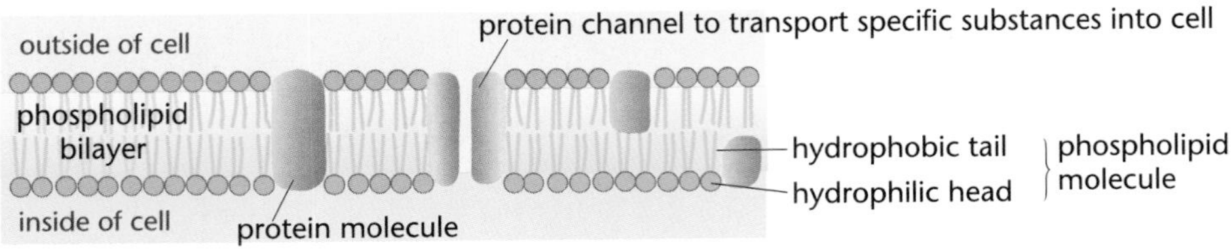

Nucleus

This controls all cellular activity using coded instructions located in DNA. These coded instructions enable the cell to make specific proteins (see protein synthesis page 83). RNA is produced in the nucleus and leaves via the nuclear pores. The nucleus stores, replicates and decodes DNA.

Be ready to identify all cell organelles in either a diagram or electron micrograph. A mitochondrion is often sausage shaped but the end view is circular. Look out for the internal membranes.

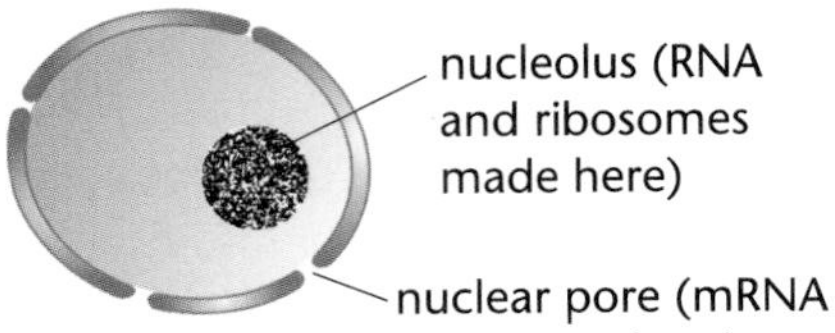

nucleus

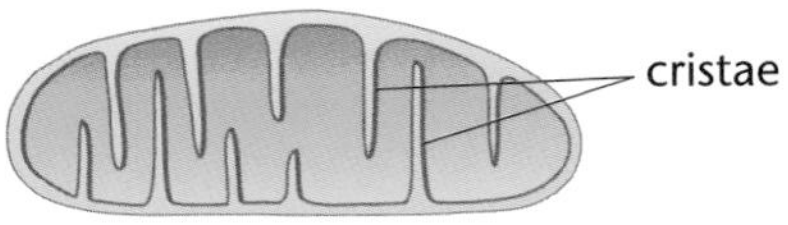

mitochondrion

Mitochondria

These consist of an outer membrane enclosing a semi-fluid matrix. Throughout the matrix is an internal membrane, folded into cristae. The cristae and matrix contain enzymes which enable this organelle to carry out aerobic respiration. It is the key organelle in the release of energy, making ATP available to the cell.

Mitochondria are needed for many energy requiring processes in the cell, including active transport and the movement of cilia.

Cytoplasm is often seen as grey and granular. If the image is 'clear' then you are probably looking at a vacuole.

Look for tiny dots in the cytoplasm. They will almost certainly be ribosomes. A membrane adjacent to a line of ribosomes is probably the rough endoplasmic reticulum.

Cytoplasm

Each organelle in a cell is suspended in a semi-liquid medium, the cytoplasm. Many ions are dissolved in it. It is the site of many chemical reactions.

Ribosomes

There are numerous **ribosomes** in a cell, located along **rough endoplasmic reticulum**. They aid the manufacture of proteins, being the site where mRNA meets tRNA so that amino acids are bonded together.

Endoplasmic reticulum (ER)

This is found as **rough ER** (with ribosomes) and **smooth ER** (without ribosomes). It is a series of folded internal membranes. Substances are transported in the spaces between the ER. The smooth ER aids the synthesis and transport of lipids.

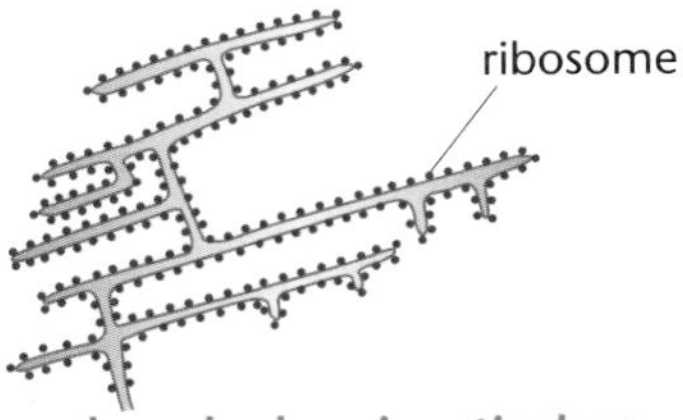

rough endoplasmic reticulum

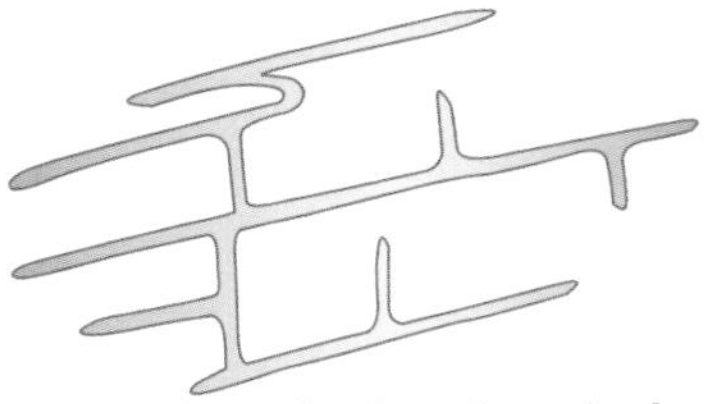

smooth endoplasmic reticulum

Look for vesicles 'pinching off' the main Golgi sacs.

Golgi body

This is a series of flattened sacs, each separated from the cytoplasm by a membrane. The **Golgi body** is a packaging system where important chemicals become membrane wrapped, forming **vesicles**. The vesicles become detached from the main Golgi sacs, enabling the isolation of chemicals from each other in the cytoplasm. The Golgi body aids the production and secretion of many proteins, carbohydrates and glycoproteins. Vesicle membranes merge with the plasma membrane to enable secretions to take place.

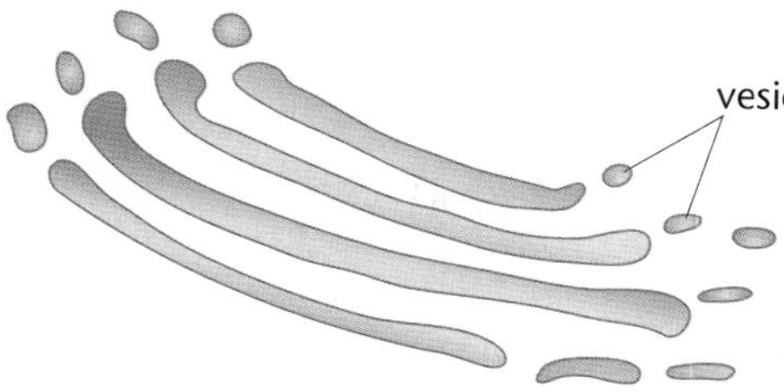

Golgi body

Lysosomes

These are specialised vesicles because they contain digestive enzymes. The enzymes have the ability to break down proteins and lipids. If the enzymes were free to react in the cytoplasm then cell destruction would result.

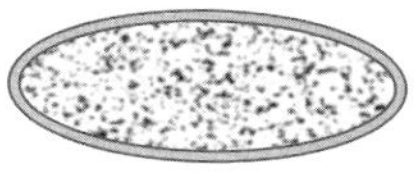

lysosome

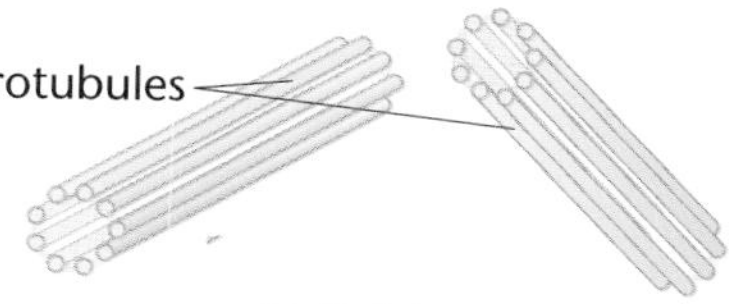

centrioles

Centrioles

In a cell there are two short cylinders which contain microtubules. Their function is to aid cell division. During division they move to opposite poles as the spindle develops.

The plant cell and its organelles

All of the structures described for animal cells are also found in plant cells. Additionally there are three extra structures shown in the diagram below.

Did you spot the three extra structures in the plant cell? Remember that a root cell under the soil will not possess chloroplasts. Nor does every plant cell above the soil have chloroplasts.

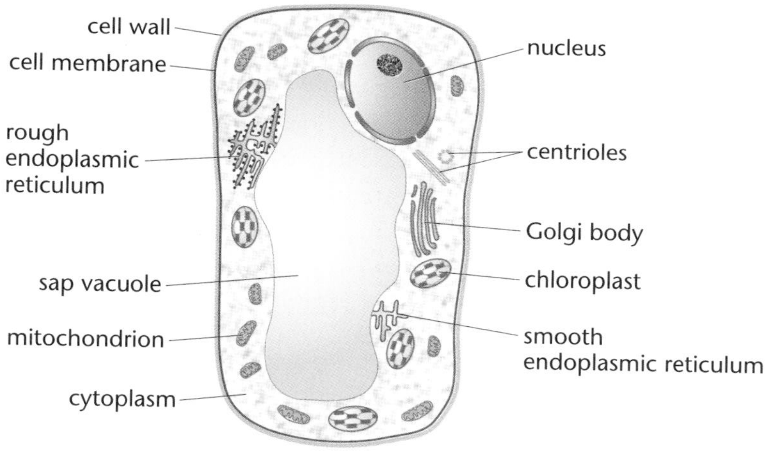

a plant cell

Cell wall

Around the plasma membrane of plant cells is the cell wall. This is secreted by the cell and consists of cellulose microfibrils embedded in a layer of calcium pectate and hemicelluloses. Between the walls of neighbouring cells calcium pectate cements one cell to the next in multi-cellular plants. Plant cell walls provide a rigid support for the cell but allow many substances to be imported or exported by the cell. The wall allows the cell to build up an effective hydrostatic skeleton. When the cell has a maximum amount of water content, it has maximum strength, and is said to be turgid. Some plant cells have a cytoplasmic link which crosses the wall. These links of cytoplasm are known as plasmodesmata.

Cells other than plant cells can have cell walls, e.g. bacteria have polysaccharides other than cellulose.

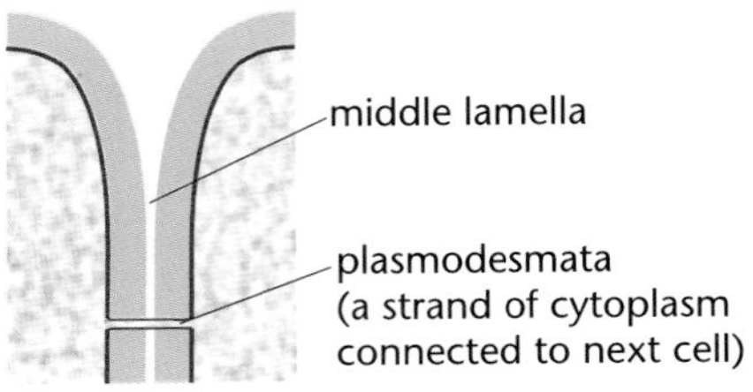

plasmodesmata

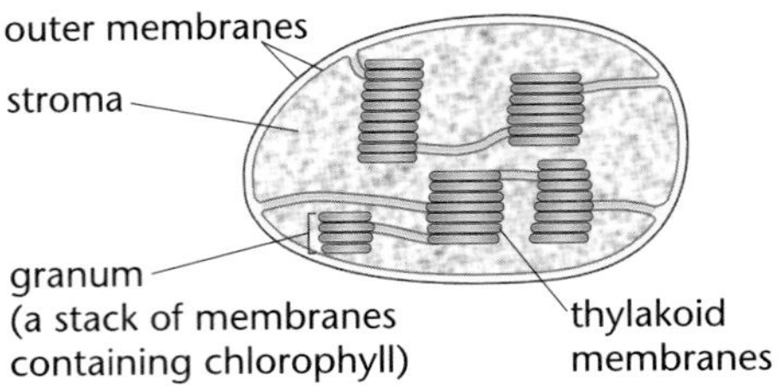

a chloroplast

Chloroplasts

These enable the plant to photosynthesise, making glucose. Each consists of an outer covering of two membranes. Inside are more membranes stacked in piles called **grana**. The membranes enclose a substance vital to photosynthesis, **chlorophyll**. Inside the chloroplast is a matrix known as the **stroma** which is also involved in photosynthesis.

Sap vacuole

This is a large space in a plant cell, containing chemicals such as glucose and mineral ions in water. This solution is the sap. It is surrounded by a membrane known as the **tonoplast**. It is important that a plant cell contains enough water to maintain internal hydrostatic pressure. When this is achieved the cell is turgid, having maximum hydrostatic strength.

Prokaryotic and eukaryotic cells

AQA A M1
AQA B M1
EDEXCEL M1
OCR M1
WJEC M1
NICCEA M1

Organisms can be classified into two groups, **prokaryotic** or **eukaryotic** according to their cellular structure.

> **KEY POINT**
> The former type of cell is characteristic of two groups of organisms, bacteria and blue-green algae. Prokaryotic cells are less complex than the eukaryotic ones and are considered to have evolved earlier.

The table below states similarities and differences between the two types of organism.

In an examination you will often be given a diagram of a cell from an organism you have not seen before. This is not a problem! The examiners are testing your recognition of the organelles found in typical prokaryotic and eukaryotic organisms.

	Prokaryotic cells	*Eukaryotic cells*
Kingdom	Prokaryotae	Protoctista, Fungi, Animalia, Plantae
Organelles	**1** small ribosomes	large ribosomes
	2 DNA present but there is no nuclear membrane	DNA is enclosed in a membrane i.e. has nucleus, mitochondria, (Golgi body vesicles and ER are present)
	3 cell wall present consisting of mucopeptides	cell walls present in plant cells – cellulose cell walls present in fungi – chitin
	4 if cells have flagellae there is no 9+2 microtubule arrangement	if cells have flagellae there is a 9+2 microtubule arrangement

Progress check

1 Describe the function of each of the following cell organelles:

nucleus, centrioles, Golgi body, mitochondria, ribosomes, cell (plasma) membrane

2 Give **three** structural differences between a plant and animal cell.

1 **nucleus** – mRNA is produced in the nucleus with the help of DNA
mitochondria – release energy during aerobic respiration
centrioles – help produce the spindle during cell division
ribosomes – aid the manufacture of proteins, being the site where mRNA meets tRNA so that amino acids are bonded together
Golgi body – is a packaging system where chemicals become membrane wrapped, forming vesicles
Cell (plasma) membrane – gives physical protection to the outside of a cell, allows the import and export of *selected* chemicals.

2 A plant cell has a cellulose cell wall, chloroplasts, and a sap vacuole lined by a tonoplast.

2.2 Isolation of cell organelles

After studying this section you should be able to:

- *understand how cell fractionation and ultracentrifugation are used to isolate cell organelles*
- *understand the principles of light and electron microscopes*
- *understand how microscopic specimens and microbial populations are measured*

LEARNING SUMMARY

Cell fractionation

AQA A M1
AQA B M1

Occasionally it is necessary to isolate organelles to investigate their structure or function, e.g. mitochondria could be used to investigate aerobic respiration away from the cell's internal environment. **Cell fractionation** consists of two processes, **homogenisation** followed by **differential centrifugation**. Cell fractionation depends on the different densities of the organelles.

Technique

Cells are kept:

- cool at around 5°C *(this slows down the inevitable autolysis, destruction by the cell's own enzymes)*
- in an isotonic solution, i.e. equal concentration of substances inside and outside of the cell membrane *(this ensures that the organelles are not damaged by osmosis and can still function)*
- at a specific pH by a buffer solution *(this ensures that the organelles can still function, as they are kept in suitable conditions)*.

Homogenisation

The cells are homogenised in either a pestle homogeniser or blender. This breaks the cells up releasing the organelles and cytoplasm. Many organelles are not damaged at all by this process. At this stage there is a suspension of mixed organelles.

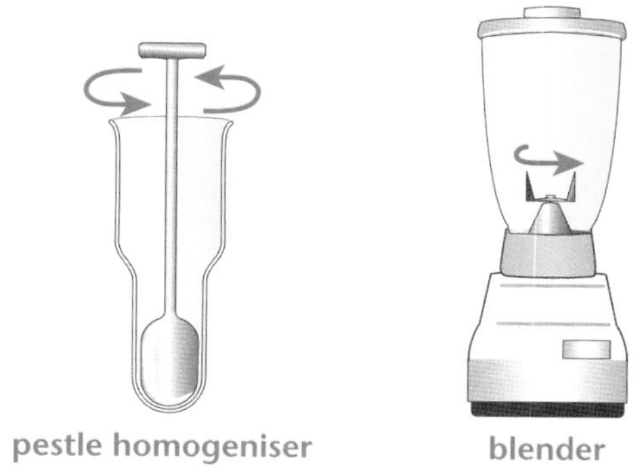

Differential centrifugation

600 g means 600 times the force of gravity. If a plant cell was centrifuged at around this speed then chloroplasts would be contained in the sediment as well as nuclei.

Equal amounts of homogenised tissue samples are poured into the tubes of an **ultracentrifuge**. This instrument spins the cell contents at a force many times greater than gravity. Organelle separation by this technique is **density dependent**.

First spin

The sample is spun at 600 g for 10 minutes. **Nuclei**, the organelles of greatest density, collect in the **sediment** at the base of the tube. All other cell contents are

The principle of pouring off the supernatant to leave the pure sediment behind can be repeated at the end of each spin. In this way the main organelles can be isolated.

Note that it is much easier to obtain nuclei, because they are isolated in the first spin. Ribosomes are isolated at the final spin.

found in the **supernatant** (the fluid above the sediment). Pouring off the supernatant leaves the sediment of relatively pure nuclei.

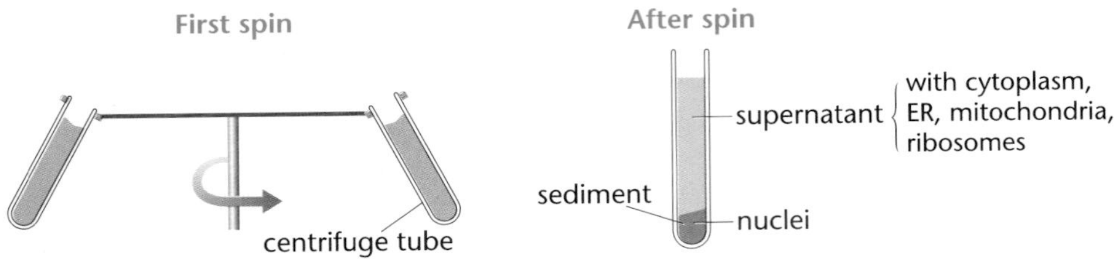

Second spin

The remaining supernatant fluid is spun at 10 000 to 20 000 g for a further 20 minutes. **Mitochondria**, the most dense of the remaining organelles collect in the sediment. All other cell contents are found in the **supernatant**.

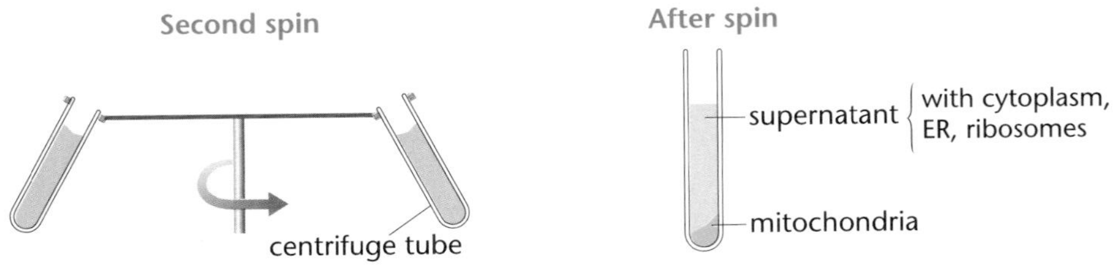

Third spin

The remaining supernatant fluid is spun at 100 000 g for a further 60 minutes. In this sediment are fragments of endoplasmic reticulum and ribosomes. Other cell contents e.g. cytoplasm and proteins remain in the supernatant.

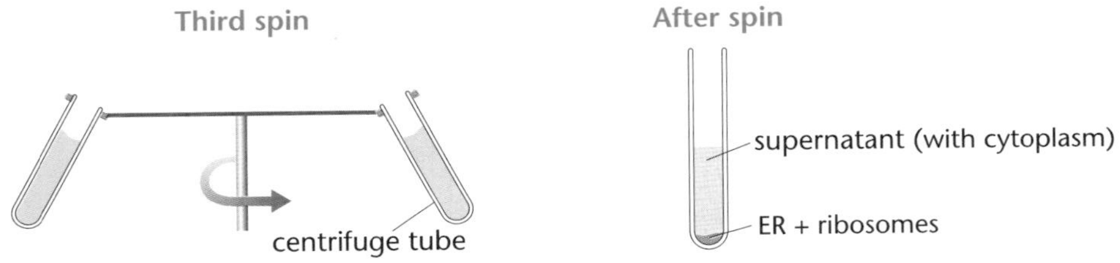

Using this technique the organelles are isolated. By providing them with suitable conditions they remain active for a time and can be used in investigations, e.g. chloroplasts given isotonic solution, suitable (warm) temperature, light, carbon dioxide and water, will continue to photosynthesise.

Electron and light microscopy

AQA A	M1
AQA B	M1
EDEXCEL	M1
OCR	M1
WJEC	M1
NICCEA	M1

Microscopes **magnify** the image of a specimen to enable the human eye to see minute objects not visible to the naked eye. **Resolution** of a microscope is the ability to distinguish between two objects as separate entities. At low resolution only one object may be detected. At high resolution two distinct objects are visible. At high resolution the image of such a specimen would show considerable detail.

The light microscope has limited resolution (0.02 μm) due to the wavelength of light so that organelles such as mitochondria, although visible, do not have clarity. Electron microscopes have exceptional resolution. The transmission electron microscope has a high resolution (0.2 to 0.3 nm). This enables even tiny organelles to be seen.

The light microscope

This type of microscope uses white light to illuminate a specimen. The light is focused onto the specimen by a **condensing lens**. The specimen is placed on a microscope slide which is clipped onto a platform, known as the **stage**. The image is viewed via an eyepiece or ocular lens. Overall magnification of the specimen depends on the individual magnification of the eyepiece lens and objective lens. For example, if a specimen is being observed with an eyepiece $\times 10$ and an objective lens of $\times 40$, then the image is 400 times the true size of the specimen.

> **KEY POINT**
> Many specimens need **staining** with chemicals so that tissues and, perhaps, organelles can be seen clearly, e.g. methylene blue is used to stain nuclei. Sometimes more than one stain is used, e.g. in differential staining, so that sub-cellular parts contrast against each other.

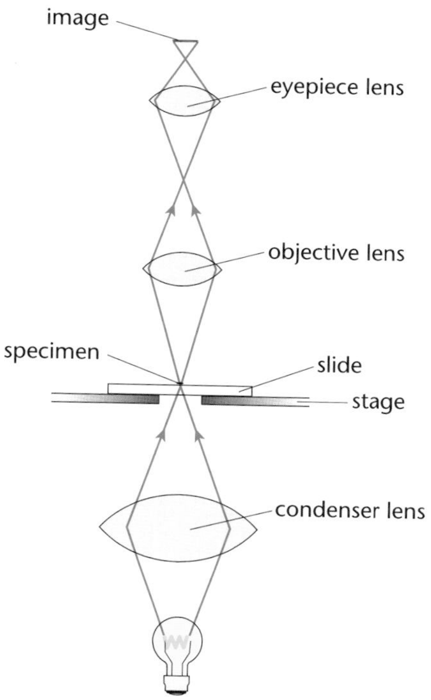

light microscope

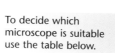

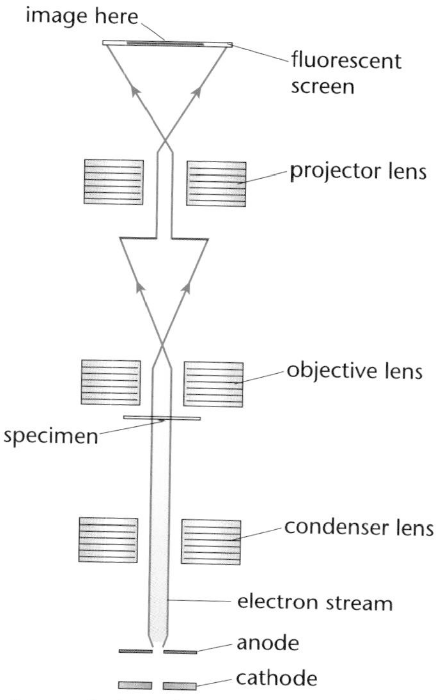

transmission electron microscope

To decide which microscope is suitable use the table below.

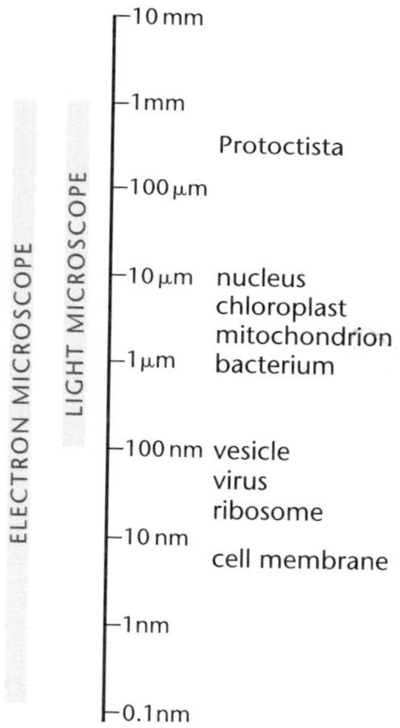

The electron microscope

This uses an electron stream which is directed at the specimen. The **transmission electron microscope (TEM)** has extremely high magnification and resolution properties. Specimens are placed in a vacuum within the microscope, to ensure the electrons do not collide with air molecules and distort the image. **Stains** such as **osmium** and **uranium** salts are used to make organelles distinct. These salts are absorbed by organelles and membranes differentially, e.g. the nuclear membrane absorbs more of the salts than other parts. In this way the nuclear membrane becomes more dense. When the electron beam hits the specimen, electrons are unable to pass through this dense membrane. The membrane shows up as a dark shadow area on the image, because it is in an electron shadow. Cytoplasm allows more electrons to pass through. When these electrons hit the fluorescent screen visible light is emitted.

Artefacts

When microscopic specimens are prepared there are often several chemical and physical procedures. Often the material is dead so changes from the living specimen are expected. Microscopic material should be analysed with care because there may have been some artificial change in the material during preparation, e.g. next to some cells a student sees a series of small circles. They look like eggs but are merely air bubbles. These are **artefacts**; structures alien to the material which should not be interpreted as part of the specimen.

Microscopic measurement

It is sometimes necessary to measure microscopic structures. There are two instruments needed for this process, a graticule and stage micrometer.

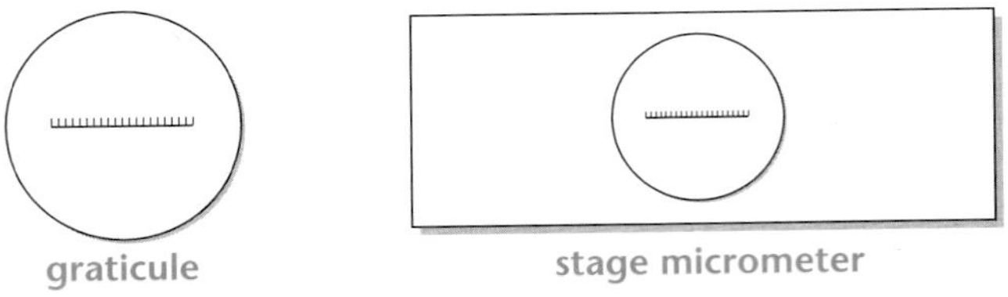

Calibration and measurement technique

- Put a graticule into the eyepiece of a microscope
- look through the eyepiece lens and the graticule line can be seen
- put a stage micrometer on the microscope stage
- look through the eyepiece lens
- line up the ruled line of the graticule with the ruled line of the stage micrometer
- calibrate the eyepiece by finding out the number of eyepiece units (e.u.) equal to one stage unit (s.u.); each is 0.01 mm
- if three eyepiece units equal 1 stage unit, then 1 eyepiece unit is equal to 0.01/3 (0.0033 mm)
- take away the stage micrometer and replace it with a specimen
- measure the dimensions of the specimen in terms of eyepiece units.

Important! Every time you change the objective lens, e.g. move from low power to high power, recalibration is necessary. In an examination this may be tested. Many candidates forget to recalibrate. Don't miss the mark!

Example

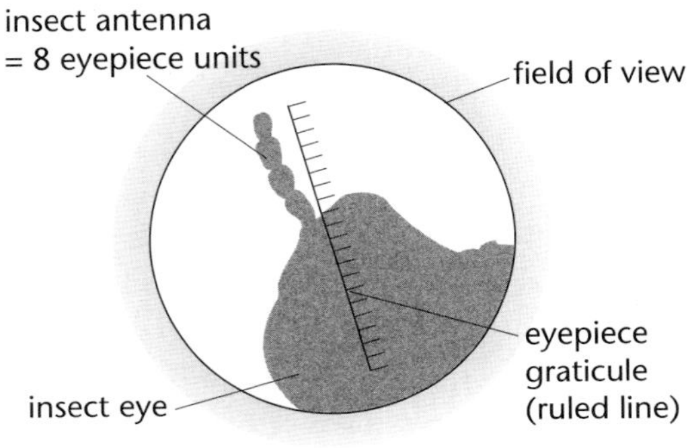

1 s.u. = 0.01 mm
3 e.u. = 1 s.u.
therefore 1 e.u. = 0.0033 mm
length of insect antenna = 8 e.u.
= 8 × 0.0033 mm
= 0.0264 mm

Estimation of populations

There are several techniques which can be used depending on the size of the cells or organisms. A haemocytometer can be used to estimate the numbers of red blood cells or minute organisms such as yeasts. A haemocytometer is a microscope slide on which an etched grid of squares has been drawn.

Technique:

- put a suspension of cells on the haemocytometer
- put a cover slip over the cell suspension to make sure that the depth is uniform (known depth, 0.1 mm)
- each small square is 0.0025 mm^2 in area and the volume above each square is 0.00025 mm^3
- look through the microscope and count the number of cells per square in a number of squares
- if a cell touches the sides of the square then only count vertical left and horizontal bottom cells
- calculate the average number of cells per square and then the number of cells per mm^3 or cm^3.

Important! In an examination you may be tested for your awareness of dilution. There are millions of red blood cells in even a small amount of blood (too many to count accurately). It is therefore always diluted before the haemocytometer count. You will need to multiply the amount of cells per mm^3 or cm^3 by the dilution factor (the question will supply this).

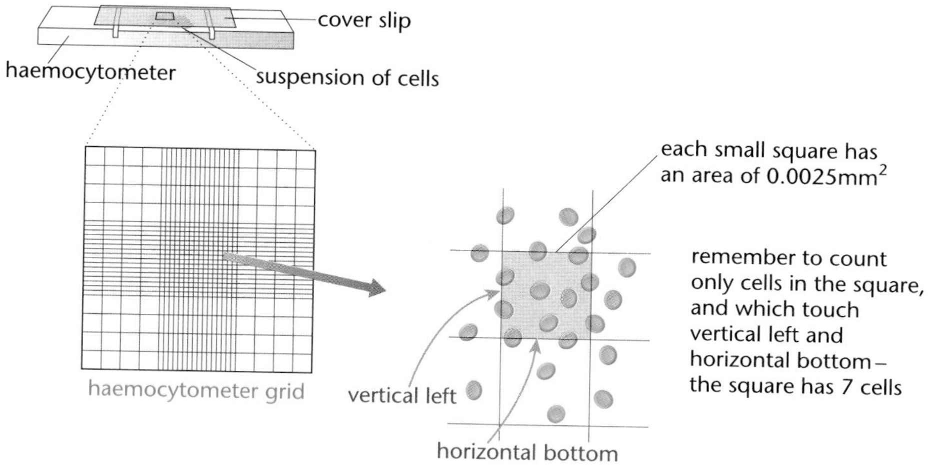
cover slip
haemocytometer
suspension of cells
each small square has an area of 0.0025mm²
remember to count only cells in the square, and which touch vertical left and horizontal bottom – the square has 7 cells
haemocytometer grid
vertical left
horizontal bottom

Progress check

1 Describe how the width of an insect's leg could be measured using a microscope, graticule and stage micrometer.

2 A student measured the insect leg but considered that a higher magnification was needed to improve accuracy. What is the significance of changing magnification to the measuring technique?

1 Put a graticule into the eyepiece of a microscope; put a stage micrometer on the microscope stage; look through the eyepiece lens; line up the ruled line of the graticule with the ruled line of the stage micrometer; calibrate the eyepiece by finding out the number of eyepiece units equal to one stage unit; a stage unit is a known length, so an eyepiece unit length can be calculated; take away the stage micrometer and replace with specimen; measure width of insect leg in eyepiece units.

2 Recalibration is needed for each new magnification.

2.3 Specialisation of cells

After studying this section you should be able to:

LEARNING SUMMARY

- *understand cell specialisation and how cells aggregate into tissues and organs*
- *recall a range of cell adaptations*

The earlier parts of this chapter informed of the structure and function of generalised animal and plant cells. The described features are found in many unicellular organisms where all the life-giving processes are carried out in one cell. Additionally many multicellular organisms exist. A few show no specialisation and consist of repeated identical cells, e.g. Volvox, a colonial alga. Most multicellular organisms exhibit specialisation, where different cells are adapted for specific roles.

Cell adaptations

AQA A	M1
AQA B	M1
EDEXCEL	M1
OCR	M1
WJEC	M1
NICCEA	M1

Some important features:

Red blood cell

- no nucleus
- high surface area
- contains haemoglobin which has an affinity for oxygen

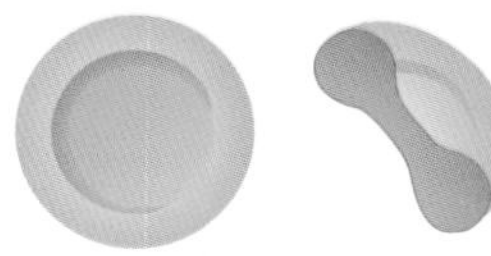

red blood cell

Endothelial cell

- very thin
- allows exchange of chemicals

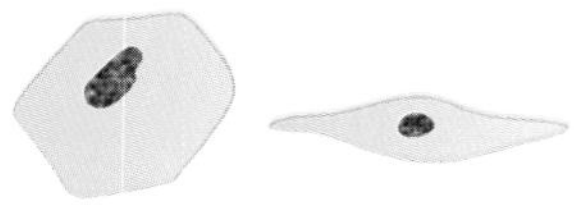

endothelial cell

Plant palisade cell

- chloroplasts for photosynthesis
- chloroplasts can move to absorb more light
- contains chlorophyll which absorbs light
- sap vacuole stores important chemicals

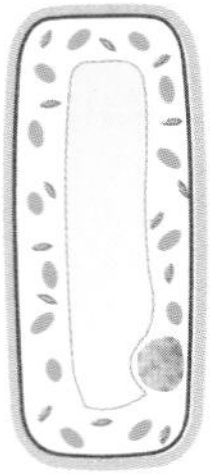

Motor neurone

- can transmit electrical impulses
- has an insulative fatty sheath
- motor end plates to stimulate muscles to contract.

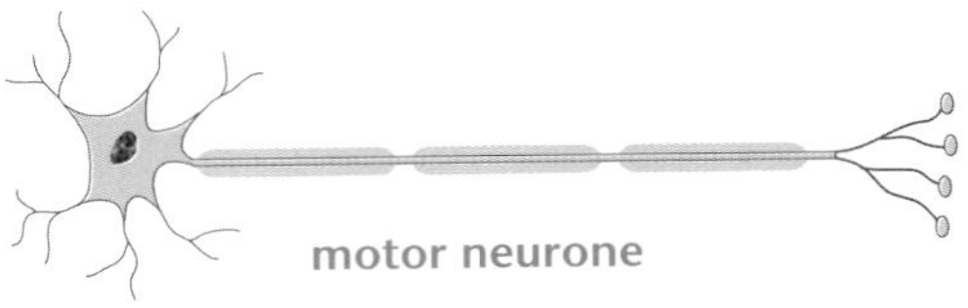

Tissues and organs

AQA A	M1
AQA B	M1
EDEXCEL	M1, M2
OCR	M1
WJEC	M1
NICCEA	M1

A **tissue** is a collection of similar cells, derived form the same source, all working together for a specific function, e.g. palisade cells of the leaf which photosynthesise or the smooth muscle cells of the intestine which carry out peristalsis.

An **organ** is a collection of tissues which combine their properties for a specific function, e.g. the stomach includes the tissues; smooth muscle, epithelial lining cells, connective tissue, etc. Together they enable the stomach to digest food.

A range of tissues and organs combine to form a system, e.g. the **respiratory system**.

In multicellular organisms specific groups of cells are specialised for a particular role. This increased efficiency helps the organism to have better survival qualities in the environment.

The photomicrograph below shows some of the cells which are part of a bone.

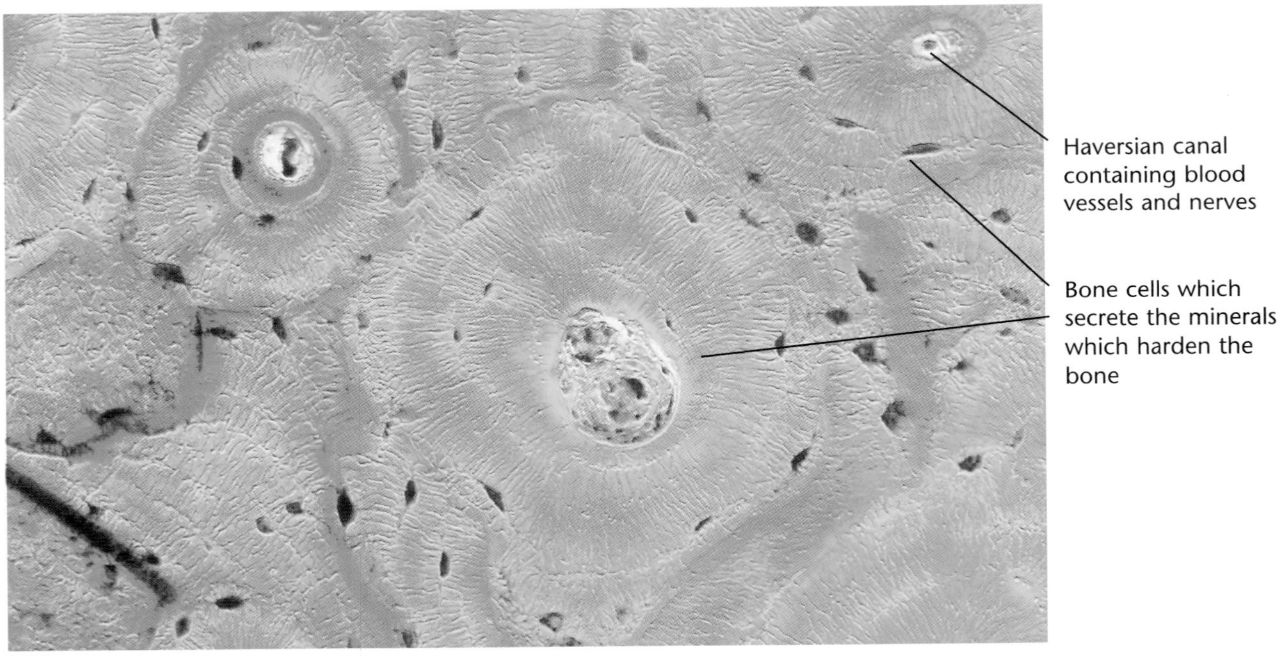

Combinations of cells each contribute their specific adaptations to the overall function of an organ. Compact bone, spongy bone and articular cartilage all have distinct but vital qualities.

Sample question and model answer

The electron micrograph below shows a lymphocyte which secretes antibodies. Antibodies are proteins.

Analyse electron micrographs carefully. Learn the typical structures of all the organelles then you will be prepared.

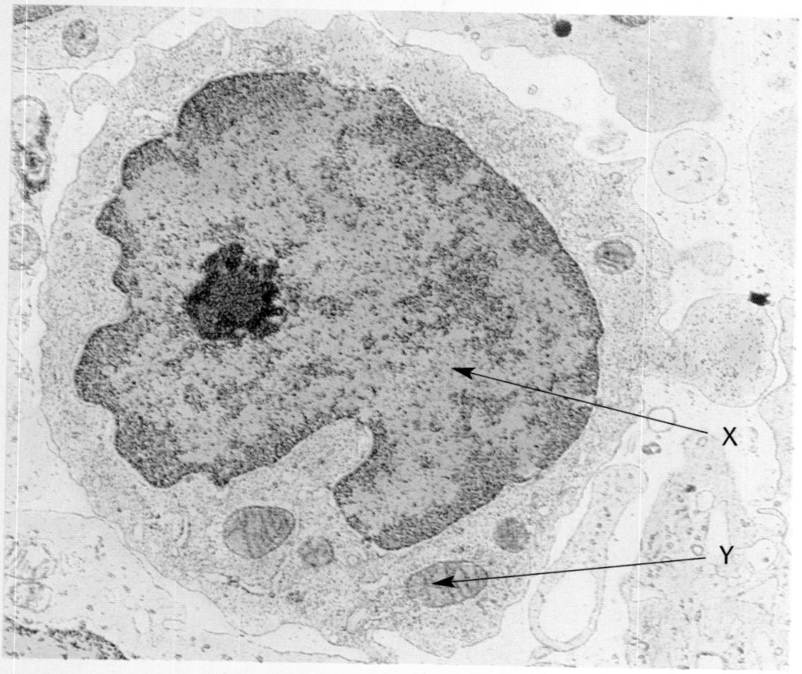

(a)

(i) Name the organelles X and Y. [2]

X = nucleus

Y = mitochondria

(ii) The cell was stained with uranium salts in preparation for a transmission electron microscope. Explain how this stain caused the nucleus to show a dark shade compared to the light shade of the cytoplasm. [4]

The stain was taken up by the nucleus more than the cytoplasm; the electrons could not pass through the stained (dense) parts of the nucleus so the dark nucleus parts on the screen are in electron shade. Electrons pass through the cytoplasm and cause light emission (fluorescence) at the screen.

There are many different stains. Most examination boards require that you know the principle of how they work, but not specific names.

(b)

(i) Given a piece of liver how would you isolate mitochondria from the cells? [7]

Put the liver in isotonic solution;
homogenise the liver or grind with a pestle and mortar;
filter the homogenate through muslin layers to remove cell debris;
put in a centrifuge; spin at 500 – 600 g for 10 minutes;
discard the pellet or sediment; centrifuge the supernatant;
spin at 10 000 – 20 000 g for 20 minutes;
mitochondria are now in the pellet or sediment.

Note that there are 7 marks maximum for this question. Any seven of the responses shown would achieve maximum credit. The ideal answer given shows 9 potential creditable points.

(ii) Why is it important to keep fresh liver cells at a temperature of around 5°C during the preparation of the sample? [2]

They keep alive for a longer period since a low temperature slows down the action of the enzymes which break down the mitochondria; i.e. prevents or slows down cell autolysis (self-digestion of the cells).

Practice examination questions

1 The diagram shows the structure of a cell surface membrane.

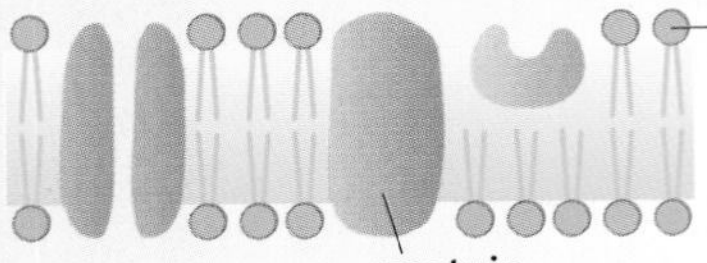

(a) Name molecule A. [1]

(b) Describe the role of protein molecules in:
  (i) active transport
  (ii) facilitated diffusion. [4]

2 (a) Complete the table by ticking boxes to show the correct statement(s) for each method by which molecules cross a cell surface membrane.

	diffusion	***facilitated diffusion***	***active transport***
molecules move from where they are in high concentration to low concentration			
molecules move from where they are in low concentration to high concentration			
a protein carrier is needed			

[3]

(b) Name **two** other methods by which molecules can pass through the cell surface membrane. [2]

3 The diagram shows a section through a leaf.

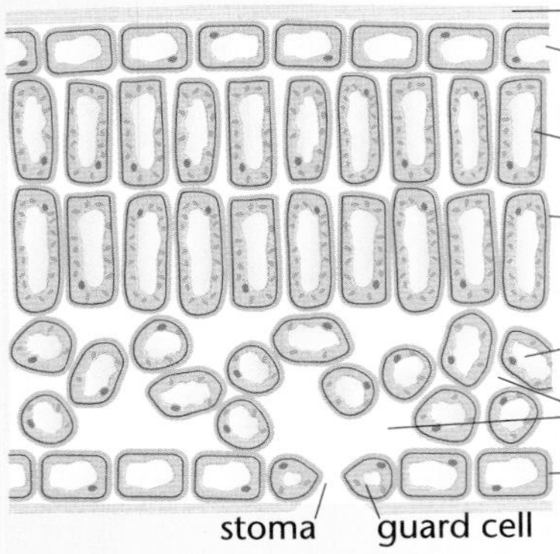

Explain how the leaf is adapted to achieve the maximum rate of photosynthesis. [7]

4 The diagram below shows a bacterium.

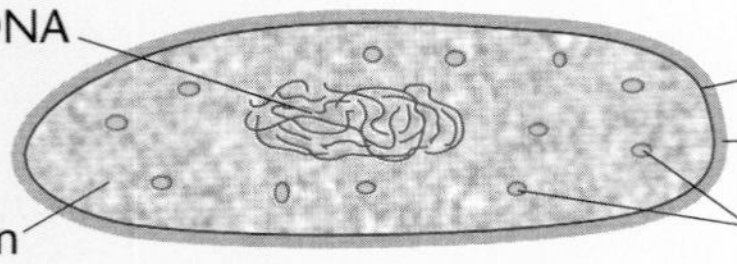

(a) Describe **two** ways, visible in the diagram, which show that the bacterium is a prokaryotic organism. [2]

(b) Name **two** organelles from a human cell which show that it is a eukaryotic organism. [2]

Practice examination questions (continued)

Remember to use the dilution factor when calculating the original population.

5 Yeast population growth was investigated with the help of a haemocytometer. A sample from a yeast culture was diluted to 0.1 of the original concentration. The haemocytometer squares (below) show some of the yeast cells.

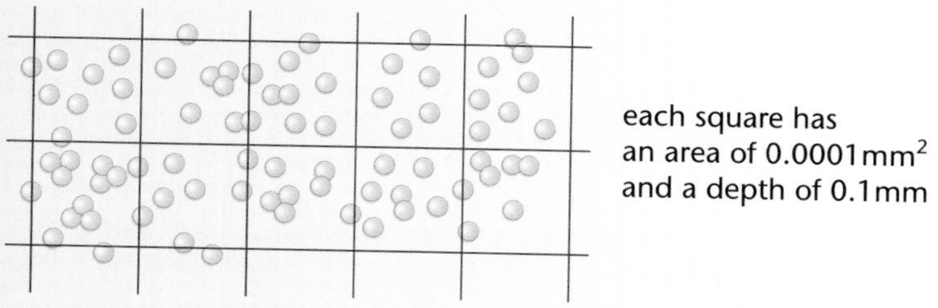

(a) (i) Using the 10 haemocytometer squares in the diagram, calculate the average number of yeast cells per square. [2]

(ii) How many yeast cells would there be in 1 cm^3 of the original yeast suspension? (1 cm^3 = 1000 mm^3)

Show your working. [3]

(b) Why was it important to stir the yeast culture before putting the sample onto the haemocytometer? [1]

6 This diagram below shows the structure of a transmission electron microscope (TEM).

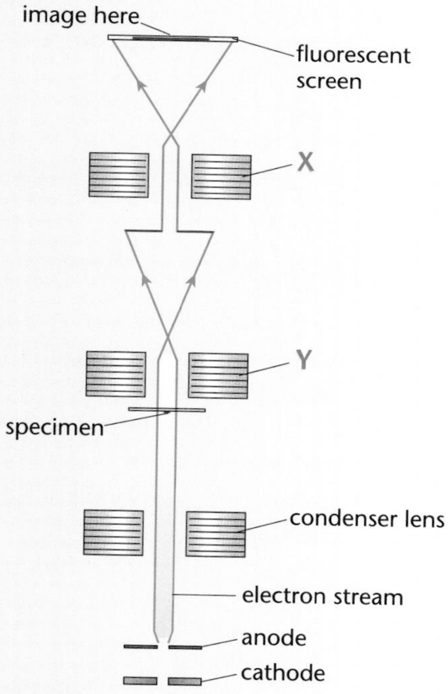

transmission electron microscope

(a) Name lens X and lens Y. [2]

(b) Why is it necessary for the specimen to be put in a vacuum? [1]

(c) Occasionally an image seen when using the electron microscope shows an item not present in the living organism.

(i) What name is given to this type of item? [1]

(ii) How should the presence of the item be interpreted? [1]

Chapter 3

Enzymes

The following topics are covered in this chapter:

- *Enzymes in action*
- *Inhibition of enzymes*
- *Digestive enzymes*
- *Applications of enzymes*

3.1 Enzymes in action

LEARNING SUMMARY

After studying this section you should be able to:

- *understand the role of the active site and the enzyme–substrate complex in enzyme action*
- *understand how enzymes catalyse biochemical reactions by lowering activation energy*
- *understand the factors which affect the rate of enzyme catalysed reactions*

How enzymes work

AQA A	M1
AQA B	M1
EDEXCEL	M1
OCR	M1
WJEC	M1
NICCEA	M1

Living cells carry out many biochemical reactions. These reactions take place **rapidly** due to the presence of enzymes. All enzymes consist of **globular proteins** which have the ability to 'drive' biochemical reactions. Some enzymes require additional non-protein groups to enable them to work efficiently. The enzyme dehydrogenase needs a coenzyme NAD to function.

The tertiary folding of polypeptides are responsible for the special shape of the active site.

KEY POINT

The ability of an enzyme to function depends on the specific shape of the protein molecule. The intricate shape created by polypeptide folding (see page 27) is a key factor in both theories of enzyme action.

Lock and key theory

In an examination the lock and key theory is the most important model to consider. Remember that both catabolic and anabolic reactions may be given.

- Some part of the enzyme has a cavity with a precise shape (**active site**)
- a substrate can fit into the active site
- the active site (lock) is exactly the correct shape to fit the substrate (key)
- the substrate binds to the enzyme forming an **enzyme–substrate complex**
- the reaction takes place immediately
- certain enzymes break a substrate down into two or more products (**catabolic** reaction)
- other enzymes bond two or more substrates together to assemble one product (**anabolic** reaction).

metabolic reaction = anabolic reaction + catabolic reaction

Remember that metabolism is a summary of **build up** and **break down reactions.**

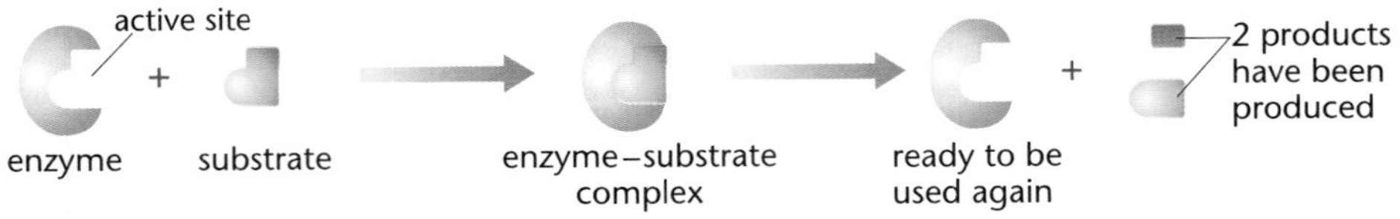

a catabolic reaction (substrate broken down)

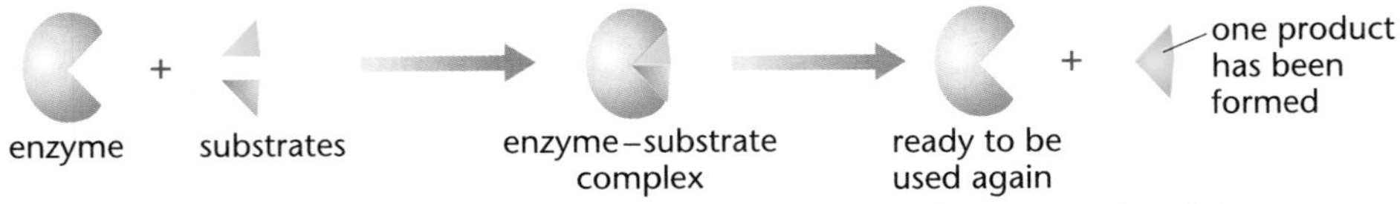

an anabolic reaction (substrates used to build a new molecule)

Induced fit theory

- The active site is a cavity of a particular shape
- initially the active site is not the correct shape in which to fit the substrate
- as the substrate approaches the active site, the site changes and this results in it being a perfect fit
- after the reaction has taken place, and the products have gone, the active site returns to its normal shape.

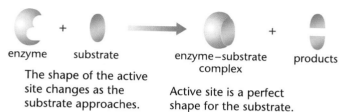

Lowering of activation energy

Every reaction requires the input of energy. Enzymes reduce the level of activation energy needed as shown by the graph.

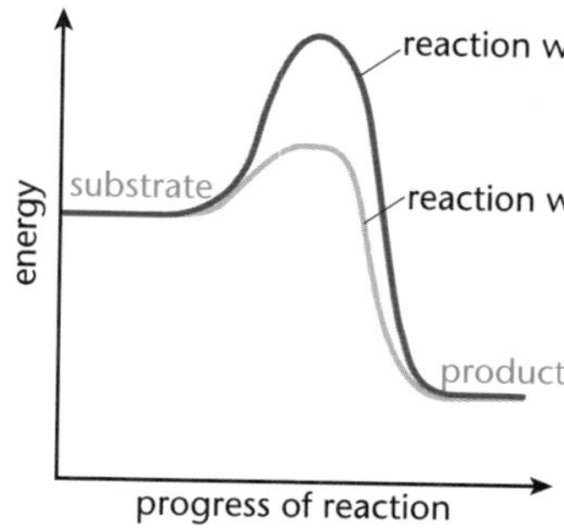

The higher the activation energy the slower the reaction. An enzyme reduces the amount of energy required for a biochemical reaction. When an enzyme binds with a substrate the available energy has a greater effect and the rate of catalysis increases. The conditions which exist during a reaction are very important when considering the rate of progress. Each of the following has an effect on the rate:

- concentration of substrate molecules
- concentration of enzyme molecules
- temperature
- pH.

You may be questioned on the factors which affect the rate of reaction. Less able candidates tend to remember just one or two factors. Learn all 4 factors here and achieve a higher grade!

What is the effect of enzyme concentration?

When considering the rate of an enzyme catalysed reaction the proportion of enzyme to substrate molecules should be considered. Every substrate molecule fits into an active site, then the reaction takes place. If there are more substrate molecules than enzyme molecules then the number of active sites available is a **limiting factor**. The **optimum rate** of reaction is achieved when all the active sites are in use. At this stage if more substrate is added, there is no increase in rate of product formation. When there are fewer substrate molecules than enzyme molecules the reaction will take place very quickly, as long as the conditions are appropriate.

Look out for questions which show the rate of reaction graphically. The examiners often test your understanding of limiting factors (see practice question).

How does temperature affect the rate of an enzyme catalysed reaction?

- **Heat energy** reaching the enzyme and substrate molecules causes them to **increase random movement**.
- The greater the heat energy the more the molecules move and so **collide** more often.
- The more **collisions** there are the greater the chance that substrates will fit into an **active site**, up to a specific temperature.

Remember that particles in liquids (and gases) are in constant random motion, even though we cannot see them.

- At the optimum temperature of an enzyme, the reaction rate is maximum.
- Heat energy also affects the shape of the active site, the active site being best at the optimum temperature.
- At temperatures above optimum, the rate of reaction decreases because the active site begins to distort.
- Very high temperature causes the enzyme to become denatured, i.e. bonding becomes irreversibly changed and the active site is permanently damaged.
- At very high temperatures, the number of collisions is correspondingly high, but without active sites no products can be formed.
- At lower temperatures than the optimum, the rate of the reaction decreases because of reduced enzyme/substrate collisions.

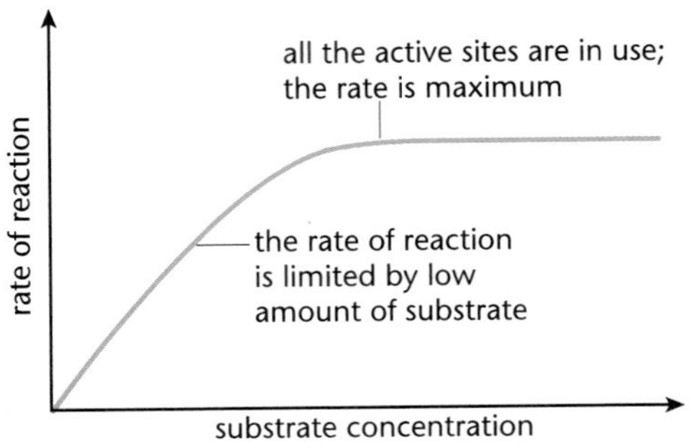
all the active sites are in use; the rate is maximum
the rate of reaction is limited by low amount of substrate
rate of reaction
substrate concentration

It is interesting to consider that some microbes can spoil ice cream in a freezer whereas a different microbe, with different enzymes, can decompose grass in a 'steaming' compost heap.

Most enzymes have an optimum between 30°C and 40°C, but there are many exceptions. An example of this is shown by some bacteria:

- thermophiles – enzymes optimum above 40°C
- mesophiles – enzymes optimum between 20°C and 40°C
- psychrophiles – enzymes efficient below 20°C.

How does pH affect the rate of an enzyme catalysed reaction?

Remember that other factors affect an enzyme catalysed reaction:

- substrate concentration
- enzyme concentration
- temperature.

Each can be a limiting factor.

The pH of the medium can have a direct effect on the bonding responsible for the secondary and tertiary structure of enzymes. If the active site is changed then enzyme action will be affected. Each enzyme has an optimum pH.

- Many enzymes work best at neutral or slightly alkaline conditions, e.g. salivary amylase.
- Pepsin works best in acid conditions around pH 3.0, as expected considering that the stomach contains hydrochloric acid.

For the two enzyme examples above, the active sites are ideally shaped at the pHs mentioned. An inappropriate pH, often acidic, can change the active site drastically, so that the substrate cannot bind. The reaction will not take place. On most occasions the change of shape is not permanent and can be returned to optimum by the addition of an alkali.

Progress check

How does temperature affect the rate of the reaction by which protein is changed to polypeptides by the enzyme pepsin, in the human stomach?

$$\text{protein} \xrightarrow{\text{pepsin}} \text{polypeptides}$$

- Heat energy causes the enzyme and substrate molecules to increase random movement, increasing the chance of collision.
- At 37°C (optimum temperature) there is a greater chance that the protein will fit into an active site, so the production of polypeptides is at maximum rate.
- At 37°C (optimum temperature) the shape of the active site is best suited to fit the protein.
- At temperatures higher than 37°C the rate of reaction decreases because the active site begins to distort.
- Very high temperature causes the pepsin to become denatured, i.e. bonding has been irreversibly changed and the active site is permanently damaged.
- At very high temperatures the number of collisions is correspondingly high, but without active sites no polypeptides can be formed.
- At lower temperatures than optimum the rate of reaction decreases because of reduced enzyme–substrate collisions.

3.2 Inhibition of enzymes

LEARNING SUMMARY

After studying this section you should be able to:

- *understand the action and effects of competitive and non-competitive inhibitors*
- *understand the process of end-product inhibition*

What are inhibitors?

AQA A	M1
AQA B	M1
EDEXCEL	M1
OCR	M1
WJEC	M1

If enzyme reactions inside the cell were to continue without regulation, there would be many problems. Cells possess **regulatory chemicals** which **slow down** or **stop** enzyme catalysed reactions. These chemicals are the inhibitors.

Competitive inhibitors

- These are molecules of **similar shape** to the normal substrate and are able to bind to the active site.
- They do not react within the active site, but leave after a time without any product forming.
- The enzymic reaction is **reduced** because while the inhibitor is in the active site, **no substrate can enter**.
- Substrate molecules **compete** for the active site so the rate of reaction decreases.
- The higher the proportion of competitive inhibitor the slower the rate of reaction.

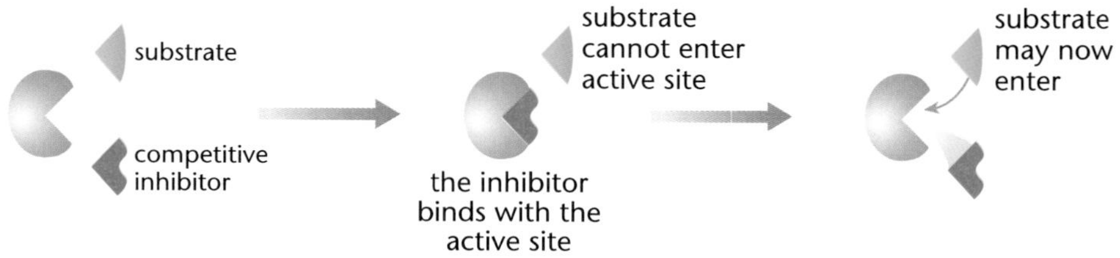

Some enzymes have two sites, the active site and one other. An **allosteric** molecule fits into the alternative site. Here it changes the shape of the active site. This can stimulate the reaction if the active site becomes a better shape **(allosteric activation)**. It can also inhibit if the active site becomes an inappropriate shape **(allosteric inhibition)**.

Non-competitive inhibitors

- These are molecules which bind to some part of an enzyme other than the active site.
- They have a different shape to the normal substrate.
- They change the shape of the active site which no longer allows binding of the substrate.
- Some substrate molecules may reach the active site before the non-competitive inhibitor.
- The rate of reaction is reduced.
- Finally they leave their binding sites, but substrate molecules do not compete for these, so they have a greater inhibitory effect.

The graph below shows the relative effects of competitive and non-competitive inhibitors, compared to a normal enzyme catalysed reaction.

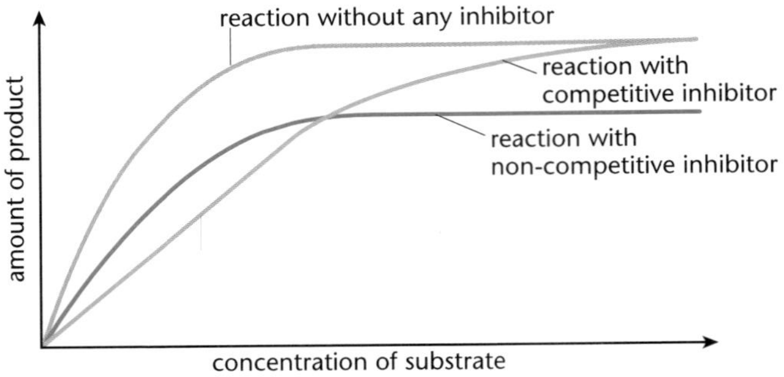

End-product inhibition

This mechanism is needed to regulate certain enzyme catalysed processes in organisms. It involves allosteric sites. The diagram below shows one example of end-product inhibition.

Stage 1

A substrate binds with the active site of enzyme X. A product is formed.

Stage 2

This product then binds with the active site of enzyme Y. Another product is formed.

Stage 3

The stage 2 product then binds with the active site of enzyme Z. Another product is formed.

Stage 4

This final product is the feedback product. It is the correct shape to bind with the allosteric site of enzyme X. Once in position it distorts the active site, inhibiting the first reaction and those which follow.
The final end product has caused its own decrease.

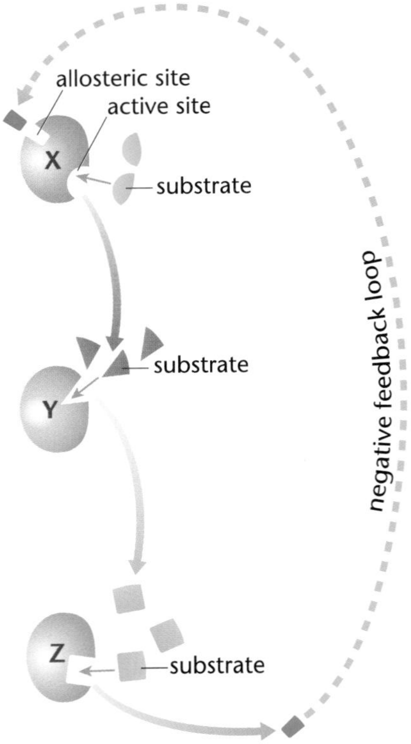

Progress check

1 Does the substrate compete with a non-competitive inhibitor to bind with the active site of an enzyme? Give a reason for your answer.

2 How does a non-competitive inhibitor reduce the rate of an enzyme catalysed reaction?

1 No. Non-competitive inhibitors have a different shape to the normal substrate. They bind to some part of an enzyme other than the active site.

2 They change the shape of the enzyme's active site which is less suitable for the binding of the substrate, so the rate of reaction decreases.

3.3 Digestive enzymes

After studying this section you should be able to:

LEARNING SUMMARY

- recall the sites of secretion and action of a range of human digestive enzymes
- recall extracellular digestion by saprobiotic microorganisms

Human digestive enzymes

AQA B M1
EDEXCEL M2
NICCEA M1

Animals which feed **heterotrophically** take in complex organic substances. These are subjected to physical breakdown, giving enzymes a more exposed surface area on which to act. The human digestive enzymes are **hydrolases** (see page 23). Each time a molecule is broken down water is required during the reaction. The table below includes some human digestive enzymes.

Lipase is aided by bile, an alkaline secretion. It reaches the duodenum and emulsifies lipids, breaking them up into tiny globules of lipid (a high surface area for the lipase to act on). It helps to neutralise acid from the stomach so that enzymes in the duodenum and small intestine have a suitable environment.

site in alimentary canal	*secretion*	*enzyme*	*substrate*	*product*
mouth	saliva	amylase	starch	maltose
stomach	gastric juice	pepsin	protein	polypeptides
duodenum	pancreatic juice	lipase	lipids	fatty acid glycerol
duodenum	pancreatic juice	amylase	starch	maltose
small intestine	intestinal juice	maltase	maltose	glucose

KEY POINT

Pepsin is an **endopeptidase**. This means that it breaks peptide bonds in the middle of a polypeptide chain. **Exopeptidases** break peptide bonds to remove individual amino acids from the ends of polypeptides.

These two types of protease work together, the endopeptidases producing shorter polypeptide chains, consequently the exopeptidases have more ends to work on.

Saprobiotic bacteria and fungi

AQA A M1
AQA B M1
EDEXCEL M1
OCR M1
WJEC M1
NICCEA M1

These microorganisms secrete **extracellular** enzymes to obtain nutrients by decaying organic matter. The enzymes act outside the cell, so that smaller nutrient molecules can be absorbed in solution. The diagram below shows a saprobiotic fungus decaying a starch-rich potato.

Most examination boards use the term saprobiotic instead of saprophytic. Both refer to decomposers.

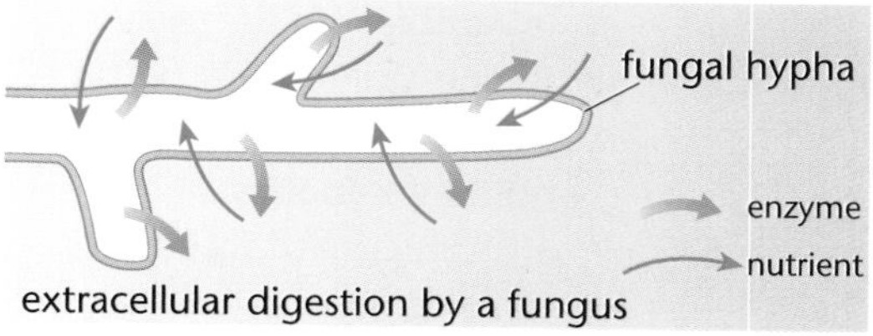

extracellular digestion by a fungus

Progress check

The diagram shows a saprobiotic fungus feeding on starch.

Describe and explain how the fungus is able to obtain a supply of soluble glucose.

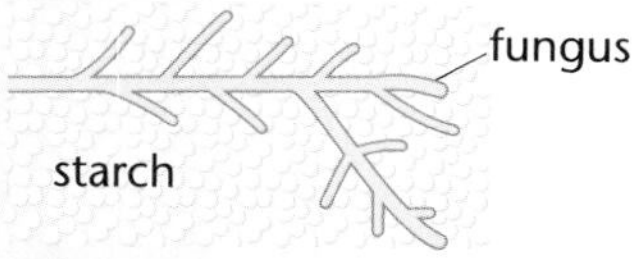

The fungus secretes an extracellular enzyme, amylase. This breaks down starch into maltose. It also secretes maltase which breaks down maltose into glucose. These are soluble compounds which can be absorbed through the fungal cell membrane by the process of diffusion.

3.4 Applications of enzymes

After studying this section you should be able to:

- *describe and understand a range of home, medical and industrial applications of enzymes*
- *understand the advantages of immobilised enzymes*

LEARNING SUMMARY

Home, medical and industrial applications of enzymes

AQA A	M1
AQA B	M1
EDEXCEL	M1
WJEC	M1
NICCEA	M1

There are a wide range of applications of enzymes used in processes throughout the world. Historically enzymes have been exploited for many years, e.g. yeast cells are still used in fermentation to produce ethanol. The yeast is really used as an enzyme 'package' to change sugar into ethanol via a sequence of enzyme catalysed reactions.

We currently live in a golden age of biotechnology and will witness many new applications of enzyme use within the coming years.

Biological detergents

These are products such as biological washing and dishwasher powders. The common link between them is they contain a range of **hydrolysing enzymes**. Manufacturers rarely inform the public of the specific enzymes in their detergents, but invariably they are:

Note the pattern – enzymes often end in -ase.

- **amylases** – break down starch stains
- **cellulases** – break down the ends of damaged cotton fibres to remove the 'fuzz' produced during washing
- **lipase** – breaks down lipid stains into fatty acids and glycerol
- **proteases** break down the many different proteins found in food stains.

This enzyme 'cocktail' has a low temperature optimum around 50°C, so that much less electricity is needed for washing; additionally, difficult stains are removed.

The enzymes are produced in fermenters (see page 88).

Fruit juice extraction

Crushing fruit such as apples releases juice, a valuable food product. Extraction of the juice is aided by an enzyme as follows :

You could be given a question about a different enzyme which you have not studied before. Do not panic! Enough information will be supplied and all you need to do is apply your knowledge of enzyme principles.

- **insoluble pectin** causes plant cell walls to adhere to adjacent cells
- during storage this pectin changes to a **soluble** form which **binds water strongly**
- **pectinase** is used to break down the pectin chains which **reduces** its water-holding capacity
- after pectinase treatment, crushing releases a greater yield of juice
- the pectinase even clears the juice of 'cloudiness' caused by pectin.

Lactose removal from milk

This is necessary because some people have allergic reactions to lactose, the sugar in milk. **Lactase** is added to change the lactose to glucose and galactose. As a result, lactose-free milk is available to consumers.

Clinistix

These are strips of cellulose which have the enzyme **glucose oxidase** stuck to one end. When dipped into urine containing glucose the reaction produces **hydrogen**

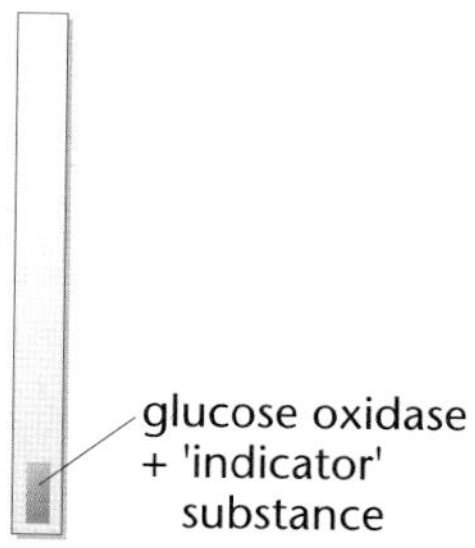

a clinistix strip

peroxide. This reacts with another compound to give a colour change. This colour change signals that the patient is potentially diabetic.

Biosensors

These are devices which are used to detect specific molecules. All biosensors use a biological component such as a layer of enzymes or antibodies. These produce a signal in the presence of a specific chemical. They work as follows:

- a sample is placed in contact with the biosensor
- when enzymes are used in the 'detection membrane', if the chemical being investigated is present, the molecules fit into the active sites of the enzyme
- this causes a transducer to produce an electrical signal
- the level of electrical signal is proportional to the level of chemical, so the device is quantitative.

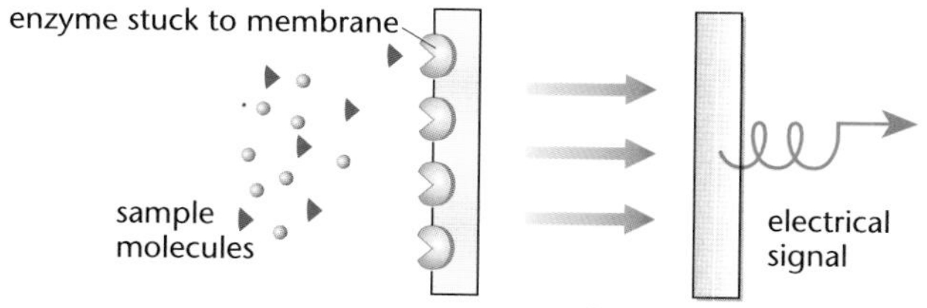

one type of biosensor

ELISA (Enzyme-linked immunosorbent assay)

This is used to detect minute quantities of protein in fluids such as blood plasma. It works as follows:

- if protein X is to be detected
- antibodies known to bind to protein X, are fixed to a plate
- protein X, *if present*, binds to the antibody whereas all other proteins wash away
- a second type of antibody, linked to an enzyme, is added and binds to X at a different site to the first antibody
- a specific substrate is added which binds to the active site of this enzyme
- the product formed is easily detectable, e.g. brightly coloured
- this product would not form in the plate at all if protein X was absent.

Some diseases can be diagnosed by ELISAs, as specific proteins are detected in blood plasma. This technique has many applications including the detection of pregnancy, bacteria and viruses.

Immobilised enzymes

Consider the methods of immobilised enzymes. The more bullet points you remember, the more marks you will gain. Top exam candidates can recall most points. Look at the number of marks available at the end of a question. This informs you of the number of creditable points you need to make to score highly!

After completion of an enzyme catalysed reaction the enzyme remains unchanged and can be used again. Unfortunately the enzyme can contaminate the product, as they can be difficult to separate out from the reaction mixture. For this reason immobilised enzymes have been developed. They are used as follows:

- enzymes are attached to insoluble substances such as resins and alginates
- these substances usually form membranes or beads and the enzymes bind to the outside
- substrate molecules readily bind with the active sites and the normal reactions go ahead
- the immobilised enzymes are easy to recover, remaining in the membranes or beads
- there is no contamination of the product by free enzymes
- expensive enzymes are re-used
- processes can be continuous unlike batch, where the process is stopped for 'harvesting'.

Sample questions and model answers

1

The graph below shows the rate of an enzyme catalysed reaction, with and without a **non-competitive inhibitor**, at different substrate concentrations.

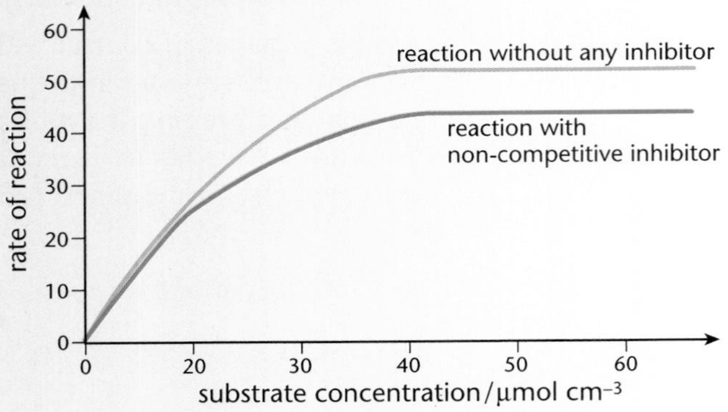

(a) Give **one** piece of evidence from the graph which shows that the inhibitor was non-competitive rather than competitive. [1]

When the non-competitive inhibitor is present the maximum rate of the inhibitor-free reaction is not reached.

A competitive inhibitor would still allow the maximum rate at high substrate concentration.

(b) Explain why the rates of the inhibited and non-inhibited reactions were very similar up to a substrate concentration of 20 μmol cm^{-3}. [2]

Before a concentration of 20 μmol cm^{-3}

- in both reactions substrate molecules are similarly successful in reaching active sites
- few inhibitor molecules have become bound to the alternative sites on the enzyme
- few active sites have been changed so are still available for the substrate.

Remember that the non-competitive inhibitor binds to a different part of an enzyme and NOT the active site. It still causes a change in the active site which cannot then bind with the substrate.

(c) Give **two** factors that are needed to be kept constant when investigating both the inhibited and non-inhibited reactions. [2]

- temperature
- pH

2

The sequence below shows a biochemical pathway which involves three enzymes E_1, E_2 and E_3 to form molecule X.

Be ready to use any visual clues about the active sites and *alternative* sites.

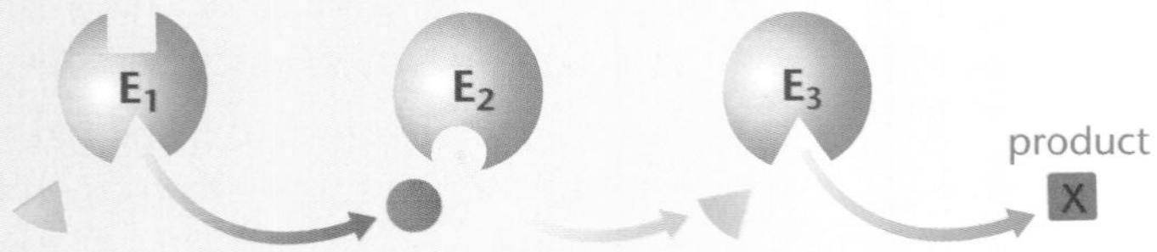

(a) Explain how product X is an allosteric inhibitor of E_1 [2]

The molecule fits into an alternative site on E_1 and the shape of active site is changed, the substrate therefore cannot bind to active site.

(b) Name the type of inhibition shown by this sequence. [1]

End-product inhibition.

Practice examination questions

1 The diagram below shows a biosensor which can detect very small quantities of urea in blood and urine.

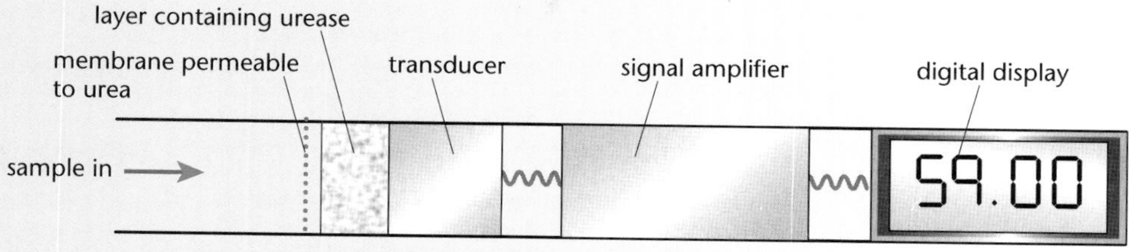

Biosensor

(a) Explain how the biosensor shown can be used to detect a minute quantity of urea molecules in a sample of blood. [3]

(b) How is the biosensor able to detect different amounts of urea in each sample? [1]

2 Describe each of the following pairs to show that you understand the main differences between them:

(a) the lock and key enzyme theory **and** the induced fit enzyme theory

(b) endopeptidases **and** exopeptidases. [4]

3 In an industrial process silver is reclaimed from a waste fluid. The silver is held on cellulose film by protein. An expensive enzyme is used to remove the protein. It is immobilised in a gel layer as fluid is passed over it.

State the advantages of using an immobilised enzyme in this process. [2]

4 In terms of the tertiary structure of the enzyme, explain why amylase can break down starch but has no effect on a lipid. [3]

5 Bacterial α-amylase works best at around 80°C.

(a) Name the substrate which it breaks down. [1]

(b) Why is this enzyme described as a thermostable enzyme? [1]

6 ***Biox*** is a biological washing powder which contains a wide spectrum protease. The graph shows the effect of a range of concentrations of protease on the removal of protein stains.

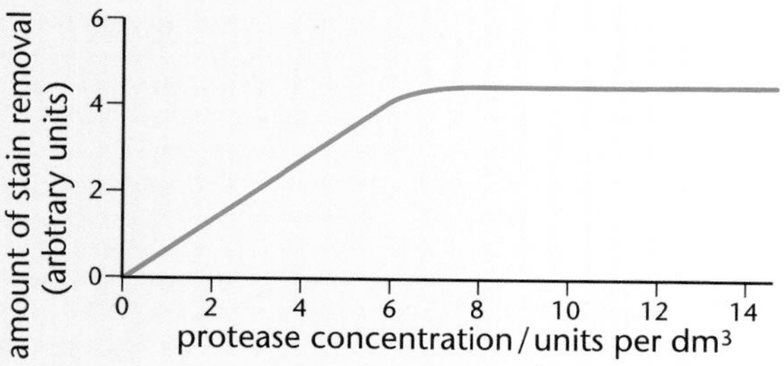

Practice examination questions (continued)

(a) What is the effect of the concentration of protease on stain removal between 2 and 6 units of protease? [1]

(b) Instructions on the washing powder box advised people to use an amount of powder containing 12 units of protease dm^{-2}. This was not good advice.

(i) Which concentration of protease removed the stains at the fastest and most economical rate? [1]

(ii) The protease is a hydrolytic enzyme. Explain, precisely, how this enzyme removes protein stains. [3]

(iii) Why is it necessary to use a wide-spectrum protease in the washing powder? [1]

(iv) Name a molecule which will be found in the waste water as a result of protein breakdown. [1]

(c) Name **two** other types of enzyme that would remove different stain components. [2]

7 The diagram represents an enzyme and its substrate.

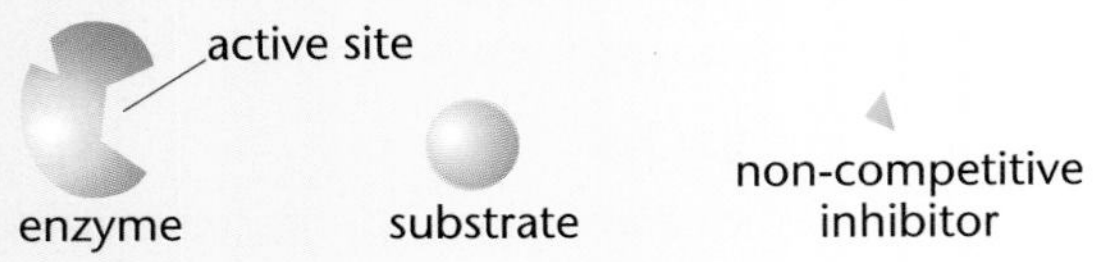

(a) Referring to information in the diagram explain the activity of this enzyme in terms of the **induced fit theory**. [2]

(b) Molecule X is a non-competitive inhibitor. Explain how this inhibitor has an effect on the structure and function of the enzyme. [3]

8 The diagram below shows a long polypeptide.

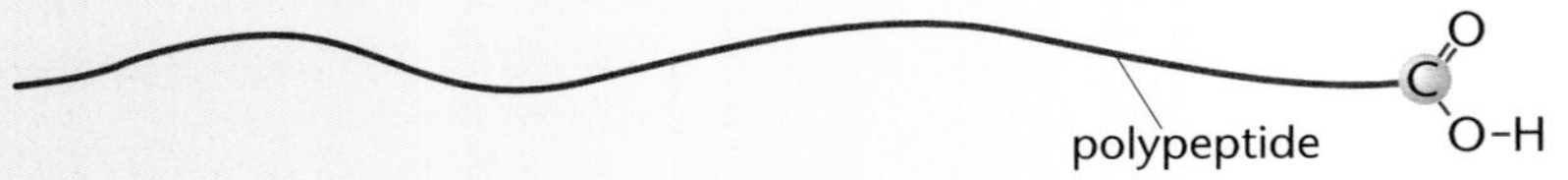

(a) The carboxylic acid is found at one end of the polypeptide. Which group is found at the other end? [1]

(b) What is the advantage of using both an exopeptidase and an endopeptidase to break down the polypeptide? [3]

Chapter 4

Exchange

The following topics are covered in this chapter:

- *The cell surface membrane*
- *The movement of molecules in and out of cells*
- *Gaseous exchange*

4.1 The cell surface membrane

After studying this section you should be able to:

- *understand the importance of surface area to volume ratio*
- *recall the fluid mosaic model of the cell surface (plasma) membrane*

LEARNING SUMMARY

How important is the surface area of exchange surfaces?

AQA A	M1
AQA B	M1
EDEXCEL	M1
OCR	M1
WJEC	M1
NICCEA	M1

Unicellular organisms like amoeba have a very high **surface area to volume ratio**. All chemicals needed can pass into the cells directly and all waste can pass out efficiently. Organisms which have a high surface area to volume ratio have no need for special structures like lungs or gills.

Nutrients and oxygen passing into an organism are rapidly used up. This gives a limit on the ultimate size to which a microorganism can grow. If vital chemicals did not reach all parts of a cell then death would be a consequence.

A unicellular organism may satisfy all its needs by direct diffusion. However, in larger organisms cells join to adjacent ones, surfaces exposed for exchange of substances are reduced. The larger an organism the lower is its surface area to volume ratio. For this reason many multicellular organisms have specially adapted exchange structures.

Fluid mosaic model of the cell surface (plasma) membrane

AQA A	M1
AQA B	M1
EDEXCEL	M1
OCR	M1
WJEC	M1
NICCEA	M1

Ultimately the exchange of substances takes place across the cell surface membrane. This must be selective, allowing some substances in and excluding others. The cell membrane consists of a bilayer of phospholipid molecules (see page 25). Each phospholipid is arranged so that the hydrophilic head (attracts water) is facing towards either the cytoplasm or the outside of the cell. The hydrophobic (repels water) tails meet in the middle of the membrane. Across this expanse of phospholipids are a number of protein molecules. Some of the proteins (intrinsic) span the complete width of the membrane, some proteins (extrinsic) are partially embedded in the membrane.

Remember that plant cells have a cellulose cell wall. This gives physical support to the cell but is permeable to many molecules. Water and ions can readily pass through.

The fluid mosaic model of the cell membrane

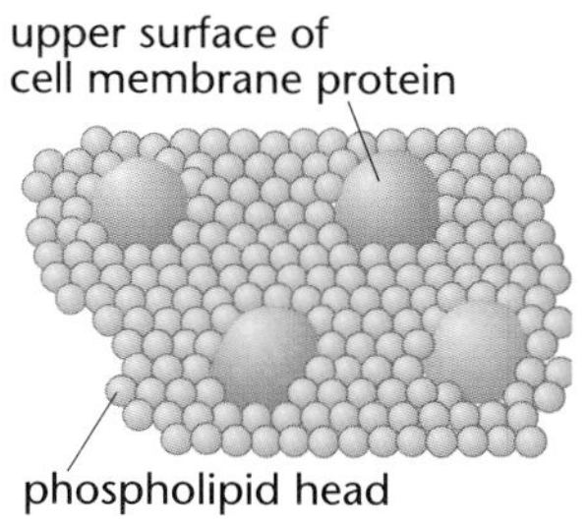

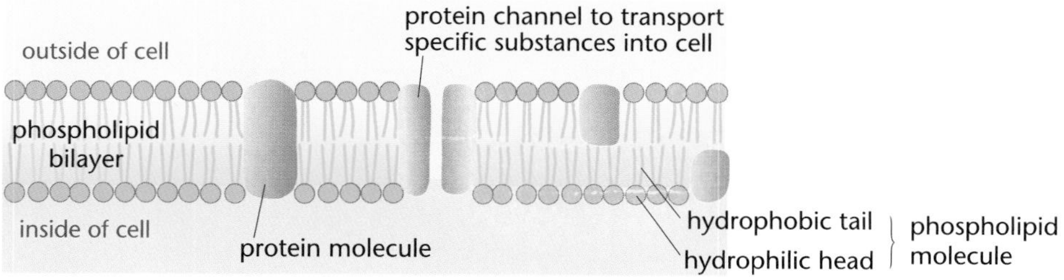

Functions of cell membrane molecules

The term 'fluid mosaic' was given because of the dynamic nature of the component molecules of the membrane. Many of the proteins seem to 'float' through an apparent 'sea' of phospholipids. Few molecules are static.

Phospholipid

Small lipid-soluble molecules pass through the membrane easily because they dissolve as they pass through the phospholipid bilayer. Small uncharged molecules also pass through the bilayer.

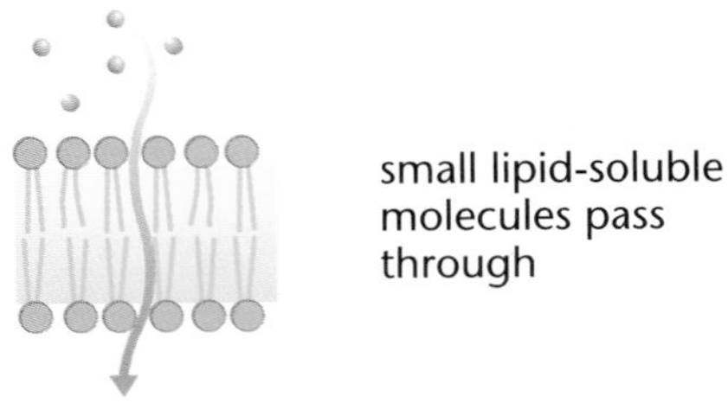

Channel proteins (ion gates)

Larger molecules and charged molecules can pass through the membrane due to channel proteins. Some are adjacent to a receptor protein, e.g. at a synapse a transmitter substance binds to a receptor protein. This opens the channel protein or ion gate and sodium ions flow in.

Not all channel proteins need a receptor protein.

When the molecule binds to a receptor molecule it is similar to a substrate binding with an enzyme's active site. On this occasion the receptor site is the correct shape.

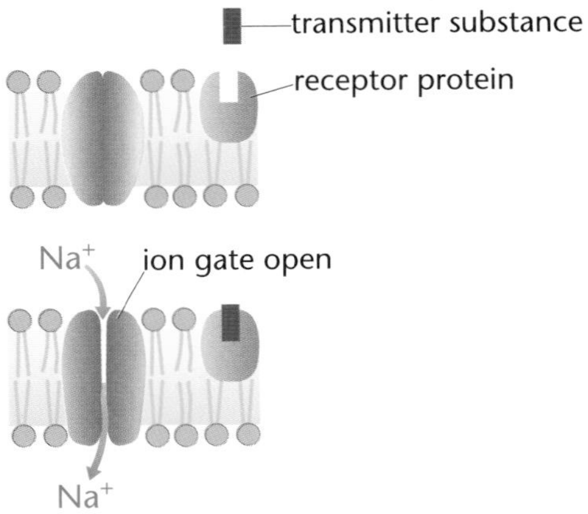

Carrier protein molecule

Some molecules which approach a cell may bind with a carrier protein. This has a site which the incoming molecule can bind to. This causes a change of shape in the carrier protein which deposits the molecule into the cell cytoplasm.

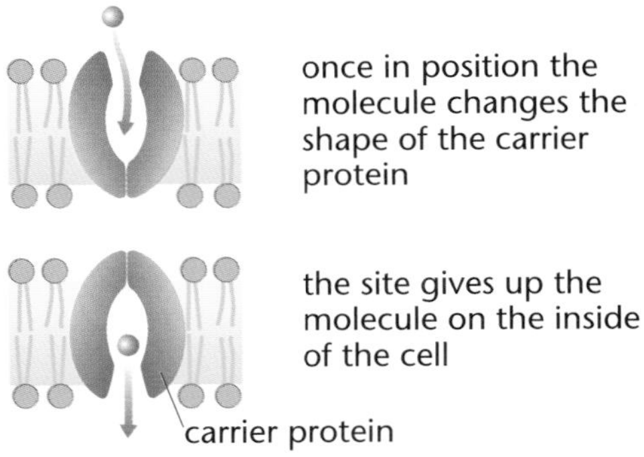

Recognition proteins

These are extrinsic proteins, some having carbohydrate components, which help in cell recognition and cell interaction, e.g. foreign protein on a bacterium would be recognised by white blood cells and the cell would be attacked.

White blood cells continually check the proteins on cell membranes. Those recognised as 'self' are not attacked, whereas those which are not 'self' are attacked.

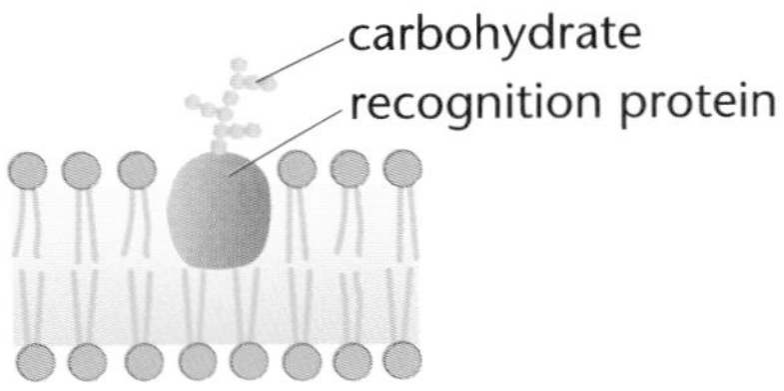

KEY POINT

The cell surface membrane is the key structure which forms a barrier between the cell and its environment. Nutrients, water and ions must enter and waste molecules must leave. Equally important is the exclusion of dangerous chemicals and inclusion of vital cell contents. It is no surprise that the cell makes further compartments within the cell using membranes of similar structure to the cell surface membrane.

4.2 The movement of molecules in and out of cells

After studying this section you should be able to:

LEARNING SUMMARY

- *understand the range of methods by which molecules cross cell membranes*
- *understand the processes of diffusion, facilitated diffusion, osmosis and active transport*

How do substances cross the cell surface membrane?

AQA A	M1
AQA B	M1
EDEXCEL	M1
OCR	M1
WJEC	M1
NICCEA	M1

Cells need to obtain substances vital in sustaining life. Some cells secrete useful substances but all cells excrete waste substances. There are several mechanisms by which molecules move across the cell surface membrane.

Diffusion

Note that diffusion is the movement of molecules down a concentration gradient.

Molecules in liquids and gases are in constant random motion. When different concentrations are in contact, the molecules move so that they are in equal concentration throughout. An example of this is when sugar is put into a cup of tea. If left, sugar molecules will distribute themselves evenly, even without stirring. Diffusion is the movement of molecules from where they are in high concentration to where they are in low concentration. Once evenly distributed the *net* movement of molecules stops.

Factors which affect the rate of diffusion

- surface area
  the greater the surface area the greater the rate of diffusion
- the difference in concentration at either side of the membrane
  the greater the difference the greater the rate
- the size of molecules
  smaller molecules may pass through the membrane faster than larger ones
- the presence of pores in the membrane
  pores can speed up diffusion
- the width of the membrane
  the thinner the membrane the faster the rate.

Sometimes the membrane is stated as being selectively permeable, partially permeable or semi-permeable. It depends on which Examination board sets your papers.

Facilitated diffusion

This is a special form of diffusion in which protein carrier molecules (see page 58) are involved. It is much faster than regular diffusion because of the carrier molecules. Each carrier will only bind with a specific molecule. Binding changes the shape of the carrier which then deposits the molecule into the cytoplasm. No energy is used in the process.

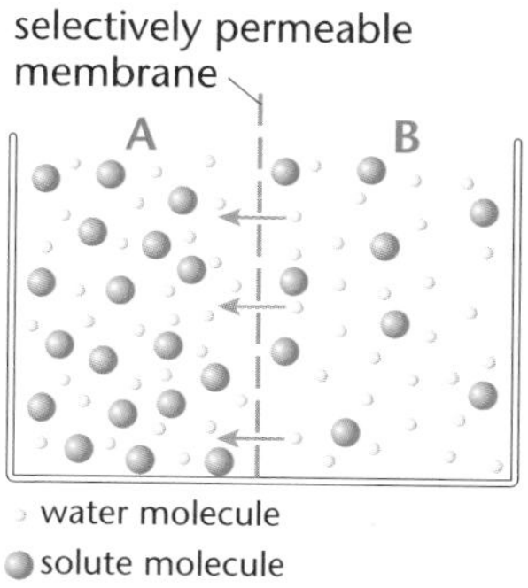

water molecules move from B to A

Osmosis

This is the movement of water molecules across a selectively permeable membrane:

- from a lower concentrated solution to a higher concentrated solution
- from where water molecules are at a higher concentration to where they are at a lower concentration
- from a hypotonic solution to a hypertonic solution
- from a hyperosmotic solution to a hypo-osmotic solution
- from an area of higher water potential to lower water potential.

The diagram on the left shows a model of osmosis.

Remember that osmosis is about the movement of **water molecules**. No other substance moves!

What is the relationship between water potential of the cell and the concentration of an external solution?

The term water potential is used as a measure of water movement from one place to another in a plant. It is measured in terms of pressure and the units are either kPa (kilopascals) or MPa (megapascals). Water potential is indicated by the symbol ψ *(pronounced psi)*. The following equation allows us to work out the water 'status' of a plant cell.

KEY POINT

ψ (cell) water potential (of cell)	=	ψs solute potential (of ions inside cell)	+	ψp pressure potential (of cell wall)

Remember that water moves from an area of higher water potential to an area of lower water potential. When a cell at −4 MPa is next to a cell at the less negative value the water moves to the more negative value, i.e. −4 MPa > −6 MPa

Note that pressure potential only has a value **above** zero when the cell membrane **begins** to contact the cell wall. The greater the pressure potential the more the cell wall resists water entry. At turgidity $\psi s = \psi p$ when net water movement is zero.

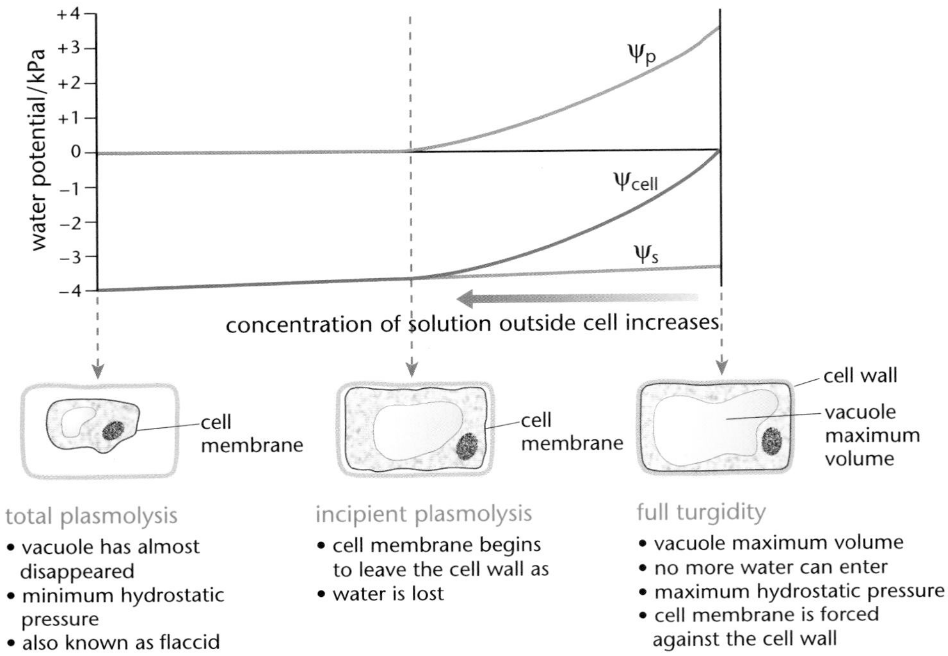

Active transport

Note that active transport is the movement of molecules up a concentration gradient.

In **active transport** molecules move from where they are in lower concentration to where they are in higher concentration. A protein carrier molecule is used (see page 58). This is **against the concentration gradient** and always **needs energy**. A plant may contain a higher concentration of Mg^{2+} ions than the soil. It obtains a supply by active transport through the cell surface membranes of root hairs. Only Mg^{2+} ions can bind with the specific protein carrier molecules responsible for their entry into the plant. This is also known as active ion uptake, but is a form of active transport.

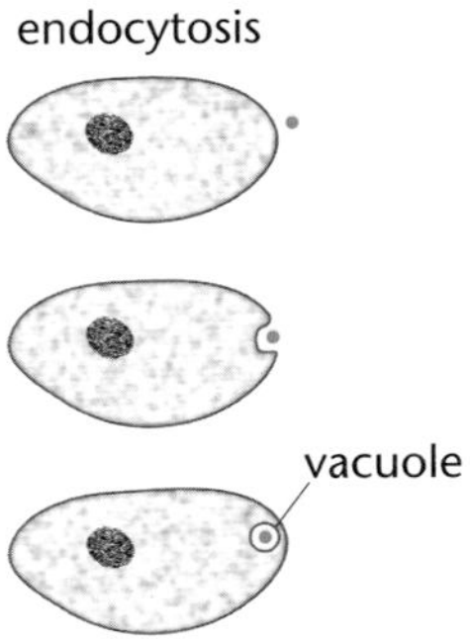

Endocytosis, exocytosis and pinocytosis

Some substances, often due to their large size, enter cells by **endocytosis** as follows:

- the substance contacts the cell surface membrane which indents
- the substance is surrounded by the membrane, forming a vacuole or vesicle
- each vacuole contains the substance and an outer membrane which has detached from the cell surface membrane.

When fluids enter the cell in this way this is known as **pinocytosis**. Some substances leave the cell in a reverse of endocytosis. Here the membrane of the vacuole or vesicle merges with the cell surface membrane depositing its contents into the outside environment of the cell. This is known as **exocytosis**.

Progress check

1 A plant contains a greater concentration of Fe^{2+} ions than the soil in which it is growing. Name and describe the process by which the plant absorbs the ions against the concentration gradient.

2 Explain the following:
(a) Endocytosis of an antigen by a phagocyte
(b) Exocytosis of acetylcholine molecules from a cell.

1 **Active transport:** molecules move from a lower concentration to a higher concentration; through the cell surface membranes of root hairs; protein carrier molecules in membranes used; energy needed; Fe^{2+} ions can bind with the protein carrier molecules which allow entry into the plant.

2 (a) **Endocytosis:** antigen contacts the cell membrane of the phagocyte; cell membrane surrounds the antigen, forming a vacuole; the vacuole contains the antigen and an outer membrane which has detached from the cell surface membrane.
(b) **Exocytosis:** a vesicle in the cell contains acetylcholine molecules; the vesicle merges with the cell membrane; acetylcholine contents deposited outside of the cell.

4.3 Gaseous exchange

After studying this section you should be able to:

- *understand gaseous exchange in a dicotyledonous leaf, the gills of a bony fish and the lungs of a mammal*
- *show awareness of the adaptations of leaves, gills and lungs for efficient gaseous exchange*

LEARNING SUMMARY

How are organisms adapted for efficient gaseous exchange?

AQA A	M1
AQA B	M1
EDEXCEL	M1
OCR	M1
WJEC	M2
NICCEA	M2

The range of respiratory surfaces in this chapter each have common properties, such as high surface area to volume ratio, one cell thick lining tissue, many capillaries.

Remember that all cells without chloroplasts must be supplied by cells capable of photosynthesis.

The exchange of substances across cell surface membranes has been described. Larger organisms have a major problem in exchange because of their low surface area to volume ratio. They satisfy their needs by having tissues and organs which have special adaptations for efficient exchange. In simple terms, these structures achieve a very high surface area, e.g. a leaf, and link to the transport system to allow import and export from the organ.

A dicotyledonous leaf

The diagram below shows a section through a leaf. Leaves of plants give a high surface area over which exchange takes place. Specialised tissues increase the efficiency of exchange to allow photosynthesis to supply the plant with *enough* energy-rich carbohydrates.

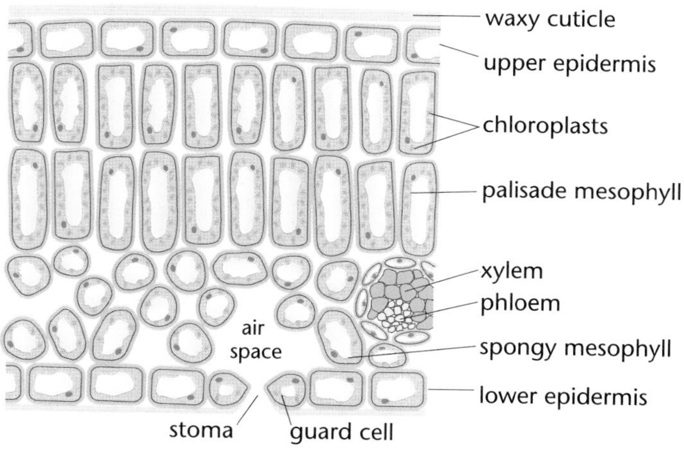

Note that the leaf gives off oxygen during the day whilst the leaf is photosynthesising but gives off carbon dioxide at night during dark conditions when only respiration takes place.

Adaptations of a leaf for photosynthesis

- A flat, thin blade (lamina) to allow maximum light absorption.
- Cells of the upper epidermis have a waxy cuticle to reflect excess light but allow entry of enough light for photosynthesis.
- Each leaf has many chloroplasts to absorb a maximum amount of light.
- Chloroplasts contain many thylakoid membranes, stacked in grana to give a high surface area to absorb the maximum quantity of light.
- Palisade cells, containing chloroplasts, pack closely together to 'capture' the maximum amount of light.
- Many guard cells open stomata to allow carbon dioxide in and oxygen out during photosynthesis.
- Air spaces in the mesophyll store lots of carbon dioxide for photosynthesis or lots of oxygen for respiration.
- Xylem of the vascular bundles brings water to the leaf for photosynthesis.
- Phloem takes the carbohydrate away from the leaf after photosynthesis.

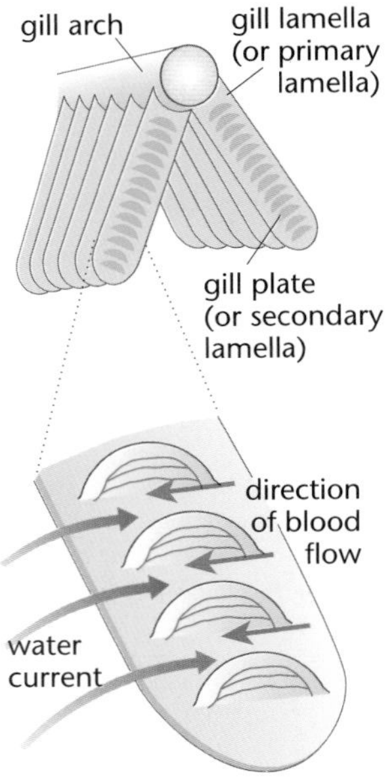

Gills of a bony fish

The ventilation mechanism of a fish allows intake of water, and passes it across the gills. The diagram (left) shows the structures of the gills which allow maximum exchange to take place.

Adaptations of gills for gaseous exchange

- The gills of a bony fish have a very high surface area to volume ratio.
- Gills consist of many flat gill filaments, stacked on top of each other, to give a high surface area for maximum exchange.
- Each gill filament has many gill plates which further increase surface area.
- Gill plates are very thin and full of blood capillaries to aid exchange.
- The gradients of O_2 and CO_2 are kept at a maximum by the **counter-current flow** mechanism. By allowing water to flow over the gills in an opposite direction to blood, maximum diffusion rate is achieved.

Remember that all respiratory surfaces are damp to allow effective transport across cell membranes.

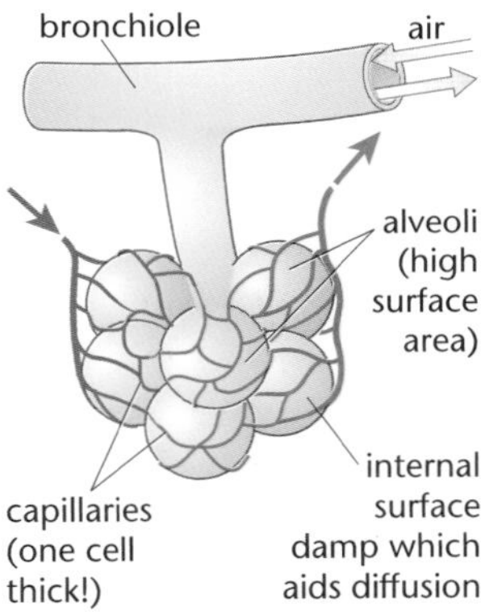

Lungs of a mammal

The ventilation mechanism of a mammal allows inhalation of air, which is passed into alveoli to exchange the respiratory gases. Completion of ventilation takes place when gases are expelled into the atmosphere. The diagram on the left shows the structure of alveoli.

Adaptations of lungs for gaseous exchange

- Air flows through a trachea (windpipe) supported by cartilage.
- It reaches the alveoli via tubes known as bronchi and bronchioles.
- Lungs have many alveoli (air sacs) which have a high surface area.
- Each alveolus is very thin (diffusion is faster over a short distance).
- Each alveolus has many capillaries, each one cell thick, to aid diffusion.
- There are many blood vessels in the lungs to give a high surface area for gaseous exchange and transport of respiratory substances.

Progress check

Describe and explain how the gills of a bony fish are adapted for efficient gaseous exchange.

Each gill consists of many thin gill filaments, stacked on top of each other which give a high surface area to volume ratio, for maximum exchange of gases; each gill filament has many gill plates which further increase surface area; each gill plate is very thin and full of blood capillaries; the gradients of O_2 and CO_2 are kept at a maximum by counter-current flow; water flows over the gills in an opposite direction to blood to achieve maximum diffusion rates.

Sample question and model answer

The diagram below shows two adjacent plant cells A and B.
The water potential equation is:

$\psi(\text{cell}) = \psi s + \psi p$

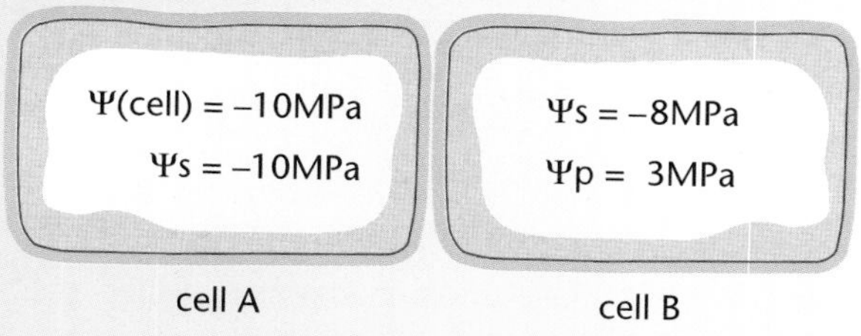

(a) (i) Calculate the water potential of cell B. [1]

Using the equation:

$\psi(\text{cell}) = \psi s + \psi p$
$= -8\text{ MPa} + 3\text{ MPa}$
$= -5\text{ MPa}$

> In this question you were given the equation. Try to remember it because it could earn you a mark. Additionally, if there were calculations you need the equation to access the other marks.
>
> When given any two of the values you can work out the other.

(ii) Draw an arrow on the diagram to show the direction of water flow. Show how you worked out the direction. [2]

The arrow should be drawn from cell B to cell A.
Direction from −5 MPa to −10 MPa.

(iii) What is the value of the pressure potential (ψp) of cell A? [1]

$\psi(\text{cell}) = \psi s + \psi p,$
$-10\text{ MPa} = -10\text{ MPa} + \psi p$
$\psi p = -10\text{ MPa} + 10\text{ MPa}$
$= 0\text{ MPa}$

> Note that from total plasmolysis up to incipient plasmolysis the resistance of the cell, i.e. ψp is zero.
>
> Only when the cell membrane contacts with the wall does it have an effect.

(iv) Name the condition of the cell when $\psi(\text{cell}) = 0$ [1]

full turgor or fully turgid

(b) Give **one** difference between the following terms: [2]

facilitated diffusion

molecules move down a gradient

active transport

energy is needed for the process

> Be careful with this type of question. You may believe that 'up a gradient' could be given for active transport. It is correct, but it's too close to the 'down a gradient' idea for facilitated diffusion.
>
> Go for a completely different idea, as shown.

(c) What effect would the following temperatures have on the active transport of Mg^{2+} ions across a cell surface membrane of a plant cell? Assume the plant is a British native. [4]

(i) 30°C

It is likely that active transport would be efficient because the temperature would be ideal for the Mg^{2+} to bind with a carrier molecule.

(ii) 80°C

process likely not to work;
protein carrier denatured;
Mg^{2+} would not be able to bind.

Practice examination questions

1

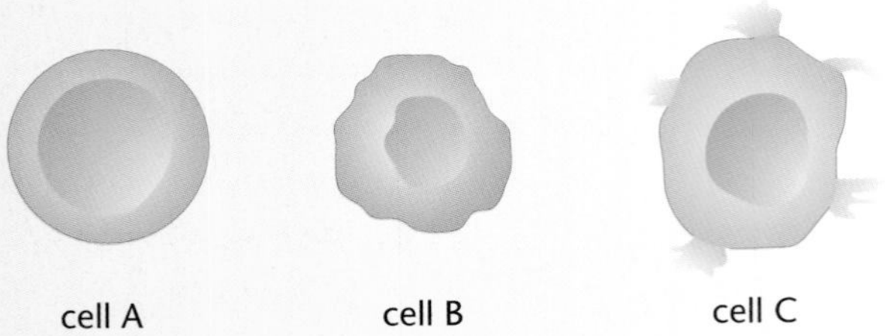

(a) Explain each of the following in terms of water potential.
  (i) Cell A did not change size at all.
  (ii) Cell B decreased in volume.
  (iii) Cell C became swollen and burst. [3]

(b) Which process is responsible for the changes to cells B and C? [1]

2 (a) Give one similarity between active transport and facilitated diffusion. [1]

(b) Give one difference between active transport and facilitated diffusion. [1]

3 The diagram shows a section through a leaf.

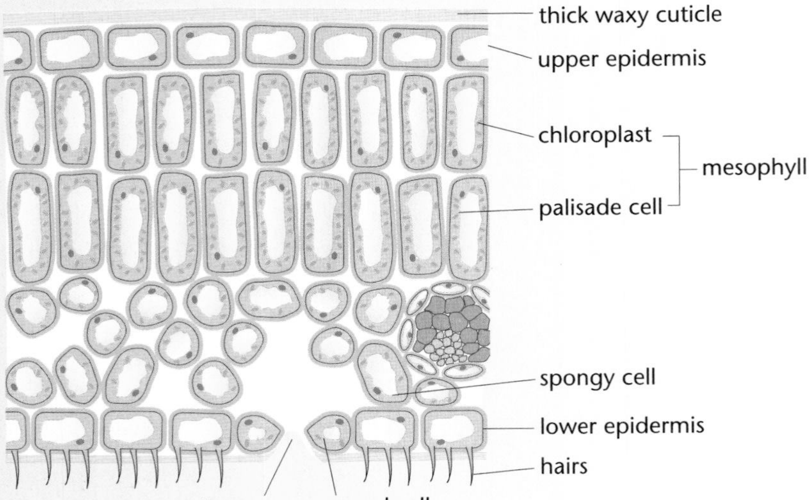

(a) Describe how the leaf is adapted for efficient photosynthesis. [6]

(b) Suggest how the leaf is adapted to xerophytic conditions. [3]

4 Describe and explain how the following are adapted to efficient gaseous exchange.

(a) The alveoli of lungs. [4]

(b) The gills of a fish. [4]

Chapter 5

Transport

The following topics are covered in this chapter:

- The importance of mass transport systems
- Heart: structure and function
- Blood vessels
- The transport of substances in the blood
- The transport of substances in a plant
- Water loss in a plant

5.1 The importance of mass transport systems

After studying this section you should be able to:

- explain why most multicellular organisms need a mass transport system
- understand the importance of a high surface area to volume ratio

LEARNING SUMMARY

Why do most multicellular organisms need a mass transport system?

AQA A	M1
AQA B	M3
EDEXCEL	M2
OCR	M3
WJEC	M2
NICCEA	M2

The bigger an organism is, the lower its surface area to volume ratio. Substances needed by a large organism could not be supplied through its exposed external surface. Oxygen passing through an external surface would be rapidly used up before reaching the many layers of underlying cells. Similarly waste substances would not be excreted quickly enough. This problem has been solved, through evolution, by specially adapted tissues and organs.

> KEY POINT
>
> Leaves, roots, gills and lungs all have high surface area to volume properties so that supplies of substances vital to **all** the living cells are made available by these structures. Movement of substances to and from these structures is carried out by efficient **mass transport systems**.

Across the range of multicellular organisms found in the living world are a number of mass transport systems, e.g. the mammalian circulatory system and the vascular system of a plant.

Mass transport systems are just as important for the rapid removal of waste as they are for supplies. Supplies include an immense number of substances, e.g. glucose, oxygen and ions. Even communication from one cell to another can take place via a mass transport system, e.g. hormones in a blood stream.

The greater the metabolic rate of an organism, the greater are the demands on its mass transport system. Rapid movement through the transport system is improved by an organ which has a pumping mechanism. The heart is an excellent example of how this is achieved.

Mammals have a **double circulation** system. This means that as blood enters the heart it is pumped to the lungs, exchanges oxygen for carbon dioxide, and returns to the heart where further pumping propels it through the rest of the body. The blood moves through the heart twice during each cardiac cycle. This double circulation has, through evolution, enabled some species to achieve a greater size because essential substances can reach cells efficiently, over longer distances. The extra pumping action acts as a boost so that greater distances can be achieved.

5.2 Heart: structure and function

After studying this section you should be able to:

LEARNING SUMMARY

- *recall the structure, cardiac cycle and electrical stimulation of a mammalian heart*

The mammalian heart

AQA A	M1
AQA B	M3
EDEXCEL	M2
OCR	M3
WJEC	M2
NICCEA	M2

The heart consists of a range of tissues. The most important one is cardiac muscle. The cells have the ability to contract and relax through the complete life of the person, without ever becoming fatigued. Each cardiac muscle cell is **myogenic**. This means it has its own inherent rhythm. Below is a diagram of the heart.

Note that tricuspid and bicuspid valves are known as atrioventricular valves.

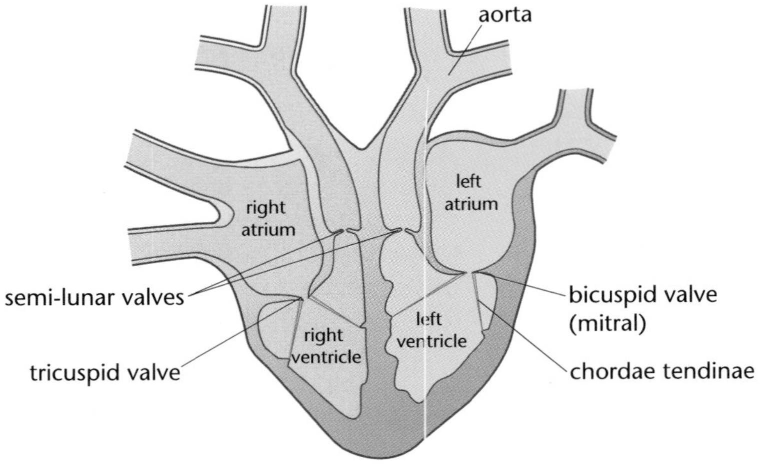

Structure

The heart consists of four chambers, **right** and **left atria** above **right** and **left ventricles**. The functions of each part are as follows.

If blood moved in the wrong direction, then transport of important substances would be impeded.

- The **right atrium** links to the **right ventricle** by the **tricuspid valve**. This valve prevents backflow of the blood into the atrium above, when the ventricle contracts.
- The **left atrium** links to the **left ventricle** by the **bicuspid valve (mitral valve)**. This also prevents backflow of the blood into the atrium above.
- The **chordae tendonae** attach each ventricle to its **atrioventricular valve**. Contractions of the ventricles have a tendency to force these valves up into the atria. Backflow of blood would be dangerous, so the chordae tendonae hold each valve firmly to prevent this from occurring.
- Semi-lunar (pocket) valves are found in the blood vessels leaving the heart (pulmonary artery and aorta). They only allow exit of blood from the heart through these vessels following ventricular contractions. Contraction of these arteries and relaxation of the ventricles closes each semi-lunar valve.
- Ventricles have thicker muscular walls than atria. When each atrium contracts it only needs to propel the blood a short distance into each ventricle.
- The left ventricle has even thicker muscular walls than the right ventricle. The left ventricle needs a more powerful contraction to propel blood to the systemic circulation (all of the body apart from the lungs). The right ventricle propels blood to the nearby lungs. The contraction does not need to be so powerful.

Check out these diagrams of a valve.

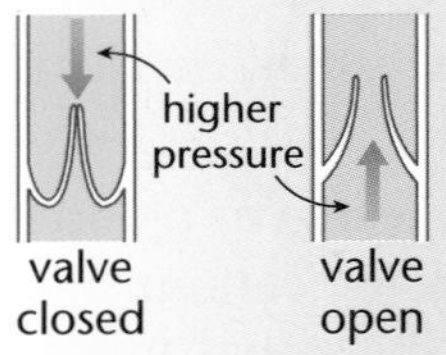

You can work out if a valve is open or closed in terms of pressure. Higher pressure above than below a semi-lunar valve closes it. Higher pressure below the semi-lunar valve than above, opens it.

Cardiac cycle

Blood must continuously be moved around the body, collecting and supplying vital substances to cells as well as removing waste from them. The heart acts as a pump using a combination of systole (contractions) and diastole (relaxation) of the chambers. The cycle takes place in the following sequence.

Examination questions often test your knowledge of the opening and closing of valves. Always analyse the different pressures given in the question. A greater pressure behind a valve opens it. A greater pressure in front closes it.

Stage 1

Ventricular diastole, atrial systole

Both ventricles relax simultaneously. This results in lower pressure in each ventricle compared to each atrium above. The atrioventricular valves open partially. This is followed by the atria contracting which forces blood through the atrioventricular valves. It also closes the valves in the vena cava and pulmonary vein. This prevents backflow of blood.

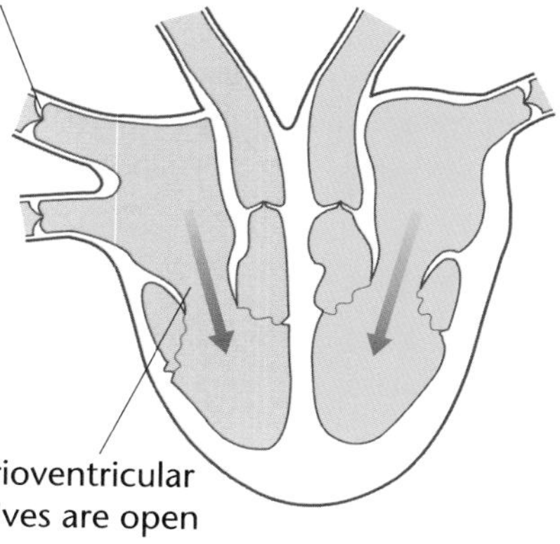

Stage 2

Ventricular systole, atrial diastole

Both atria then relax. Both ventricles contract simultaneously. This results in higher pressure in the ventricles compared to the atria above. The difference in pressure closes each atrioventricular valve. This prevents backflow of blood into each atrium. Higher pressure in the ventricles compared to the aorta and pulmonary artery opens the semi-lunar valves and blood is ejected into these arteries. So blood flows through the systemic circulatory system via the aorta and vena cava and through the lungs via the pulmonary vessels.

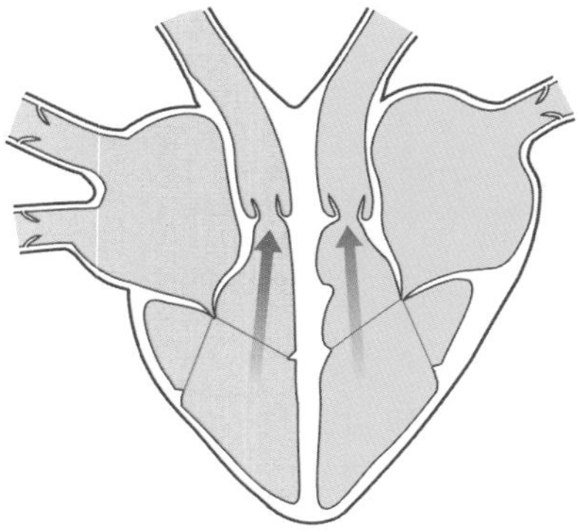

Stage 3

Ventricular diastole, atrial diastole

Immediately following ventricular systole, both ventricles and atria relax for a short time. Higher pressure in the aorta and pulmonary artery than the ventricles closes the semi-lunar valves. This prevents the backflow of blood. Higher pressure in the vena cava and pulmonary vein than the atria results in the refilling of the atria.

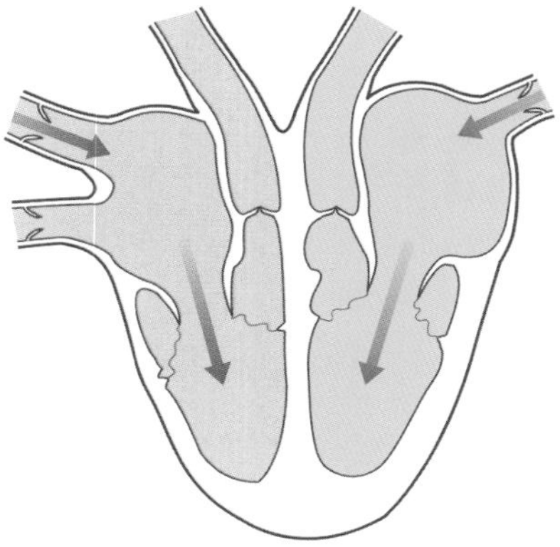

Returning to stage one the cycle begins again. The hormone adrenaline increases the heart rate still further. Even your examinations may increase your heart rate!

The cycle is now complete – ***GO BACK TO STAGE 1!***

The whole sequence above is one cardiac cycle or heartbeat and it takes less than one second! The number of heartbeats per minute varies to suit the activity of an organism. Vigorous exercise is accompanied by an increase in heart rate to allow faster collection, supply and removal of substances because of enhanced blood flow. Conversely during sleep, at minimum metabolic rate, heart rate is correspondingly low because of minimum requirements by the cells.

How is the heart rate controlled?

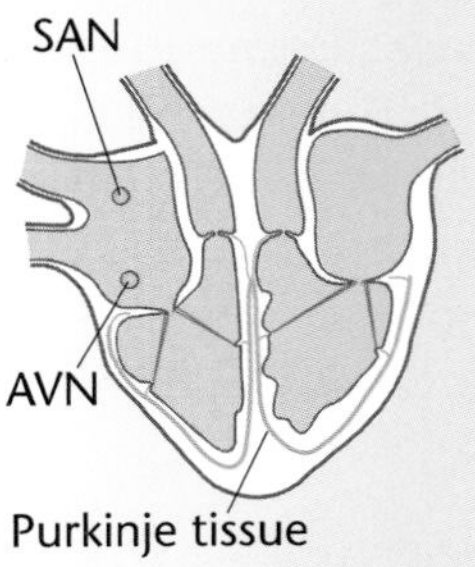

The SAN is the natural pacemaker of the heart.

It has already been stated that the cardiac muscle cells have their own inherent rhythm. Even an individual cardiac muscle cell will contract and relax on a microscope slide under suitable conditions. An orchestra would not be able to play music in a coordinated way without a conductor. The cardiac muscle cells must be similarly coordinated, by electrical stimulation from the brain.

- The heart control centre is in the medulla oblongata.
- The sympathetic nerve stimulates an increase in heart rate.
- The vagus nerve stimulates a decrease in heart rate.
- These nerves link to a structure in the wall of the right atrium, the **sinoatrial node (SAN)**.
- A wave of electrical excitation moves across both atria.
- They respond by contracting (the right one slightly before the left).
- The wave of electrical activity reaches the **atrioventricular node (AVN)** which conducts the electrical activity through the **Purkinje fibres**.
- These Purkinje fibres pass through the septum of the heart deep into the walls of the left and right ventricles.
- The ventricle walls begin to contract from the apex (base) upwards.
- This ensures that blood is ejected efficiently from the ventricles.

All of the Purkinje fibres together are known as the **Bundle of His**.

Graphs to show the changes in pressure and volume during the cardiac cycle

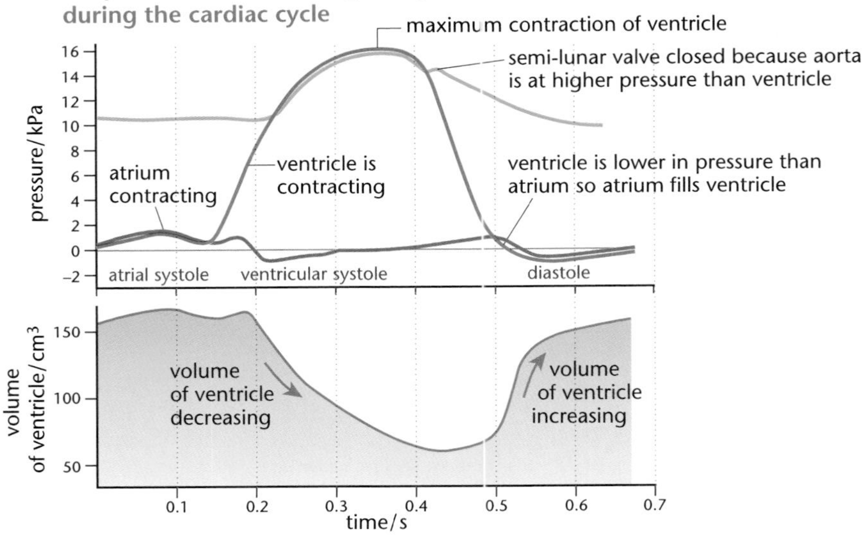

This is one of the examiners' favourite ways to test heart-related concepts. Look at the **peak** of the **ventricular contraction**. It coincides with the **trough** in the **ventricular volume**. This is not surprising, because as the ventricle contracts it empties! Use the data of higher pressure in one part and lower in another to explain:

(a) movement of blood from one area to another
(b) the closing of valves.

Progress check

The medulla oblongata can increase the heart rate. The statements below include all of the events which take place, but in the wrong order. Write them out in the correct sequence.

A this ensures that blood is ejected efficiently from the ventricles
B the wave of electrical activity reaches the **atrioventricular node (AVN)** which conducts the electrical activity through the **Purkinje fibres**
C a wave of electrical excitation moves across both atria
D the sympathetic nerve conducts electrical impulses
E electrical impulses are received at the **sinoatrial node (SAN)**
F as a result the atria contract
G the ventricle walls begin to contract from the apex (base) upwards

D E C F B G A

5.3 Blood vessels

LEARNING SUMMARY

After studying this section you should be able to:

- *describe the structure and functions of arteries, veins and capillaries*
- *understand the importance of valves in the return of blood to the heart*

Arteries, veins and capillaries

AQA A	M1
AQA B	M3
EDEXCEL	M2
OCR	M3
WJEC	M2
NICCEA	M2

The blood is transported to the tissues via the vessels. The main propulsion is by the ventricular contractions. Blood leaves the heart via arteries, reaches the tissues via the capillaries, then returns to the heart by the veins. Each blood vessel has a space through which the blood passes; this is the **lumen**. The structure of the vessels is shown below.

Note that the pressure in the **arteries** is highest because:

(a) they are closest to the ventricles
(b) they contract forcefully themselves.

Capillaries are the next highest in pressure, the main factor being their resistance to blood flow.

Finally, the pressure of **veins** is the lowest because:

(a) they are furthest from the ventricles
(b) they have a low amount of muscle.

If given blood pressures of vessels, be ready to predict the correct direction of blood flow.

Artery

- It has a thick **tunica externa** which is an outer covering of tough collagen fibres.
- It has a **tunica media** which is a middle layer of **smooth muscle** and **elastic fibres**.
- It has a lining of **squamous endothelium** (very thin cells).
- It can contract using its **thick muscular layer**.

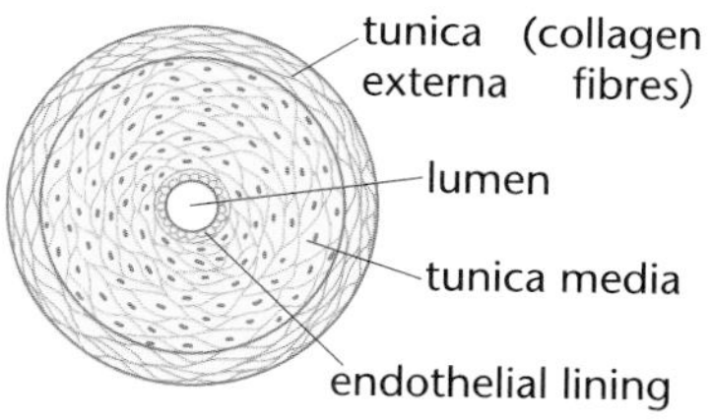

Capillary

- It is a very thin blood vessel, the endothelium is just one cell thick.
- Substances can exchange easily.
- It has such a high resistance to blood flow that blood is slowed down. This gives more time for efficient exchange of chemicals at the tissues.

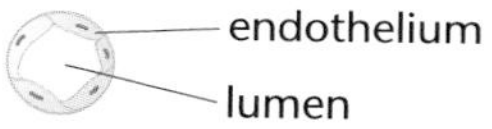

Vein

- It has a thin **tunica externa** which is an outer covering of tough collagen fibres.
- It has a very thin **tunica media** which is a middle layer of **smooth muscle** and **elastic fibres**.
- It has a lining of **squamous endothelium** (very thin cells).
- It is lined with semi-lunar valves which prevent the backflow of blood.

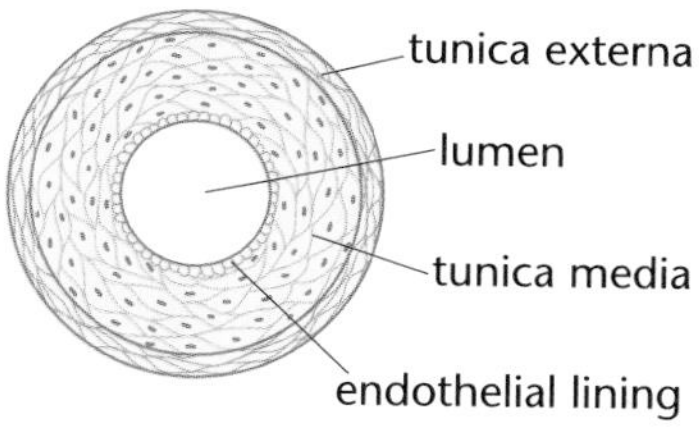

How do the veins return the blood to the heart?

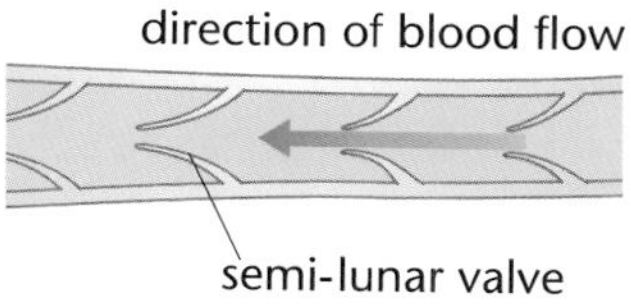

Veins have a thin tunica media, so only mild contractions are possible. They return blood in an unexpected way. Every time the organism moves physically, blood is squeezed between skeletal muscles and forced along the vein.

KEY POINT

It must travel towards the heart because of the direction of the semi-lunar valves. Any attempt at backflow and the semi-lunar valves shut tightly!

Capillary network

In the skin the superficial capillaries have the arteriole/shunt vessel/venule arrangement as shown opposite. When the arteriole is dilated (**vasodilation**) more heat can be lost from the skin. When the arteriole is constricted (**vasoconstriction**) the blood cannot enter the capillary network so is diverted to the core of the body. Less heat is lost from the skin.

Every living cell needs to be close to a **capillary**. The arteries transport blood from the heart but before entry into the capillaries it needs to pass through an **arteriole**. The arteriole is a ring of muscle known as a **pre-capillary sphincter**. When this is contracted the constriction shuts off blood flow to the capillaries, but when dilated blood passes through. Some capillary networks have a shunt vessel. When the arteriole is constricted blood is diverted along the shunt vessel so the capillary network is by-passed. After the capillary network has permeated through an organ the capillaries link into a **venule** which joins a **vein**.

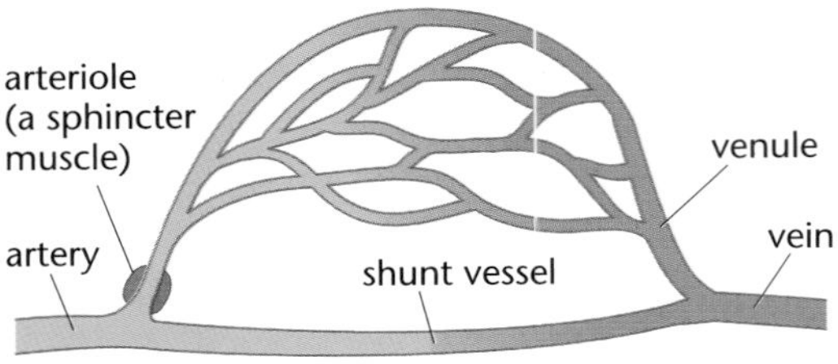

Blood

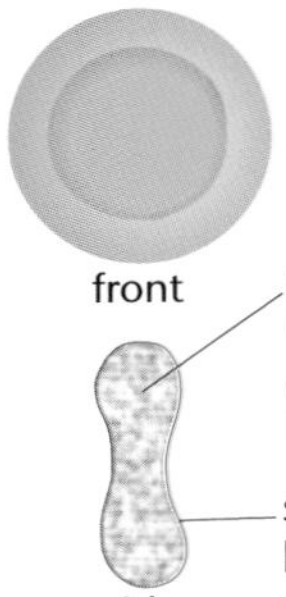

The blood consists of a fluid in which many solutes are dissolved and blood cells are suspended. It is constantly circulated around the body. Additionally it has roles in combating infections (see page 135). The shape of a red blood cell is biconcave. This allows a greater amount of oxygen to be transported, because of the greater surface area to volume ratio. It important that the blood has enough red blood cells and that each red blood cell contains enough haemoglobin to transport the oxygen efficiently.

The human body can adapt well to different environmental conditions, e.g. if a person who lives close to sea level moves to a much higher altitude, like Mexico City, they experience much thinner air, and take in correspondingly less oxygen. The breathing rate of the person would, initially, be more rapid than usual. After several months the bone marrow makes more red blood cells, so oxygen transport is much improved even though the air is less dense than in the person's normal environment. Athletes use this technique to prepare for important events. Even when they return to compete at lower altitude oxygen transport is so improved that they usually compete very well and often exceed their previous best.

Progress check

The diagram shows the structure of a blood vessel.

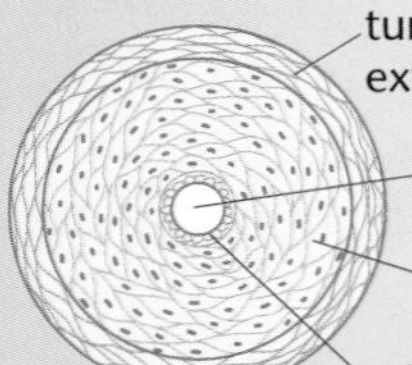

(a) (i) Which type of vessel, artery, vein or capillary is shown? Give a reason for your choice.

(ii) What is the function of the tunica media?

(b) The pressure values 30 kPa, 10 kPa and 5 kPa correspond to the different types of vessel. Give the correct value for each vessel so that blood flows around the body.

(a) (i) artery; the vessel has a thick tunica externa
(ii) contracts to help transport blood.
(b) artery, 30 kPa, capillary, 10 kPa and vein, 5 kPa.

5.4 The transport of substances in the blood

After studying this section you should be able to:

- *describe the transport of oxygen in the blood and explain how oxygen is released at the tissues*
- *describe the transport of carbon dioxide*

LEARNING SUMMARY

How is oxygen transported?

AQA B	M3
EDEXCEL	M2
OCR	M3
WJEC	M2
NICCEA	M2

Oxygen is absorbed in the lungs from fresh air which has been breathed in. Red blood cells (erythrocytes) contain the protein haemoglobin which has an affinity (attraction) for oxygen. This means that oxygen readily binds with the haemoglobin. Even when oxygen is in short supply oxygen will effectively bind with the haemoglobin and the red blood cells will carry the oxyhaemoglobin.

The red blood cells have no nucleus, which increases the surface area to volume ratio, which increases the amount of oxygen taken up. Efficient transport is important but crucial is the ability to give up the oxygen to the tissues which need it. The Bohr effect explains the way that oxygen moves from the red blood cells to the tissues. It is shown by the graph below.

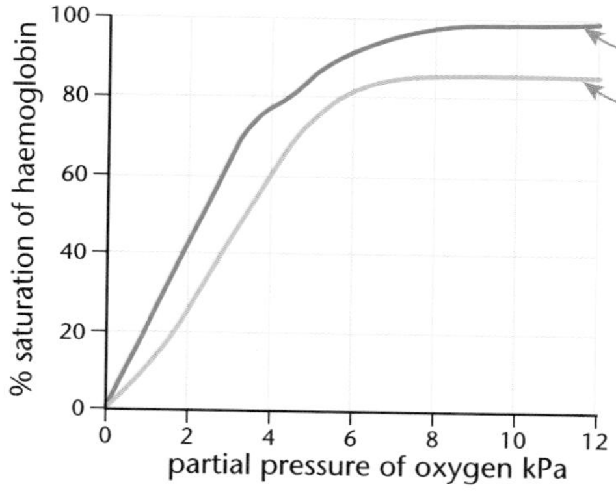

Features of the Bohr effect

- The graph is known as the oxygen dissociation curve and its shape is sigmoid ('S' shaped).
- Even in a low partial pressure of oxygen, the percentage saturation of haemoglobin is very high as shown by the steep incline on the graph at low partial pressures.
- Haemoglobin holds the oxygen strongly as the blood is transported.
- Once they reach the tissues, the red blood cells encounter carbon dioxide which causes the dissociation curve to move downwards and to the right.
- The net effect is that some oxygen is released from the haemoglobin and supplied to the tissues.
- The greater the amount of carbon dioxide at the tissues, the more the dissociation curve is moved to the right, and the more oxygen is 'off-loaded' to the tissues.

The term **oxygen tension** can be used instead of partial pressure.

The answers to Bohr effect questions revolve around:

(a) the uptake of oxygen by haemoglobin even at low partial pressures
(b) the 'offloading' of oxygen by carbon dioxide at the tissues.

Fetal haemoglobin has a greater affinity for oxygen than adult haemoglobin. This allows the fetus to take oxygen from the mother's haemoglobin. There is a substance with a greater affinity for oxygen than haemoglobin. It is myoglobin. Sea lions have high quantities in their muscles. The myoglobin acts as an oxygen store so the animals can remain under water for a long period of time.

Lymphatic system

AQA A	M1
AQA B	M3
EDEXCEL	M2
OCR	M3
WJEC	M2
NICCEA	M2

There is a network of vessels other than the blood system. They are the **lymphatic vessels**. They collect surplus tissue fluid, similar to blood plasma.

The lymph vessels have valves to ensure transport is in one direction. Along some parts of the lymphatic system are lymph nodes. These are swellings lined with white blood cells (macrophages and lymphocyte cells, see page 135).

Transport of carbon dioxide

AQA A	M1
AQA B	M3
EDEXCEL	M2
OCR	M3
WJEC	M2
NICCEA	M2

Take great care when answering questions about carbon dioxide transport. You will need to give details about the role of the red blood cell in carbon dioxide transport. Just stating that the red cell transports carbon dioxide is wrong! The process is much more complex than that and the HCO_3^- ions diffuse out of the red cells into the plasma.

This is done with the help of the red blood cells as follows:

- carbon dioxide diffuses into red blood cells from the tissues
- the carbon dioxide reacts with water to produce carbonic acid, this reaction being catalysed by the enzyme **carbonic anhydrase** in the cell *(a very fast reaction!)*.

carbonic anhydrase

$$H_2O + CO_2 = H_2CO_3$$

water carbon dioxide carbonic acid

- the carbonic acid **ionises** into H^+ and HCO_3^-

$$H_2CO_3 = H^+ + HCO_3^-$$

- haemoglobin combines with H^+ ions forming **haemoglobinic acid** which is very weak

$$H^+ + Hb = HHb$$

- HCO_3^- ions diffuse into the blood plasma to be transported to the lungs
- Cl^- ions diffuse into the red blood cell from the plasma; this counteracts the build up of positive charge from the H^+ ions. This is known as the **chloride shift**.

The whole process is reversed once the blood reaches the lungs.

Plasma

AQA A	M1
AQA B	M3
EDEXCEL	M2
OCR	M3
WJEC	M2
NICCEA	M2

Water has many important functions in the body, including being transported to the sweat glands to cool the body down.

Note that the list outlines just some of the functions of plasma-transported substances. There are many more!

This is the fluid in which all of the blood contents are transported. Listed below are some substances transported in the plasma:

- **water** – dissolves substances such as glucose for transport, stores dissolved prothrombin and fibrinogen which may be used later in clotting
- **proteins** – some are used to buffer the pH of the blood
- **glucose** – on its way to releasing energy in respiration
- **lipids** – on their way to releasing energy in respiration
- **amino acids** – on their way to cells to help assemble proteins or release energy in respiration
- **salts** – contribute to the water potential of blood, so that cells are not dehydrated by osmosis
- **hormones** – chemical messenger-molecules on their way to a target organ
- **antigens** – recognition proteins preventing white blood cells from destroying the person's own blood
- **antibodies** – made by lymphocytes to destroy antigens
- **urea** – made in the liver from excess amino acids, extracted by the kidneys.

Blood has a major role in the defence against disease (see the immune system page 134).

5.5 The transport of substances in a plant

After studying this section you should be able to:

LEARNING SUMMARY

- recall the structure of a root and understand how water and ions are absorbed
- recall the structure of xylem and phloem and explain the processes by which they transport essential chemicals

Root structure and functions

AQA B	M3
EDEXCEL	M2
OCR	M1, M3
WJEC	M2
NICCEA	M2

The roots of a green plant need to exchange substances with the soil environment. The piliferous zone just behind a root tip has many root hairs which have a high surface area to volume ratio.

- Root hairs are used for absorption of water and mineral ions and the excretion of carbon dioxide.
- They have a cell membrane with a high surface area to volume ratio to efficiently absorb water, mineral ions and oxygen and excrete carbon dioxide.
- They project out into the soil particles which are surrounded by soil water at high water potential compared to the low water potential of the contents of the root hairs.
- They have a cell membrane which is partially permeable to allow water absorption by osmosis (see page 59).
- As they absorb more water by osmosis, a cell sap becomes more dilute compared to neighbouring cells. Water therefore moves to these adjacent cells which become more diluted themselves, so osmosis continues across the cortex.
- They have carrier proteins in the cell membranes to allow mineral ions to be absorbed by active transport.

Note that the root hairs also absorb oxygen from the air to aid aerobic respiration. The high surface area to volume ratio certainly helps!

Remember that water moves from a higher water potential to a more negative water potential.

Remember that active transport needs energy, so mitochondria will be close to the carrier molecules on the membranes.

Passage of water into the vascular system

Once absorbed by osmosis, water needs to pass to the xylem vessels in order to move up the plant. First it must move across the cortex of the root and through the endodermis before entering the xylem. The mechanism of passage is not known but there are three theories:

- **apoplast** route, where the water is considered to pass on the outside of the cells
- **symplast** route, where the water is considered to pass via the cytoplasm of the cells via **plasmodesmata** (cytoplasmic strands connecting one cell to another)
- **vacuolar** route, where the water is considered to pass through the tonoplast then through the sap vacuole of each cell.

Note the different theories for water transport across the width of the root.

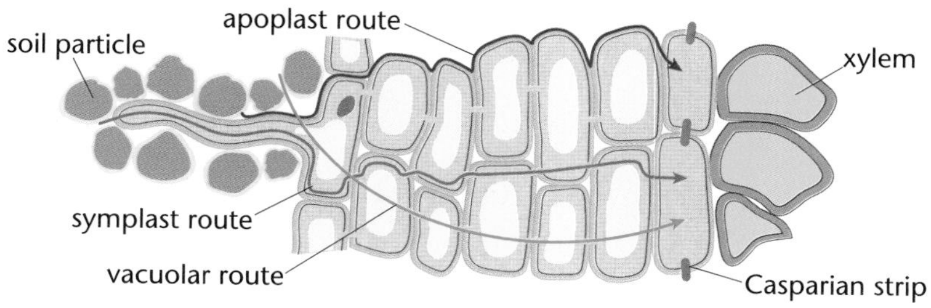

movement of water across the cortex

Casparian strip

Water moves across the cortex and needs to pass through the endodermal cells before entering the xylem vessels of the vascular system. Each cell of the endodermis has a waterproof band around it, just like a ribbon around a box. This means that water must pass through the cell in some way, rather than around the outside. If water moves by the apoplast route up to this point, then it must now move into the symplast or vacuolar pathways.

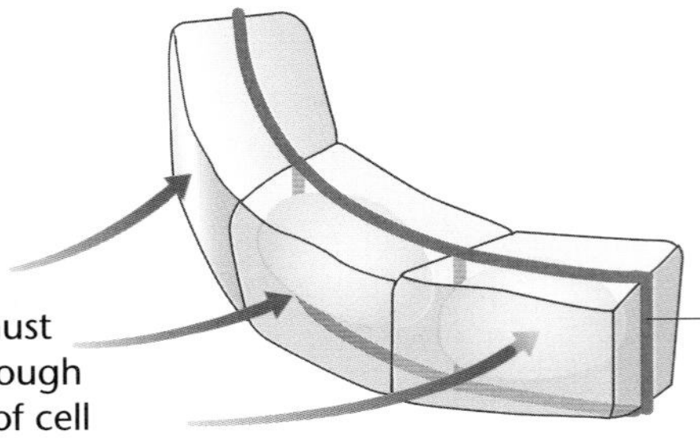

Casparian strip of the endodermal cells

Once the water has passed through the endodermis and navigated the pericycle then it must pass into the xylem for upward movement to the leaves and to the tissues.

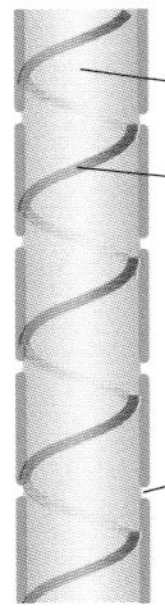

How does water move up the vascular system to the leaves?

Water moves into the **xylem** vessels in the vascular system in the centre of the root; it enters via **bordered pits**. The xylem is internally lined with **lignin**. This substance is waterproof and it also gives great strength to the xylem vessels, which are tube shaped. Much of the strength of a plant comes from cells toughened by lignin. A Giant Redwood tree is many metres high but water is still able to reach all the cells. Water moves up the xylem for the following reasons.

Remember that the xylem is part of the mass flow system ensuring that all cells receive their requirements.

- Root pressure gives an initial upward force to water in the xylem vessels. This can be shown by cutting off a shoot near soil level. Some sap will pour vertically out of the xylem of the remaining exposed xylem.
- Water moves up the xylem by capillarity which is the upward movement of a fluid in a narrow bore tube – xylem has very narrow vessels.
- Capillarity occurs because the water molecules have an attraction for each other (cohesion) so when one water molecule moves others move with it.
- Capillarity has another component – the fact that the water molecules are attracted to the sides of the vessels pulls the water upwards (adhesion).
- Transpiration causes a very negative water potential in the mesophyll of the leaves. Water in the xylem is of higher water potential and so moves up the xylem.

The factors in the list are known as the cohesion-tension theory and explain how water moves up the xylem.

Xylem vessels die at the end of their maturation phase. The lignin produced inside the cells finally results in death. The young xylem cells end to end, finally produce a long tube-like structure (vessel) through which water passes. Xylem can still transport water after the death of the plant.

Mineral ions are also transported in the xylem.

Translocation

This is an **active process** by which **sugars** and **amino acids** are transported through the phloem. Sugar is produced in the photosynthetic tissues and must be exported from these **sources** to areas of need, i.e. usually areas which have large energy requirements. These areas are called sinks, e.g. terminal buds and roots.

> **KEY POINT**
> Roots cannot photosynthesise so they need carbohydrates to be supplied by other parts of the plant such as the leaf or storage organs.

The sugars are transported in the phloem which consists of two types of cell, the **sieve tube** and **companion cell**. Unlike the xylem the cells of the phloem are living.

The sieve tube has no nucleus so that essential proteins for life are made by the companion cell which does possess a nucleus. The companion cell maintains services to the sieve tube.

Structure of the phloem tissue

- Each **sieve tube** links to the next via a **sieve plate** which is perforated with pores.
- The sieve tube has cytoplasm and a few small mitochondria.
- Sugars are thought to pass through the sieve tubes by **cytoplasmic streaming**.
- The sieve tubes have no nucleus but are alive because of **cytoplasmic connections (plasmodesmata)** with the companion cell.
- Each companion cell has a nucleus and mitochondria.

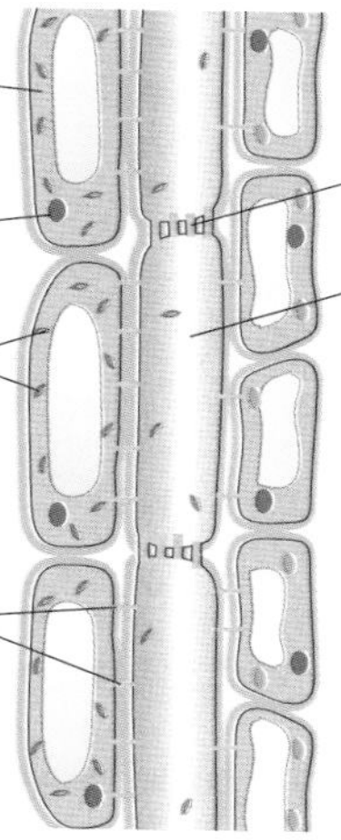

Radioactive labelling

This technique has been used to investigate the mechanism of translocation. It involves the use of a substance such as radioactive CO_2. The radioactive isotope, ^{14}C is used to make $^{14}CO_2$. A leaf is allowed to photosynthesise in the presence of $^{14}CO_2$ and makes the radioactive sugar ($^{14}C_6H_{12}O_6$). The route of the radioactive sugar can be traced using a Geiger-Mueller counter. The greater the number of radioactive disintegrations per unit time, the greater is the concentration of the sugar in that part of the plant

5.6 Water loss in a plant

After studying this section you should be able to:

- *understand how guard cells open and close*
- *understand the process of transpiration*
- *know how to use a potometer to measure the rate of transpiration*
- *recall the adaptations of xerophytes*

LEARNING SUMMARY

How is water lost from a leaf?

AQA A	M2
AQA B	M3
EDEXCEL	M2
OCR	M3
WJEC	M2
NICCEA	M2

Water moves up the xylem and into the mesophyll of a leaf. The process by which water is lost from any region of a plant is transpiration. Water can be lost from areas such as a stem, but most water is lost by evaporation through the stomata. Each stoma is a pore which can be open or closed and is bordered at either side by a guard cell. The diagrams show an open stoma and a closed stoma.

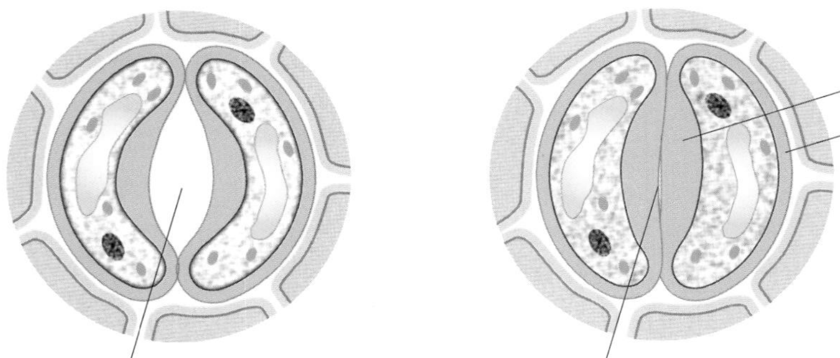

Transpiration from a leaf takes place as follows:

- the air spaces in the mesophyll become saturated with water vapour (higher water potential)
- the air outside the leaf may be of lower humidity (more negative water potential)
- this causes water molecules to diffuse from the mesophyll of the leaf to the outside.

KEY POINT

Some water can escape through the cell junctions and membranes. This is known as cuticular transpiration. In the dark all stomata are closed. Even so, there is still water loss by cuticular transpiration.

How do the guard cells open and close?

In the presence of light:

- K^+ ions are actively transported into the guard cells from adjacent cells
- malate is produced from starch
- K^+ ions and malate accumulate in the guard cells
- this causes an influx of water molecules
- the cell wall of each guard cell is thin in one part and thick in another
- the increase in hydrostatic pressure leads to the opening of the stomata.

Closing of the stomata is the reverse of this process. Under different conditions the stomata can be partially open. The rate of transpiration can increase in warm, dry conditions or decrease at the opposite extreme.

Measuring the rate of transpiration

This is done indirectly by using a potometer. This instrument works by the following principle; for every molecule of water lost by transpiration, one is taken up by the shoot.

Potometer

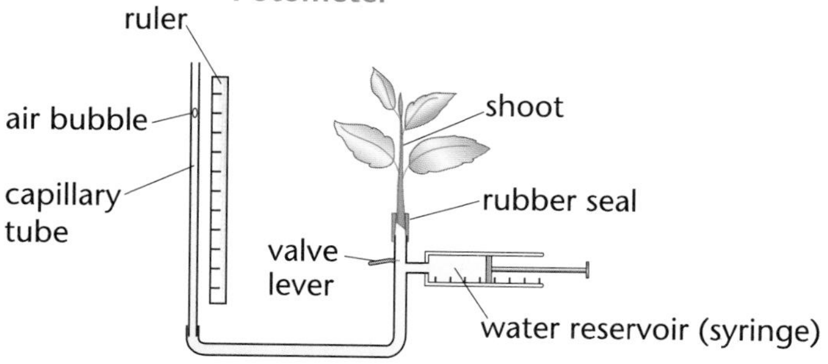

Note that a living shoot may be photosynthesising whilst attached to the instrument. Only a minute amount of water would be used in this process. The instrument gives an accurate measure of transpiration.

The potometer is used as follows:

- a shoot is cut and the end is quickly put in water to prevent an air lock in the xylem
- the potometer is filled under water so that the capillary tube is full
- all air bubbles are removed from the water
- the shoot is put into the rubber seal
- the valve is changed to allow water uptake
- the amount of water taken up by the shoot per unit time is measured
- the shoot can be tested under various conditions.

Xerophytes

AQA A	M2
AQA B	M3
EDEXCEL	M2
OCR	M3
WJEC	M2
NICCEA	M2

These are plants which have **special adaptations** to survive in drying, environmental conditions where many plants would become desiccated and die. The plants survive well because of a combination of the following features:

- thick cuticle to reduce evaporation
- reduced number of stomata
- smaller and fewer leaves to reduce surface area
- hairs on plant to reduce air turbulence
- protected stomata to prevent wind access
- aerodynamic shape to prevent full force of wind
- deep root network to absorb maximum water
- some store water in modified structures, e.g. the stem of a cactus.

In an exam you may be given a photomicrograph of a xerophytic plant which you have not seen before. Look for *some* of the features covered in the bullet points opposite.

A cactus is an excellent example of a xerophyte. It makes excellent use of what little water there is available, and holds on to what it does manage to absorb really well. Its cuticle and epidermis are so thick that metabolic water released from the cells during night time respiration is retained for photosynthesis during the day. Nothing is wasted!

Progress check

Water is absorbed into a plant by the root hairs.

(a) The water potential of the root hair cells are more negative than in the soil water. Is this statement true or false?

(b) Describe:

(i) the apoplast route across the cortex

(ii) the symplast route across the cortex.

(a) true

(b) (i) water is considered to pass on the outside of the cell membrane

(ii) water passes through the cytoplasm of the cells through plasmodesmata.

Sample question and model answer

(a) The graph below shows the oxygen dissociation curve for human haemoglobin.

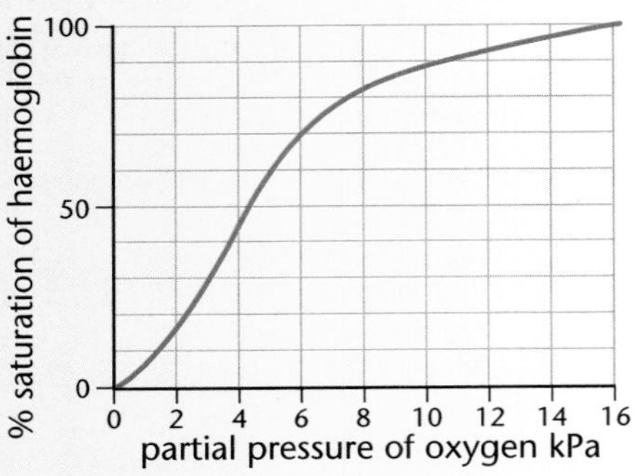

Note that haemoglobin is able to pick up a lot of oxygen, even at low partial pressure.

Use the information in the graph to help you answer the following questions.

(i) What is the advantage of haemoglobin as a respiratory pigment when oxygen in the air is at the low partial pressure 6 kPa? [1]

Even at a low partial pressure a lot of oxygen (70%) is taken up by the haemoglobin of a red blood cell.

The fact that haemoglobin is able to carry oxygen is important. However, it is just as important that the oxygen is offloaded at tissues needing it. This is only possible because carbon dioxide is found at the tissues.

(ii) Explain the effect on the oxygen dissociation curve of a high partial pressure of carbon dioxide at a muscle. [2]

The curve is moved to the right and down so that oxygen is released.

(iii) Fetal haemoglobin has a greater affinity for oxygen than maternal haemoglobin. Draw a curve on the graph to show the oxygen dissociation curve for fetal haemoglobin. [1]

See graph opposite.

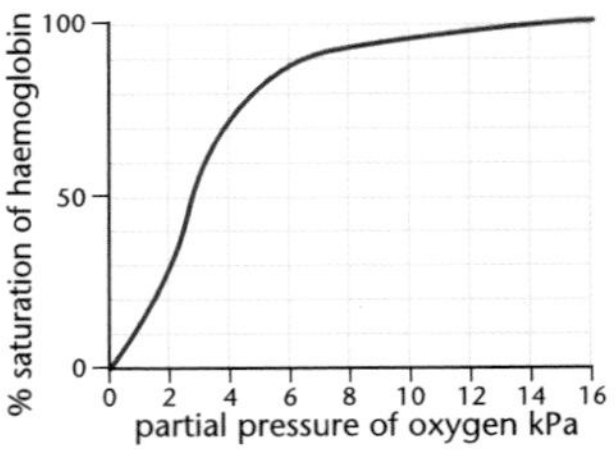

(b) The diagram shows **one** stage in the cardiac cycle.

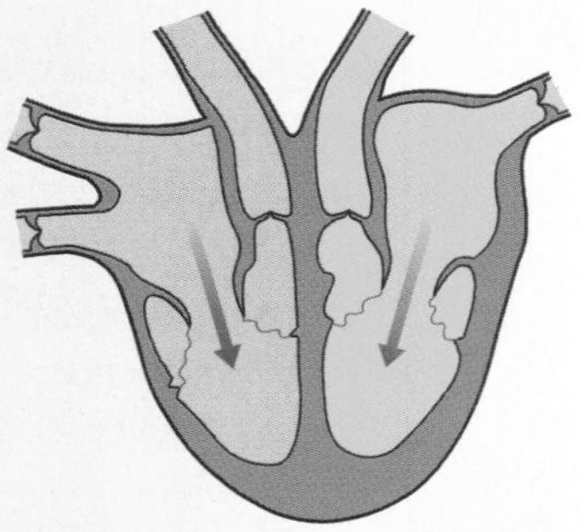

Always look for the valves. If the heart valve is open then the chamber behind it is contracting.

(i) Which stage of the cardiac cycle is shown in the diagram? Give **two** reasons for your answer. [3]

atrial systole
the atrioventricular valves are open/blood flows through the atrioventricular valves,
semi-lunar valves are closed.

(ii) Write an X in one chamber to show the position of the atrioventricular node (AVN). [1]

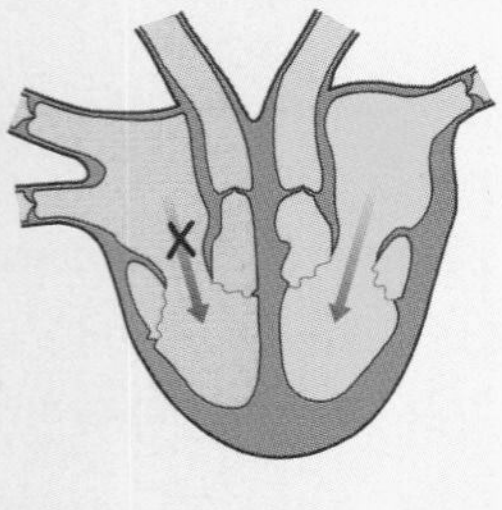

(iii) How does the AVN stimulate the contraction of the ventricles? [1]

Passes electrical impulses to Purkinje tissue/Bundle of His.

Practice examination questions

1 The diagram shows a capillary bed in the upper part of the skin. The arteriole is constricted.

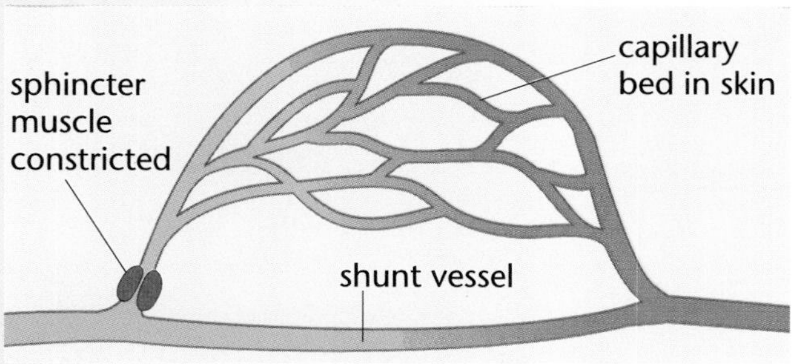

Use the information in the diagram and your own knowledge to answer the questions below.

(a) As a result of arteriole constriction, to where would the blood flow? [1]

(b) Explain how this would help maintain the body temperature. [4]

2 The table shows data about a person's heart before and after a training programme.

	Before training	***After training***
heart stroke rate	90 ml	120 ml
heart rate at rest	75 bpm	60 bpm
maximum heart rate	170 bpm	190 bpm

(a) Over a five minute period at rest before training, the cardiac output of the person was 33.75 litres.

How much blood would leave the heart, during the same time, whilst the person was at rest, after training? [2]

(b) After training, the maximum heart rate increased by 20 bpm. Explain the advantage of this increase to an athlete. [4]

(c) After training there are other changes in the body.

Explain:

(i) **two** changes which would improve the efficiency of the respiratory system. [2]

(ii) the effect of training on the muscles. [2]

3 Smoking causes respiratory disease. Outline the course and symptoms of each disease:

(a) lung cancer

(b) bronchitis

(c) emphysema. [6]

Practice examination questions (continued)

4 The diagram shows a freshly cut, leafy shoot attached to a potometer. This was used to measure the amount of water taken up by the shoot under different conditions.

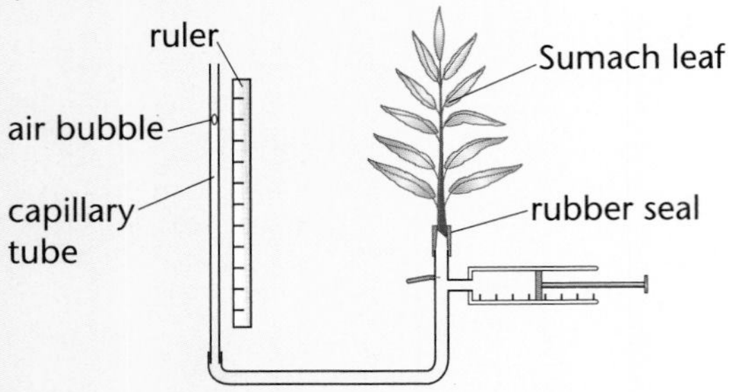

(a) What assumption must be made when using this apparatus to measure the rate of transpiration? [1]

(b) An air-lock can occur in the shoot which prevents water uptake.

(i) In which plant tissue could an air-lock occur? [1]

(ii) Describe the practical details by which a student could make sure that there was no air-lock in the shoot. [2]

(c) The radius of the capillary tube of the potometer was 1 mm. When a Sumach leaf was measured the air bubble moved 32 mm in one minute. Calculate the volume of water in mm^3 which would be taken up by the leaf in one hour under the same environmental conditions. [3]

5 *Agave americana* is a xerophytic plant which grows in the deserts of Mexico.

Agave americana

Suggest **three** ways in which the plant is adapted to survive periods of very low rainfall. [3]

6 The diagram shows nerves linking the medulla oblongata with the heart.

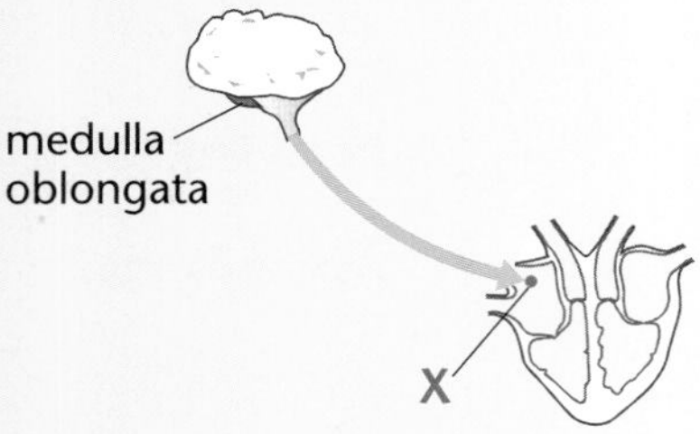

(a) Name part X. [1]

(b) What effect do the following have on the heart:

(i) vagus nerve

(iii) sympathetic nerve

(iv) adrenaline? [3]

Practice examination questions (continued)

7 The diagram shows an aphid feeding on a plant. The sharp stylet is inserted into the phloem tissue which supplies the aphid with sucrose, plus organic and inorganic ions.

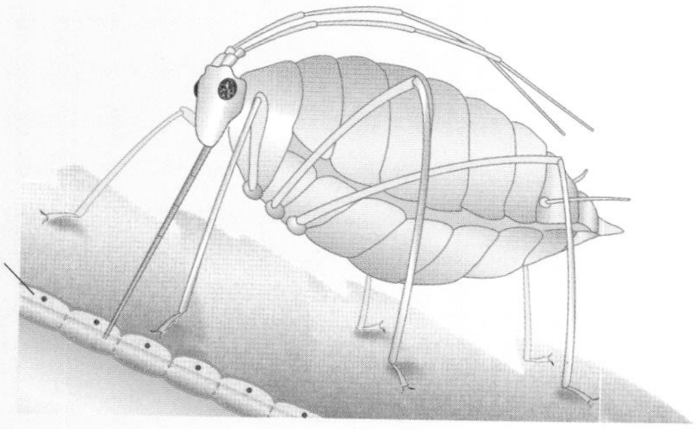

(a)

(i) Name the phloem cell X from which the aphid obtains sucrose. [1]

(ii) Cell X does not have a nucleus or ribosomes, but still contains enzymes. Explain how this is possible. [3]

(b)

(i) Feeding aphids obtain the contents of the phloem without any sucking action being necessary. What does this indicate about the transport of substances through the phloem? [3]

(ii) Scientists investigated phloem contents by anaesthetising feeding aphids, then cutting their bodies from their stylets. Phloem contents oozed from the cut end of each stylet. The phloem contents were tested using iodine and heating with Benedict's solution.

	Tested with iodine	***Heated with Benedict's solution***
Contents of phloem	brown colour	brick-red colour

Referring to the results of the tests, explain what the scientists found out about the phloem contents using this method. [4]

(iii) Hot-wax ringing is a technique where hot wax is poured around a stem. This technique was used with the aphid method described in (ii). Radioactive carbon dioxide was supplied to one leaf so that a radioactive carbohydrate was made.

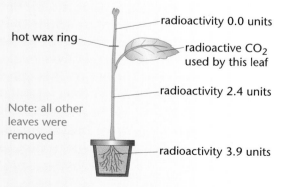

Explain the effect of hot-wax ringing on the phloem tissue. [3]

Chapter 6
The genetic code

The following topics are covered in this chapter:

- Chromosomes
- Cell division
- Gene technology
- Genetically modified organisms

6.1 Chromosomes

After studying this section you should be able to:

LEARNING SUMMARY

- recall the structure of DNA
- describe the roles of DNA and RNA in the synthesis of protein
- use organic base codes of DNA and RNA to identify amino acid sequences

Chromosome structure and function

AQA A	M2
AQA B	M2
EDEXCEL	M1
OCR	M1
WJEC	M1
NICCEA	M1

Each chromosome in a nucleus consists of a series of genes. A gene is a section of **DNA** and each controls the production of a protein important to the life of an organism.

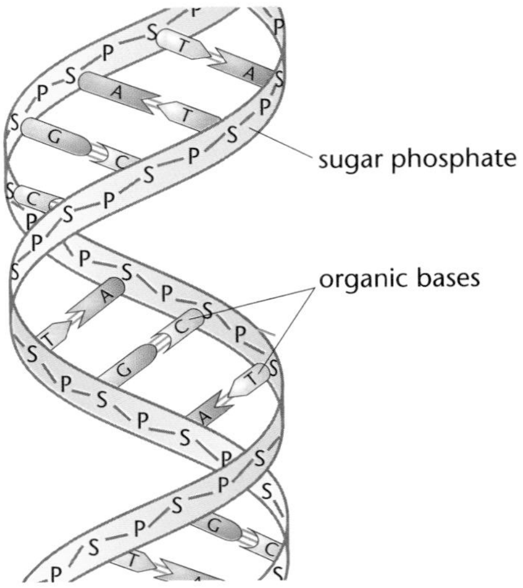

Deoxyribonucleic acid (DNA)

You need to be aware that many nucleotides join together to form the polymer, DNA.

Deoxyribonucleic acid (DNA) is made up of a number of **nucleotides** joined together in a double helix shape.

Why does the DNA of one organism differ from the DNA of another?

The answer lies in the structure of their nucleotides. Look at the structure of one nucleotide – **monomer**.

Each strand of DNA is said to be complementary to the other. **Examination tip:** be ready to identify one strand when given the matching complementary strand.

The organic base of each nucleotide can be any one of **adenine**, **thymine**, **cytosine** or **guanine**. Nucleotides join together at their bases by hydrogen bonds. Adenine bonds with thymine and cytosine with guanine.

A single nucleotide

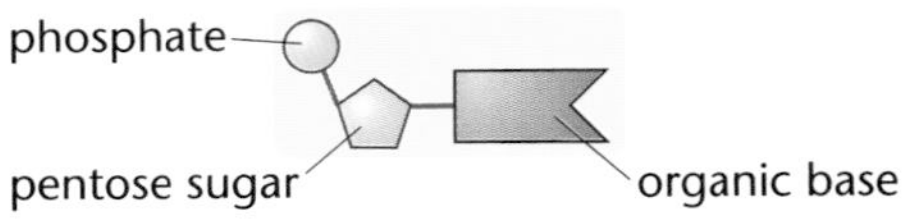

Phosphate and pentose sugar units link to form the backbone of the DNA. The twisting pattern formed as nucleotides bond to each other produces the double helix shape of DNA. Repeated linking of the monomer nucleotides forms the polymer structure of DNA.

Differences in the DNA of organisms such as humans and houseflies lie in the **different sequences** of the organic bases. Each sequence of bases is a code to make a protein, usually vital to the life of an organism.

DNA

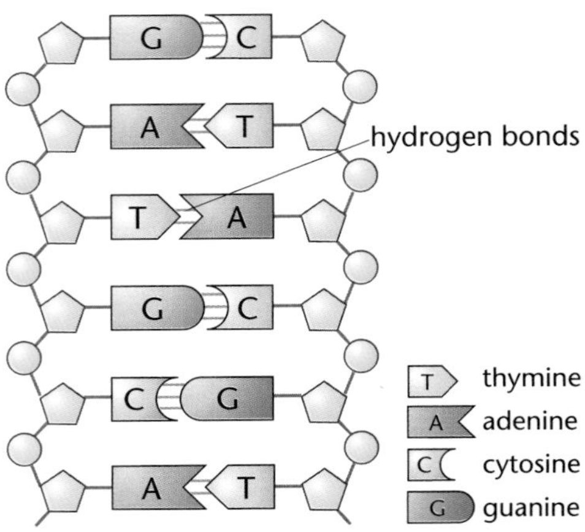

How does a cell make protein?

AQA A	M2
AQA B	M2
EDEXCEL	M1
OCR	M1
WJEC	M1
NICCEA	M1

This is called **protein synthesis**. It begins by linking amino acids in a chain sequence to form a **polypeptide**. Later a number of polypeptides can bond together to form an entire protein. The following diagrams show protein synthesis.

1 In the nucleus **RNA polymerase** links to a start code along a DNA strand.

2 RNA polymerase moves along the DNA. For every organic base it meets along the DNA a complementary base is linked to form mRNA **(messenger RNA)**.

Transcription

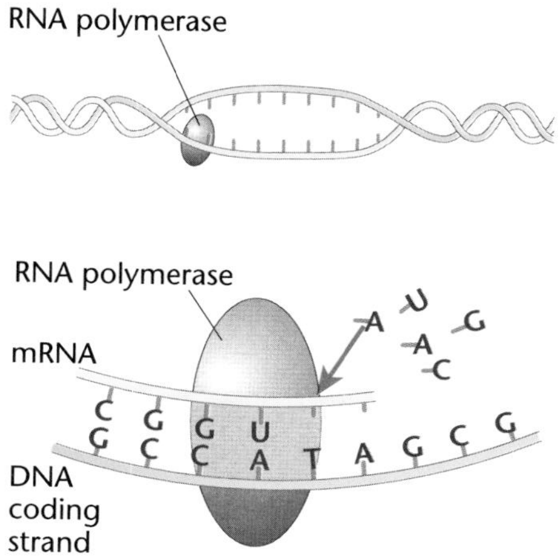

There is no thymine in mRNA. Instead there is another base, uracil.

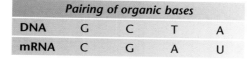

Pairing of organic bases				
DNA	G	C	T	A
mRNA	C	G	A	U

3 RNA polymerase links to a finish code along the DNA and finally the mRNA **moves** to a **ribosome**. The DNA stays in the nucleus for the next time it is needed.

4 Every three bases along the mRNA make up one **codon** which codes for a specific amino acid. Three complementary bases form an **anti-codon** attached to one end of tRNA **(transfer RNA)**. At the other end of the RNA is a specific amino acid.

5 All along the mRNA the tRNA 'partner' molecules enable each amino acid to bond to the next. A chain of amino acids **(polypeptide)** is made, ready for release into the cell.

Note the link between each pair of amino acids along a polypeptide – the peptide link.

Translation

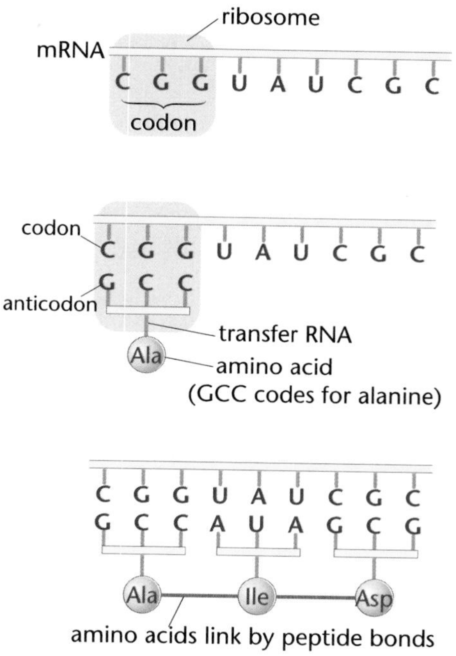

DNA codes

AQA A	M2
AQA B	M2
EDEXCEL	M1
OCR	M1
WJEC	M1
NICCEA	M1

The table below shows all the triplet sequences of organic bases found along DNA strands and the coding function of each. During the process of protein synthesis triplet codes along the DNA result in specific amino acids being linked in chains known as **polypeptides**. Firstly, each triplet in the table codes for the production of complementary bases along mRNA.

Here is an example of a coding strand of DNA

DNA	A A A G A G G A C A C T	*(coding strand)*
mRNA	U U U C U C C U G U G A	*(messenger RNA)*

Use the key to identify the amino acids in the table opposite.

Amino acid	Abbreviation
alanine	Ala
arginine	Arg
asparagine	Asn
aspartic acid	Asp
cysteine	Cys
glutamine	Gln
glutamic acid	Glu
glycine	Gly
histidine	His
isoleucine	Iso
leucine	Leu
lysine	Lys
methionine	Met
phenylalanine	Phe
proline	Pro
serine	Ser
threonine	Thr
tryptophan	Trp
tyrosine	Tyr
valine	Val

guanine (G) on DNA codes for cytosine (C) on mRNA
cytosine (C) on DNA codes for guanine (G) on mRNA
thymine (T) on DNA codes for adenine (A) on mRNA
adenine (A) on DNA codes for uracil (U) on mRNA

Special note: There is no thymine found on mRNA. Instead, the organic base uracil is found.

Genetic code functions of DNA

	second organic base								
	A		*G*		*T*		*C*		*third organic base*
	AAA	Phe	AGA		ATA	Tyr	ACA	Cys	**A**
A	AAG		AGG	Ser	ATG		ACG		**G**
	AAT	Leu	AGT		ATT	stop	ACT	stop	**T**
	AAC		AGC		ATC	stop	ACC	Trp	**C**
	GAA		GGA		GTA	His	GCA		**A**
G	GAG	Leu	GGG	Pro	GTG		GCG	Arg	**G**
	GAT		GGT		GTT	Gln	GCT		**T**
	GAC		GGC		GTC		GCC		**C**
	TAA		TGA		TTA	Asn	TCA	Ser	**A**
T	TAG	Ile	TGG	Thr	TTG		TCG		**G**
	TAT		TGT		TTT	Lys	TCT	Arg	**T**
	TAC	Met	TGC		TTC		TCC		**C**
	CAA		CGA		CTA	Asp	CCA		**A**
C	CAG	Val	CGG	Ala	CTG		CCG	Gly	**G**
	CAT		CGT		CTT	Glu	C CT		**T**
	CAC		CGC		CTC		CCC		**C**

Do not learn all of the triplet codes. Be ready to use the supplied data in the examination. You will be given a key of different codes and functions.

If you are given a table of codes check them carefully. If the bases are from mRNA then there will be uracil in the table.

Each triplet code is non-overlapping. This means that each triplet of three bases is a code, then the next three, and so on along the DNA.

- AAA codes for the amino acid phenylalanine
- GAG codes for the amino acid leucine
- GAC codes for the amino acid leucine
- ACT codes for a stop, the mRNA to be released at the end of transcription.

There are more triplet codes than there are amino acids. This is known as the degenerate code, because an amino acid such as leucine can be coded for by up to six different codes.

Mutation

This is a change in the DNA of an organism. There are different effects on DNA causing different types of mutation. Here is a strand of DNA before mutation.

C T A T C G C A A A T A C G T

Mutation type 1 C T A T C G C A A A T A T G C

This is inversion: The TGC triplet now codes for a different amino acid.

Mutation type 2 C T A T C G C A A A T A C G T C A A

This is addition: The CAA triplet now codes for an extra amino acid.

Mutation type 3 C T A T C G C A A A T A

CGT is missing. This is deletion. One amino acid is missing from the polypeptide.

Mutation type 4

Large sections of DNA can be added, whole chromosomes or sets of chromosomes. Mutation types 1 to 3 are point mutations because they affect one amino acid code.

Addition is a key type of mutation. A regular question is to ask why addition of one base may be more harmful than adding a triplet of new bases. One base may change every amino acid code along the DNA whereas one triplet may add **just one** amino acid.

Progress check

(a) Name the parts of a nucleotide.

(b) (i) By which bonds do the two strands of DNA link together?

(ii) How would these bonds be broken in the laboratory to produce single strands of the DNA?

(c) Which organic base is found in DNA but not in RNA?

(d) During protein synthesis:

(i) which enzyme enables the mRNA to be produced?

(ii) which process produces mRNA?

(iii) which process enables amino acids to link together as tRNA 'reads' the mRNA codons?

(a) pentose sugar, phosphate and organic base. The organic base may be thymine, adenine, cytosine, or guanine

(b) (i) hydrogen bonds (ii) heat

(c) thymine (d) (i) RNA polymerase (ii) transcription (iii) translation

6.2 Cell division

After studying this section you should be able to:

LEARNING SUMMARY

- *describe and explain the semi-conservative replication of DNA*
- *understand that DNA must replicate before cell division can begin*
- *recognise each stage of cell division by mitosis*

How do cells prepare for division?

AQA A	M2
AQA B	M2
EDEXCEL	M2
OCR	M1
WJEC	M1
NICCEA	M1

Remember that as the DNA unwinds each single strand is a **complement** to the other. This means that each has the **matching** series of organic bases.

Before cells divide they must first make an exact copy of their DNA by using a supply of organic bases, pentose sugar molecules and phosphates. This is known as the semi-conservative replication of DNA. The diagram (right) shows this taking place.

The DNA begins to unwind, exposing its two single strands. Each complementary strand then acts as a template to build its opposite strand. This process results in the production of two identical copies of double stranded DNA.

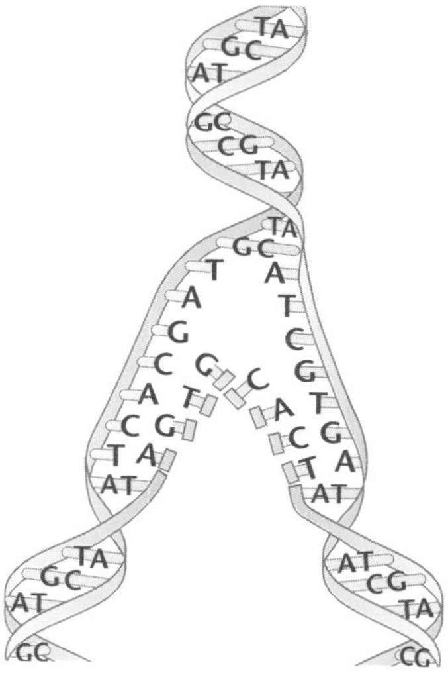

Semi-conservative replication of DNA

Exam questions are often based on experimental data. Apply your knowledge of principles learned during the course and this will be helpful.

What does semi-conservative mean?

The answer lies in the results of this experiment carried out by researchers.

Bacteria were cultured with a radioactive isotope of nitrogen located in the organic bases of their DNA.

The bacteria were then supplied with non-radioactive bases. They replicated their DNA using these bases. Their population increased.

Each molecule of DNA of the next generation had one radioactive strand and one normal strand.

Semi-conservative replication

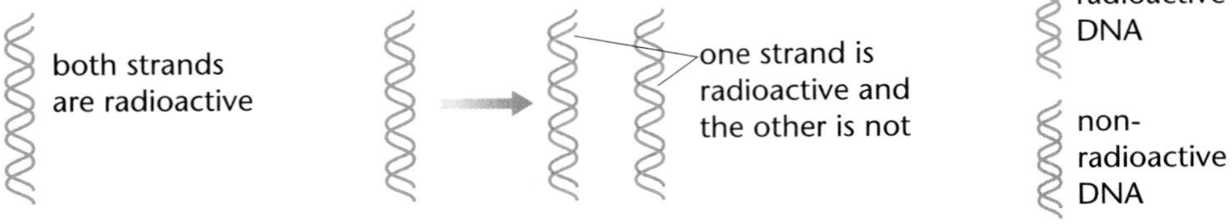

Semi-conservative means that as DNA splits into its two single strands, each of the new strands is made of newly acquired bases. The other strand, part of the original DNA, remains.

Cell division

Cells divide for the purposes of growth, repair and reproduction. Not all cells can divide but there are two ways in which division may occur, i.e. mitosis and meiosis.

Just before either mitosis or meiosis begin, **interphase** takes place. This is when the DNA of the chromosomes replicates (see page 85). The sequence of diagrams below shows a cell dividing into two daughter cells by mitosis.

> Remember that DNA replication takes place before cell division in **interphase** (see page 85). This is not an integral phase of mitosis or meiosis.

1 Prophase

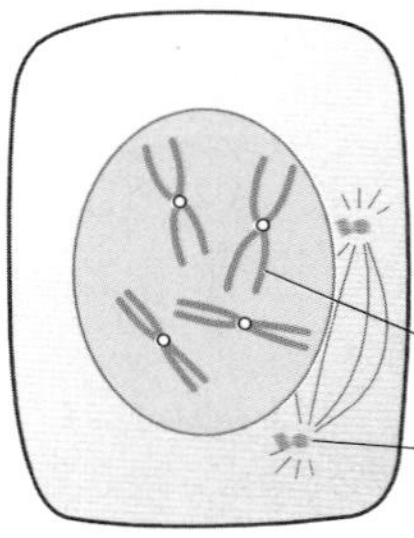

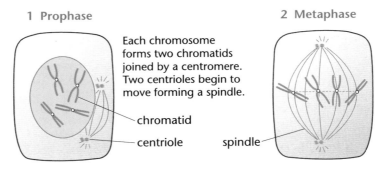

Each chromosome forms two chromatids joined by a centromere. Two centrioles begin to move forming a spindle.

2 Metaphase

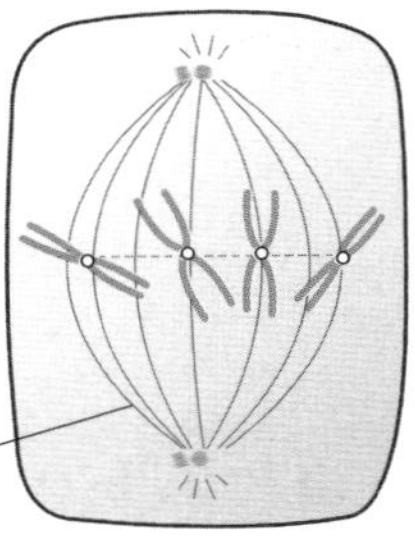

The chromatids, still joined by a centromere move to middle of cell. Each of the two chromatids has identical DNA to the other.

> Be ready to analyse photomicrographs of all phases of mitosis. If you can spot 10 pairs of chromosomes at the end of telophase, then this is the original diploid number of the parent cell.

3 Anaphase

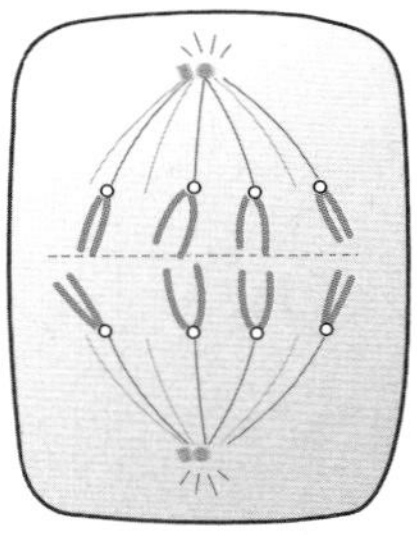

The spindle fibres join to the centromeres. The spindle fibres shorten and the centromeres split. The separated chromatids are now chromosomes.

4 Telophase

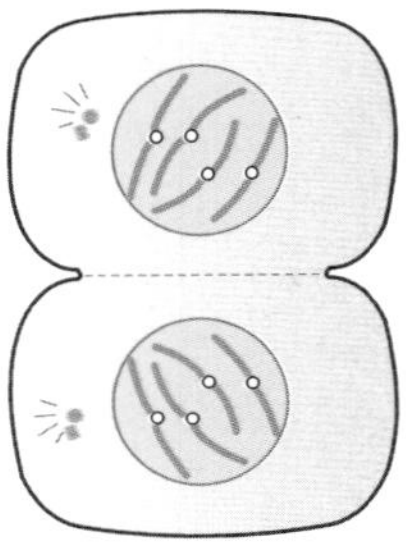

Identical chromosomes move to each pole.The nuclear membrane re-forms. The cell membrane narrows at the middle and two daughter cells are formed.

The table below shows differences between mitosis and meiosis.

	Mitosis	*Meiosis*
How many daughter cells are produced?	2	4
Are the daughter cells identical or different to the parent cell?	identical (clones)	different
Are the chromosomes of daughter cells single or in pairs?	in pairs **(diploid)**	single **(haploid)**

6.3 Gene technology

LEARNING SUMMARY

After studying this section you should be able to:

- *define genetic engineering*
- *describe and explain the roles of key enzymes in genetic engineering*
- *understand the process of electrophoresis and recall its applications*

Manipulating DNA

AQA A M2
AQA B M2
OCR M1
NICCEA M1

Scientists have developed methods of manipulating DNA. It can be transferred from one organism to another. Organisms which receive the DNA then have the ability to produce a new protein. This is one example of **genetic engineering**.

KEY POINT

Changes in the DNA of an organism by a range of methods use the knowledge and skills acquired during research into **gene technology**. The examples which follow show different ways of utilising gene technology.

Gene transfer

AQA A M2
AQA B M2
OCR M1
NICCEA M1

The gene which produces human insulin was transferred from a human cell to a bacterium. The new microbe is known as a **transgenic bacterium**. The process which follows shows a similar technique.

Restriction endonucleases are produced by some bacteria as a defence mechanism. They cut up the DNA of invading viruses. This can be exploited during gene transfer.

Note that **both** the donor DNA and recipient plasmid DNA are cut with the same enzyme. This allows the new gene to be a matching fit.

Many exam candidates fail to state that the plasmids are cloned inside the bacterium.

The bacteria themselves are also cloned. There may be two marks in a question for each cloning point!

1 An enzyme known as **restriction endonuclease** cuts the DNA and the gene was removed. Each time a cut was made the two ends produced were known as 'sticky ends'.

2 Circles of DNA called **plasmids** are found in bacteria.

3 A plasmid was taken from a bacterium and cut with the same restriction endonuclease.

4 The human gene was inserted into the plasmid. It was made to fix into the open plasmid by another enzyme known as **ligase**.

5 The plasmid **replicated** inside the bacterium.

6 Large numbers of the new bacteria were produced. Each was able to secrete perfect human insulin, helping diabetics all over the world.

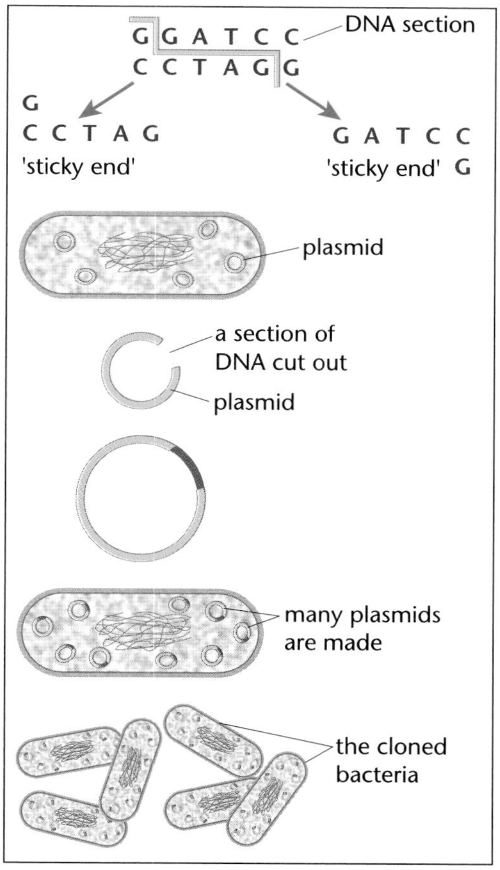

Transgenic bacteria are cultured in huge industrial **fermenters**, like the one on the next page. They secrete their products which can be collected. Many microbes are exploited in this way. The enzymes found in biological washing powders are produced in this way. Where microbes are exploited for human use, this is known as **biotechnology**.

Modern industrial fermenters

- There are several different types of fermenter used to grow microorganisms on a large scale. They all have the common purpose of producing food, or chemicals such as antibiotics, hormones, or enzymes. The fermenter (right) shows a typical design.

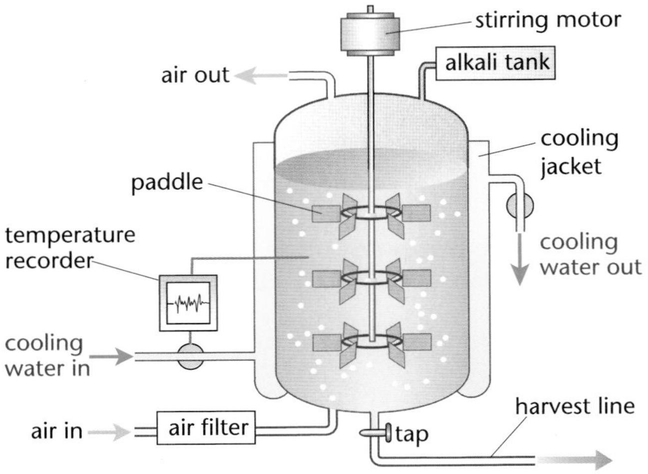

New transgenic organisms are continually being developed. Many hit the headlines in the media. Be aware that the examiners may use these high-profile organisms in questions. Do not become disorientated – the principle is always the same.

Conditions inside fermenters should be suitable for the optimal metabolism and rapid reproduction of the microorganisms. Products should be harvested without contamination. Note the conditions which need to be controlled.

- Fermenters are sterilised using steam before adding nutrients and the microorganisms used during the process. Conditions are **aseptic**.
- Nutrients which are specifically suited to the needs of the microorganisms are supplied.
- Air is supplied if the process is aerobic. This must be filtered to avoid contamination from other microorganisms.
- Temperature must be regulated to keep the microorganisms' enzymes within a suitable range. An active 'cooling jacket' and heater, both controlled via a thermostat, enable this to be achieved.
- pH must remain close to the optimum. Often the development of low pH during fermentation would result in the process slowing down or stopping. The addition of alkaline substances allows the process to continue and maximises yield.
- Paddle wheel mixing or 'bubble agitation' make sure that the microorganisms meet the required concentrations of nutrients and oxygen.

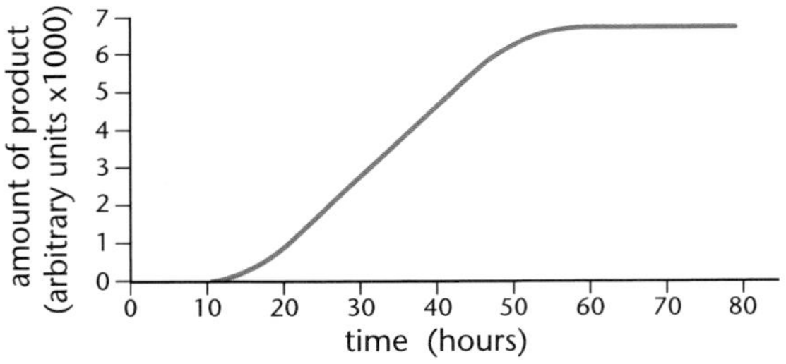

Questions about fermentation usually explore your understanding of how the optimal (best) conditions can be achieved. Also graphs may be given. You may be asked about the best time for harvesting the product. This will be at the earliest stage of the graph becoming level.

Electrophoresis

Restriction endonucleases can be used to cut up an organism's DNA (see page 87).

- DNA sections are put into a well in a slab of agar gel.
- The gel and DNA are covered with buffer solution which conducts electricity.
- Electrodes apply an electrical field.
- Phosphate groups on DNA are negatively charged causing DNA to move towards the anode.
- Smaller pieces of DNA move more quickly down the agar track, larger ones move more slowly, leading to the formation of bands.

a view looking down on the agar slab

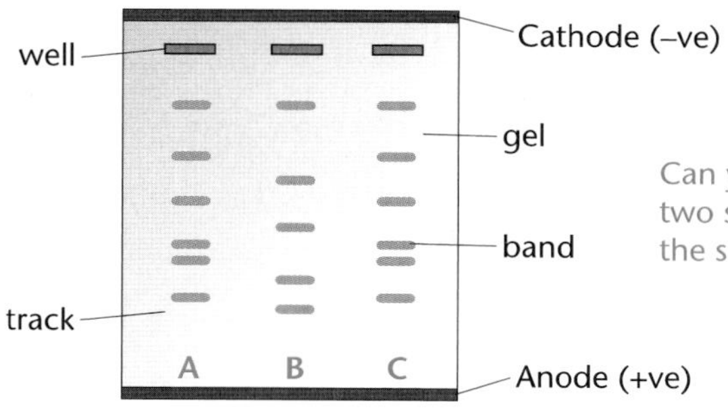

Can you spot which two samples were from the same person?

Genetic fingerprinting is applied to organisms other than humans. Illegal egg collectors have been successfully prosecuted when egg DNA has been compared against the DNA profile of parent birds.

Genetic fingerprinting

Electrophoresis has many applications. DNA is highly specific so the bands produced using this process can help with identification. In some crimes DNA is left at the scene. Blood and semen both contain DNA specific to an individual. DNA evidence can be checked against samples from suspects. This is known as **genetic fingerprinting**. Genetic fingerprinting can be used in paternity disputes. Each band of the DNA of the child must correspond with *either* a band from the father or mother.

In examinations you may experience questions on a wide range of applications.

(a) Someone with leukaemia must have a bone-marrow transplant. The DNA of the marrow cells after transplant must be the same as the donor if the operation has been successful.

(b) When breeding animals, the DNA of potential breeding pairs can be checked to make sure that they come from different families. Inbreeding is avoided.

Isolating genes

Along chromosomes are large numbers of genes. Scientists may need to identify and isolate a useful gene; one way of doing this is to use the enzyme **reverse transcriptase**. This is produced by viruses known as **retroviruses**. Reverse transcriptase has the ability to help make DNA from mRNA.

Stage 1

When a polypeptide is about to be made at a ribosome, reverse transcriptase allows a strand of its coding DNA to be made.

mRNA UAA GCC GAU
single DNA ATT CGG CTA

Stage 2

The single stranded DNA is parted from the mRNA.

single DNA ATT CGG CTA

Stage 3

The other strand of DNA is assembled using DNA polymerase.

DNA TAA GCC GAT
ATT CGG CTA

Using this principle the exact piece of DNA which codes for the production of a vital protein can be made.

Progress check

1 A length of DNA was prepared then electrophoresis was used to separate the sections. The statements below describe the process of electrophoresis but they are in the wrong order. Write the letters in the correct sequence.

A electrodes apply an electrical field
B DNA sections are put into a well in a slab of agar gel
C smaller pieces of DNA move more quickly down the agar track with larger ones further behind
D the gel and DNA are then covered with buffer solution which conducts electricity
E restriction endonucleases can be used to cut up the DNA

2 Reverse transcriptase is an enzyme which enables the production of DNA from RNA. Work out the sequence of organic bases along the DNA of the following RNA sequence. AAUGCCCGGAUU

1 E B D A C
2 RNA AAUGCCCGGAUU
DNA_2 AATGCCCGGATT
DNA_1 TTACGGGCCTAA

6.4 Genetically modified organisms

After studying this section you should be able to:

- *outline the main features of a range of genetically modified organisms*
- *explain the advantages and disadvantages of using a range of genetically modified products*

LEARNING SUMMARY

Examples of genetic modification

AQA A	M2
AQA B	M2
OCR	M1
NICCEA	M1

Animals and plants can also have their DNA changed. A new gene can be added to give the organism a new property or feature.

Gene transfer can be achieved in a number of ways; e.g. *Agrobacterium tumefaciens* specialises in invading plants through roots. It sends a plasmid into the host cell which becomes incorporated into the host cell's chromosomes. The genetic engineer puts a new gene into the plasmid which takes the gene into the cell. This results in a new feature.

Genetically modified soya bean plants

In the USA large quantities of soya beans are produced. Selective herbicides (weed killers) are effective against broad-leaved plants. They could not be used in soya fields because the crop is also broad-leaved. Farmers needed to use expensive mechanical methods to kill the weeds. Genetic engineers transferred a gene using a **vector** into a soya bean plant which gave resistance to selective herbicides. The vector was a bacterium which entered the soya bean plant taking the useful gene with it. Since then the modified soya seeds have been grown all over the world. Farmers can use selective herbicides in their soya fields and keep them weed free.

Genetically modified potato plants

A gene which allows the production of insecticide has been transferred into a new breed of potato plant. Aphids which feed on the sap of the plants take in the insecticide which kills many of them. It is not 100% effective so there are many resistant aphids in the environment. Ladybirds are natural predators which eat the aphids. It has been found that ladybird fertility has decreased, and they live half as long as normal. In the long term the aphid pests may increase even more, becoming a greater problem. Ladybirds could even become extinct. Gene transfer may have problems in store for the human race.

Ethical issues

AQA A	M2
AQA B	M2
OCR	M1
WJEC	M1
NICCEA	M1

The applications of gene technology have huge implications. People must assess the advantages against the potential dangers.

- It is possible to locate a defective gene in a fetus. The gene may lead to a condition such as muscular dystrophy. Consider potential action and the responsibility of knowing this information.
- Companies now are able to change a species drastically to produce something useful to humans. They even patent the new life form so that its reproduction is under their licence. Is it moral to change a species?
- If potatoes contain insecticide which kills aphids and their ladybird predators, then what effect may it have on human consumers of the genetically modified potatoes?
- If genetically modified soya plants resistant to herbicides breed with weeds, they may pass this feature on. What effect would this have on crop yields?

Life is based on DNA. Different species possess DNA with different sequences of organic bases. Adding new sections to give new properties has advantages but should be handled with care. There may be consequences.

In the examination you may be asked to consider a scenario involving genetic engineering. You will not be credited for simply stating that you agree or disagree. Show that you have a balanced view giving advantages *and* disadvantages. Show awareness of the consequences which may take place. Give details of possible sequential effects.

Sample questions and model answers

Always remember to read all information given. You must be aware of what the examiner is testing. Try to link the question with the part of the syllabus the topic comes from.

You will not be expected to remember all the genetic code! In this question you are given data. Make sure you have revised all key words so that you can apply the principles you have learned to the data.

Exam boards never give the full name of amino acids. There will always be a key.

The table below shows some mRNA codons and the amino acids which are coded by them.

	second position					
	U	*C*	*A*	*G*		
first position U	Phe	Ser	Tyr	Cys	U	third position
	Phe	Ser	Tyr	Cys	C	
	Leu	Ser	stop	stop	A	
	Leu	Ser	stop	Trp	G	

Key to amino acids

Ser – serine
Phe – phenylalanine
Leu – leucine
Tyr – tyrosine
Trp – tryptophan
Cys – cysteine

Use the information in the table to help you answer the following questions.

1

There are two codes to choose from.

(a) Give a sequence of mRNA bases which would code for leucine. [1]

UUA or UUG

(b) What does the mRNA base sequence UAC code for? [1]

Tyrosine

Follow the table headings to indicate U (first base), A (second base) and C (third base).

This can be tricky! Remember that you need to work backwards. Given mRNA you know that it is coded for by one strand of DNA. Work out one DNA strand then use T – A, and G – C links.

2

The mRNA sequence UCA codes for serine. Work out the base pairs on the DNA. [3]

UCA is coded for by these bases, AGT
AGT links to the bases TCA
So the DNA is AGT
TCA

If you failed to learn the definition of the degenerate code then you would fail to apply it to this data.

3

Use evidence from the table to show that serine is an example of the degenerate code. [1]

It is coded for by four different base sequences.

4

UAG codes for 'stop'. Explain the effect of the 'stop' code during the process of protein synthesis. [2]

It is responsible for the polypeptide being terminated which allows it to leave the tRNA once all the amino acids have been linked.

Take care that you do not confuse the two terms.

5

During protein synthesis,

(i) where does translation take place?

At a ribosome

(ii) where does transcription take place? [2]

In a nucleus

Practice examination questions

Try all of the questions and check your answers with the mark scheme on page 141.

1 The two DNA sequences below are cut by the enzymes *Eco*R1 and *Hin*d111.

G | AATTC   A | AGCTT
CTTAA | G   TTCGA | A

*Eco*R1   *Hin*d111

Two identical pieces of DNA were cut with each enzyme, separately. The resulting pieces are shown below.

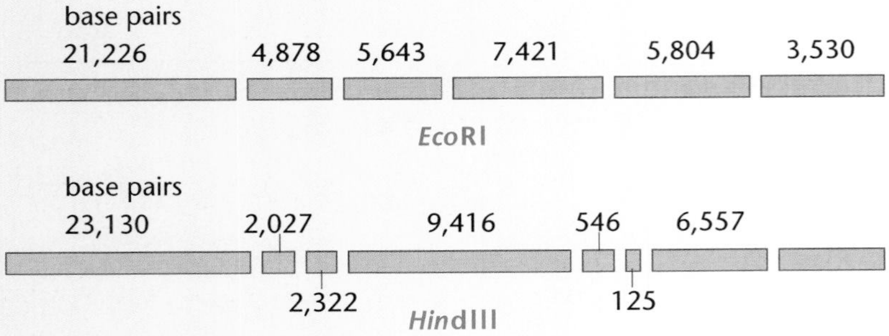

(a) How many times did the base sequence cut by *Eco*R1 occur along the DNA? Give a reason for your answer. [2]

(b) What term is given to each end of a piece of cut DNA? [1]

(c) How many base pairs were there on the final piece of DNA cut by *Hin*d111? Show your working. [2]

(d) Describe how the use of the enzymes *Eco*R1 and *Hin*d111 are useful in genetic fingerprinting. [3]

2 The diagram below shows a stage in the process of mitosis.

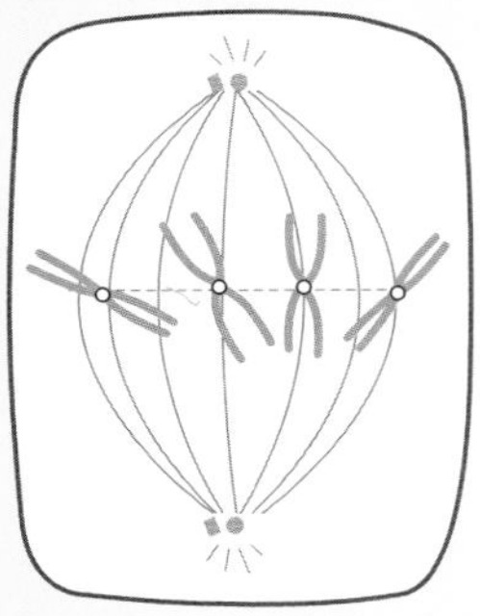

(a) Give the stage of mitosis shown. [1]

(b) How many chromosomes would there be in the daughter cells? [2]

3 (a) Explain how a useful gene can be transferred from a human pancreas to a bacterium. [6]

(b) Describe how the transgenic bacteria could be cultured in an industrial fermenter to produce a useful product. [5]

(c) Give ONE example of a hormone which is produced as a result of gene transfer from pancreas cells. [1]

Practice examination questions (continued)

4 The table below shows the relative organic base proportions found in human, sheep, salmon and wheat DNA.

	Proportion of organic bases in DNA (%)			
Organism	***Adenine***	***Guanine***	***Thymine***	***Cytosine***
human	30.9	19.9	29.4	19.8
sheep	29.3	21.4	28.3	21.0
salmon	29.7	20.8	29.1	20.4
wheat	27.3	22.7	27.1	22.8

(a) Refer to the proportion of organic bases in salmon DNA to explain the association between specific bases. [2]

(b) Suggest a reason for the small difference in proportion of the organic bases adenine and thymine in sheep. [1]

(c) All species possess adenine, guanine, thymine and cytosine in their DNA. Account for the fact that each species is different. [2]

5 It was suspected that a person had taken an egg from the nest of a rare bird. DNA samples were taken from the egg and both parent birds. The DNA profiles shown below were made using electrophoresis.

a view looking down on the agar slab

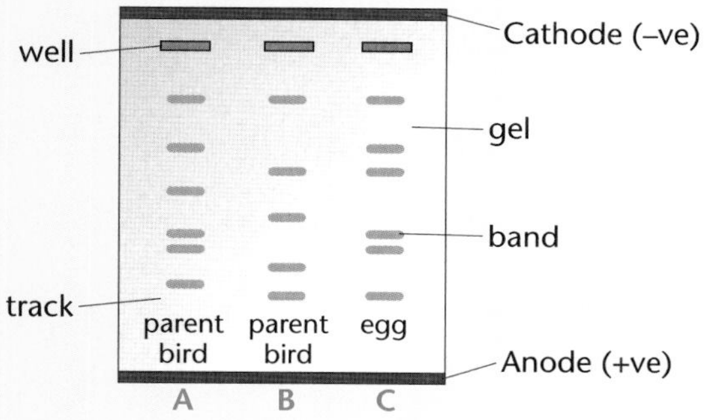

(a) Which type of enzyme is used to cut DNA before electrophoresis? [1]

(b) Do the electrophoresis results suggest that the egg was taken from the nest? Give a reason for your answer. [1]

(c) Suggest TWO other applications for electrophoresis. [2]

6 A new genetically modified soya bean plant has been developed. It has a new gene which prevents it from being killed by herbicide (weed killer).

(a) Describe the stages which enable a gene to be transferred from one organism to another. [5]

(b) Explain how the genetically modified soya plants result in higher bean yields. [3]

(c) What would be the danger if the genetically modified soya plants interbred with the plants of the hedgerows? [3]

(d) Suggest why people may object to the growing of genetically modified soya bean plants. [2]

Chapter 7

Continuity of life

The following topics are covered in this chapter:

- *Variation*
- *Plant reproduction*
- *Human reproduction*

7.1 Variation

After studying this section you should be able to:

- *understand the significance of meiosis to sexual reproduction*

LEARNING SUMMARY

Why is meiosis so important in sexual reproduction?

AQA A	M2
AQA B	M2
OCR	M1
WJEC	M1
NICCEA	M1

When sexual reproduction takes place the male and female must produce gametes (sex cells). These are produced by the process of meiosis. This is sometimes called reduction division because a **diploid** parental cell divides to produce four **haploid** cells.

- parental cell has chromosomes in pairs **(diploid)**
- four daughter cells each have single **chromosomes**, half the number of the parental cell **(haploid)**

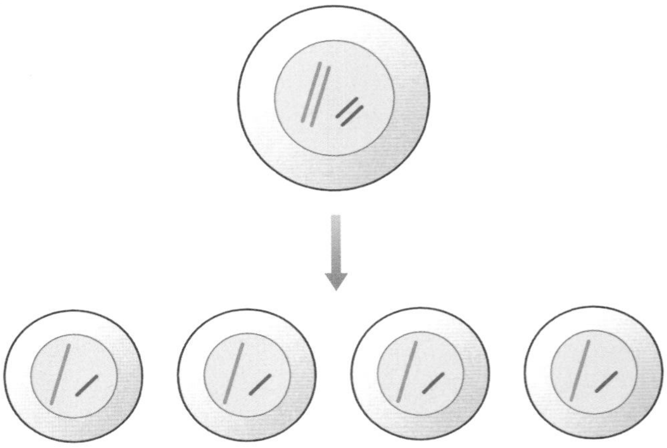

Note that the diploid number in a human body cell is 46 (23 pairs of chromosomes).

All cells produced by meiosis are **different** to the parental cell and to each another. This is highly significant and is a major factor in the **genetic variation** within a species. Consider human reproduction as an example. Every person inherits a set of chromosomes from the mother (23) and a set from the father (23). The matching chromosomes of each corresponding pair have the same gene in the same position (locus) along their length. They may be exactly the same gene but can be different **alleles**.

An allele is a different expression of a gene. Each pair of alleles along homologous chromosome pairs can be homozygous, e.g. **AA**, **aa** or heterozygous, e.g. **Aa** (where **A** is **dominant**, and **a** is **recessive**).

Note that the haploid number in a human body cell is 23 (single) chromosomes.

How are genetically different cells produced during meiosis?

The key event in producing genetically different gametes takes place during the first stage of meiosis – **prophase 1**. The diagrams on the next page show the process of **crossing over** of a pair of homologous chromosomes and the consequences this has on producing **different allele combinations**.

KEY POINT

If this diagram represents one cross-over or chiasma then imagine what happens when there are **many** cross-overs along a pair of chromosomes. Each person has 23 pairs of homologous chromosomes. What a lot of cross-overs!

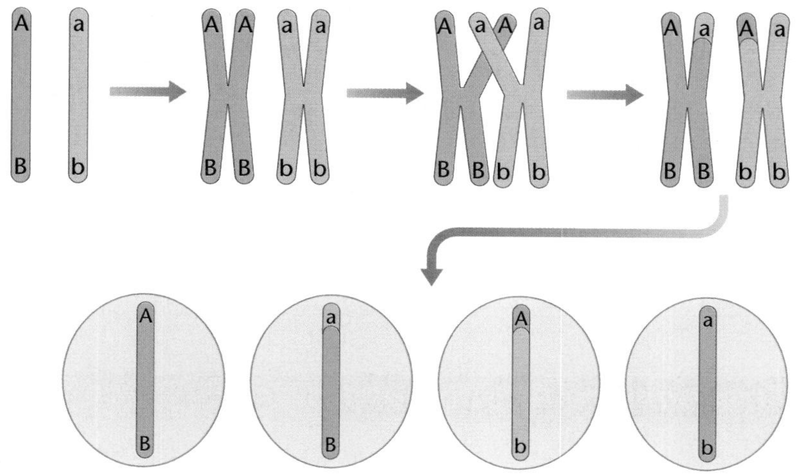

Note that the pair of homologous chromosomes shown have different alleles.

A represents an allele dominant to a, a recessive allele.

B represents an allele dominant to b, a recessive allele.

The chromosomes would have many more genes than merely ones shown by A, a, B, b. The diagram above shows the consequence of only one cross-over or chiasma. Cross-overs cause a difference in the combinations of alleles along a chromosome. The cross-over, as shown above, results in chromosomes with AB, Ab, aB and ab combinations.

With many cross-overs taking place along all 23 pairs of chromosomes it is not surprising that every cell produced by meiosis is genetically different.

Meiosis takes place by two divisions. Consider these two divisions in relation to the cross-over above.

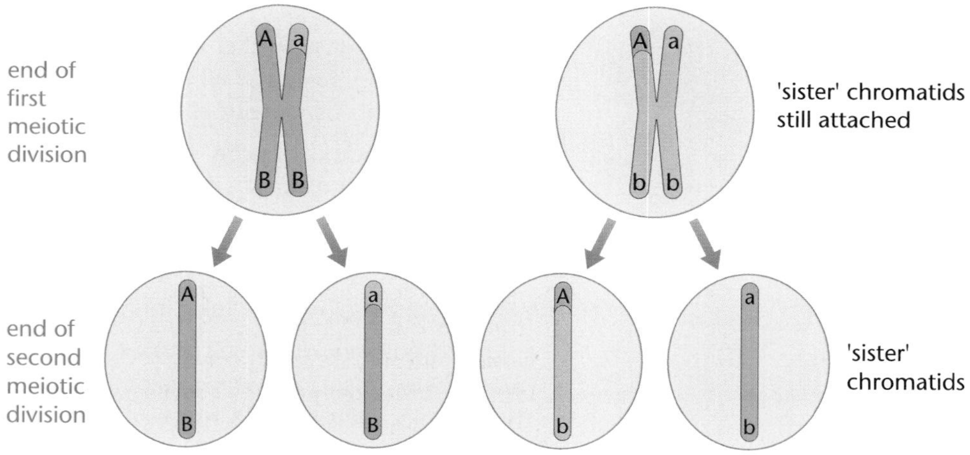

The combination of each of these chromosomes with the others, results in further genetic variation.

Humans are given as examples of the consequences of a meiotic division. Plants and other organisms divide by **exactly the same principles**. Only the chromosome numbers and alleles differ.

The combination of each of these chromosomes with 22 others, results in further genetic variation; the random segregation of chromosomes. Human gametes are produced by meiosis. Only 1 homologous pair is shown in the diagram but there would be 22 other pairs. If each gamete is different, then the male gamete fusing with a female gamete is yet another source of variation.

7.2 Plant reproduction

LEARNING SUMMARY

After studying this section you should be able to:

- *describe the structures and functions of flowers*
- *understand the development of pollen and ovules*
- *understand the significance of cross-pollination*
- *describe typical seed structure*
- *describe the special features of wind- and insect-pollinated plants*

Structure and function of flowers

EDEXCEL M2

Sexual reproduction in plants takes place as a result of the activity of specific parts of flowers. The diagram below shows a section through a flower.

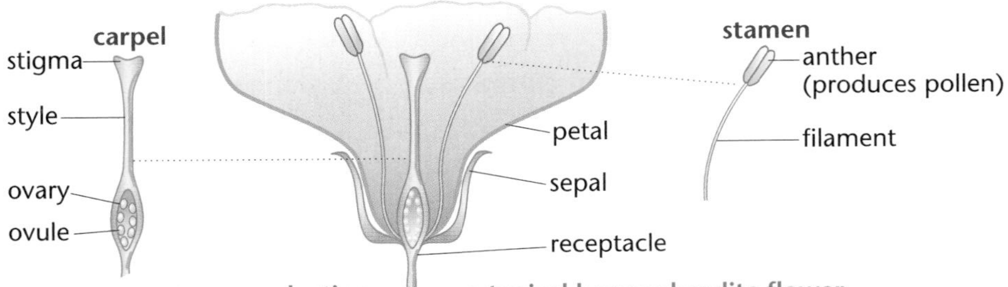

reproduction a typical hermaphrodite flower

The functions of the parts are as follows.

- Sepals – collectively known as the calyx, protect the flower whilst in bud.
- Petals – if they are large and brightly coloured attract insects for the process of pollination.
- Stamens – consist of anther and filament. The anthers produce the male gametes (pollen) each of which contains a haploid set of chromosomes. The anther does this by meiotic division.
- Carpels are made of stigma, style and ovary. In the ovary are the female gametes (ovules) each of which also contains a haploid set of chromosomes.

Candidates often confuse the male and female structures. Learn the structure names and functions carefully.

How does the anther make pollen?

The complete development takes place in a pollen sac inside an anther.

- A diploid pollen mother cell divides by meiosis.
- Each division forms 4 pollen grains.
- The haploid nucleus of each pollen grain divides by mitosis to form 2 haploid nuclei per pollen grain.
- One nucleus is the tube nucleus and one is the generative nucleus.
- The male gamete is contained inside the pollen grain.
- The outer cellular layer of the pollen grain is smooth for wind-pollinated flowers and rough for insect-pollinated flowers.

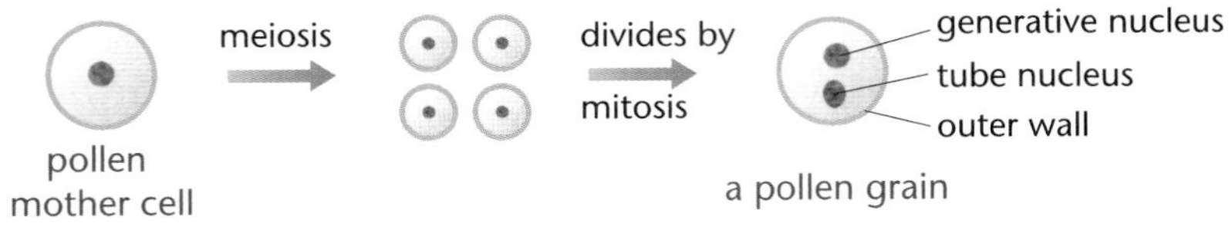

formation of a pollen grain

How does the ovary make ovules?

The complete development of each ovule takes place beginning with an **embryosac mother cell**.

Try to understand each part of the process in a logical sequence then you will build up an understanding.

- The embryosac mother cell (diploid cell) divides by meiosis to form 4 haploid cells.
- 3 of them degenerate.
- The nucleus of the 1 haploid cell remaining divides by mitosis.
- This produces 2 haploid nuclei, which again divide by mitosis.
- This produces 4 haploid nuclei, which again divide by mitosis.
- Finally this produces 8 haploid nuclei, and the structure is known as a mature **embryosac**.

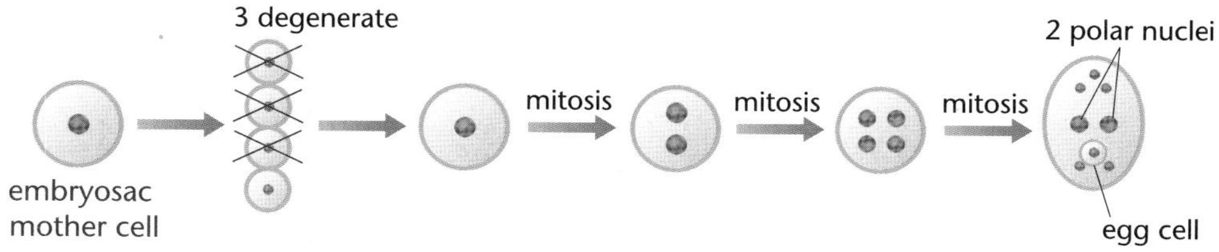

formation of an embryosac

Pollination

This is the movement of pollen from an anther to a stigma. The stigma often has a surface covered with a sticky sugary substance, acting as a super-glue to hold onto pollen grains.

What is fertilisation? This takes place during sexual reproduction. The male gamete fuses with a female gamete to produce a zygote. This first diploid zygote then divides many times by mitosis to produce a new organism.

Fertilisation

Pollen reaches a stigma and sticks to the surface, the following events then take place.

- A **pollen tube** begins to grow from the pollen grain.
- The proteins for this tube are produced with the help of the **tube nucleus** which remains near the tip of the tube.
- The **generative nucleus** divides into **2 male nuclei** which follow down the tube.
- The pollen tube grows into an ovule.
- One male nucleus fuses with the egg cell forming a diploid **zygote**; this divides many times to form the **embryo** of the seed.
- The other male nucleus fuses with the two polar nuclei forming a triploid cell; this divides many times to form the endosperm (food store) of the mature seed.
- This is double fertilisation because of the fusion to form the **diploid zygote** and the triploid **primary endosperm cell**.

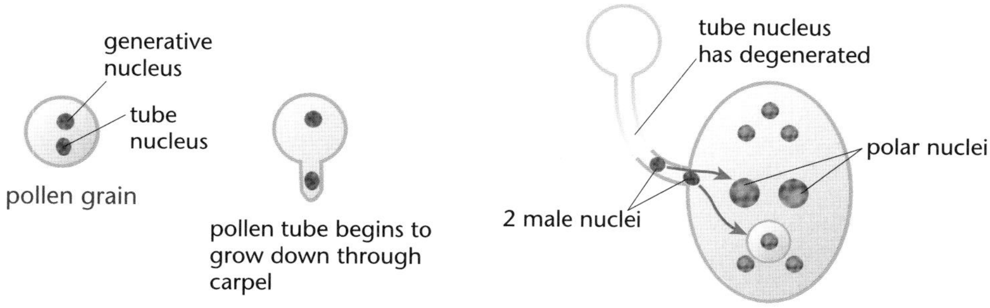

fertilisation

Seed structure

EDEXCEL M2

After fertilisation the flower parts die off leaving the ovary surrounded by its wall. A variety of different types of fruit form after this depending on the species of plant, e.g. in a plum the ovary wall becomes fleshy and swells. This protective outer wall is now known as the **pericarp**. A typical seed has an outer protective covering known as the **testa**.

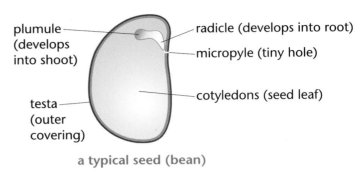

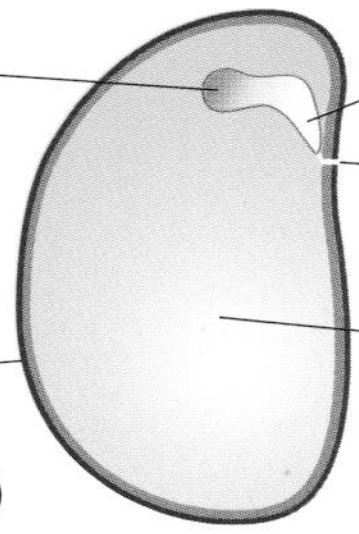

a typical seed (bean)

What special adaptations do plants have for reproduction?

There are many different structures and mechanisms which help plants to reproduce successfully. Each has evolved over a considerable period.

Many flowers are able to self-pollinate but there is an increased probability of disadvantageous alleles being exhibited in the phenotype of offspring.

> **KEY POINT**
> Cross-pollination is better as it increases the probability of advantageous alleles, strengthening the gene pool of a species.

Mechanisms of pollination

Plants have evolved a number of adaptations to make sure that self-pollination does **not** take place before pollen is transferred from one flower to another.

Protandry

This means that the **anthers ripen first**, to produce pollen before the carpel has ovules ready for fertilisation. Reproduction can only take place by pollen being taken to another flower, e.g. Rosebay Willowherb (*Chamaenerion angustifolium*). Correspondingly, the later-ripening ovules can only receive pollen from another flower.

Note that protandry and protogyny are different mechanisms, but the outcome is similar, i.e. they ensure that cross-pollination takes place.

Protogyny

This means that the **stigmas ripen first**, to produce ovules before the anther has pollen ready for fertilisation. Reproduction can only take place by pollen being received from another flower, e.g. Bluebell (*Endymion non-scriptus*). Correspondingly, the later-ripening anthers can only produce pollen capable of pollinating another flower.

Dioecious plants

These are plant species which have a **separate plant** which produces just **male flowers** and **another** which produces **exclusively female ones**, e.g. Holly (*Ilex* species). This means that cross-pollination must take place if reproduction is to be successful. In a garden two holly trees, a male and a female, must be planted if reproduction is to be successful. Just the female alone will not successfully produce berries. It is possible that a single holly plant produces berries but there is always a male plant close by!

Every female holly tree needs a male pollinator, otherwise there will be no berries! Holly flowers are dull and insignificant. Do you think they are insect- or wind-pollinated?

Features of wind-pollinated and insect-pollinated plants

The transport of pollen from one plant to another requires some mechanism to carry the pollen since, unlike a sperm, it is non-motile. The table below shows the typical features of wind- and insect-pollinated plants.

Features	
Wind-pollinated plants	***Insect-pollinated plants***
Petals are small or absent so that anthers and stigmas are exposed to the wind	Petals are large to attract insects
Stamens hang out of the flower so that pollen can be blown away on the air currents. Long styles allow the stigma to be exposed to catch the pollen blown by the wind	Stamens and stigmas are found inside the flower. Petals often in a tubular arrangement. This forces the insect to brush against anthers for pollen pick up and brush against stigmas which releases pollen.
If petals are present they are are often green	Petals are coloured to attract insects
No scent produced	Scent often produced, e.g. perfumed roses or the stinking-flesh scent of *Fritillaria*
No nectaries are present	Nectaries are present which contain (nectar) carbohydrate as an attractant for insects. They are deep in the receptacle of the flower, increasing the probability of the insect brushing against anther and stigma.
Flowers are well above the leaves, exposed to air currents, often found on tall stems	Many flowers are at a lower level, e.g. pansy
Very high pollen quantity produced which increases the probability of successful pollination	Lower quantity of pollen produced because insect pollination has a high chance of success
Pollen smooth and aerodynamic	Pollen rough, enabling it to cling to insect bodies

Wind-pollinated plants have flowers which are hardly noticeable. The diagram below shows a typical grass flower.

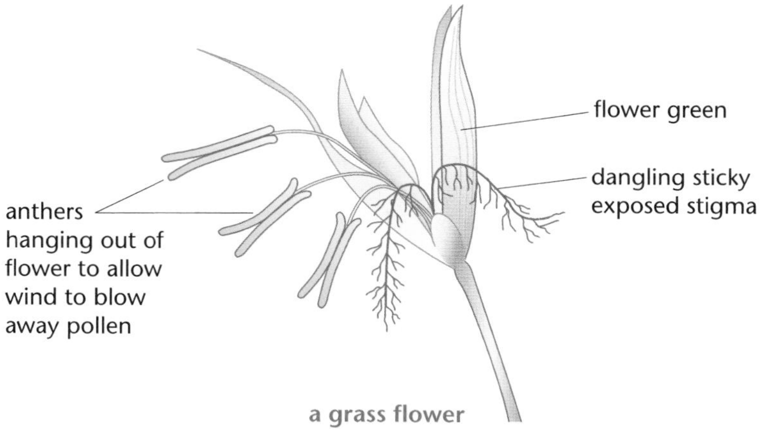

a grass flower

Progress check

Explain the function of protandry and protogyny in flowering plants.

Protandry ensures that the pollen ripens first and protogyny causes the ovules to ripen before the pollen. Both ensure that self-pollination does not take place.

7.3 Human reproduction

After studying this section you should be able to:

- *describe the structure and functions of male and female reproductive systems in humans*
- *describe the roles of the hormones which control the menstrual cycle*
- *describe the transfer of gametes leading to fertilisation in humans*
- *outline implantation and fetal development in humans*
- *understand the process of birth and lactation*

LEARNING SUMMARY

The reproductive structures

AQA A M2
EDEXCEL M2

When a baby is born it already has the structures which can eventually result in the production of offspring. Once adolescence is reached the sex organs of a person begin to function, as they mature.

The male reproductive system

The diagram below shows the male reproductive system.

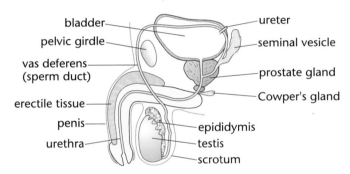

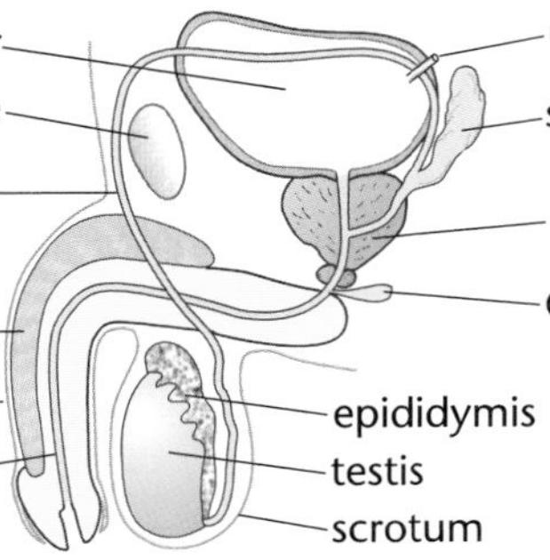

What are the functions of the male reproductive structures?

- The key structures are the two **testes** in which the sperm develop. Precisely, it is in the many **seminiferous tubules** where the millions of sperm are formed.
- The seminiferous tubules all lead to the **epididymis**, a coiled tube. Mature sperm are stored in the epididymis which in turn leads to the **vas deferens** (sperm duct).
- Sperm move through the vas deferens during ejaculation – a muscular spasm by which sperm are ejected from the male reproductive system.
- Each sperm is equipped with a tail which enables it to swim to the female gamete. The sperms need fluid to swim in, which they acquire on their journey from three structures:

  (a) prostate gland
  (b) Cowper's gland
  (c) seminal vesicle.

  These secrete alkaline fluid which aids sperm survival, but additionally the seminal vesicle produces sucrose, an energy source for the sperm.
- The sperm and fluid together are known as semen.
- Semen leaves the body via the penis. Here it passes through the urethra, a central tube in the penis which is shared with urine excretion, although not at the same time!
- The penis can become firm and erect by the inflow of blood in the erectile tissue around the urethra.

You will probably remember a lot of this information from GCSE. Build on what you already know. Additional facts about the glands, vesicles and vas deferens will widen your knowledge.

- A sac, the scrotum, covers each testis. This gives limited protection and helps keep the testes 2°C below the normal body temperature. Sperm need this lower temperature to develop. They must not overheat!
- The testes also produce the hormone **testosterone**, which helps develop secondary sexual characteristics.

The female reproductive system

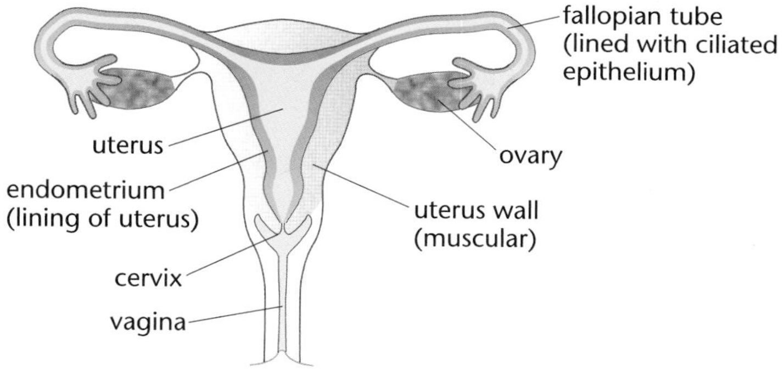

What are the functions of the reproductive structures?

- The key structures are the two **ovaries** which produce hormones and develop the ova (female gametes).
- A **fallopian tube** connects each ovary to the uterus. Each fallopian tube is a muscular tube lined with **ciliated epithelia** and **glandular** cells which secrete mucus.
- The action of the cilia of the cells lining the fallopian tube moves the ovum progressively towards the uterus after **ovulation**.
- The mucus is propelled along by the **cilia**, so that the ovum moves smoothly **without dehydration**.
- The uterus is a cavity lined by a thick layer of smooth muscle. This will, by contractions, help the mother to give birth in the final stage of pregnancy.
- The uterus is lined by the **endometrium**, a mucous membrane which has a rich supply of capillaries. This is used to supply the embryo with services during pregnancy.
- The vagina is a muscular tube which is connected to the uterus via the narrow 'neck' of the uterus, the **cervix**.

How are the sperms produced in the testes?

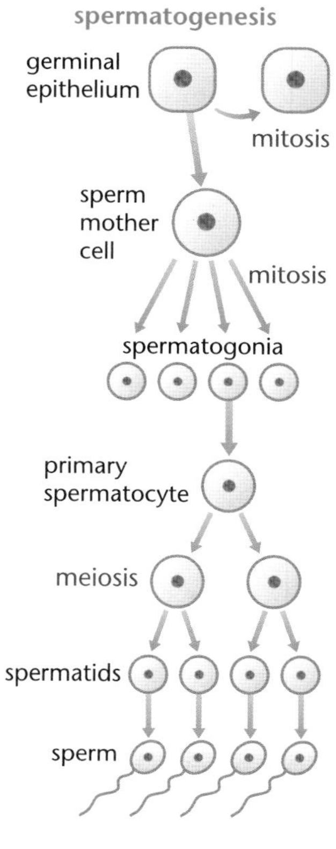

The process is called **spermatogenesis**. The sequence of this process takes place as follows:

- cells from the germinal epithelium on the outside of the seminiferous tubules divide by mitosis
- this produces sperm mother cells (spermatogonia)
- each sperm mother cell divides by mitosis to produce many more identical cells
- each spermatogonium grows to form a primary spermatocyte which divides by the first meiotic division to form secondary spermatocytes
- each secondary spermatocyte then completes the second meiotic division to form spermatids
- Sertoli cells are a source of nutrition for the spermatids; the heads grow a tail and become mature sperms after feeding at these cells
- finally they fall away to be transported to the epididymis for storage.

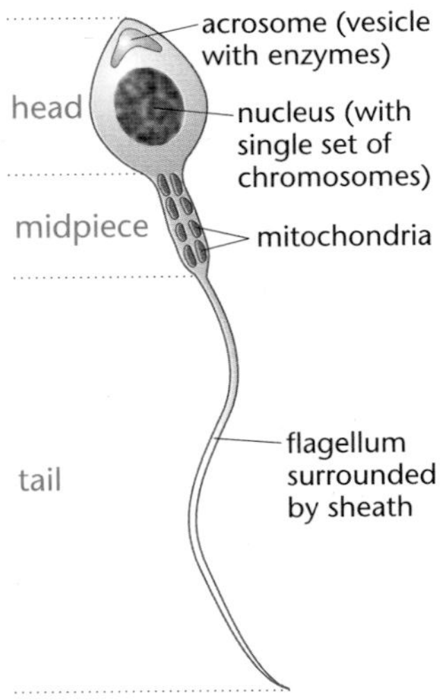

The structure of a human sperm

- The head consists of a haploid nucleus, carrying a single set of chromosomes from the male. Near the front of the head is the acrosome, a package of proteolytic enzymes which enable the sperm to pass through the protective layer around an ovum.
- The mid-piece is full of mitochondria which release energy necessary to fuel the life processes of the sperm on its journey.
- The tail consists of a sheath around a flagellum. Much of the energy released in the mid-piece powers the swimming action of the flagellum.

How are the ova produced in an ovary?

When a female baby is born, each ovary contains thousands of primary follicles. All remain dormant until adolescence begins. At maturity it is usual that one follicle will develop each month and produce an ovum.

The process is by oogenesis. The sequence of this process begins as a female fetus is developing in a uterus.

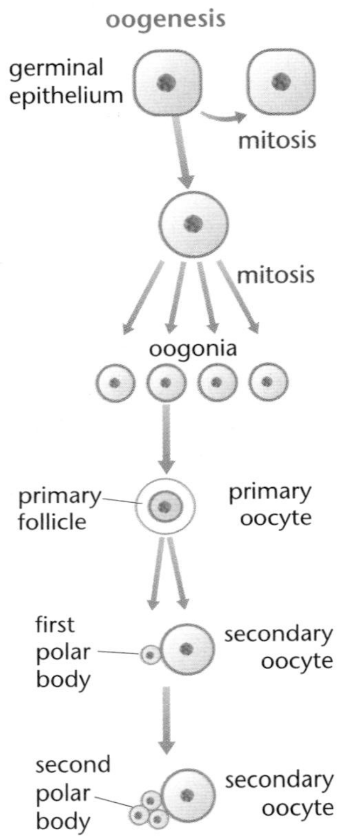

Stage 1 (foetus to birth)

- Fetal cells from the germinal epithelium on the outside of its ovaries divide by mitosis to form oogonia.
- Each oogonium grows to form a primary oocyte.
- Each primary oocyte becomes surrounded by a layer of follicle cells. It is then known as the primary follicle (Graafian follicle).
- A female baby has thousands of primary follicles at birth, but all remain dormant until adolescence begins.

Stage 2 (maturity to menopause)

- At maturity, during each month it is normal for just one primary follicle to develop to maturity stimulated by a hormone 'trigger' (see page 104).
- The primary oocyte divides by the first meiotic division to form a secondary oocyte and a smaller polar body.
- A second meiotic division takes place to form the large secondary oocyte and much smaller second polar body.
- The secondary oocyte is known as the ovum as it is released from the primary follicle.
- The release of the ovum is known as ovulation.
- The ruptured primary follicle still has an important role! It changes into a corpus luteum (yellow body) which produces an important hormone – progesterone.

The ovary shown below shows the events leading to ovulation.

The diagram of the ovary shows the events which take place from the development of the primary oocyte to the degeneration of a corpus luteum. The diagram shows the sequence for one primary follicle in its development. All stages are not present at the same time! The sequence shown would only be visible if a time-lapse sequence followed the **same** follicle during development.

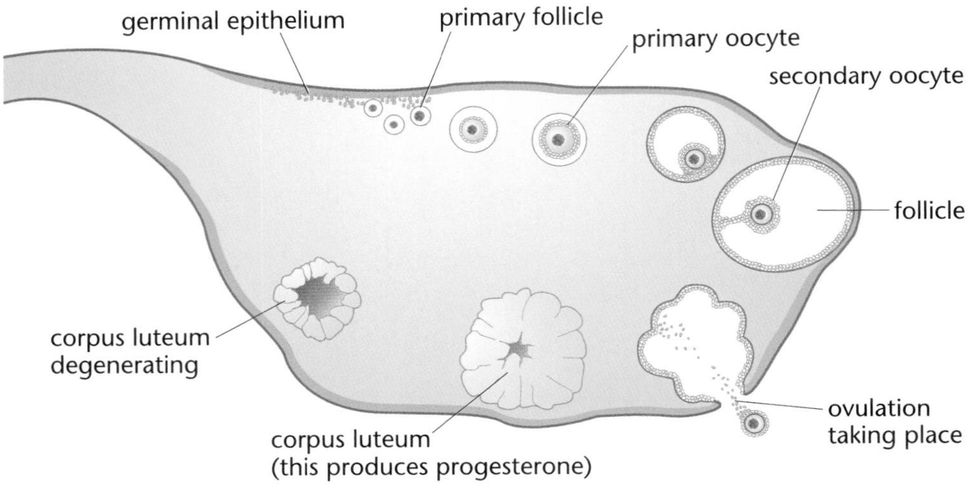

The events leading to fertilisation

During copulation the erect penis is inserted into the vagina. When ejaculation takes place the semen is released at the cervix. The semen immediately coagulates so that the female retains the sperm. Within a few minutes the sperm then begin to swim in a fluid produced by the female. Fertilisation normally takes place in the fallopian tube, where one sperm fuses with an ovum. The diagram below shows fertilisation.

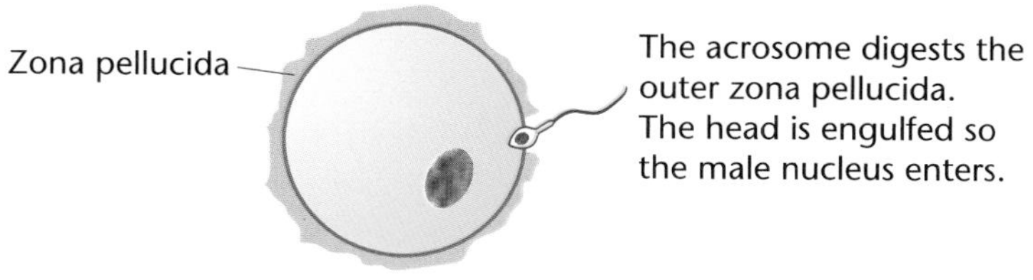

Remember that the ovum can also be called the secondary oocyte.

- Many sperm are attracted to the ovum by chemotaxis.
- The acrosome, a vesicle containing hydrolytic enzymes, breaks down part of the **zona pellucida** to allow the sperm entry into the secondary oocyte.
- The cell membrane of the sperm head fuses with the cell membrane of the secondary oocyte.
- The sperm nucleus is engulfed and moves into the cytoplasm of the secondary oocyte.
- Finally the two sets of haploid nuclei fuse together to form the diploid nucleus of the zygote, which may go on to produce the fetus.

What controls the menstrual cycle?

Events which take place within a female, such as ovulation and menstruation, need to be coordinated. Menstruation, the break down and loss of the lining of the uterus, would have a devastating consequence if a woman was pregnant. The foetus would be miscarried. The menstrual cycle is controlled by the secretion of **hormones** by the **endocrine system**. The flow diagram below shows how the process achieves coordination.

Note that at the start of the menstrual cycle FSH is supported by a smaller quantity of LH to stimulate the development of a follicle. Later the proportion reverses so that a larger amount of LH is aided by a smaller amount of FSH resulting in ovulation.

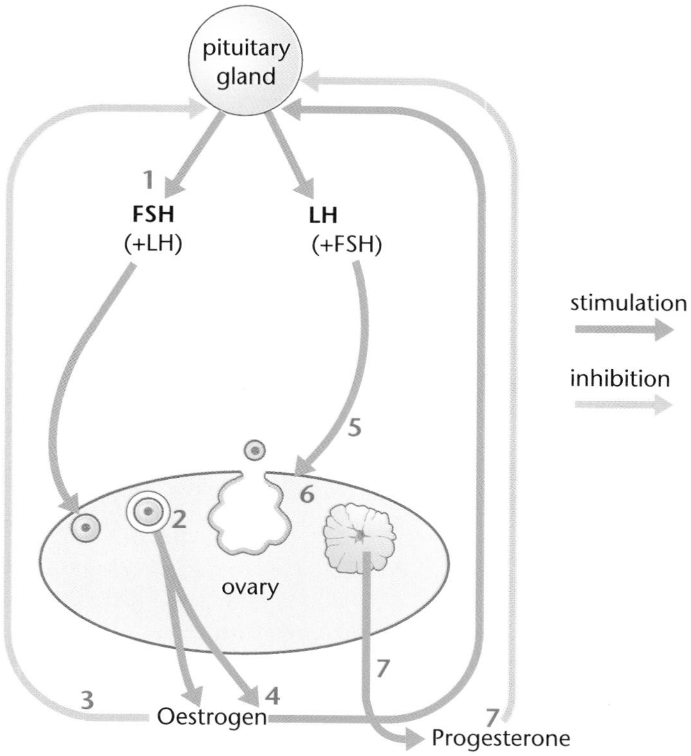

Stages of the menstrual cycle

1 (a) FSH (follicle stimulating hormone) is secreted into the bloodstream by the pituitary gland. It stimulates the development of a Graafian follicle and so triggers the development of an ovum.
(b) At the same time a small amount of LH (luteinising hormone) is secreted by the pituitary gland which reinforces the effect of FSH.

2 As a follicle develops, its wall (**theca**) begins to secrete oestrogen which stimulates the building of the endometrium (lining of uterus).

3 The oestrogen inhibits the secretion of FSH *temporarily* but LH secretion continues.

4 A peak of oestrogen is reached which results in a surge of LH with some FSH which is no longer inhibited.

Remember that all hormones are secreted into the bloodstream.

5 When LH peaks it causes ovulation – the follicle ruptures releasing the ovum.

6 The empty follicle now changes role and becomes a corpus luteum which begins to secrete progesterone.

7 (a) Progesterone keeps the endometrium in position, as it will be needed if a foetus is to develop in the uterus.
(b) Progesterone also inhibits the secretion of any FSH or LH by the pituitary gland. Ovulation is ultimately prevented by high concentrations of progesterone.

8 If no sperm fertilises an ovum during the cycle then the corpus luteum degenerates and a drop in progesterone takes place. Low progesterone does not inhibit the FSH and LH so that they are both able to be secreted again.

The cycle is now complete – ***GO BACK TO STAGE 1!***

Pregnancy

During fertilisation the **zygote** is produced. This **diploid** cell is moved down the **fallopian tube** by the **cilia**. On this journey it undergoes cell division by mitosis. It takes about four days to reach the uterus by which time it has become a **ball of cells (blastocyst)**.

the journey: from ovulation to implantation

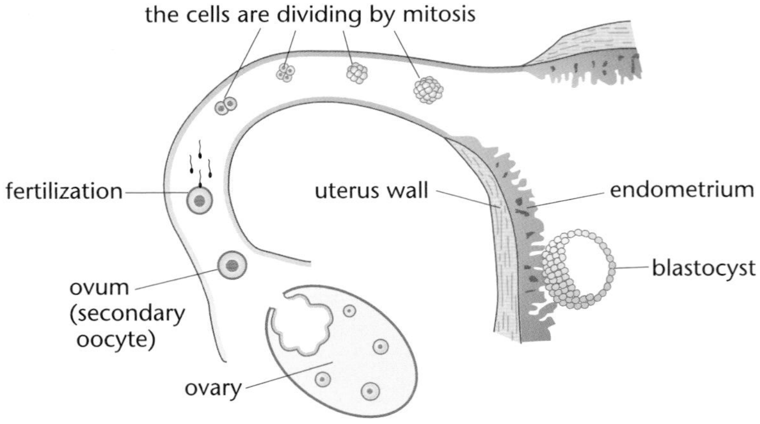

- The **blastocyst** is hollow and ready to become attached to the uterus.
- It becomes securely lodged into the **endometrium (lining of uterus)**. This process of becoming fixed into the surface of the endometrium is known as **implantation**.
- The blastocyst secretes the hormone **human chorionic gonadotrophin (HCG)** which **prevents degeneration** of the **corpus luteum** so that **progesterone** secretion continues into pregnancy.

- Cells of the blastocyst divide further resulting in the development of a placenta.
- The placenta secretes oestrogen and progesterone. Together they maintain the endometrium and prepare the mammary glands for lactation (milk production).
- The placenta also secretes relaxin. This relaxes the elastin fibres joining the bones of the pelvic girdle together and helps to expand the cervix during the final stages of pregnancy.

Further development of the placenta

After the blastocyst implants into the endometrium it has access to a range of nutrients and oxygen as well as the ability to allow waste products such as carbon dioxide to diffuse away into the mother's blood. All this is possible because the outer layer of cells of the blastocyst form the chorionic villi, finger-like projections of fetal origin which embed into the endometrium. They are surrounded by spaces filled by the mother's blood (maternal blood spaces). The combination of the chorionic villi and maternal blood spaces gives a high surface area enabling the exchange of chemicals between embryo and mother.

Remember that the chorionic villi have the fetal nuclei, whereas the endometrium is parental, having identical nuclei to the mother.

- Chemicals which diffuse from mother to fetus include, oxygen, glucose, water, amino acids, fatty acids, glycerol, minerals, vitamins, some hormones and some antibodies.
- Chemicals which diffuse from embryo to mother include urea and carbon dioxide as well as some hormones and water.
- Harmful chemicals including drugs and alcohol and even some viruses can cross the placenta into the foetus. Fetal development can be impaired.
- The umbilical artery takes waste substances to the placenta for excretion and the umbilical vein collects useful substances from the placenta and transports them to the fetus.

Birth

The 40-week period during which time the fetus develops in the uterus is known as gestation. The final stage involves birth (parturition) as follows:

- the foetus moves into the 'head-down' position
- the cervix begins to dilate and eventually becomes wide enough to allow even the widest part of the baby (the head) to pass through

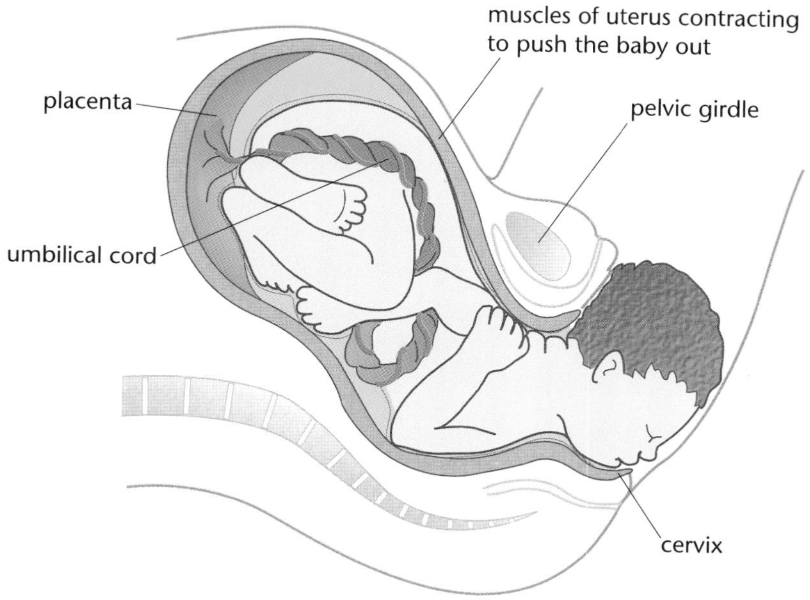

Many births in hospital are induced using oxytocin artificially.

- contractions of the uterus wall, (known as **labour**) are stimulated by the hormone **oxytocin**, secreted by the **pituitary gland**.
- another hormone, **prostaglandin**, is secreted by the **placenta** which increases the **frequency** and **force** of contractions of the uterus
- birth finally takes place as the baby is expelled from the uterus, closely followed by the **umbilical cord** and **placenta**.

Lactation

This is the production of milk and includes its ejection from the mammary glands to feed the baby. Preparation of these glands takes place during gestation due to the effect of oestrogen and progesterone. However, milk production cannot take place when the level of progesterone in the blood is high. In the final stages of gestation progesterone falls which initiates lactation. Prolactin, yet another hormone, is secreted by the pituitary gland which finally results in the mother lactating. The physical effect of the baby's sucking reflex at the nipples stimulates the lactation process to continue.

The first milk of the lactating mother is most important. It contains a high concentration of antibodies which gives the baby a degree of immunity from a range of diseases.

Progress check

1 (a) In the mammalian male reproductive system what is the function of:
   (i) the epididymis
   (ii) Cowper's and prostate glands?
(b) In the sperm, what is the function of:
   (i) the acrosome
   (ii) mitochondria in the mid-piece?

2 Beginning with the production of FSH by the pituitary gland, describe the role of hormones during the menstrual cycle.

1 (a) (i) storage of sperm; (ii) addition of fluid for sperm to swim and nutrients.
(b) (i) contains enzymes to break down the ovum membrane for sperm entry; (ii) energy release for flagellum to move.

2 Primary follicle develops and begins the development of an ovum: oestrogen is secreted into the blood; this stimulates the building of the endometrium; oestrogen inhibits the secretion of FSH; a surge of LH secreted by pituitary gland occurs; ovulation takes place; the follicle becomes a corpus luteum which begins to secrete progesterone. Progesterone keeps the endometrium in position, and is needed to develop the foetus. Progesterone inhibits the secretion of FSH, ovulation is prevented by high concentrations of this hormone. Corpus luteum degenerates, progesterone level falls and FSH can be produced again.

Sample question

The diagram shows a sperm. Immediately you may think, 'This is like GCSE.'. The question builds on GCSE knowledge. Learn the structures which are 'new' to you.

(a) The diagram below shows a mammalian sperm cell.

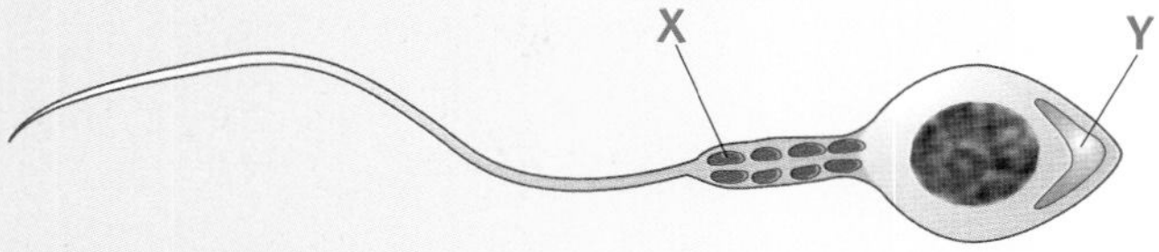

Remember to learn all structures and their functions. Here you need to recognise the mitochondrian and relate the energy release to produce a swimming action.

(i) Name each organelle labelled in the diagram and describe its function.

Organelle X [2]

This is a mitochondrion; it releases energy by aerobic respiration, to move the flagellum.

Organelle Y [2]

This is an acrosome, it is an enzyme package which helps the sperm penetrate through the zona pellucida and plasma membrane.

(ii) What is the function of the nucleus? [1]

Carries a haploid set of chromosomes.

(b) (i) Where in the testes are the sperm stored? [1]

Epididymis.

(ii) Give **two** functions of the seminal vesicles and Cowper's glands during ejaculation. [2]

Fluid is added for sperm to swim in.
Nutrients are added to supply energy which enables sperm to swim.

(c) The graph below shows the levels of oestrogen and progesterone in the blood of a woman during one month.

Many concepts you learn may be examined using graphs. Always look for peaks and troughs which mark significant events.

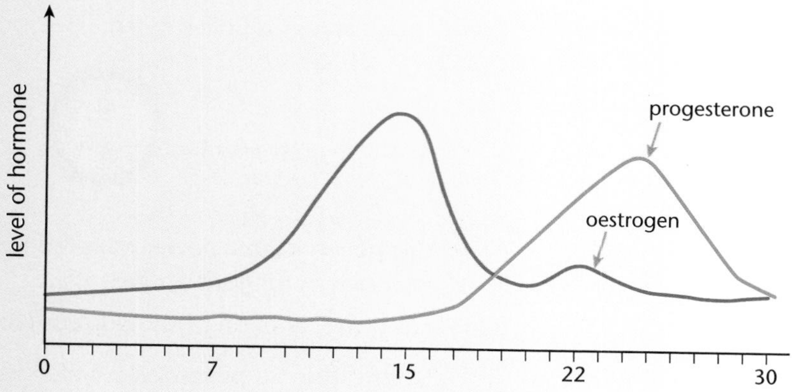

You would only score this mark about the peak of oestrogen if you could *work backwards* and link the hormone (FSH) to the stimulation of oestrogen.

(i) Which hormone, produced by the pituitary gland, would have resulted in the peak of oestrogen? [1]

FSH or follicle stimulating hormone.

(ii) What evidence shown on the graph shows that the woman is not pregnant? [1]

Progesterone level has fallen.

Practice examination questions

1 The graph shows the relative level of progesterone in the blood of a woman during one menstrual cycle.

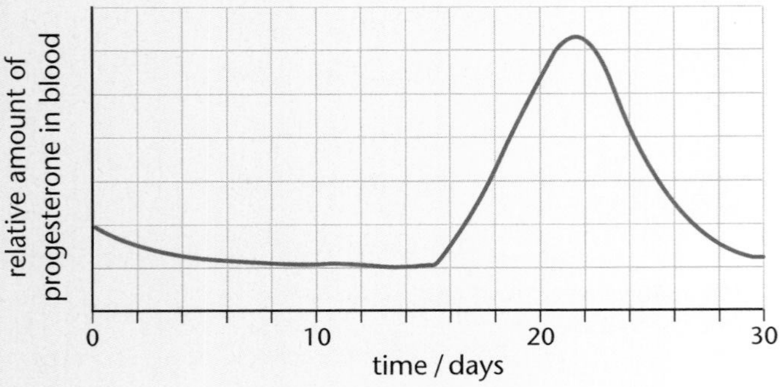

(a) (i) Precisely what produced the progesterone? [1]

(ii) How does progesterone reach the uterus? [1]

(b) Was the woman pregnant? Give a reason for your answer. [1]

(c) The role of the progesterone is to maintain the endometrium (lining of the uterus). Suggest what would happen if no progesterone was produced during pregnancy. [1]

2 (a) Some plant species have adaptations for cross-pollination. Explain how each of the following species ensures that cross-pollination takes place.

(i) Bluebell (*Endymion non-scriptus*) using protogyny

(ii) White dead nettle (*Lamium album*) using protandry. [2]

(b) The flowers of the Conference pear tree (*Pyrus communis*) self-pollinate.

(i) Explain **one** advantage to a gardener, of self-pollination. [1]

(ii) Explain **two** disadvantages to the species of self-pollination. [2]

3 (a) The diagram shows a pollen grain.

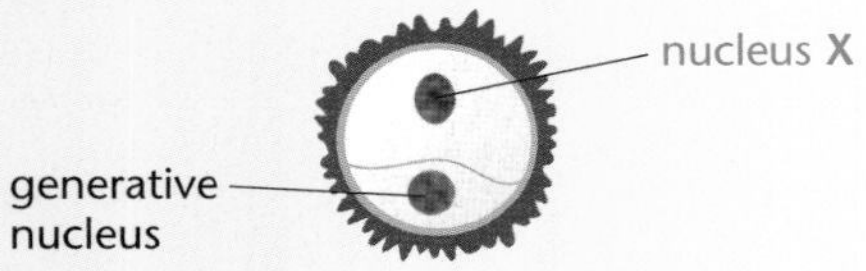

(i) Is this pollen from a flower adapted for wind or insect pollination? Give a reason for your answer. [1]

(ii) What is the function of the nucleus labelled X? [1]

(b) The diagram shows a pollen tube which has just penetrated an embryosac.

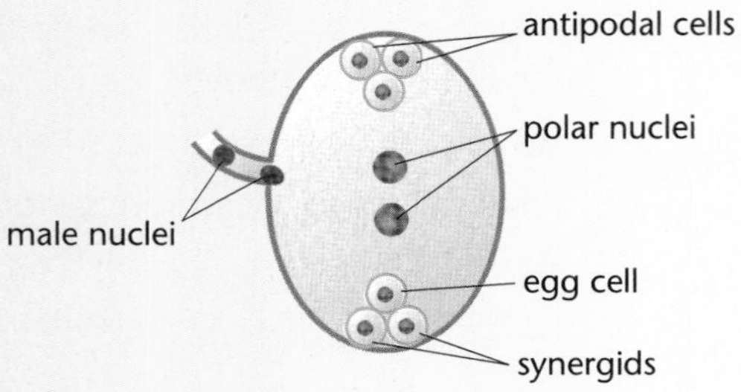

Describe the role of each male nucleus in fertilisation. [4]

Chapter 8

Energy and ecosystems

- Energy flow through ecosystems
- Energy transfer and agriculture
- Nutrient cycles
- Colonisation and succession
- Effects of human activity on the environment

8.1 Energy flow through ecosystems

After studying this section you should be able to:

- outline the process of photosynthesis
- identify the biotic and abiotic factors of an ecosystem
- understand the roles of producers, consumers, and decomposers
- understand the flow of energy through an ecosystem

LEARNING SUMMARY

Photosynthesis

EDEXCEL M3
WJEC M2
NICCEA M2

Before energy is available to organisms in an ecosystem photosynthesis must take place. This is the process by which green plants make carbohydrates. The main stages take place in the chloroplasts.

Photosynthesis is often summarised as the production of glucose and oxygen, from carbon dioxide and water, with the help of light and chlorophyll. The true details of the process are much more complex than this!

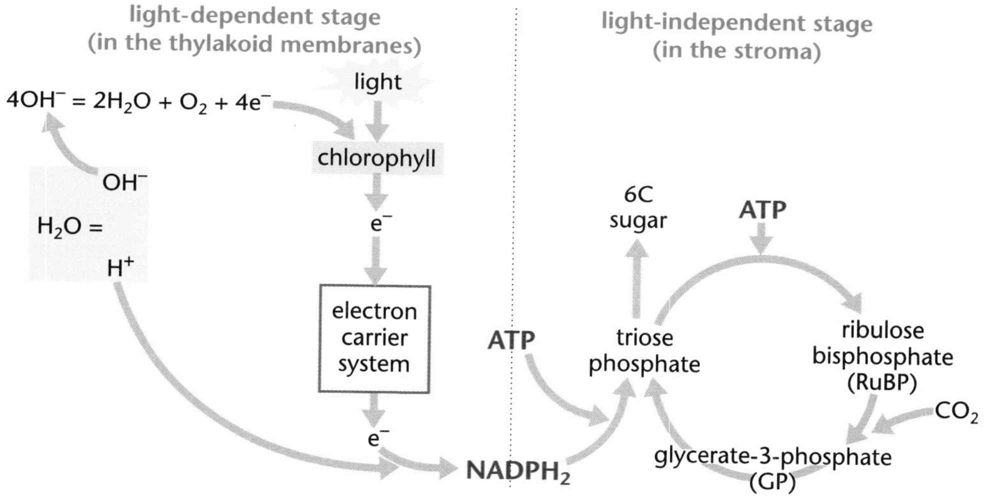

Light-dependent reaction

Look out for the useful substances produced by the light-dependent stage. **ATP** and **$NADPH_2$** are regularly needed in answers!

- Light energy results in the excitation of electrons in the chlorophyll.
- These electrons are passed along a series of electron acceptors collectively known as the electron carrier system.
- Energy from excited electrons funds the production of ATP (adenosine triphosphate).
- The final electron acceptor is $NADP^+$.
- Electron loss from chlorophyll causes the splitting of water (photolysis).

  $H_2O = H^+ + OH^-$ then $4OH^- = 2H_2O + O_2 + 4e^-$
- Oxygen is produced, water to re-use, and electrons stream back to replace those lost in the chlorophyll.
- Hydrogen ions (H^+) from photolysis, together with $NADP^+$ form $NADPH_2$.

Light-independent reaction

- Two useful substances are produced by the light-dependent stage – ATP and $NADPH_2$.
- They react with **glycerate-3-phosphate** (GP) to produce a triose sugar – **triose phosphate**.
- Triose phosphate is used to produce a 6C sugar.
- Some $NADPH_2$ is used, together with ATP to form **ribulose bisphosphate** (RuBP).
- RuBP together with carbon dioxide form more GP to complete the Calvin cycle.

Progress check

(a) Where in a chloroplast do the following take place:
(i) the light-dependent stage
(ii) the light-independent stage?

(b) At the end of the light-dependent stage, which **two** substances are produced that are needed for the light-independent stage?

(c) When does the light-independent stage take place?

(d) What is the function of carbon dioxide in the light-independent stage?

(a) (i) thylakoid membranes (ii) stroma.
(b) ATP and $NADPH_2$ or reduced NADP.
(c) Immediately after the light-dependent stage (Never state in the dark!).
(d) Used in the reaction to convert ribulose bisphosphate into glycerate-3-phosphate.

What is an ecosystem?

EDEXCEL	M3
OCR	M1
WJEC	M2
NICCEA	M2

The study of **ecology** investigates the inter-relationships between organisms in an area and their environment. The importance of photosynthesis to all organisms of an ecosystem must be considered. The plants (producers) make carbohydrates and are the source of most energy available to the organisms of an ecosystem. Before explaining the term ecosystem some important terms need to be defined:

- **habitat** is the area where an organism lives
- **population** is the number of organisms of one species living in an area
- **community** is a number of different populations living in an area
- **biotic factors** are factors caused by living organisms which influence other organisms in their environment, e.g. plants being consumed by herbivores or one species predating upon another
- **abiotic factors** are non-living factors which influence organisms in their environment, e.g. pH of the soil or the temperature of the environment
- **niche** is the precise way in which an organism fits into its environment and what it does there, e.g. a fish may survive within a temperature range of 30°C –35°C, and a pH range of 5–8 and eat a specific type of plant. All of its specific requirements for life are its niche
- **competition** is where different organisms occupy a similar niche, e.g. slugs and snails living in a garden both consume lettuce leaves.

Green plants are also known as photo-autotrophs. An autotroph is an organism which takes in simple inorganic chemicals and assembles more complex organic chemicals. Some of these can be later respired to release energy needed for life.

An **ecosystem** is a distinctive and stable ecological unit in an area and consists of the following features:

- different populations of organisms living and interacting together within a **community**
- all **abiotic factors** of their environment
- the **energy flow** through food chains and webs
- the **cycling of nutrients** to be re-used by the community.

Note that the term ecosystem is difficult to define! Make sure that you remember all four parts of this definition.

There may be no physical barrier between one ecosystem and the next, e.g. a desert ecosystem may exist alongside a tropical ecosystem, which has much more rainfall. Each specific ecosystem is self-sustaining and relies on the cycling of nutrients and special adaptations of the component organisms.

Some organisms may move from one ecosystem to another, e.g. a dragonfly larva is part of a food web in a pond, but after reaching the maturity of adulthood it flies into a terrestrial ecosystem. Also a migratory bird such as the insectivorous swallow flies from Britain to South Africa to avoid the winter but makes the return journey for summer. In this instance it occupies a similar niche in both countries.

Energy flow though an ecosystem

Sunlight energy enters the ecosystem and *some* is available for photosynthesis. *Not all* light energy reaches photosynthetic tissues. Some totally misses plants and may be absorbed or reflected by such items as water, rock or soil. Some light energy which does reach plants may be reflected by the waxy cuticle or even miss chloroplasts completely!

> Around 4% of light entering an ecosystem is actually used in photosynthesis.
>
> KEY POINT

The green plant uses the **carbohydrate** as a first stage substance and goes on to make **proteins** and **lipids**. Plants are a rich source of nutrients, available to the herbivores which eat the plants. Some energy is not available to the herbivores for two reasons:

1 green plants **respire** (releasing energy)
2 **not all parts** of plants may be **consumed**, e.g. roots.

Food chains and webs

Energy is passed along a food chain. Each food chain always begins with an autotroph (producer) then energy is passed to a primary consumer, then secondary consumer, then tertiary consumer and so on.

direction of energy flow →

Producer → primary consumer (herbivore) → secondary consumer (1st carnivore) → tertiary consumer (2nd carnivore)

The following example shows four food chains linked to form a food web.

Note that a small bird is a secondary consumer when it eats apple codling moths but a tertiary consumer when it eats greenfly.

The producers always have more energy than the primary consumers, the primary consumers more than the secondary consumers and so on, up the food web. Energy is released by each organism as it respires. Some energy fails to reach the next organism because not all parts may be eaten.

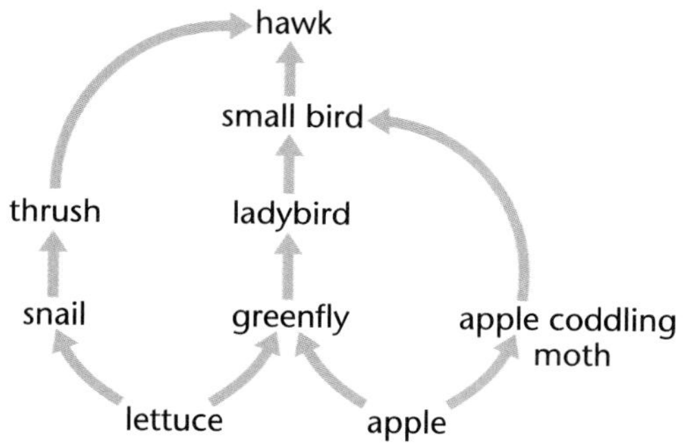

Each feeding level along a food chain can also be represented by a **trophic level**. The food chain on the next page is taken from the food web above and illustrates trophic levels.

Energy may be used by an organism in a number of different ways:

- respiration releases energy for movement or maintenance of body temperature, etc.
- production of new cells in growth and repair
- production of eggs.

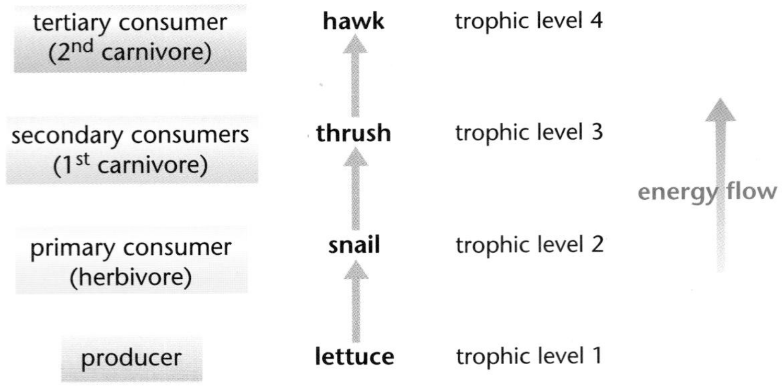

Examiner's tip! Note that the primary consumer is at trophic level 2. It is easy to make a mistake with this concept. Many candidates do!

Predators and prey

There can be many examples of this type of relationship in an ecosystem. **Primary consumers** rely on the **producers**, so a flush of new vegetation may give a corresponding increase in the numbers of primary consumers. Predators which eat the primary consumers may also follow with a population increase. Each population of the ecosystem may have a **sequential effect** on other populations. Ultimately the ecosystem is in **dynamic equilibrium** and has limits as to how many of each population can survive, i.e. its **carrying capacity**.

Note that graphs are often given in predator–prey questions. A flush of spring growth is often responsible for the increase in prey. Plant biomass may not be shown on the graph! Candidates are expected to suggest this for a mark. Also remember that as prey increase, their numbers will go down when eaten by the predator. Predator numbers rise after this!

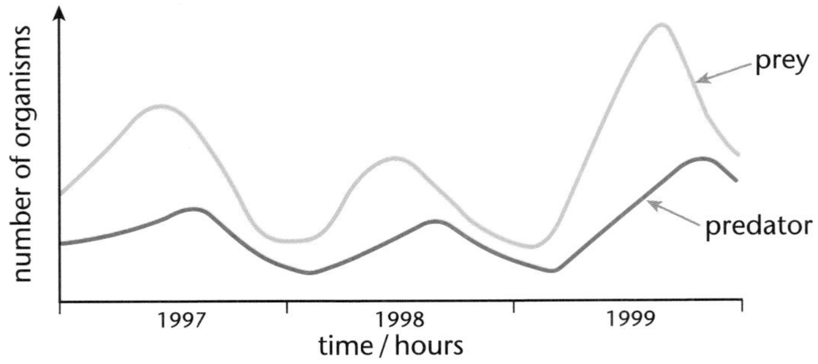

Pyramids of numbers, energy and biomass

A food chain gives limited information about feeding relationships in an area. Actual proportions of organisms in an area give more useful data. Consider this food chain from a wheat field.

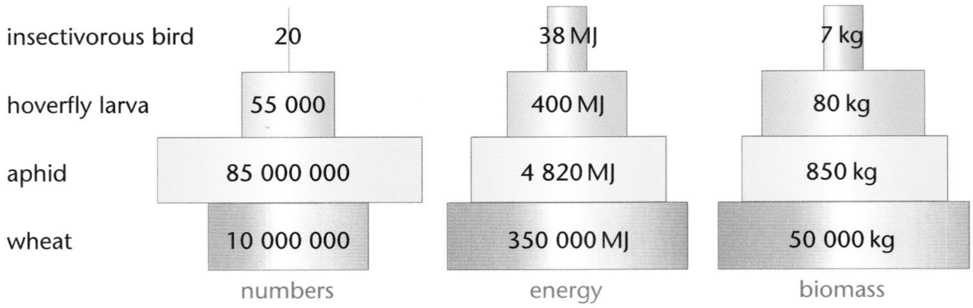

Biomass is the mass of organisms present at each stage of the food chain. The biomass of wheat would include leaves, roots and seeds. (All parts of the plant are included in this measurement.)

The pyramid of numbers sometimes does not give a suitable shape. In the example shown there are more aphids in the field than wheat plants. This gives the shape shown above (not a pyramid in shape!). Both the pyramids of energy and biomass are always the correct shape.

The organisms in the above food chain may die rather than be consumed. When this happens the decomposers use extracellular enzymes to break down any organic debris in the environment. Dead corpses, faeces and parts that are not consumed are all available for decay.

8.2 Energy transfer and agriculture

After studying this section you should be able to:

- *understand a range of agricultural methods used to increase yield*

LEARNING SUMMARY

How are high yields achieved in agriculture?

AQA A M2
WJEC M2
NICCEA M2

The aim in agriculture is often to obtain good quality produce at maximum yield. Farmers grow crops and rear domesticated animals, like cattle, for meat and milk. Humans usually end the food chain as the top consumer. The human population is increasing constantly so **efficient** methods of agriculture have been developed.

Reduction of competition

Weeds reduce water, minerals and light reaching the crop plant; ultimately its rate of growth would be limited by the competing weeds. This is **interspecific competition** and takes place when different species need the same resources. Weeds can be removed **chemically** by use of a **herbicide** (weedkiller) or physically by an implement such as a rotavator which cuts up the weeds into tiny pieces, eventually killing them.

Intraspecific competition can also take place. This is where neighbouring plants of the same species compete for identical resources. This problem is reduced by making sure that crop plants are a suitable distance apart to achieve a maximum yield.

Use of fertilisers

It is important that crop plants have access to all the minerals they require to give a maximum yield. Farmers supply these minerals in fertilisers, usually in the form NPK (nitrogen, phosphates and potassium). By supplying them with these minerals nitrogen is available to make protein, a key substance for growth. Phosphates help the production of DNA, RNA and ATP. Potassium helps with protein synthesis and chlorophyll production. Other minerals are also needed like iron and calcium. The more a plant grows, the more its biomass increases and usually the greater is the surface area for light absorption. The amount of photosynthesis increases proportionally. If a farmer is to reach the maximum productivity of a crop, fertiliser is vital.

Increasing photosynthetic rate

As well as fertilisers helping to achieve a high productivity, other factors have a positive influence on growth:

- **irrigation** ensures that a plant has enough water for photosynthesis
- **suitable temperature** can be achieved by use of a greenhouse to give ideal conditions for the process. If a gas heater is used then the **high concentration of carbon dioxide** excreted can be harnessed in photosynthesis.

Pest control

If pests such as aphids or caterpillars begin to damage crops then both quality and yield are reduced. Farmers combat pests in different ways.

- **Pesticides**, sprayed onto crops, kill pests. Chemicals used to kill insects are

> Examination questions on this topic often test knowledge of the advantages and disadvantages of each method. Chemicals may pass along food chains, and accumulate in greater quantities higher in the food chain due to the consumption of many smaller organisms, each carrying a small amount of the toxin. Biological control does not usually rely on a chemical agent so that the chemical risk is removed.
>
> Biological control is usually much cheaper in the long term. If predators are used they go on to breed. Several repeat sprays of insecticides are needed through the growing season.

insecticides. **Contact insecticides** kill insects directly but **systemic insecticides** are absorbed into the cell sap. Any insect consuming part of the plant or sucking the sap then dies.

- **Biological control** includes a range of different methods to get rid of pests.
  (a) The most commonly used method is to use **predators** to reduce pest numbers, e.g. in greenhouses infested with whitefly (*Trialeurodes vaporariorum*) the predatory wasp (*Encarsia formosa*) is introduced. The female wasp lays eggs into the scale (larva) of the whitefly. A young wasp emerges from each larva, having used the larva as a nutrient supply. The whitefly young are killed so its population decreases. Wasps increase in numbers and remain as long as some whiteflies still remain.
  (b) **Genetic engineering** can be used. A gene has been transferred to potato plants which enables them to produce a natural insecticide. This destroys 50% of aphids that attack the plants. The amount of damage is decreased.
  (c) **Pheromones** are also used. These are compounds secreted by organisms which affect the **behaviour** within the species, e.g. the apple codling moth larva spoils the fruit by tunneling through apples. Female adult moths secrete a powerful chemical which attracts many males. This pheromone is now used in a trap. The sticky tent-shaped trap (below) shows how male moths are attracted and stick to the sides of the trap. Here they die and thousands of female moths out in the orchards are not mated and their eggs are not fertilised.

a codling moth trap

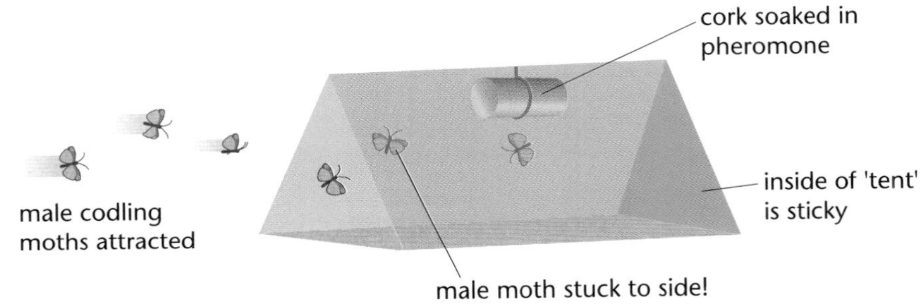

  (d) **Irradiation** is used on insect pests which mate only once, e.g. the New World screw fly lays eggs in cattle (and humans!). Larvae attack the internal systems having a devastating effect. Millions of screw worm flies are bred then **irradiated**. They are subsequently released into cattle-producing regions. Irradiated males cannot produce fertile gametes. Any male mating with a female from the cattle fields results in unfertilised eggs so the population decreases. Cattle productivity is maintained.

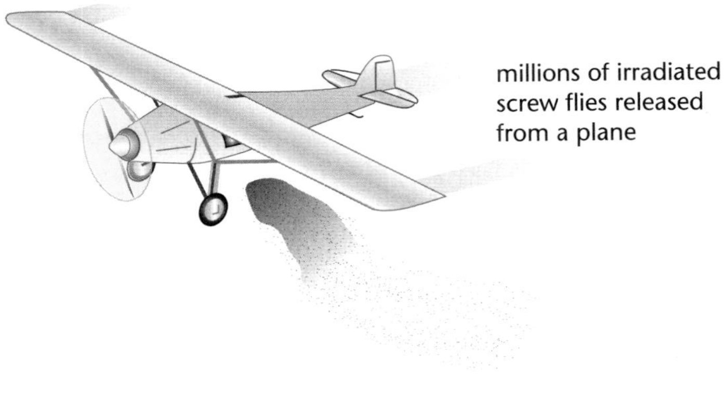

8.3 Nutrient cycles

After studying this section you should be able to:

- *recall how carbon and nitrogen are recycled*

LEARNING SUMMARY

The nitrogen cycle

EDEXCEL	M3
OCR	M1
WJEC	M1
NICCEA	M2

Nitrogen is found in every amino acid, protein, DNA and RNA. It is an essential element! Most organisms are unable to use atmospheric nitrogen directly so the nitrogen cycle is very important.

There are three parts of the nitrogen cycle which are regularly examined:

- nitrogen fixation in leguminous plants
- nitrification
- denitrification.

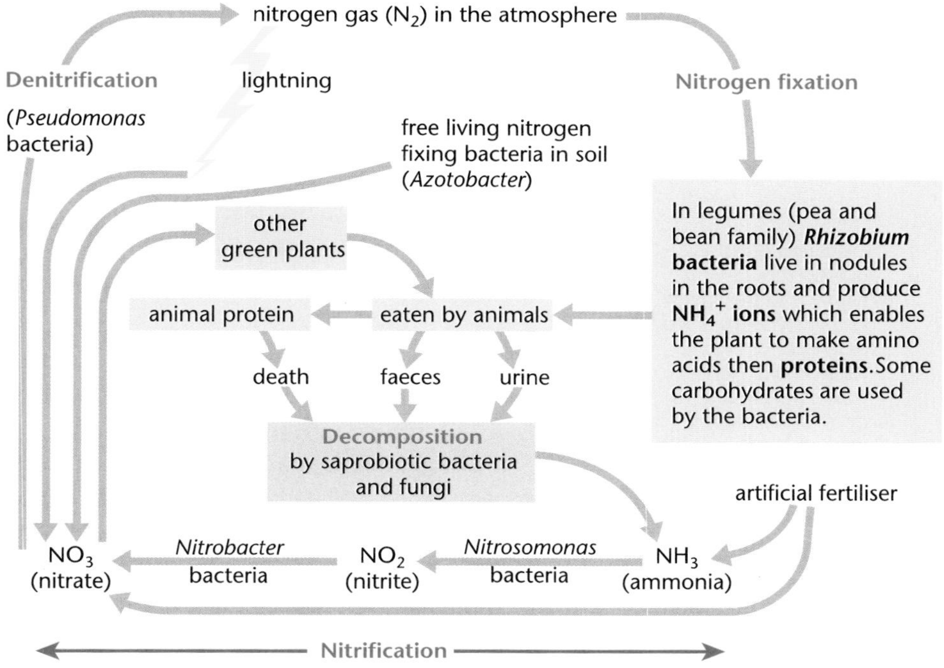

Some important points

The association of *Rhizobium* bacteria with legume plants give advantages to both organisms. This relationship is known as **mutualism**.

- **Nitrogen gas** from the atmosphere is used by ***Rhizobium* bacteria**. These bacteria, living in nodules of legume plants, convert nitrogen gas into **ammonia** (NH_3) then into amine($-NH_2$) compounds. The plants transport the amines from the nodules and make amino acids then proteins. *Rhizobium* bacteria gain carbohydrates from the plant, therefore each organism benefits.

Saprobiotic bacteria and fungi secrete extracellular enzymes. They obtain nutrients in this way.

- Plants support food webs, throughout which excretion, production of faeces and death take place. These resources are of considerable benefit to the ecosystem, but first **decompostion** by **saprobiotic** bacteria takes place, a waste product of this process is **ammonia**.

The biochemical route from ammonia to nitrate is **nitrification**. This is helped by ploughing which allows air into the soil. Nitrifying bacteria are aerobic. Draining also helps.

- Ammonia is needed by *Nitrosomonas* bacteria for a special type of nutrition (chemo-autotrophic). As a result another waste product, **nitrite** (NO_2) is formed.
- Nitrite is needed by *Nitrobacter* bacteria, again for chemo-autotrophic nutrition. The waste product from this process is **nitrate**, vital for plant growth. Plants absorb large quantities of nitrates via their roots.
- Nitrogen gas is returned to the atmosphere by **denitrifying bacteria** such as *Pseudomonas*. Some nitrate is converted back to nitrogen gas by these bacteria. The cycle is complete!

The carbon cycle

EDEXCEL M3
OCR M1
NICCEA M2

Carbon is the key element in all organisms.The source of this carbon is atmospheric carbon dioxide which proportionally is 0.03% of the volume of the air. Most organisms cannot use carbon dioxide directly so the carbon cycle is very important.

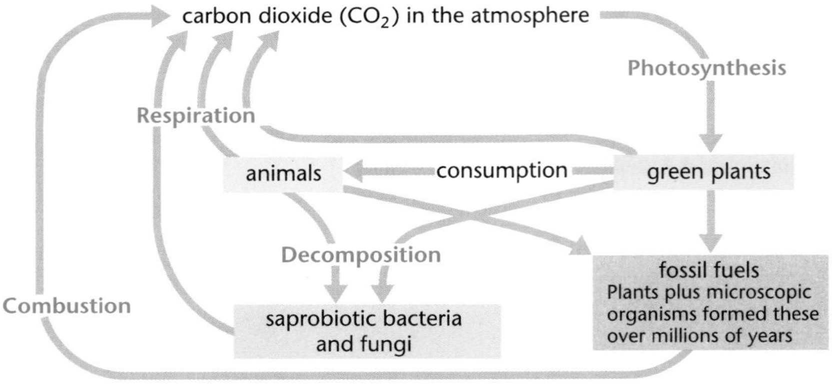

Some important points

Examiners often give a question about what happens to the energy in the chemicals of dead organisms or organic waste. Many candidates correctly state that microorganisms rot down the materials but then go on to state that energy goes into the ground. Big mistake! Energy is released by the respiration of the decomposers to support their life.

- Producers carry out photosynthesis. This process incorporates the carbon dioxide into carbohydrates. These chemicals are used as a starting point to make lipids and proteins. Some of the carbon helps to form structures in the producers and some is released as carbon dioxide as a waste product of respiration.
- Producers are the starting point of food chains. After the plants are eaten by primary consumers carbon can be passed along to subsequent consumers. It can be incorporated into tissues, respired or excreted.
- Even after the death of a plant or animal, carbon dioxide can still be released. Saprobiotic bacteria and fungi respire using the organic chemicals in dead organisms as well as faeces and urine, etc.
- Compression of organisms millions of years ago resulted in the formation of fossil fuels. Combustion of these fuels releases carbon dioxide back into the atmosphere.
- The return of carbon dioxide to the air completes the cycle!

Other elements are also recycled. The decomposers have a major role in maintaining the availability of vital chemicals.

8.4 Colonisation and succession

After studying this section you should be able to:

- *understand how colonisation is followed by changes*
- *understand how colonisation and succession lead to a climax community*

LEARNING SUMMARY

How decolonisation and succession take place

WJEC M2
NICCEA M2

Any area which has never been inhabited by any organisms may be available for **primary succession**. Such areas could be a garden pond filled with tap water, lava having erupted from a volcano, or even a concrete tile on a roof. The latter may become colonised by lichens.

Occasionally an ecosystem may be destroyed, e.g. fire destroying a woodland. This allows **secondary succession** to begin, and signals the reintroduction of plant and animal species to the area.

Colonisation and succession also take place in water. Even an artificial garden pond would be colonised by organisms naturally. Aquatic algae would arrive on birds' feet.

The process of succession can take place as follows.

- **Pioneer species (primary colonisers)** begin to exploit a 'new' habitat. Mosses may successfully grow on newly exposed heathland soil. These are the **primary colonisers** which have adaptations to this environment. Fast germination of spores and the ability to grow in waterlogged and acid conditions, aid rapid colonisation. These plants may support a specific food web. In time, as organic matter drops from these herbaceous colonisers it is decomposed (see nitrogen cycle page 115), nutrients are added to the soil and acidity increases. In time the changes caused by the primary colonisers cause the habitat to be unsuitable.
- Conditions unsuitable to primary colonisers may be ideal for other organisms. In early heathland, mosses are replaced by heathers which can thrive in acid and xerophytic (desiccating) conditions. This is **succession**, where one community of organisms is replaced with another. In this example the secondary colonisers have replaced the primary colonisers; this is known as **seral stage 1** in the succession process. Again, a different food web is supported by the secondary colonisers.

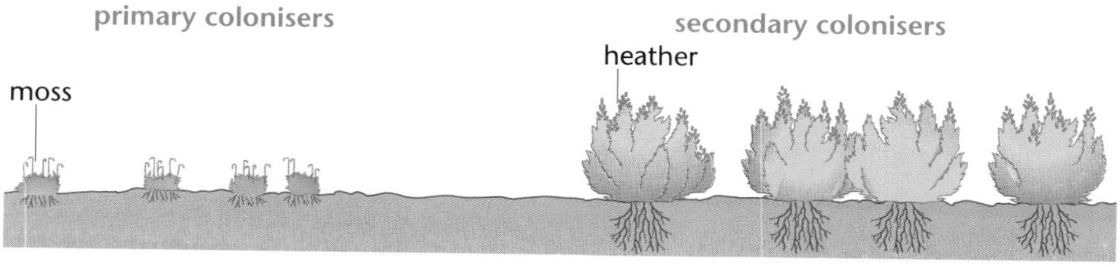

- At every seral stage there are changes in the environment. The **second seral stage** takes place as the tertiary colonisers replace the previous organisms. In heathland, the new conditions would favour shrubs such as gorse and bilberry plus associated animals.
- The shrubs are replaced in time with birch woodland, the **third seral stage**. Eventually acidic build-up leads to the destruction of the dominant plant species.
- Finally conditions become suitable for a dominant plant species, the oak. Tree saplings quickly become established. Beneath the oak trees, grasses, ferns, holly and bluebells can grow in harmony. This final stage is **stable** and can continue for hundreds of years. This is the **climax community**. Associated animals survive and thrive alongside these plant resources. Insects such as gall wasps exploit the oak and dormice eat the wasp larvae. Jays are birds which eat some acorns but spread others which they store and forget. The acorns germinate; the woodland spreads.

In Britain, an excellent example of a climax community is Sherwood Forest where the 'Major Oak' has stood for 400 years. Agricultural areas grow crops efficiently by **deflecting succession**. Plants and animals in their natural habitat are 'more than a match' for domesticated crops. Herbicides and pesticides are used to stop the invaders!

8.5 Effects of human activities on the environment

After studying this section you should be able to:

- *understand some causes and effects of pollution*
- *understand the effects of deforestation*
- *understand the problems of over-fishing*

LEARNING SUMMARY

How human activities affect the environment

AQA A	M2
EDEXCEL	M3
WJEC	M2
NICCEA	M2

Activities carried out by the human population to supply food, power, and industrial needs have a considerable effect on the environment. These effects include atmospheric and water pollution, and destroying habitats and communities.

What is the greenhouse effect?

This is caused by specific gases which form a thin layer around the atmosphere. These gases include water vapour, carbon dioxide, methane, ozone, and nitrogen oxides and CFCs. CFCs (CCl_2F_2, CCl_3F) have a greenhouse factor of 25 000 based on the same amount of carbon dioxide at a factor of 1.0. The **quantity** of the greenhouse factor gas needs to be considered to work out the overall greenhouse effect, e.g.

KEY POINT

carbon dioxide is 0.035% of the troposphere × greenhouse factor value 1= 0.035

CCl_2F_2 is 4.8×10^{-8} % of the troposphere × greenhouse factor value 25 000 = 0.012

Water vapour is 1% of the troposphere × greenhouse factor 0.1 = 0.1

Examiner's tip.
Do not mix up the greenhouse effect with the 'hole in the ozone layer' – that is different! The ozone layer around the Earth absorbs some ultra-violet radiation from the sun. If a lot of ultra-violet radiation reaches the Earth's surface then many people succumb to skin cancer. CFCs cause a hole to form in the ozone layer. Not using these chemicals is the answer to this problem.

It is clear that carbon dioxide has the greatest overall greenhouse effect!

- The greenhouse gases allow short wavelength radiation from the sun to reach the Earth's surface.
- Some of the infra-red radiation fails to pass back through the greenhouse layer resulting in **global warming**.
- Polar ice caps may melt causing the sea to rise and subsequent reduction of land mass. Some aquatic populations could increase and some terrestrial populations decrease.
- Climatic changes are expected, so rainfall changes and heat increases will have significant effects.

Follow the numbers to remember sequence in correct order!

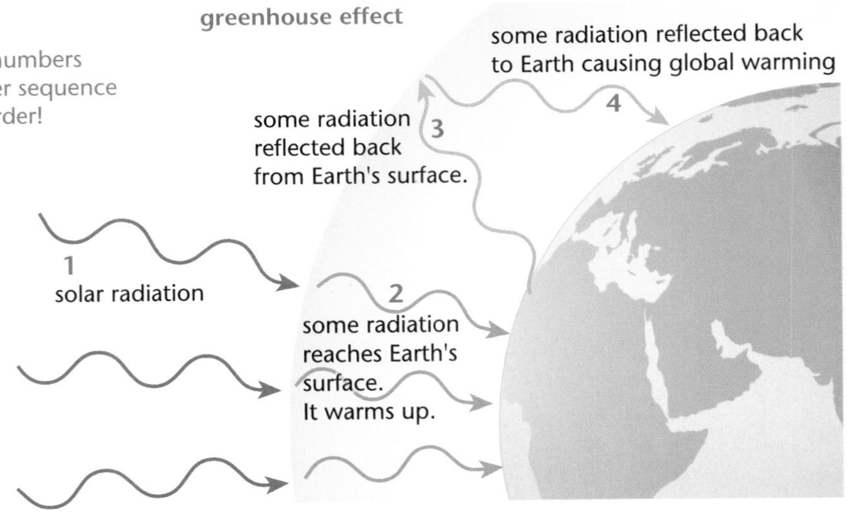
greenhouse effect
1
solar radiation
2
some radiation reaches Earth's surface. It warms up.
3
some radiation reflected back from Earth's surface.
4
some radiation reflected back to Earth causing global warming

Deforestation

In countries such as Brazil, forests have been burned down. Large quantities of carbon dioxide and water vapour released into the atmosphere contribute to the greenhouse effect. However, the long-term effects are highly significant. Habitats and complete food webs are lost. Biodiversity is decreased so that many less species are represented on the land left after deforestation. The canopy of a forest intercepts and holds rain water, so too much rain does not reach the ground and cause flooding. Instead, much water evaporates back into the atmosphere. Without the forest, flooding is a danger, and without the tree roots, soil erosion takes place. If the deforestation was to make way for agriculture then there are major problems. Top soil is lost and nutrients leach into the ground and in the long term agriculture fails.

Water pollution

'Run off', containing fertilisers, enters rivers from fields. Similarly, sewage also pollutes rivers. The diagrams below show a river before and after sewage entry.

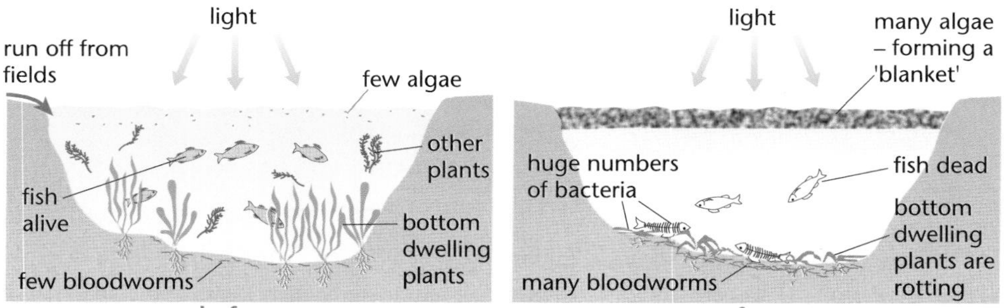

The polluting effect of fertilisers and sewage are caused by the constituent ions such as nitrates and phosphates. They result in **eutrophication**.

- **Nitrates and phosphates** enter the river and are absorbed by plants. This promotes plant growth.
- **Algae** float near the water surface and their population increases dramatically. A 'blanket' of algae soon covers the surface.
- Bottom dwelling plants do not share the same advantage. Initially the ions promote growth but **surface algae block the sunlight**. Plants beneath the algae die.
- **Bacteria** and other decomposers begin to **break down** the **dead plants** and some short lived algae. The **bacterial population increases** and proportionally takes more oxygen from the river water.
- **Fish die** as the oxygen content becomes much too low. Rotting dead fish contribute to even lower oxygen levels, again aerobic bacteria are responsible.
- Often there is an **increase in bloodworms** (tubifex). These are mud dwellers and possess a protein similar to haemoglobin which helps them to take in enough oxygen for survival, even at low concentration. Without fish to eat them numbers of bloodworm increase even more.

Examiner's tip.
The sequence of stages of eutrophication are important. Take care to learn the correct sequence. Do not miss out any stage. Some candidates merely state nitrates enter the river and fish die. Give the detail and score more marks!

How can the water pollution be measured?

There are many ways to measure both pollutants and their effects. Populations of algae, bloodworms or fish can be estimated. A key measurement is **biological oxygen demand (BOD)**. This is the amount of oxygen taken up by a sample of water at 20°C over 5 days. Clean water takes up much less oxygen than that polluted with organic material. Aerobic bacteria take up a large proportion of this oxygen. A river, heavily polluted with organic matter, has a very high BOD.

Indicator species

The presence or absence of a species in the river can be used as a sign of pollution. Mayfly larvae can only tolerate well oxygenated water. Bloodworms are only found in large numbers in water heavily polluted with organic matter. As the river flows downstream, organisms change the organic matter and eventually the oxygen content increases. A large population of mayfly larvae found in water downstream suggests that there is:

- a low BOD
- organic material further upstream which has been changed by bacteria so the water is no longer polluted.

Acid rain

There are other acid gases apart from sulphur dioxide, e.g. nitrogen oxides.

This is caused by the combustion of fossil fuels, e.g. coal. This releases a number of acidic gases which dissolve in rain water. One of the most significant of these gases is sulphur dioxide.

H_2O	+	SO_2	=	H_2SO_3
rain water		sulphur dioxide		sulphurous acid

Rain of low pH can have a devastating effect on the organisms of an ecosystem.

- Low pH results in many mineral ions being less soluble and consequently less available to plants.
- Phosphate (PO_4^-) ions become bound to clay particles and are unavailable to plants.
- Positively charged ions such as calcium (Ca^{2+}) are more easily leached.
- Aluminium ions (Al^{3+}) are an exception and may accumulate to a toxic level.
- Plants may be defoliated and die. This has a sequential effect on all consumers which rely directly or indirectly on the plants in food webs.
- In lakes the low pH destroys organisms, e.g. fish, often as a result of Al^{3+} build up.
- Levels of other minerals are normally low and cannot sustain much plant growth. A lake is said to be **oligotrophic** in this condition.

Remember that 'oligotrophic' is an opposite term to eutrophic.

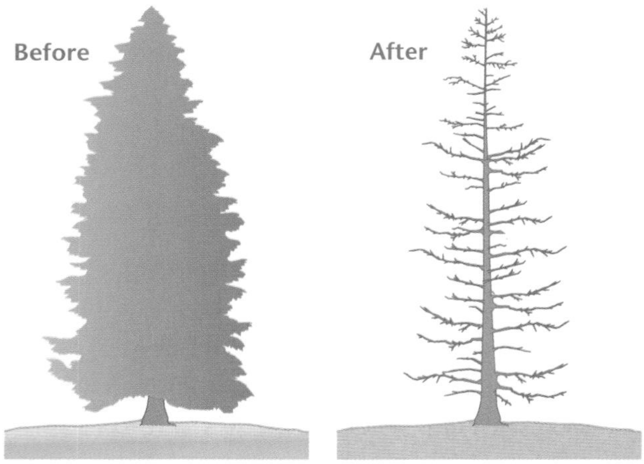

Examiners often give questions about the acid rain problem. Higher grade students note the consequences of trees dying. Complete food webs can be destroyed!

What is the answer to pollution?

People need to make personal choices. Do they support the use of products which have involved pollution? Do they support the use of legislation to prevent pollution?

> **KEY POINT**
> In Europe currently there is legislation to ensure that each country complies with targets to reduce both water and air pollution. It is vital that we make the correct decisions if biodiversity is to be maintained.

Progress check

(a) Explain how acid rain is formed.

(b) Suggest the effects that acid rain may have on a woodland ecosystem.

(c) A student states that all power stations contribute to acid rain. Is this true or false? Give a reason for your answer.

(a) Acid rain is caused by the burning of fossil fuels, e.g. oil. Acidic gases dissolve in rain water, e.g. sulphur dioxide. Cloud water vapour condenses to produce acid rain.

$$H_2O + SO_2 = H_2SO_3$$

rain water + sulphur dioxide = sulphurous acid

(b) Plants become defoliated and die; some minerals cannot be absorbed; phosphate ions become bound to clay particles and are unavailable to plants; positively charged ions such as calcium are leached; aluminium ions accumulate to a toxic level; there is a sequential effect on all consumers which rely directly or indirectly on the plants in food webs.

(c) False. Only power stations which are fuelled by fossil fuels emit acid gases. Nuclear power stations just emit water vapour from the cooling towers.

Remember that over-fishing may have a sequential effect on other organisms of an ecosystem. Some organisms may increase in numbers because fish are no longer eating them, e.g. zooplankton. Other organisms may decrease in numbers, e.g. phytoplankton, because fewer zooplankton are consuming them.

Problems in over-fishing

The human population needs food, but as the World population has increased more food is required. Just as agriculture has improved productivity, the fishing industry has improved techniques of catching fish.

- Echo-sounding equipment is used to locate precisely fish populations.
- Giant trawler nets drag across the sea floor to catch demersal (bottom dwelling) fish.
- Giant drift nets are suspended in the sea so that unsuspecting pelagic (surface dwelling) fish bump into the nets and become trapped by their gill flaps.
- Nets often have a small mesh so that both small and large fish are caught.

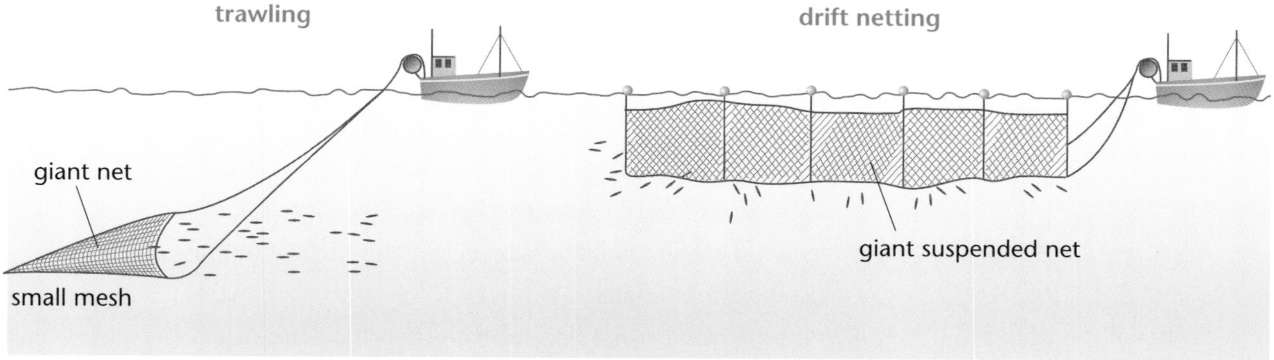

Fish are returned to the sea if the numbers caught are beyond the fishing quota or if the fish are too small. Perhaps fish farms are the answer.

Techniques are so efficient that breeding stocks have decreased dramatically. Many small fish never reach maturity. Legislation is the answer to increase mesh size, enforce quotas and exclusion zones. By international agreement, breeding stocks may be allowed to become re-established.

Sample question and model answer

Some questions give information that you can use to deduce the answers (a) (i) is one of them!

(a) The sequence below shows how nitrate can be produced from a supply of oak leaves.

		decomposers		Nitrosomonas bacteria		Nitrobacter bacteria	
dead oak leaves	----->	NH_3 (ammonia)	----->	NO_2 (nitrite)	----- >	NO_3 (nitrate)	

This question targets the nitrogen cycle. Be ready to answer questions about *any part* of the cycle. Pure recall of the cycle is not enough! You need to apply your knowledge.

(i) Suggest the consequences of death of the Nitrosomonas bacteria. [4]

build up of ammonia; build up of dead leaves; death of Nitrobacter bacteria; no nitrite/no nitrate

(ii) Name the process by which bacteria produce nitrate from ammonia. [1]

nitrification

(iii) Name **two** populations of organisms not shown in the sequence which would be harmed by a lack of nitrate. [2]

denitrifying bacteria or Pseudomonas; plants or producers

(iv) Which organisms fix atmospheric nitrogen on the nodules of bean plants? [1]

(Rhizobium) bacteria

In questions targeting yield in agriculture make sure that you have clarified all terms, e.g. do not confuse herbicide with pesticide.

(b) Apart from adding fertiliser or irrigating a crop, how can a farmer make sure of producing a high yield ? [4]

make sure that the plants are the correct distance apart; use of pesticide or use of insecticide; use of herbicide or fungicide; use of biological control or named biological control; use of variety produced by selective breeding [any four]

Note that the reverse explanation for pigs reared outside can be given, i.e. more energy used for movement, etc.

(c) (i) A farmer rears pigs by a factory-farming method. Pigs are kept indoors 24 hours per day in warm, confined cubicles.

How can this method result in the production of a greater yield of pork than from animals reared outside? [3]

less energy is released for movement; less energy is used to maintain body temperature; more energy is used for biomass

(ii) Why do many consumers object to this factory farming method? [1]

cruel or not ethical

(iii) Pigs are often given copper with their food because it promotes their growth. Suggest **one** disadvantage of using this method. [2]

it may contaminate the pork; people eat the pork and may be harmed

Practice examination questions

1 The number of species of grass and the number of leguminous plants growing in two fields was measured over a 10-year period. Field A was given nitrogenous fertiliser each year, but field B was given none. The results are shown in the graphs.

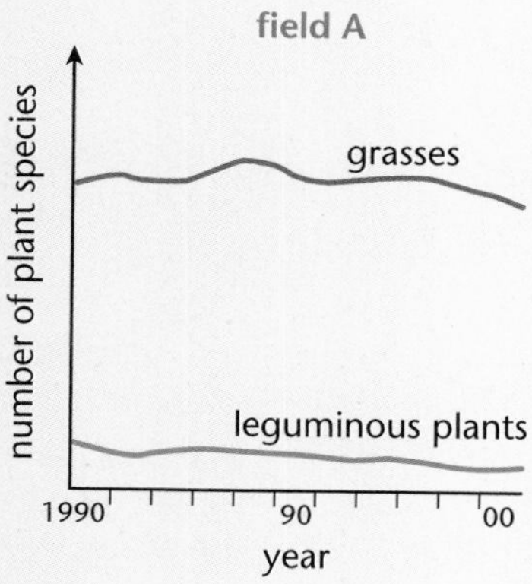

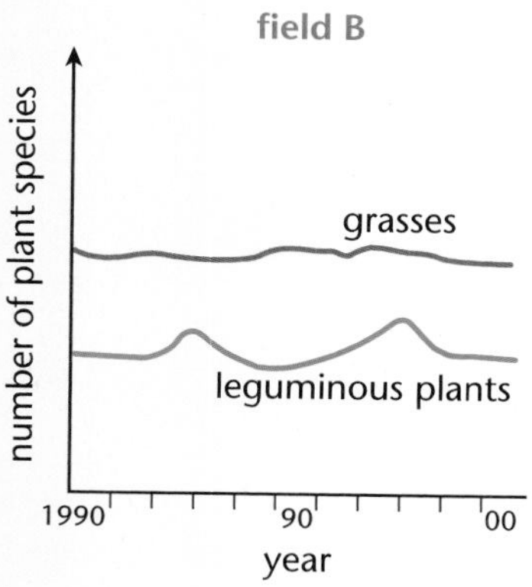

(a) (i) Suggest why there were fewer leguminous plant species in field A. [2]

(ii) Suggest why there were more leguminous plant species in field B. [2]

(b) After the main investigation no fertiliser at all was used in either field. Cattle were allowed to graze in both fields. At the end of five years the number of legume species in each field had decreased. Suggest why the number of legume plants decreased. [1]

2 The following article appeared in a newspaper.

> **ATLANTIC COD IN DANGER OF EXTINCTION!**
>
> The cod stocks of the Atlantic Ocean are in urgent need of protection. Deep-water trawling is so efficient that in the last 10 years numbers have fallen drastically. A survey found that the average length of the fish has decreased by 10 cm since 1990. This will have a harmful effect on the population and could ultimately lead to extinction. One of the problems is improved technology which locates complete shoals of the fish. Trawl nets are dragged along the sea floor stirring up sediment and killing many delicate invertebrates. This will affect biodiversity. So many countries fish the waters that a political agreement must be found.

Extract from 'Action Ecology' 2000

(a) Suggest **two** ways in which trawling is considered 'efficient'. (line 2) [2]

(b) Why was the decrease in the average length of the cod considered to have a 'harmful effect' on the population of the species? (line 5) [2]

(c) How may trawling result in reduced biodiversity? (line 10) [3]

(d) Suggest how 'political agreement' may help to increase breeding stocks. (line 11) [2]

Practice examination questions *(continued)*

3 The diagrams show stages in the development of a garden pond over a 10-year period.

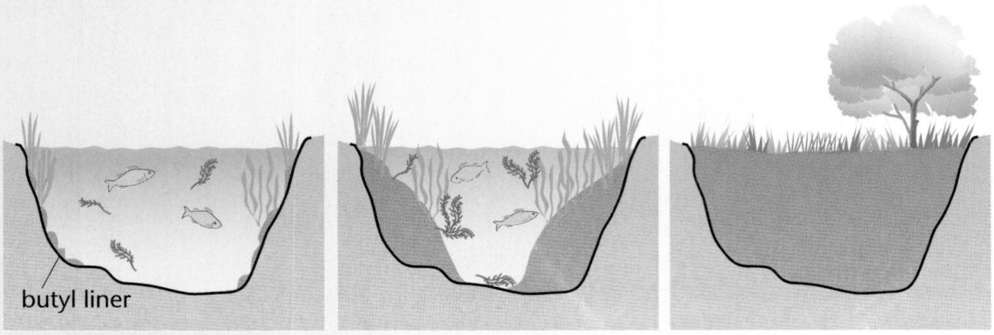

A hole was dug, lined with butyl and new plants were placed in the pond.
1990

Marginal plants grow, spread and die down in the winter. As they rot sediment falls to the bottom of the pond.
1995

After a number of years the pond has completely covered over.
2000

(a) In 1990 irises, oxygenating pondweed and a water lily were planted in the pond. Algae were not planted but arrived in the pond in some other way.

(i) What term describes an organism that grows in a new habitat that previously supported no life? [1]

(ii) After a time the algae produced a thick 'carpet' of growth on the surface of the pond. Explain the effect this may have on organisms under the water. [5]

(b) Describe the stages which took place to produce the stable grassland after 10 years. [2]

4 (a) Explain how the increase in mesh size of trawling nets can help increase fish stocks in the sea. [2]

(b) Apart from the increase of mesh size, how can governments increase fish stocks in the sea? [1]

(c) A herbivorous species of fish is part of a food chain. If the fish species increased in number, suggest **two** effects this may have on the other organisms of the food chain. [2]

5 The following two gases help cause the greenhouse effect.

	Greenhouse effect factor	*Relative amount in troposphere*
Water vapour	0.1	1%
CFC'S	25 000	4.8×10^{-8}

(a) Work out which gas has the greatest influence on the greenhouse effect. [2]

(b) Suggest **one** reason for the greenhouse effect resulting in:

(i) an increase in the population of a species [1]

(ii) a decrease in the population of a species. [1]

9 Human health and disease

- *Health and lifestyle*
- *Disease*
- *Immunity*

9.1 Health and lifestyle

After studying this section you should be able to:

- *define health*
- *understand the features of good health*
- *understand how good health can be maintained through diet and exercise*
- *describe the specific effects of smoking tobacco*

LEARNING SUMMARY

How can we achieve good health?

AQA A M1
OCR M2

Good health is not just an absence of disease or infirmity. It is the physical, mental and social well-being of a person. The development of a healthy person begins in the uterus. It is important that the mother supplies the fetus with suitable nutrients for development, e.g. amino acids for proteins essential for healthy growth. The mother's diet is important for both her and the fetus.

Following birth, the emotional and social development are equally as important as physical development.

If a person is healthy then they may expect the following:

- an absence of disease
- an absence of pain
- to be fit and have good muscle tone
- an absence of stress
- to get along with other people in society
- to have a long life expectancy.

Examiner's tip
It is likely that you will be supplied with data about dietary constituents. Be ready to analyse the data and apply the principles of a balanced diet. Try to remember the main function of each substance. Analyse the dietary reference values for food energy and nutrients in the UK. The values indicate amounts of individual food components required per day and those which should not be exceeded.

The importance of diet

The human diet is vital to good health. A newly born baby needs to feed on mother's first milk **(colostrum)** which is rich in antibodies. This gives immunity against some diseases. It is important that each of the following food classes are included in a person's diet, in a suitable proportion.

The balanced diet

- **Carbohydrates** – sugars and starch supply metabolic energy; cellulose (dietary fibre) stimulates peristalsis so that constipation is prevented.
  Source – potato and bread
- **Proteins** – supply metabolic energy and are needed in growth and repair. **All enzymes are proteins**. Very important!
  Source – meat and nuts
- **Fats and oils** – supply metabolic energy and are needed in cell membrane formation, as they help to make phospholipids.
  Source – butter and cooking oil
- **Vitamins** – organic substances needed in minute quantities to maintain health, e.g. vitamin A. This is essential to make the pigment in the rods of the retina.
  Source (vitamin A) – butter and carrots

- **Minerals** – inorganic ions needed for a number of important roles in the body, e.g. iron. This is essential for the production of haemoglobin and so is vital for oxygen transport.
  Source (iron) – red meat, spinach
- **Water** – makes up over 50% of the content of blood plasma. It is needed for many functions including as a solvent and cooling the body down.

Remember that carbohydrates, proteins, lipids, vitamins, minerals, water and dietary fibre are all essential.

If a person does not eat enough of any one constituent of their diet then there is a deficiency disease, e.g. a protein deficiency causes kwashiorkor. If a person eats too much carbohydrate and fats then obesity and cardiovascular problems can result. A balanced diet is vital!

Essential amino acids

All the parts of a balanced diet are vital if good health is to be maintained. Proteins supply amino acids which can be used as an energy source or to build different proteins. There are 20 different amino acids used to make important proteins. Children need 10 essential amino acids but adults need just 8.

Essential amino acids must be supplied in the diet and cannot be made in the body. A person who eats foods with all the essential amino acids is able to make the others.

Daily energy requirement

Exercise does much more than reduce weight! It develops good muscle tone, keeps joints supple and even mental health is positively affected.

Eating, then respiring carbohydrates, proteins, fats and oils, supplies the energy needed for good health. Energy content of food is usually measured in **kilojoules (kJ)**. A diet rich in carbohydrates and/or fats and oils which exceeds daily requirements results in **obesity**. Large quantities of fat are stored around the body resulting in cardiovascular problems. If the kilojoule intake is regularly less than the daily requirement then a condition known as **anorexia nervosa** can develop. People with this condition are unable to eat enough food and they lose body mass.

What are the energy needs of different people?

Energy needs are determined by age, gender and activity. Additionally, if a woman is pregnant or lactating, extra food is needed. The table below shows typical daily energy requirements.

Person	*Energy used in one day (kilojoules)*	
baby (0–3 months)	2400	
infant (1 year)	4300	
child (8 years)	8900	
teenager (15 years)	Male 12600	Female 9600
adult (office work)	Male 11600	Female 9500
adult (heavy work)	Male 16600	Female 12600
pregnant woman	10500	
lactating mother	11400	

When a person is sleeping their respiratory rate is at a minimum, so the amount of energy released from food is also at a minimum. A person may be involved in a very physical activity like building work or mountain biking; on these occasions energy requirement is large. Exercise is important for health. It can prevent excessive weight increase since more kilojoules of energy are released by increased respiratory activity.

If the energy component and the other components of the diet are less than the recommended daily values, malnutrition takes place. This resembles multiple deficiency diseases. Muscle wastage follows and the individual is in great danger.

Saturated fat and coronary heart disease

The diet is important if we are to maintain health. People can make choices. They can eat a balanced diet and avoid problems caused by eating food components in the wrong proportions.

An example of part of the diet which should be eaten in small quantities is **saturated fat**. Saturated fats (see lipid structure page 24) are found in large quantities in animal tissues.

> **KEY POINT**
>
> Eating red meat such as beef, fatty pork chops, sausages and dairy products can result in health problems. The way that the food is cooked can also result in health problems. Frying food in animal fat adds to the danger! Many people consume the above foods but in smaller quantities. Dietary balance is important.

Atherosclerosis

This is a major health problem caused by eating saturated fats. This circulatory disease may develop as follows:

- yellow fatty streaks develop under the lining of the **endothelium** on the inside of an artery
- the streaks develop into a fatty lump called an **atheroma**
- the atheroma is made from **cholesterol** (taken up in the diet as well as being made in the liver)
- dense **fibrous tissue** develops as the atheroma grows
- the endothelial lining can **split**, allowing blood to contact the fibrous atheroma
- the damage may lead to a blood clot and an artery can be blocked.

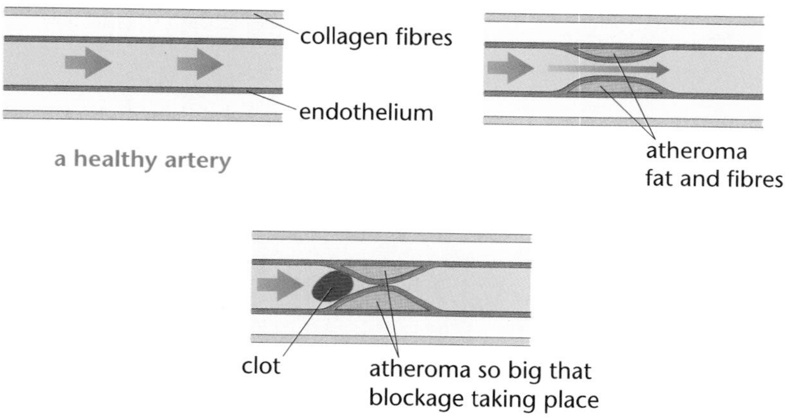

Remember that the clotting of blood can occur for other reasons. There may be damage at other positions around the body. Blockage of this type is **thrombosis**.

Increasing constriction of an artery caused by **atherosclerosis** and **blood clots** reduces blood flow and increases blood pressure. If the artery wall is considerably weakened then a bulge in the side appears, just like a weakened inner tube on a cycle tyre. There is a danger of bursting and the structure is known as an **aneurysm**.

It is possible for a blood clot formed at an atheroma to break away from its original position. It may completely block a smaller vessel, this is known as an **embolism**.

If the artery which supplies the heart (coronary artery) is partially blocked, then there is a reduction in oxygen and nutrient supply to the heart itself. This causes **angina**, the main symptom being sharp chest pains. If total blockage occurs then **myocardial infarction** (heart attack) takes place.

Other aspects of lifestyle influence the condition of the cardiovascular system. A combination of factors are responsible for our health.

Progress check

1 (a) The diet of an infant must contain 10 **essential** amino acids to help maintain health. What is an essential amino acid?
(b) How many essential amino acids are needed by an adult person?

2 (a) Name a specific substance in food which can result in atherosclerosis.
(b) Describe and explain the structural changes which take place in a blood vessel as atherosclerosis develops.
(c) How can the damage caused by an atheroma result in a heart attack?

1 (a) an amino acid which must be supplied in the diet. Non-essential amino acids can be made within the body. (b) 8
2 (a) saturated fat
(b) yellow fatty streaks develop under the cells lining the inside of a blood vessel, the streaks develop into a lump known as an atheroma, the atheroma is made of cholesterol, dense fibrous tissue develops and the lining of the vessel can split.
(c) a blood clot forms which can block the blood vessel completely. Prevention of oxygen supply to the heart results in myocardial infarction (heart attack).

Effects of lifestyle

AQA A M1
OCR M2

Statistically people have a greater chance of living longer if they:

- do not smoke
- do not drink alcohol excessively
- consume a low amount of salt
- consume a low amount of saturated fat in their diet
- are not stressed most of the time
- exercise regularly.

Exercise has a **protective effect** on the **heart** and **circulation**. Activities such as jogging, walking, swimming and cycling can build up the person's endurance.

It is not enough to do a minor amount of exercise, infrequently. The **intensity**, **frequency** and **duration** of the exercise are all important if a programme is to be effective. Frequent exercise:

- reduces the resting heart rate
- increases the strength of contraction of the heart muscle
- increases the stroke volume of the heart (the volume of blood which is propelled during the contractions of the ventricles)
- aids mobility and subtlety of the body
- increases the rate of recovery after a strenuous activity so that heart rate and breathing rates return to resting levels more quickly.

Recommended amount of exercise per week:

- **Intensity** – should allow your heart to beat at a minimum of 60% of your maximum heart rate and increase as you become more fit
- **Frequency** – around three times weekly
- **Duration** – about 30–60 minutes per session.

The diagrams below show the typical effect of training on a person's heart.

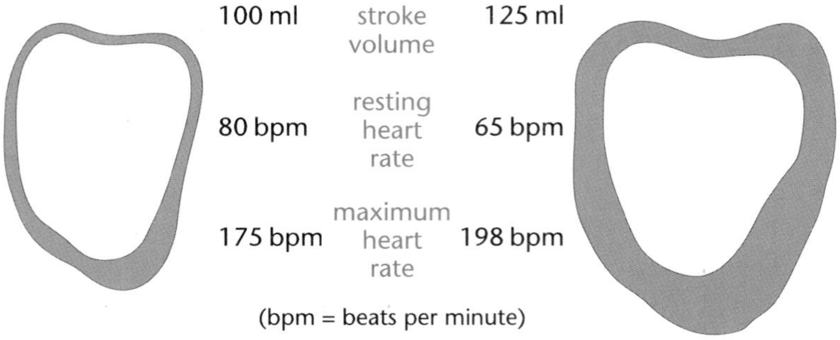

heart before training　　heart after training

What are the dangers of smoking tobacco?

OCR M2

Each person has another choice to make, to smoke or not to smoke. The government health warning on every cigarette packet informs of health dangers but many young people go ahead and ignore the information.

Effects of tobacco smoking

- **Nicotine** is the active component in tobacco which **addicts** people to the habit.
- **Tars** coat the alveoli which **slows down exchange** of carbon dioxide and oxygen. If less oxygen is absorbed then the smoker will be less active than their true potential.
- **Cilia** lining bronchial tubes are coated then **destroyed**, this reduces the efficiency in getting rid of pollutants which enter the lungs. These pollutants include the cigarette chemicals themselves.
- **Carbon monoxide** from the cigarette gases **combines with haemoglobin** of red blood cells rather than oxygen. This **reduces oxygen transport** and the smoker becomes less active than their potential. Ultimately it may lead to heart disease.
- The **bronchi** and **bronchioles** become **inflamed**, a condition known as **bronchitis**. This causes irritating fluid in the lungs, **coughing** and increased risk of heart disease. A number of bronchitis sufferers die each year.
- The walls of the alveoli break down reducing the surface area for gaseous exchange. Less oxygen can be absorbed by the lungs, leaving the **emphysema** sufferer extremely breathless. They increase their breathing rate to compensate but still cannot take in enough oxygen for a healthy life. A chronic emphysema sufferer needs an oxygen cylinder to prolong their life. Death is a regular conclusion, especially when combined with other symptoms.
- **Blood vessel elasticity is reduced** so that serious damage may occur. Ultimately a heart attack can follow.
- The **carcinogens** (cancer-causing chemicals) of the tobacco can result in **lung cancer. Malignant growths** in the lungs develop uncontrollably and cancers may spread to other parts of the body. Death often follows. Smokers have a greater risk of developing other cancers than non-smokers, e.g. more smokers develop cervical cancer.

Learn the characteristics of each disease carefully. There are so many consequences of smoking that you may well mix them up.

Even non-smokers can develop any of the above symptoms, but the probability of developing them is increased by smoking. Being in a smoky atmosphere each day, such as a non-smoker working in a pub, also increases the chances.

The role of statistics

The government health warning on cigarette packets informs people of the risks of smoking. The WHO (World Health Organisation), governments and local authorities have collected statistics on many diseases over the years. These are used in education packs and posters to warn of risk factors. People can take precautions and use the information to avoid health dangers and take advantage of vaccination programmes.

Where education is not successful then related diseases follow. This acts as a drain on the National Health Service. Many operations which would have been unnecessary are performed to save people's lives, e.g. where coronary blood vessels are dangerously diseased a by-pass operation is the answer.

The ideal situation is that education is successful, but realistically the aim is to balance prevention and cure.

9.2 Disease

After studying this section you should be able to:

LEARNING SUMMARY

- *define disease*
- *recall the causes, symptoms and control of a range of diseases including cholera, tuberculosis, malaria and AIDS*

What is a disease?

OCR M2

A disease is a disorder of a tissue, organ or system of an organism. As a result of a disorder, symptoms are evident. Such symptoms could be the failure to produce a particular digestive enzyme, or a growth of cells in the wrong place. Normal bodily processes may be disrupted, e.g. efficient oxygen transport is impeded by the malarial parasite, *Plasmodium*.

Different types of disease

Infectious disease by pathogens

Pathogens attack an organism and can be passed from one person to another. Many pathogens are spread by a vector which carries it from one organism to another without being affected itself by the disease. Pathogens include bacteria, viruses, protozoa, fungi, parasites and worms.

Most exam candidates recall that pathogens are responsible for disease. However, there are more causes of disease! If a question asks for different types of disease then giving a range of pathogens will not score many marks. Give genetic diseases, etc.

Genetic diseases

These can be passed from parent to offspring. Also known as congenital diseases, they include haemophilia and cystic fibrosis.

Dietary related diseases

These are caused from the foods that we eat. Too much or too little food may cause disorders, e.g. obesity or anorexia nervosa. Lack of vitamin D causes the bone disease rickets, the symptoms of which are soft weak bones which bend under the body weight (see page 126 deficiency diseases).

Environmentally caused diseases

Some aspects of the environment disrupt bodily processes, e.g. as a result of nuclear radiation leakage, cancer may develop.

An **auto-immune disease** may be **environmentally** caused, e.g. the form of leukaemia where phagocytes destroy a person's red blood cells may be caused by radiation leakage.

Auto-immune disease

The body in some way attacks its own cells so that processes fail to function effectively.

How are infectious diseases transmitted?

The pathogens which cause infectious diseases are transmitted in a range of ways.

- Direct contact – sexual intercourse enables the transmission of syphillis bacteria; a person's foot which touches a damp floor at the swimming baths can transfer the Athlete's foot fungus.
- Droplet infection – a sneeze propels tiny droplets of nasal mucus carrying viruses such as those causing influenza.
- Via a vector – if a person with typhoid bacteria in the gut handles food the bacteria can be passed to a susceptible person.
- Via food or water – chicken meat kept in warm conditions encourages the reproduction of *Salmonella* bacteria which are transferred to the human consumer, who has food poisoning as a result.

Be prepared to answer questions about diseases not on your syllabus. The examiners will give data and other information which you will need to interpret. Use your knowledge of the principles of disease transmission, infection, symptoms and cure.

- Via blood transfusion – as a result of receiving blood a person can contract AIDS.

Some infectious diseases have serious consequences to human life. The incidence of infectious diseases may vary according to the climate of the country, the presence of vectors, the social behaviour of people and other factors.

The infectious diseases in an area may be classified by using the following terms:

(a) **endemic**, which means that a disease or its vector is invariably found in an area

(b) **epidemic**, which means that there is an outbreak of a disease attacking many people in an area

(c) **pandemic**, which means that a there is an outbreak of a disease over a very large area, e.g. the size of a continent.

Disease file – cholera

OCR M2

Cause of disease

Vibrio cholerae (bacteria) in the faeces or vomit of a human sufferer or human carrier which contaminate water supplies.

Transmission of microorganism

Contaminated water spreads the bacteria. Poor sanitary behaviour of people who are carriers and those who have contracted the disease are responsible. Faeces enters rivers which may be used for bathing, drinking, or irrigation. The bacteria survive outside the human body for around 24 hours. They can also contaminate vegetables and can be passed to a person in this way.

Outline of the course of the disease and symptoms

The bacteria reach the intestines where they breed. They secrete a toxin which stimulates adenyl cyclase in epithelial cells. This enzyme causes much fluid to be secreted into the intestine, giving severe diarrhoea. Death is a regular consequence, due to dehydration, but some people do recover.

Prevention

Education about cleanliness and sewage treatment. Good sanitation is vital. Suitable treatment of water to be consumed by people, e.g. chlorination which kills the bacteria. Use of disinfectant also kills the bacteria. Early identification of an outbreak followed by control.

Cure

Tetracycline antibiotics kill organisms in the bowel. Immunisation is not very effective. It will help some individuals but not stop them from being carriers, so epidemics are still likely.

Disease file – tuberculosis

OCR M2

Cause of disease

Mycobacterium tuberculosis (bacterium) via droplet infection.

Transmission of microorganism

Coughs and sneezes of sufferers spread tiny droplets of moisture containing the pathogenic bacteria. People then inhale these droplets and may contract the disease.

Outline of the course of the disease and symptoms

The initial attack takes place in the lungs. The alveoli surfaces and capillaries are vulnerable and lesions occur. Some epithelial tissues begin to grow in number but these cannot carry out gaseous exchange. Inflammation occurs which stimulates painful coughing. Intense coughing takes place which can cause bleeding. There is much weight loss. Weak groups of people, like the elderly, or someone underweight are more prone to the disease.

Prevention

Mycobacterium bovis causes tuberculosis in cattle. It can be passed to humans via milk. It causes an intestinal complaint in humans. It is important that cows are kept free of *M. bovis* by antibiotics.

The BCG vaccination is the injection of a weakened form of this microbe. This vaccination stimulates antibodies which are effective against both *M. tuberculosis* and *M. bovis*.

Mass screening using **X-rays** can identify 'shadows' in those people with scar tissue in the lungs.

Sputum testing identifies the presence of the bacteria in sufferers. Sufferers can be treated with antibiotics. Once cured they cannot pass on the pathogen so an epidemic may be prevented.

Skin testing is used. Antigens from dead *Mycobacteria* are injected just beneath the skin. If a person has been previously exposed to the organism then the skin swells which shows that they already have resistance, i.e. they have antibodies already. Anyone whose skin does not swell up is given the **BCG vaccination**. This contains attenuated *Mycobacterium bovis* to stimulate the production of antibodies against both *M. bovis* and *M. tuberculosis*.

Cure Use of antibiotics such as streptomycin.

Disease file – malaria

OCR M2

Cause of disease

There are many variants of the malarial parasite, *Plasmodium* (protozoa).

Transmission of the microorganism

The vector which carries the *Plasmodium* is a female *Anopheles* mosquito. The mosquito feeds on a mammal which may be suffering from malaria. It does this at night by inserting its 'syringe-like' stylet into a blood vessel beneath the skin. The mosquito feeds on blood and digests the red blood cells which releases the malarial parasites. These burrow into the insect's stomach wall where they breed; some then move to the salivary glands. Next time the mosquito feeds it secretes saliva to prevent clotting of the blood. This secretion introduces the parasites into the person's blood, who is likely to contract the disease.

Malaria is endemic in the Middle East and Southern Asia, where the vectors of the disease live successfully. Global warming is beginning to have an effect on the distribution of the disease. New areas suitable as habitats for the *Anopheles* mosquito are appearing because of global warming.

Outline of the course of the disease and symptoms

After entry into the blood, **sporozoites** invade the **liver** releasing many **merozoites**. Each merozoites infects a **red blood cell** producing even more merozoites. Millions of these parasites are released into the blood causing a fever. As a result, the sufferer develops a range of symptoms including pains, exhaustion, aching, feeling cold, sweating and fever. The increased body temperature attracts mosquitoes even more, so a person with malaria acts as a reservoir for parasites.

Prevention

The most effective methods of prevention are those which **destroy the vector**. Spraying **insecticide** onto lake surfaces kills mosquito larvae.

Oil poured on lake surfaces prevents air entering the breathing tubes of the mosquitoes, so they die. Fish can be introduced into lakes as **predators** to eat the larvae. This is an example of **biological control**.

Combinations of these tests are used in different countries. Where there are outbreaks of the disease the systems are activated.

Sometimes ponds are **drained** to remove the mosquitoes' breeding area. People in areas where malaria is endemic **cover up** all waste **tin cans** and **plastic containers**. If they were to fill up with rain water then the mosquitoes have another habitat to breed in. The bacterium, ***Bacillus thuringiensis*** is used to destroy mosquitoes. Mosquito nets exclude mosquitoes from buildings and are even used over beds. **Electronic insect killer** techniques can be used which attract the mosquito via ultra-violet light then kill them by application of voltage. **Drugs** are used so that even if a person is bitten by a mosquito any *Plasmodia* entering the blood fail to develop further.

Cure

It is necessary to isolate and treat the sufferer. This also reduces the spread of the disease. Drugs are used to kill the parasites in the blood and reduce the symptoms. People are constantly attempting to find different ways of preventing this killer disease.

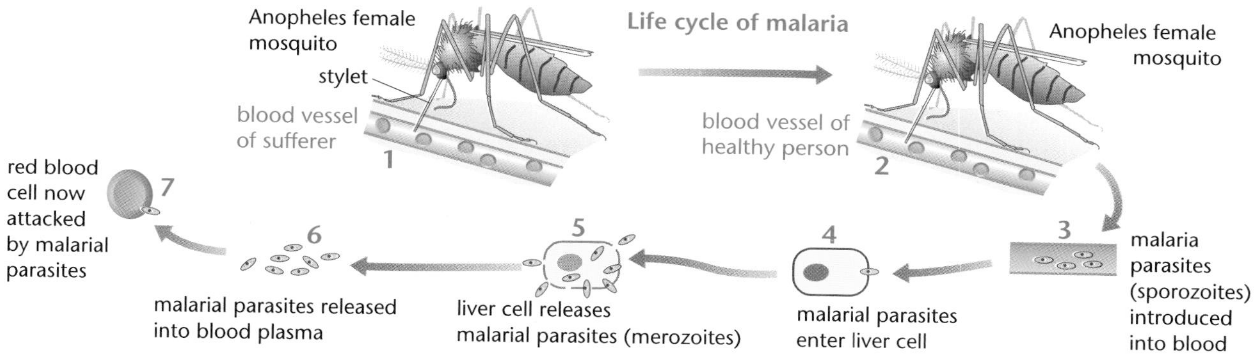

Progress check

A mosquito carries the malarial parasite, *Plasmodium*. The female mosquito feeds on a mammal by inserting its 'syringe-like' stylet into a blood vessel beneath the skin. The mosquito feeds on blood and digests the red blood cells releasing the malarial parasites. These burrow into the insect's stomach wall and breed there, then some move to the salivary glands. Next time the mosquito feeds it secretes saliva. The saliva introduces the parasites into the person's blood.

(a) (i) Which species of mosquito transmits malaria?
(ii) Which organism causes the disease, malaria?
(iii) Does every mosquito bite transmit malaria?
Give a reason for your answer.

(b) Suggest how to reduce the spread of malaria.

(a) (i) *Anopheles* (ii) plasmodium (iii) no – mosquito must feed on sufferer first.
(b) Drain ponds where the mosquitoes breed; kill the mosquitoes with insecticide; pour oil on ponds to kill the larvae; introduce insectivorous fish as a form of biological control; use drugs such as chloroquine to cure people suffering from the disease; isolate people suffering from the disease; spray mosquitoes with a suspension of *Bacillus thuringiensis*.

Disease file – AIDS (Acquired Immune Deficiency Syndrome)

OCR M2

Cause of disease

This is by HIV (human immune deficiency virus). It is a retrovirus, which is able to make DNA with the help of its own core of RNA.

Transmission of microorganism

This takes place by the exchange of body fluids, transfusion of contaminated blood, or via syringe needle 'sharing' in drug practices.

Outline of the course of the disease and symptoms

Scientists are constantly trying to find a **cure**. None has been found yet.

Destruction of T-lymphocyte cells

The HIV protein coat attaches to protein in the plasma membrane of a T-lymphocyte. The virus protein coat fuses with the cell membrane releasing RNA and reverse transcriptase into the cell. This enzyme causes the cell to produce DNA from the viral RNA. This DNA enters the nucleus of the T-lymphocyte and is incorporated into the host cell chromosomes. The gene representing the HIV virus is permanently in the nucleus from now on and can be dormant for years. It may become activated by an infection. Viral protein and viral RNA are made as a result of the infection.

Many RNA viral cores now leave the cell and protein coats are assembled from degenerating plasma membranes. Other T-lymphocytes are attacked. Cells of the lymph nodes and spleen are also destroyed. Viruses appear in the blood, tears, saliva, semen and vaginal fluids. The immune system becomes so weak that many diseases can now successfully invade the weakened body.

Prevention

Screening of blood before transfusions. Use of condoms and remaining with one partner. No use of contaminated needles.

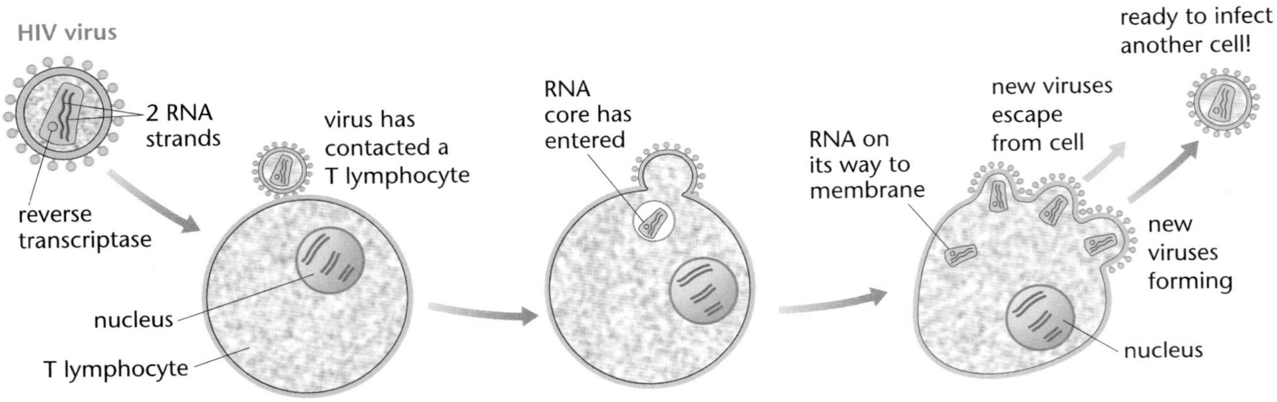

9.3 Immunity

LEARNING SUMMARY

After studying this section you should be able to:

- *describe and explain the action of the body's immune system*

Survival against the attack of pathogens

AQA A	M2
EDEXCEL	M3
OCR	M2

Many pathogenic organisms attack people. They are not all successful in causing disease. We have immunity to a disease when we are able to resist infection. The body has a range of ways to prevent the disease-causing organism from becoming established.

- A tough protein called **keratin** helps skin cells to be a formidable **barrier** to prevent pathogens entering the body.
- An enzyme, **lysozyme**, destroys some microorganisms and can be found in sebum, tears and saliva.
- **Hydrochloric acid** in the stomach kills some microorganisms.

Carefully learn all the different ways in which the body is adapted to combat disease. Questions may refer to specific diseases and the principles of immunity will often be examined in the same question. There are a range of ways in which the body achieves immunity!

- The bronchial tubes of the lungs are lined with **cilia**. Microorganisms which enter the respiratory system are often trapped in mucus which is then moved to the oesophagus. From here they move to the stomach where many are destroyed by hydrochloric acid or digested.
- **Blood clotting** in response to external damage prevents entry of microorganisms from the external environment.

The ways in which the body is adapted to prevent microorganisms entering the bloodstream are sometimes unsuccessful. When the microorganisms invade, then breed in high numbers, we develop the **symptoms**. **White blood cells** enable us to destroy invading microorganisms. They may destroy the microorganisms quickly before they have any chance of becoming established, so the person would not develop any symptoms. Sometimes there are so many microorganisms attacking that the white blood cells cannot destroy all of them. Once the pathogens are established the symptoms of a disease follow, but for most diseases, after some time, the white blood cells eventually overcome the disease-causing organisms.

The roles of the white blood cells (leucocytes)

There are a number of different types of **leucocytes**. They are all produced from **stem cells** in the **bone marrow**. Different stem cells follow alternative maturation procedures to produce a range of leucocytes. Leucocytes have the ability to recognise self chemicals and non-self. Only where non-self chemicals are recognised will a leucocyte respond. Proteins and polysaccharides are typical of the complex molecules which can trigger an immune response.

Phagocytes

Phagocytes can move to a site of infection through capillaries, tissue fluid and lymph as well as being found in the plasma. They move towards pathogens which they destroy by the process of phagocytosis. This is often called engulfment and involves the surrounding of a pathogen by pseudopodia to form a food vacuole. Hydrolytic enzymes complete the destruction of the pathogen.

Neutrophils are one type of phagocyte. Proteins in plasma called **opsonins** attach to a pathogen. These opsonins enable the phagocyte to engulf the pathogen.

Macrophages are another type of phagocyte which work alongside T-lymphocytes.

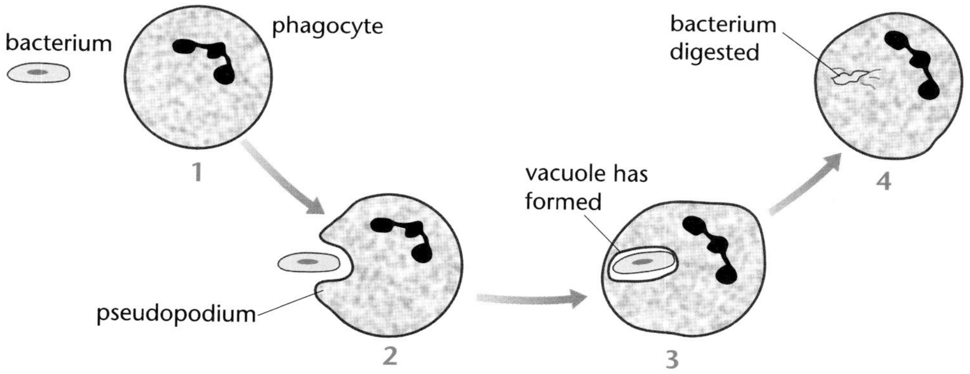

What is an antigen?

AQA A M2
EDEXCEL M3
OCR M2

As an individual grows and develops, complex substances such as proteins and polysaccharides are used to form cellular structures. Leucocytes identify these substances in the body as 'self' substances. They are ignored as the leucocytes encounter them daily. 'Non-self substances', e.g. foreign proteins which enter the body, are immediately identified as 'non-self.' These are known as **antigens** and trigger an immune response.

White blood cells (leucocytes) constantly check out proteins around the body. Foreign protein is identified and attack is stimulated.

Lymphocytes

There are two types of lymphocyte, **B-lymphocytes** and **T-lymphocytes**.

B-lymphocytes begin development and mature in the bone marrow. They produce antibodies, known as the **humoral response**.

T-lymphocytes work alongside phagocytes known as macrophages; this is known as the **cell-mediated response**. A macrophage engulfs an antigen. This antigen remains on the surface of the macrophage. T-lymphocytes respond to the antigen, dividing by mitosis to form a range of different types of T-lymphocyte cells.

- **Killer T-lymphocytes** adhere to the pathogen, secrete a toxin and destroy it.
- **Helper T-lymphocytes** stimulate the production of antibodies.
- **Suppressor T-lymphocytes** are inhibitors of the T-lymphocytes and plasma cells. Just weeks after the initial infection, they shut down the immune response when it is no longer needed.
- **Memory T-lymphocytes** respond to an antigen previously experienced. They are able to destroy the same pathogen before symptoms appear.

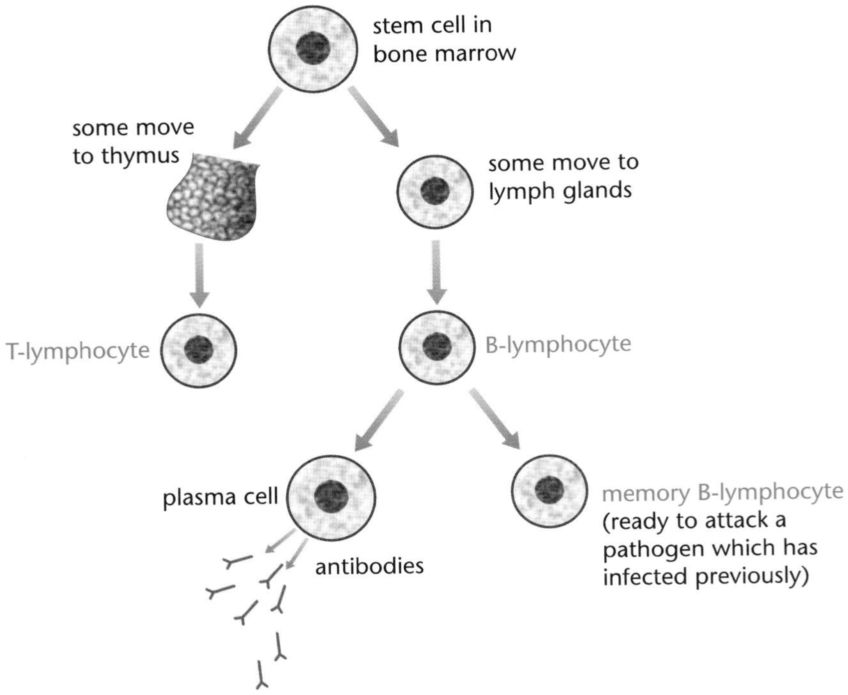

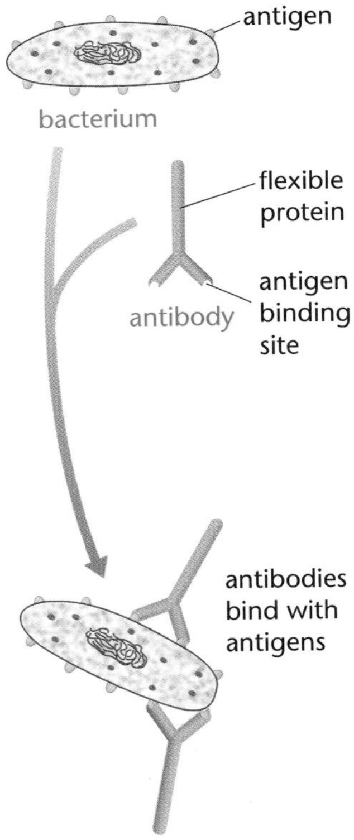

How do antibodies destroy pathogens?

The diagram above shows antibodies binding to antigens. The descriptions below show what can happen immediately after the binding takes place.

There are four main ways in which antibodies destroy pathogens.

- **Precipitation**, by linking many antigens together. This enables the phagocytes to engulf them.
- **Lysis**, where the cell membrane breaks open, killing the cell.
- **Neutralisation** of a chemical released by the pathogen, so that the chemical is no longer toxic.
- Attachment of **opsonins** to the membrane of the microorganism, which causes them to clump together. They then attach each pathogen to a phagocyte which engulfs them.

Sample question

The graph below shows the relative numbers of antibodies in a person's blood after the vaccination of attenuated viruses. Vaccinations were given on day 1 then 200 days later.

In examinations you are regularly given graphs. Make sure that you can link the idea being tested. This should help you recall all of the important concepts needed. All you need to do after this is **apply** your knowledge to the given data.

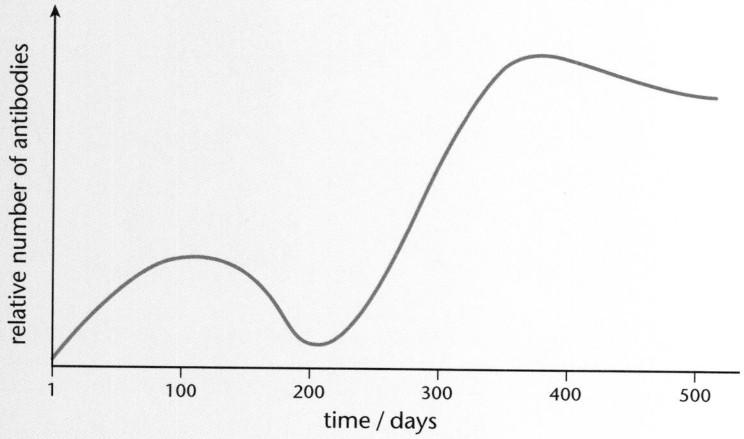

(a) Why is it important that viruses used in vaccinations are attenuated? [1]

If they were active then the person would contract the disease.

(b) Suggest **two** advantages of giving the second vaccination. [2]

A greater number of antibodies were produced.
The antibodies remain for much longer after the second vaccination.

(c) Which cells produced the antibodies during the primary response? [1]

B-lymphocytes.

(d) Why was there no delay in the secondary response to vaccination? [3]

Because the first vaccination had already been given, memory B-lymphocytes had been produced which respond to the viruses more quickly.

(e) Describe how a virus stimulates the production of antibodies? [3]

Antigen in the protein 'coat' or capsomere stimulate the B-lymphocytes.

If you gave B-lymphocytes as a response it would be wrong! B-lymphocytes secrete antibodies.

(f) Apart from producing antibodies, outline FOUR different ways that the body uses to destroy microorganisms. [4]

Phagocytes by engulfment; T-lymphocytes attach to microorganism and destroy them; hydrochloric acid in the stomach; lysozyme in tears.

Practice examination questions

1 The diagram shows how the bacterium which causes typhoid can be transmitted from one person to another.

(a) Name the method of disease transmission shown in the diagram. [1]

(b) Sometimes the bacteria infect people but they do not develop symptoms.

(i) What term is given to this group of people? [1]

(ii) Explain why these people may be a greater danger to a community than those who actually suffer from the disease. [2]

(c) (i) What can be given to a person infected with typhoid to help destroy the bacteria? [1]

(ii) Explain the role of each of the following in destroying typhoid bacteria.

Phagocyte
B-lymphocyte
T-lymphocyte [6]

2 The diagram shows the response of B-lymphocytes to a specific antigen.

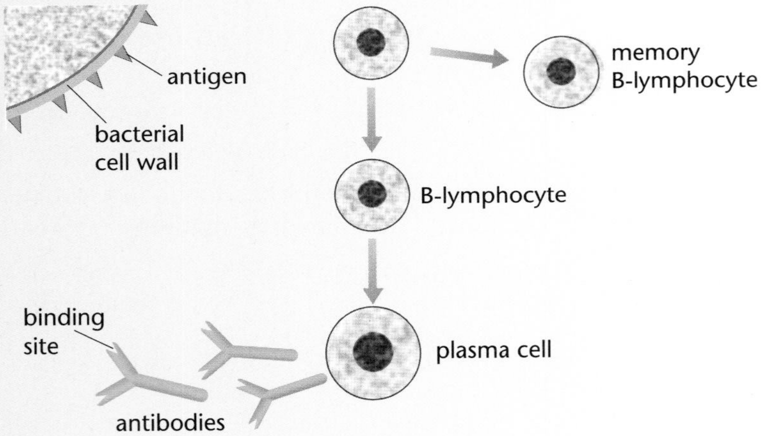

(a) (i) A plasma cell is bigger than a B-lymphocyte. Suggest an advantage of this. [1]

(ii) Describe the precise role of antibodies in the immune response. [3]

(iii) What is the advantage of memory B-lymphocytes? [2]

(b) What is an auto-immune disease? Give an example. [2]

(c) A person contracts the virus which causes the common cold. Suggest why their lymphocytes fail to destroy the pathogen. [1]

Practice examination answers

Chapter 1 Biological molecules

1 (a) $\frac{90}{100} = 0.9$ [2]

(b) X [1]

(c) The solvent front would have reached the edge of the paper. [1]

[Total: 4]

2 (a)

$$\begin{array}{lll} \text{RCOOH} & & \text{HOCH}_2 \\ \text{RCOOH} & + & \text{HOCH} \\ \text{RCOOH} & & \text{HOCH}_2 \\ \text{fatty acids} & & \text{glycerol} \end{array}$$

[2]

(b) Emulsion test: add the sample to ethanol and mix; decant or pour into water; if a fat is present a white emulsion forms on the surface. [3]

[Total: 5]

3 (a) peptide bond/peptide link [1]

(b) –COOH/carboxylic acid [1]

(c) primary structure; amino acids in a chain [2]

[Total: 4]

4 (a) The latent heat of evaporation is large so lots of energy is needed to evaporate water/in sweating, much body heat is needed for evaporation. [2]

(b) High specific heat capacity means that the water needs a lot of heat energy to increase temperature significantly, therefore an organism will not overheat easily. [2]

(c) Cohesive forces aid the movement of water up the xylem. [2]

[Total: 6]

Chapter 2 Cells

1 (a) phospholipid [1]

(b) (i) Substance approaches a carrier protein molecule; carrier protein activated by ATP; protein changes shape allowing the substance into the cell.

(ii) Substance approaches a carrier protein; this may be a channel protein and substances pass through without any ATP necessary. [4]

[Total: 5]

2 (a)

	diffusion	*facilitated diffusion*	*active transport*
molecules move from where they are in high concentration to low concentration	✓	✓	
molecules move from where they are in low concentration to high concentration		✓	✓
a protein carrier is needed			✓

[3]

(b) phagocytosis/endocytosis/exocytosis/osmosis [any two for 2 marks] [2]

[Total: 5]

3 Cuticle reflects some light so that the leaf does not have excess, which would dehydrate the leaf. [1] Palisade cells have most chloroplasts so that they can capture maximum light. [1] The chloroplasts are motile, able to move in the cytoplasm to absorb most light. [1] Large air spaces in the spongy mesophyll store carbon dioxide for photosynthesis. [1] Stomata open to allow high amounts of carbon dioxide to enter the leaf. [1] Water is supplied to photosynthetic cells by the xylem. [1] Glucose is rapidly removed by the phloem. [1] [7]

[Total: 7]

4 (a) cell wall (not cellulose); no true nucleus; no mitochondria; plasmids [any two for 2 marks] [2]

(b) mitochondria; nucleus; Golgi body; large ribosomes/rough endoplasmic reticulum [any two for 2 marks] [2]

[Total: 4]

5 (a) (i) total number of yeast cells in 10 squares = 76

$\frac{76}{10} = 7.6$ (average number per square) [2]

(ii) volume of one square = (0.0001) mm^3

number of cells in one square = 7.6

number in 1 cm^3

$= \frac{1000 \times 10 \text{ (dilution factor)} \times 7.6}{0.00001}$

$= 7.6 \times 10^9$ [3]

(b) so that the suspension is homogeneous [1]

[Total 6]

6 (a) lens X = projector; lens Y = objective [2]

(b) electrons would collide with air molecules [1]

(c) (i) artefact [1]

(ii) ignore the artefact, because it is not part of normal structure and is only present due to preparation of the specimen. [1]

[Total 5]

Chapter 3 Enzymes

1 (a) The urea molecules bind with receptor molecules on the biological recognition layer; the transducer measures and amplifies a signal; electrical signal identifies urea. [3]
(b) Level of voltage. [1]
[Total: 4]

2 (a) lock and key – the substrate is a similar shape to the active site; it fits in and binds with the active site like a key (substrate) fitting into a lock (active site); induced fit – the substrate is not a matching 'fit' for the active site, but as the substrate approaches, the active site changes into an appropriate shape.
(b) Endopeptidases break down peptide links in the middle parts of polypeptides; exopeptidases break down the peptides links at the ends of polypeptides, removing the outer amino acids. [4]
[Total: 4]

3 They do not contaminate the product; they can be used again and again. [2]
[Total: 2]

4
- The tertiary structure of the enzyme is responsible for the further folding of the protein;
- this gives the shape of the active site;
- the active site in amylase is specific to starch, lipid is unable to bind to the active site of amylase, therefore amylase cannot break down lipid. [3]

5 (a) starch [1]
(b) thermostable enzymes are effective at high temperatures [1]
[Total: 2]

6 (a) Stain removal directly proportional to protease concentration. [2]
(b) (i) At 6 units of protease dm^{-3} the maximum rate is reached; after this amount there was no further increase in stain removal. [1]
(ii) Protein molecules bind to the enzyme's active site; water molecules are part of the hydrolysis mechanism to break down the protein; polypeptides or amino acids are produced which readily move from the cloth. [3]
(iii) so that a lot of different proteins can be broken down by the same enzyme. [1]
(iv) polypeptide/amino acid [1]
(c) lipase; carbohydrase/amylase [2]
[Total: 9]

7 (a) The substrate molecule collides with the active site of the enzyme; as it approaches, the active site changes shape to become compatible with the substrate shape. [2]
(b) Non-competitive inhibitor molecule binds with part of enzyme other than the active site; as a result the active site changes shape; so the substrate can no longer bind with the active site. [3]
[Total: 5]

8 (a) NH_2 (amino group) [1]
(b) Endopeptidases break down the middle of polypeptides; exopeptidases break down the outside peptide bonds to release amino acids; every time the endopeptidase breaks the middle of the polypeptide it reveals two more ends for the exopeptidase to work on. [3]
[Total: 4]

Chapter 4 Exchange

1 (a) (i) No change in size because the water potential inside the cell equals the water potential of the solution outside the cell. [1]
(ii) The water potential of the solution outside the cell is more negative than the water potential inside the cell. [1]
(iii) The water potential of the solution outside the cell is less negative than the water potential inside the cell. [1]
(b) osmosis [1]
[Total: 4]

2 (a) They both use a protein carrier molecule. [1]
(b) Active transport needs energy or mitochondria, whereas facilitated diffusion does not.
OR Active transport allows molecules to move from a lower concentrated solution to a higher concentrated solution.
OR Active transport allows molecules to move against a concentration gradient. [1]
[Total: 2]

3 (a)
- a flat, thin blade allows maximum light absorption;
- the leaf has a waxy cuticle to reflect excess light but allow entry of enough light for photosynthesis;
- the mesophyll cells have many chloroplasts to absorb the maximum amount of light;
- the palisade cells pack closely together to absorb the maximum amount of light;
- guard cells open stomata to allow carbon dioxide in and oxygen out during photosynthesis;
- air spaces in the mesophyll store lots of carbon dioxide for photosynthesis;
- xylem of the vascular bundles bring water to the leaf for photosynthesis;
- phloem takes the carbohydrate away from the leaf after photosynthesis. [any 6 points] [6]

(b) thick waxy cuticle; low number of stomata; hairs on epidermis (which reduce turbulence). [3]
[Total: 9]

4 (a) alveoli have a very high surface area; they are very close to many capillaries; capillaries are one cell thick/very thin/have squamous epithelia; they are kept damp which facilitates diffusion. [4]
(b)
- there are many gill filaments, which give a very

high surface area;
- the gill filaments are very thin;
- they have many capillaries;
- they have gill plates which increase the surface area further;
- the blood and water directions are opposite which maximises diffusion/they use countercurrent flow to maximise diffusion. [any 4 points] [4]

[Total: 8]

Chapter 5 Transport

1 (a) to the body core [1]

(b) less blood reaches the superficial capillaries of the skin; so less heat is lost by conduction, convection and radiation; blood in body core better insulated by the adipose layer of the skin [4]

[Total: 5]

2 (a) 60 x 120 x 5 = 36 000 ml / 36 litres [2]

(b)
- blood is transported more quickly;
- more oxygen taken up at the lungs/more carbon dioxide excreted at the lungs;
- more oxygen reaches the muscles;
- more glucose reaches the muscles;
- so muscles contract more effectively.

[any 4 points] [4]

[Total: 4]

(c) (i)
- slower breathing rate;
- more alveoli accessed for exchange;
- intercostal muscles more effective.

[any 2 points] [2]

(ii)
- improved muscle tone;
- greater muscular strength;
- more capillaries in muscles. [any 2 points] [2]

[Total: 4]

3 (a) Lung cancer – cause: tobacco or tars are carcinogenic; mutates the lung cells – symptom: malignant growths/abnormal growth. [2]

(b) Bronchitis – cause: smoking/damp cold conditions; inflammation of the bronchi or bronchioles – symptoms: coughing/phlegm/increased chance of pneumonia. [2]

(c) Emphysema – cause: smoking; damaged alveoli/walls between alveoli reduce, so surface area for gaseous exchange less – symptoms: breathless, cannot obtain enough oxygen. [2]

[Total: 6]

4 (a) The amount of water lost by transpiration is exactly matched by the amount taken up by the leaf. [1]

(b) (i) xylem [1]

(ii) fill the potometer under water; operate the valve to get rid of air bubbles; when removing the leaf from the tree the stalk or petiole must be put in water immediately. [2]

(c) Volume of water $= \pi r^2 \times 32\text{ mm} \times 60$

$= \frac{22}{7} \times 1 \times 1 \times 32 \times 60$

$= 6034.3\text{ mm}^3$ [3]

[Total: 7]

5
- extensive root system to absorb maximum water;
- large amount of water storage in leaves;
- thick cuticle;
- low numbers of stomata/sunken stomata;
- hairs to reduce turbulence. [any 3 points] [3]

[Total: 3]

6 (a) SAN/Sinoatrial node [1]

(b) (i) slows heart rate [1]

(ii) speeds up the rate [1]

(iii) speeds up the rate [1]

[Total: 4]

7 (a) (i) sieve tube [1]

(ii) companion cell has nucleus plus ribosomes; which make the proteins or enzymes; supplies enzymes to sieve tube via plasmodesmata. [3]

(b) (i) It is an active process; a pump is involved; phloem contents under high pressure. [3]

(ii) no starch in the phloem contents; did not change to blue-black; contained reducing sugar; did change to brick red. [4]

(iii) Hot wax kills phloem cells; so they cannot transport the radioactive carbohydrate; transport by phloem is an active process. [3]

[Total: 14]

Chapter 6 Genetic code

1 (a) 5; There were 5 cuts along the piece of DNA. So the base sequence binding to the active site of the enzyme occurred 5 times. [2]

(b) sticky end [1]

(c) 48502 – 44123 = 4379 [1 mark for working and 1 mark for correct answer.] [2]

(d) They cut the DNA into pieces; electrophoresis then used/voltage applied; different DNA samples compared and from same person all DNA samples will form a pattern like a bar-code. [8]

[Total: 3]

2 (a) metaphase [1]

(b) 2n [2]

[Total: 3]

3 (a) The gene is cut out from the human DNA using a restriction endonuclease. [1] A bacterial plasmid is cut using the same restriction endonuclease. [1] The human DNA is incorporated into the plasmid; [1] with ligase. [1] The plasmid now returned to bacterium. [1] Bacterium clones the plasmid. [1] [6]

(b) Sterilise the fermenter to kill contaminant microorganisms; supply nutrients plus the transgenic bacteria; use paddle wheel to ensure nutrients plus microorganisms make contact; adjust the pH during process/neutralise; temperature sensor plus water jacket to keep reaction at optimum; add air via air filter to remove contaminant microorganisms. [5]

(c) insulin [1]

[Total: 12]

4 (a) adenine and thymine are similar proportions because adenine binds with thymine; cytosine and guanine are similar proportions because cytosine binds with guanine [2]
(b) They should be identical in number but the scientists were operating at the limits of instrumentation. [1]
(c) Organic bases form the codes for different amino acids. Different sequences of amino acids form the different proteins specific to a species. [2]
[Total: 5]

5 (a) restriction endonuclease [1]
(b) Yes, the egg DNA shares several common bonds with the parents DNA. [1]
(c) checking out who is the father of a child/paternity cases; crimes where blood samples or tissue or saliva is left and checked against suspects [2]
[Total: 5]

6 (a) Identify the specific section of DNA which contains the gene; this can be done using reverse transcriptase; insert DNA into a vector/insert into *Agrobacterium tumefaciens*; this bacterium/this vector then passes the DNA into the recipient cell. [5]
(b) herbicide kills weeds; which reduces competition; for light or water or minerals; soya plants unharmed [3]
(c) the ability to resist the effect of herbicide could transfer to weeds; so the herbicide no longer effective on weeds; resistant weeds spread into field [3]
(d) fear that the new gene will be passed to other plants by interbreeding; fear that potentially toxic chemicals may be consumed; fear that the beans have not been tested enough [2]
[Total: 13]

Chapter 7 Continuity of life

1 (a) (i) corpus luteum [1]
(ii) via the blood [1]
(b) no, because the progesterone level fell [1]
(c) endometrium would detach and miscarriage take place [1]
[Total: 4]

2 (a) (i) this causes the ovules to ripen before the pollen [1]
(ii) this causes the pollen to ripen before the ovules [1]
(b) (i) no need to have more than one tree [1]
(ii) do not have hybrid vigour; greater chance of recessive disadvantageous character in offspring [2]
[Total: 5]

3 (a) (i) insect, because of the rough outside which sticks to insects or the converse, because it is not aerodynamic [1]
(ii) tube nucleus or tube growth [1]
(b) one male nucleus fuses with the egg cell; to form the embryo; one male nucleus fuses with the polar nuclei; to form the endosperm [4]
[Total: 6]

Chapter 8 Energy and ecosystems

1 (a) (i) When given fertiliser the grasses competed for resources better that the legumes; some legume species could not grow in these conditions. [2]
(ii) Without fertiliser the grass species did not have enough minerals so did not compete as well; the legumes fixed nitrogen in root nodules so could grow effectively. [2]
(b) Cows grazed on some species more than others/ perhaps trampling by cattle destroyed some species but others were tougher and survived/perhaps waste encouraged the growth of some species whereas others were destroyed. [1]
[Total: 5]

2 (a) electronic systems locate shoals of fish accurately; very large nets/small-mesh nets [2]
(b) many of the breeding size fish have already been caught; some fish may never reach breeding size as they are caught before they reach this size [2]
(c)
- trawling destroys some invertebrates;
- they may be the food of other organisms in a food web, so some animals may die out as a result;
- overfishing reduces fish numbers so that their predators may ultimately die out;
- nets catch other than target fish in the nets.

[any 3 points] [3]

(d) agree to quota numbers of fish; exclusion zones/exclusion times [2]
[Total: 9]

3 (a) (i) pioneer or primary coloniser [1]
(ii)
- algae cut off light from plants underneath;
- they die as a result;
- bacteria or fungi or saprobiotics decay them;
- they use a lot of oxygen;
- fish die due to not enough oxygen;
- blood worms increase in number as they are adapted to small amounts of oxygen.

[any 5 points] [5]

(b)
- marginal plants or irises were introduced;
- they spread;
- each year the foliage died and rotted;
- this organic material or humus added to the soil or mud;
- secondary colonisers spread from other areas;
- succession took place.

[any 4 points) [4]
[Total: 10]

4 (a) more fish escape through the bigger holes; and go on to breed [2]
(b) legislation/regulations/rules/penalties/laws [1]
(c) its predators may increase correspondingly; the

plants may be over-grazed or plant numbers depleted [2]
[Total: 5]

5 (a) greenhouse effect factor x amount = water vapour
CFCs 25 000 x 4.8 x 10^{-8} % = 0.012
water vapour has greatest greenhouse effect [2]

(b) (i) new sea areas so more marine organisms or named organism/formerly cold area grows new warm-climate plants [1]
(ii) deserts formed which reduce food availability/ cold-adapted organisms not suited to new climate/terrestrial organisms destroyed by the rising seas [1]
[Total: 4]

Chapter 9 Human health and disease

1 (a) droplet infection [1]
(b) (i) carriers [1]
(ii) we do not know that they carry the pathogen as they display no symptoms, so people do not avoid contact and pass on the bacteria [2]
(c) (i) antibiotics or named antibiotics [1]
(ii) **Phagocyte** – engulfs/produces pseudopodia/ phagocytosis; digests the bacterium/causes lysis of the bacterium [2]
B-lymphocyte – changes into plasma cell; makes antibodies [2]
T-lymphocyte – whole cell links to bacterial antigen sites; cell is usually destroyed by this; reacts to bacterial antigen [2]
[Total: 6]

2 (a) (i) ability to secrete more antibodies [1]
(ii) the antibodies have specific receptor sites which bind with the antigens; they have a flexible protein which changes angle to fit the antigens; antibodies result in the destruction of the antigen in some way/ neutralise toxin/cluster around antigens then cause precipitation/cause agglutination [3]
(iii) are produced when body first exposed to antigen; remain in body to react quickly when exposed to same antigen again [2]
(b) when the immune system attacks the person's own cells; pernicious anaemia/rheumatoid arthritis [2]
(c) the influenza virus often mutates so lymphocytes take longer to produce antibodies [1]
[Total:9]

Index

Letts

Revise

A2

Biology

John Parker

Contents

Specification lists

AQA A Biology

MODULE	SPECIFICATION TOPIC	CHAPTER REFERENCE	STUDIED IN CLASS	REVISED	PRACTICE QUESTIONS
Unit 5 (M5)	Autotrophic nutrition	1.1			
	The biochemistry of photosynthesis	1.2			
	Respiration	1.3			
	Glycolysis and the Krebs cycle	1.3			
	Essential genetic terms	5.1			
	Meiosis	5.2			
	Sex linkage	5.3			
	Hardy–Weinberg Principle	5.3			
	Chi-squared: a statistical test	5.3			
	Classification of organisms	6.1			
	Investigations of ecosystems	7.1			
	Capture, mark, release, recapture	7.1			
	Water pollution	8.1			
	Pollution of the atmosphere	8.2			
Unit 6 (M6)	Digestion	2.2			
	Important structures in the small intestine	2.2			
	Digestion of food by ruminants	2.3			
	Lepidoptera; dietary changes through their life cycle	2.4			
	Structure and function neurones	3.1			
	The action potential	3.2			
	Synaptic transmission	3.2			
	Autonomic nervous system	3.4			
	The human eye	3.6			
	Homeostasis	4.1			
	The endocrine system	4.1			
	Temperature control in a mammal	4.2			
	Regulation of blood sugar level	4.3			
	Liver functions	4.3			
	The kidneys	4.4			
	The control of water balance	4.4			
	Adaptations to desert ecosystems	4.5			
	The behaviour of organisms	7.2			

Examination analysis

The A Level specification comprises 6 compulsory units, 3 AS and 3 A2. In unit tests 5, 6, and 8a, all questions are compulsory; they consist of structured questions and questions requiring extended answers.

Unit 5 *1 hr 30 min examination 15%*

Unit 6 *1 hr 30 min examination 15%*

Unit 8a *1 hr 45 min synoptic examination 10%*

8b *Centre-assessed coursework 10%*

Note: *the A2 centre-assessed coursework tests 8 different skills. Each may be assessed several times during the course. Marks awarded by your teacher are subject to change by external moderator. A key investigation is submitted as evidence of 7 of the skills. AS + A2 coursework counts towards the A Level.*

AQA B Biology

MODULE	SPECIFICATION TOPIC	CHAPTER REFERENCE	STUDIED IN CLASS	REVISED	PRACTICE QUESTIONS
Unit 4 (M4)	*The biochemistry of photosynthesis*	*1.2*			
	Respiration	*1.3*			
	The action potential	*3.2*			
	The synapse	*3.2*			
	Functions of parts of the brain	*3.4*			
	Control of skeletal muscle	*3.5*			
	The mammalian eye	*3.6*			
	Homeostasis	*4.1*			
	Hormones	*4.1*			
	Temperature control	*4.2*			
	Regulation of blood sugar level	*4.3*			
	The kidneys	*4.4*			
	Essential genetic terms	*5.1*			
	Meiosis	*5.2*			
	Monohybrid and dihybrid inheritance	*5.3*			
	Classification of organisms	*6.2*			
	Natural selection	*6.2*			
	Speciation	*6.2*			
Unit 5 (M5)	*Measurement in an ecosystem*	*7.1*			
	Water pollution	*8.1*			
	Pollution of the atmosphere	*8.2*			
Unit 6 (M6)	*Measurement in an ecosystem*	*7.1*			
	Capture, mark, release, recapture	*7.1*			
Unit 7 (M7)	*Microbial culture and measurement*	*9.2*			
	Dilution plating	*9.2*			
	Large scale production	*10.1*			
	Biotechnology	*10.1*			
Unit 8 (M8)	*Screening*	*5.4*			
	Behaviour	*7.2*			
	Sign – stimulus release factors	*7.2*			

Examination analysis

The A Level specification comprises 6 units, 3 AS and 3 A2. The unit tests consist of structured questions and questions requiring extended answers. In A2, units 4 and 5 are compulsory and you can choose **one** *unit from 6, 7 or 8. Each of units 6, 7 and 8 has compulsory questions plus a choice from two essay questions.*

Unit 4	*1 hr 30 min examination 15%*
Unit 5a	*1 hr 15 min examination 7.5% (including 3.5% synoptic questions)*
Unit 5b	*Centre-assessed coursework 7.5% (including 2.5% synoptic questions)*
Unit 6	*2 hr examination 20% (including 14% synoptic questions)* **or**
Unit 7	*2 hr examination 20% (including 14% synoptic questions)* **or**
Unit 8	*2 hr examination 20% (including 14% synoptic questions)*

Note: *the A2 centre-assessed coursework tests 5 different skills. Each may be assessed several times during the course. Marks awarded by your teacher are subject to change by external moderator. The same investigation is submitted as evidence of the 5 skills. AS + A2 coursework counts towards the A Level.*

OCR Biology

MODULE	SPECIFICATION TOPIC	CHAPTER REFERENCE	STUDIED IN CLASS	REVISED	PRACTICE QUESTIONS
Unit 4 (M4)	The biochemistry of photosynthesis	1.2			
	The biochemistry of respiration	1.3			
	The structure and functions of neurones	3.1			
	The action potential	3.2			
	Homeostasis	4.1			
	The endocrine system	4.1			
	The kidneys	4.4			
	Meiosis	5.2			
	Monohybrid and dihybrid inheritance	5.3			
	Classification and variation	6.1			
	Evolution	6.2			
	Investigation of ecosystems	7.1			
	Microbial culture and measurement	9.2			
Unit 5.01 (M5)	Plant growth regulators	3.7			
Unit 5.02 (M5)	Chi-squared: a statistical test	5.3			
	Applications of genetics	5.4			
	Classification and variation	6.1			
Unit 5.03 (M5)	Investigation of ecosystems	7.1			
	Pollution and effects	8.1, 8.2			
Unit 5.04 (M5)	Diversity of microorganisms	9.1			
	Microbial culture and measurements	9.2			
	Large scale production	10.1			
	Medical applications	10.2			
	Further gene transfer	10.3			
Unit 5.05 (M5)	Digestion and absorption	2.2			
	Ruminants and their microbial allies	2.3			
	Functions of parts of the brain	3.4			
	Control of skeletal muscle	3.5			
	The human eye and ear	3.6			
	Liver functions	4.3			

Examination analysis

The A Level specification comprises 6 units, 3 AS and 3 A2. The unit tests consist of structured questions and questions requiring extended answers. In A2 units 4 and 6.01 are compulsory. You can choose ONE option from 5.01–5.05, and choose either centre-assessed coursework or practical examination from 6.02 or 6.03.

2804 Unit 4	1 hr 30 min examination 15%		
2805 Unit 5.01	1 hr 30 min examination 15% **or**	**5.04**	1 hr 30 min examination 15% **or**
5.02	1 hr 30 min examination 15% **or**	**5.05**	1 hr 30 min examination 15% **or**
5.03	1 hr 30 min examination 15% **or**		
2806 Unit 6.01	1 hr 15 min examination 10%	**6.03**	1 hr 30 min Practical examination 10%
6.02	Centre-assessed coursework 10% **or**		

Note: *the A2 centre-assessed coursework tests 4 different skills. Each may be assessed several times during the course. Marks awarded by your teacher are subject to change by external moderator. A2 Level coursework is used to investigate the same skills as for AS Level but additional criteria must be satisfied. AS + A2 coursework counts towards the A Level. Alternatively a practical examination assesses the same practical skills.*

Edexcel Biology

MODULE	SPECIFICATION TOPIC	CHAPTER REFERENCE	STUDIED IN CLASS	REVISED	PRACTICE QUESTIONS
Unit 4 (M4)	Respiration	1.3			
	The structure and function of neurones	3.1			
	The action potential	3.2			
	The synapse	3.2			
	Homeostasis	4.1			
	Regulation of blood sugar level	4.2			
	The kidneys	4.4			
Unit 4A	Diversity of microorganisms	9.1			
	Gram positive and Gram negative	9.2			
	Microbial culture and measurement	9.2			
	Large scale production	10.1			
	Batch and continuous fermentation	10.1			
Unit 4B	Commercial production of beer	10.1			
Unit 4C	The synapse	3.2			
	Control of skeletal muscle	3.5			
Unit 5	The biochemistry of photosynthesis	1.2			
	Plant growth regulators	3.7			
	Essential genetic terms	5.1			
	Meiosis	5.2			
	Monohybrid and dihybrid inheritance	5.3			
	Applications of genetics	5.4			
	Classification	6.1			
	Evolution	6.2			
	Speciation	6.2			
	Investigation of ecosystems	7.1			
	Measurement in an ecosystem	7.1			
	Conservation	7.1			
	Further gene transfer	10.3			

Examination analysis

The A Level specification comprises 6 units, 3 AS and 3 A2. The unit tests consist of structured questions and questions requiring extended answers. In A2, units 4, 5 and 6 are compulsory. You can choose ONE option from A, B or C within unit 4. Unit 6 has a compulsory a synoptic examination, plus a choice of centre-assessed coursework or an alternative examination.

6104 Unit 4	1 hr 30 min examination 16.7% (inc. option A, B or C)
6105 Unit 5	1 hr 30 min examination 16.7%
6106 Unit 6	Centre-assessed coursework **or** 1 hr 20 min examination 1 hr 10 min examination (synoptic) 16.7% (inc. choice of **one** essay from two options)

WJEC Biology

MODULE	SPECIFICATION TOPIC	CHAPTER REFERENCE	STUDIED IN CLASS	REVISED	PRACTICE QUESTIONS
Unit 4 (M4)	*The biochemistry of photosynthesis*	1.2			
	The biochemistry of respiration	1.3			
	Glycolysis and the Krebs cycle	1.3			
	Digestion	2.2			
	Digestion in the duodenum and small intestine	2.2			
	Gram positive and Gram negative	9.2			
	Microbial culture and measurement	9.2			
	Dilution plating	9.2			
	Large scale production	10.1			
	Batch fermentation	10.1			
	Medical applications	10.2			
Unit 5 (M5)	*Structure and function of the motor neurone*	3.1			
	The action potential	3.2			
	Functions of parts of the brain	3.4			
	Control of skeletal muscle	3.5			
	The human ear	3.6			
	Homeostasis	4.1			
	The kidneys	4.4			
	Essential genetic terms	5.1			
	Monohybrid and dihybrid inheritance	5.3			
	Classification	6.1			
	Evolution	6.2			
	Artificial selection	6.2			
	Genetic conservation	6.2			
	Pollution	8.1, 8.2			
	Transgenic organisms	10.2			

Examination analysis

The A Level specification comprises 6 assessment units, 3 AS and 3 A2. The modular tests consist of structured questions and questions requiring extended answers. In A2, modules 4, 5 and 6 are compulsory.

Unit 4 *1 hr 40 min examination 15%*

Unit 5 *2 hr examination 20% (including synoptic questions)*

Unit 6 *Practical assessment by examination 15% (including synoptic)*

NICCEA Biology

MODULE	SPECIFICATION TOPIC	CHAPTER REFERENCE	STUDIED IN CLASS	REVISED	PRACTICE QUESTIONS
Module 4 (M4)	*The biochemistry of photosynthesis*	1.2			
	Respiration	1.3			
	Glycolysis and the Krebs cycle	1.3			
	The action potential	3.2			
	The synapse	3.2			
	Central nervous system	3.2			
	The human eye	3.6			
	Plant growth regulators	3.7			
	Phytochrome and the onset of flowering in plants	3.7			
	Homeostasis	4.1			
	The endocrine system	4.1			
	Temperature control in a mammal	4.2			
	Negative feedback	4.2			
	The kidneys	4.4			
	Hormone control of the kidneys; the role of ADH	4.4			
	Ecological conservation	7.1			
	Pollution	8.1, 8.2			
Module 5 (M5)	*Essential genetic terms*	5.1			
	Meiosis	5.2			
	Mendel and the laws of inheritance	5.3			
	Sex linkage	5.3			
	Hardy–Weinberg Principle	5.3			
	Applications of genetics	5.4			
	Classification of organisms	6.1			
	Continuous and discontinuous variation	6.1			
	Manipulation of reproduction	6.3			
	Artificial insemination	6.3			
	Superovulation and embryo transfer	6.3			

Examination analysis

The A Level specification comprises 6 compulsory modules, 3 AS and 3 A2. In modular tests 4, 5, and 6a, all questions are compulsory; they consist of structured questions and questions requiring extended answers.

Module 4 *1 hr 30 min examination 16.7%*
Module 5 *1 hr 30 min examination 16.7%*
Module 6a *1 hr examination (synoptic) 9.3%*
Module 6b *Centre-assessed coursework 7.4%*

Note: *the A2 centre-assessed coursework tests 8 different skill areas. Each is assessed in the context of ONE investigation during the A2 course. Marks awarded by your teacher are subject to change by external moderator. AS + A2 coursework counts towards the A Level.*

AS/A2 Level Biology courses

AS and A2

All Biology GCE A Level courses currently studied are in two parts, with a number of separate units or modules in each part. Some units are further divided into sub-units and some have options to allow you to follow a specific path of interest. Some Examination Boards offer alternative externally marked practical examinations or the internal assessment of practical skills (subject to moderation).

In using this Revision Guide most students will have already completed the first half of the course, AS (Advanced Subsidiary). Some students will study both AS and A2 in one year. Some will go on to study the second part of the A Level course, called A2. Both groups of students are advised to use the Letts AS and A2 Revision Guides.

Advanced Subsidiary is assessed at the standard expected halfway through an A Level course, i.e. between GCSE and A Level. This means that AS and A2 courses are designed so that difficulty steadily increases:

- AS Biology builds from GCSE Science/ Biology
- A2 Biology builds from AS Biology.

IMPORTANT NOTE! Each Examination Board has included a common core of subject content in AS and in A2. Beyond the common core material the Examination Boards have included more varied content. Use the Examination Board Specification book or CD-ROM to identify subject content. The AS Biology Revision Guide includes material appropriate to A2 Level. Use the references to find A2 topics for your Examination Board which are to be found in the AS Biology Guide. You can be confident that these topics in the AS Guide will help you achieve understanding at A2 Level.

What are the differences between AS and A2?

There are three main differences:

(i) A2 includes the more demanding concepts. (Understanding will be easier if you have completed the AS Biology course as a 'stepping stone'.)

(ii) There is a much greater emphasis on the skills of application and analysis than in AS. (Using knowledge and understanding acquired from AS is essential.)

(iii) A2 includes a substantial amount of synoptic material. (This is the drawing together of knowledge and skills across the modules of AS and A2. Synoptic investigative tasks and questions involving concepts across the specification are included.)

How will you be tested?

Assessment units

A2 Biology comprises three units or modules. The first two units are assessed by examinations.

The third component usually involves some method of practical assessment (this is dependent on the Examination Group). Examination Groups use either centre-assessed coursework or a practical examination.

Centre-based coursework involves practical skills marked by your teacher. The marks can be adjusted by moderators appointed by the awarding body. If a practical examination is an option, it is based on identical skills to the centre-assessed option.

Some groups also include another part to the third component. This is a short examination of further content.

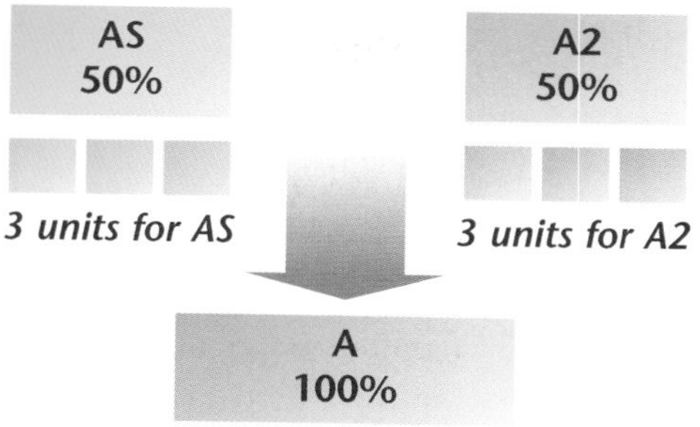

Tests are taken at two specific times of the year, January/February and June. It can be an advantage to you to take a unit test at the earlier optional time because you can re-sit the test, (only once !) The best mark from the two will be credited and the lower mark ignored.

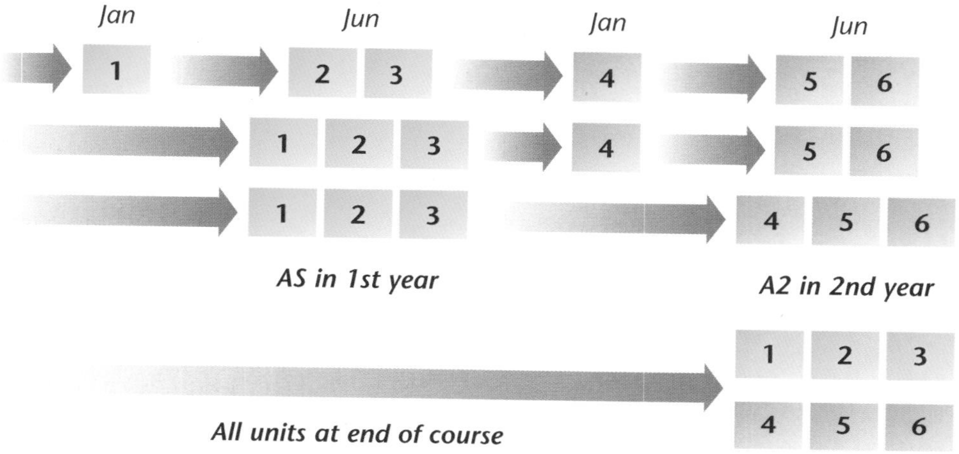

If you are disappointed with a module result, you can resit each module once. You will need to be very careful about when you take up a resit opportunity because you will have only one chance to improve your mark. The higher mark counts.

A unit or module can be retaken once but the complete course can be repeated in the future, should you wish to improve further.

A2 and synoptic assessment

Most students who study A2 have already studied to AS Level. There are three further units or modules to be studied. Some units are optional, so it is the choice of the Centre e.g. 'Applications of Genetics,' 'Environmental Biology,' or 'Microbiology and Biotechnology.'

Every A Level specification includes synoptic assessment at the end of A2. Synoptic questions draw on the ideas and concepts of earlier units, bringing them together in holistic contexts. Examiners will test your ability to inter-relate topics through the complete course from AS to A2. (See the synoptic chapter page 148).

Coursework

Coursework may form part of your work in Biology A2 course, depending on which specification you study. Where students have to undertake coursework it is usually for the assessment of practical skills.

Key skills

Your work in Biology AS and A2 can be used to gain a further award, the Key skills qualification. This helps you to develop important skills that are needed, whatever you do beyond A Level. The Key skills include: Application of number, Communication and Information Technology. There are three levels of award; Biology AS and A2 have opportunities to study one or more of the key skills, e.g. Communication – an average A2 student may be expected to achieve a Level 3.

A2 Biology is an excellent opportunity to achieve key skills. A coursework investigation can be used to achieve key skill levels. It is worth taking time to submit your coursework in a way which satisfies A2 Biology and key skill criteria. Discussing your experimental design, results and conclusions is beneficial to both you and other students. You must collect a portfolio evidence of each skill to show your level of competence. The awarding body specification will show opportunities of appropriate topics which can also be used to develop key skills. Additionally the QCA publication, *Introduction to key skills* will be helpful. Other subjects may be used to develop your key skills as well as AS and A2 Biology.

Key skills are in demand by Further Education institutions and by employers.

What skills will I need?

For A2 Biology, you will be tested by assessment objectives: these are the skills and abilities that you should have acquired by studying the course. The assessment objectives shown below.

Knowledge with understanding

- recall of facts, terminology and relationships
- understanding of principles and concepts
- drawing on existing knowledge to show understanding of the responsible use of biological applications in society
- selecting, organising and presenting information clearly and logically

Application of knowledge and understanding, and evaluation

- explaining and interpreting principles and concepts
- interpreting and translating, from one to another, data presented as continuous prose or in tables, diagrams and graphs
- carrying out relevant calculations
- applying knowledge and understanding to familiar and unfamiliar situations
- assessing the validity of biological information, experiments, inferences and statements

You must also present arguments and ideas clearly and logically, using specialist vocabulary where appropriate. Remember to balance your argument!

Experimental and investigative skills

Biology is a practical subject and part of the assessment of A2 Biology will test your practical skills. This may be done during your lessons or may be tested in a more formal practical examination. You will be tested on four main skills:

- planning
- implementing
- analysing evidence and drawing conclusions
- evaluating evidence and procedures.

The skills may be assessed in the context of separate practical exercises although more than one skill may be assessed in any one exercise. They may also be assessed all together in the context of a 'whole investigation'. An investigation may be set by your teacher or you may be able to pursue an investigation of your own choice.

You will receive guidance about how you practical skills will be assessed from your teacher. This Study Guide concentrates on preparing you for the written examinations testing the subject content of A2 Biology.

Different types of questions in A2 examinations

Questions in AS and A2 Biology are designed to assess a number of assessment objectives. For the written papers in AS Biology the main objectives being assessed are:

- recall of facts, terminology and inter-relationships
- understanding of principles and concepts and their social and technological applications and implications
- explanation and interpretation of principles and concepts
- interpreting information given as diagrams, photomicrographs, electron micrographs tables, data, graphs, passages
- application of knowledge and understanding to familiar and unfamiliar situations.

In order to assess these abilities and skills a number of different types of question are used.

In A2 Level Biology unit tests these include short answer questions, structured questions requiring both short answers and more extended answers, together with free-response and open-ended questions.

Short-answer questions

A question will normally begin with a brief amount of stimulus material. This may be in the form of a diagram, data or graph. A short-answer question may begin by testing recall. Usually this is followed up by questions which test understanding. Often you will be required to analyse data. Short answer questions normally have a space for your responses on the printed paper. The number of lines is a guide as to the amount of words you will need to answer the question. The number of marks indicated on the right side of the papers shows the number of marks you can score for each question part. Here are some examples. (The answers are shown in blue).

The diagram below shows a gastric pit.

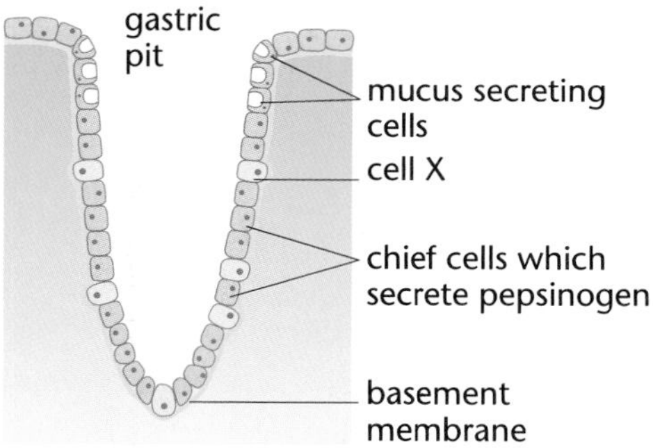

(a) (i) Label cell X (1)

oxyntic cell

(ii) What is secreted by cell X? (1)

hydrochloric acid

(b) (i) Protein enters the stomach. What must take place before the hydrolysis of the protein begins? (2)

Hydrochloric acid acts on pepsinogen, to produce pepsin

(ii) After the protein has been hydrolysed, what is produced? (1)

polypeptides

Structured questions

Structured questions are in several parts. The parts are usually about a common context and they often progress in difficulty as you work through each of the parts. They may start with simple recall, then test understanding of a familiar or unfamiliar situation. If the context seems unfamiliar the material will still be centred around concepts and skills from the Biology specification. (If a student can answer questions about unfamiliar situations then they display understanding rather than simple recall.)

The most difficult part of a structured question is usually at the end. Ascending in difficulty, a question allows a candidate to build in confidence. Right at the end technological and social applications of biological principles give a more demanding challenge. Most of the questions in this book are structured questions. This is the main type of question used in the assessment of both AS and A2 Biology.

The questions set at A2 Level are generally more difficult than those experienced at AS Level. A2 includes a number of higher level concepts, so can be expected to be more difficult. The key advice given by this author is:

- Give your answers in greater detail,

  Example: Why does blood glucose rise after a period without food?

  Answer: The hormone glucagon is produced X not enough for credit!)

  The hormone glucagon is produced which results in glycogen breakdown to glucose.

- Look out for questions with a 'sting in the tail'. A2 questions structured questions are less straight forward, so look for a 'twist'. This is identified in the example below.

When answering structured questions, do not feel that you have to complete a question before starting the next. Answering a part that you are sure of will build your confidence. If you run out of ideas go on to the next question. This will be more profitable than staying with a very difficult question which slows down progress, return at the end when you have more time.

Extended answers

In A2 and AS Biology questions requiring more extended answers will usually form part of structured questions. They will normally appear at the end of a structured question and will typically have a value of four to twenty marks. Longer questions are allocated more lines, so you can use this as a guide as to how many points you need to make in your response. Often for an answer worth ten marks the mark scheme would have around 12 $\rightarrow$ 14 creditable answers. You are awarded up to the maximum, ten marks, in this instance.

Depending on the awarding body, longer, extended questions may be set. These are often open response questions. These questions are worth up to twenty marks for full credit. Extended answers are used to allocate marks for the **quality of communication**.

Candidates are assessed on their ability to use a suitable style of writing, and organise relevant material, both logically and clearly. The use of specialist biological terms in context is also assessed. Spelling, punctuation and grammar are also taken into consideration. Here is a longer response question.

Question

Urea, glucose and water molecules enter the kidney via the renal artery. Explain what *can* happen to each of these substances.

In this question one mark is available for communication. (Total 13 marks)

Urea, glucose and water molecules can pass through the blood capillaries in a glomerulus. ✓ This is as a result of ultrafiltration, ✓ as the podocytes of Bowman's capsule cause a pressure build up. ✓

The three substances pass down the proximal tubule. 100% glucose is reabsorbed in the proximal tubule ✓ so is returned to the blood. Carrier proteins on the microvilli aided by mitochondria, actively transport the glucose across the cells. ✓ Around 80% of the water is reabsorbed in the proximal tubule. ✓ Remaining water and urea molecules continue through the loop of Henlé. Urea continues through the distal tubule to the ureter then the bladder. ✓

More water can be reabsorbed with the help of the countercurrent multiplier. ✓ The ascending limb of the loop of Henlé ✓ actively transports Na^+ and Cl^- ions into the medulla. ✓ Water molecules leave the collecting duct by osmosis due to the ions in the medulla. ✓ Cells of the collecting duct are made more permeable to water by the hormone, ADH. ✓ Some water molecules pass into the capillary network and having been successfully reabsorbed ✓ Some water molecules continue down the ureters and into the bladder. ✓

Communication mark ✓

Remember that mark schemes for extended questions often exceed the question total, but you can only be awarded credit up to the maximum. In response to this question the candidate would be awarded the maximum of 13 marks which included one communication mark. The candidate gave two more creditable responses which were on the mark scheme, but had already scored a maximum. Try to give more detail in your answers to longer questions. This is the key to A2 success.

Exam technique

Links from AS

A2 builds from the skills and concepts acquired during the AS course. This Study Guide has been written in a similar style to the AS Biology Guide and incorporates many concepts. The Guide will help you cope as the A2 concepts ascend in difficulty. The chapters explain the ideas in small steps so that understanding takes place gradually. The final aim, of complete understanding of major topics is more likely.

Can I use my AS Biology Study Guide for A2?

YES! Some examination groups cover a topic at AS Level. A different examination group may cover the same topic at AS Level. Check out the A2 table for your specification. Every topic in the AS Guide is explained at a level suitable for A2 Level.

What are examiners looking for?

Whatever type of question you are answering, it is important to respond in a suitable way. Examiners use instructions to help you to decide the length and depth of your answer. The most common words used are given below, together with a brief description of what each word is asking for.

Define

This requires a formal statement. Some definitions are easy to recall.

Define the term transport.

This is the movement of molecules from where they are in lower concentration to where they are in higher concentration. The process requires energy.

Other definitions are more complex. Where you have problems it is helpful to give an example.

Define the term endemic.

This means that a disease is found regularly in a group of people, district or country. Use of an example clarifies the meaning. Indicating that malaria is invariably found everywhere in a country confirms understanding.

Explain

This requires a reason. The amount of detail needed is shown by the number of marks allocated.

Explain the difference between resolution and magnification.

Resolution is the ability to be able to distinguish between two points whereas magnification is the number of times an image is bigger than an object itself.

State

This requires a brief answer without any reason.

State one role of blood plasma in a mammal.

Transport of hormones to their target organs.

List

This requires a sequence of points with no explanation.

List the abiotic factors which can affect the rate of photosynthesis in pond weed.

carbon dioxide concentration; amount of light; temperature; pH of water

Describe

This requires a piece of prose which gives key points. Diagrams should be used where possible.

Describe the nervous control of heart rate.

The medulla oblongata ✓ of the brain connects to the sino-atrial node in the right atrium, wall ✓ via the vagus nerve and the sympathetic nerve ✓ the sympathetic nerve speeds up the rate ✓ the vagus nerve slows it down. ✓

Discuss

This requires points both for and against, together with a criticism of each point. (**Compare** is a similar command word).

Discuss the advantages and disadvantages of using systemic insecticides in agriculture.

Advantages are that the insecticides kill the pests which reduce yield ✓ they enter the sap of the plants so insects which consume sap die ✓ the insecticide lasts longer than a contact insecticide, 2 weeks is not uncommon ✓

Disadvantages are that insecticide may remain in the product and harm a consumer e.g. humans ✓ it may destroy organisms other than the target ✓ no insecticide is 100% effective and develops resistant pests. ✓

Suggest

This means that there is no single correct answer. Often you are given an unfamiliar situation to analyse. The examiners hope for logical deductions from the data given and that, usually, you apply your knowledge of biological concepts and principles.

The graph shows that the population of lynx decreased in 1980. Suggest reasons for this.

Weather conditions prevented plant growth ✓ so the snowshoe hares could not get enough food and their population remained low ✓ so the lynx did not have enough hares (prey) to predate upon. ✓ The lynx could have had a disease which reduced numbers. ✓

Calculate

This requires that you work out a numerical answer. Remember to give the units and to show your working, marks are usually available for a partially correct answer. If you work everything out in stages write down the sequence. Otherwise of you merely give the answer and if it is wrong, then the working marks are not available to you.

Calculate the Rf value of spot X. (X is 25 mm from start and solvent front is 100 mm)

$$Rf = \frac{\text{distance moved by spot}}{\text{distance moved by the solvent front}}$$

$$= \frac{25\text{ mm}}{100\text{ mm}} = 0.25$$

Outline

This requires that you give only the main points. The marks allocated will guide you on the number of points which you need to make.

Outline the use of restriction endonuclease in genetic engineering.

The enzyme is used to cut the DNA of the donor cell. ✓

It cuts the DNA up like this A T G C C G A T = A T + G C C G A T ✓
T A C G G C T A   T A C G G C   T A

The DNA in a bacterial plasmid is cut with the same restriction endonuclease. ✓
The donor DNA will fit onto the sticky ends of the broken plasmid. ✓

If a question does not seem to make sense, you may have mis-read it. Read it again!

Some dos and don'ts

Dos

***Do** answer the question*

No credit can be given for good Biology that is irrelevant to the question.

***Do** use the mark allocation to guide how much you write*

Two marks are awarded for two valid points – writing more will rarely gain more credit and could mean wasted time or even contradicting earlier valid points.

***Do** use diagrams, equations and tables in your responses*

Even in 'essay style' questions, these offer an excellent way of communicating biology.

***Do** write legibly*

An examiner cannot give marks if the answer cannot be read.

***Do** write using correct spelling and grammar. Structure longer essays carefully*

Marks are now awarded for the quality of your language in exams.

Don'ts

***Don't** fill up any blank space on a paper*

In structured questions, the number of dotted lines should guide the length of your answer.

If you write too much, you waste time and may not finish the exam paper. You also risk contradicting yourself.

***Don't** write out the question again*

This wastes time. The marks are for the answer!

***Don't** contradict yourself*

The examiner cannot be expected to choose which answer is intended. You could lose a hard-earned mark.

***Don't** spend too much time on a part that you find difficult*

You may not have enough time to complete the exam. You can always return to a difficult calculation if you have time at the end of the exam.

What grade do you want?

Everyone would like to improve their grades but you will only manage this with a lot of hard work and determination. You should have a fair idea of your natural ability and likely grade in Biology and the hints below offer advice on improving that grade.

For a Grade A

You will need to be a very good all-rounder.

- You must go into every exam knowing the work extremely well.
- You must be able to apply your knowledge to new, unfamiliar situations.
- You need to have practised many, many exam questions so that you are ready for the type of question that will appear.

The exams test all areas of the syllabus and any weaknesses in your Biology will be found out. There must be no holes in your knowledge and understanding. For a Grade A, you must be competent in all areas.

For a Grade C

You must have a reasonable grasp of Biology but you may have weaknesses in several areas and you will be unsure of some of the reasons for the Biology.

- Many Grade C candidates are just as good at answering questions as the Grade A students but holes and weaknesses often show up in just some topics.
- To improve, you will need to master your weaknesses and you must prepare thoroughly for the exam. You must become a better all-rounder.

For a Grade E

You cannot afford to miss the easy marks. Even if you find Biology difficult to understand and would be happy with a Grade E, there are plenty of questions in which you can gain marks.

- You must memorise all definitions.
- You must practise exam questions to give yourself confidence that you do know some Biology. In exams, answer the parts of questions that you know first. You must not waste time on the difficult parts. You can always go back to these later.
- The areas of Biology that you find most difficult are going to be hard to score on in exams. Even in the difficult questions, there are still marks to be gained. Show your working in calculations because credit is given for a sound method. You can always gain some marks if you get part of the way towards the solution.

What marks do you need?

The table below shows how your average mark is transferred into a grade.

average	*80%*	*70%*	*60%*	*50%*	*40%*
grade	*A*	*B*	*C*	*D*	*E*

Four steps to successful revision

Step 1: Understand

- Study the topic to be learned slowly. Make sure you understand the logic or important concepts.
- Mark up the text if necessary – underline, highlight and make notes.
- Re-read each paragraph slowly.

GO TO STEP 2

Step 2: Summarise

- Now make your own revision note summary:
  What is the main idea, theme or concept to be learned?
  What are the main points? How does the logic develop?
  Ask questions: Why? How? What next?
- Use bullet points, mind maps, patterned notes.
- Link ideas with mnemonics, mind maps, crazy stories.
- Note the title and date of the revision notes
  (e.g. Biology: Homeostasis, 3rd March).
- Organise your notes carefully and keep them in a file.

This is now in **short term memory**. You will forget 80% of it if you do not go to Step 3.
GO TO STEP 3, but first take a 10 minute break.

Step 3: Memorise

- Take 25 minute learning 'bites' with 5 minute breaks.
- After each 5 minute break test yourself:
  Cover the original revision note summary.
  Write down the main points.
  Speak out loud (record on tape).
  Tell someone else.
  Repeat many times.

The material is well on its way to **long term memory**.
You will forget 40% if you do not do step 4. **GO TO STEP 4**

Step 4: Track/Review

- Create a Revision Diary (one A4 page per day).
- Make a revision plan for the topic, e.g. 1 day later, 1 week later, 1 month later.
- Record your revision in your Revision Diary, e.g.
  Biology: Homeostasis, 3rd March 25 minutes
  Biology: Homeostasis, 5th March 15 minutes
  Biology: Homeostasis, 3rd April 15 minutes
  ... and then at monthly intervals.

Chapter 1

Energy for life

The following topics are covered in this chapter:

- *Autotrophic nutrition*
- *The biochemistry of photosynthesis*
- *Respiration*

1.1 Autotrophic nutrition

After studying this section you should be able to:

- *understand the principles of autotrophic nutrition*
- *relate the internal structure of a chloroplast to its function*

LEARNING SUMMARY

Different types of autotrophic nutrition

AQA A	M5
AQA B	M4, M5
EDEXCEL	M5
OCR	M4, M6
WJEC	M4
NICCEA	M4, M5

Key points from AS

- **The nitrogen cycle** *Revise AS page 115*
- **Photosynthesis** *Revise AS page 109*

Autotrophic nutrition is very important! **Autotrophic nutrition** means that simple inorganic substances are taken in and used to synthesise organic molecules. Energy is needed to achieve this. In **photo-autotrophic nutrition** light is the energy source. In most instances the light source is **solar energy**, the process being **photosynthesis**. Carbon dioxide and water are taken in by organisms and used to synthesise glucose, which can be broken down later during respiration to release the energy needed for life. By far the greatest energy supply to support food chains and webs is obtained from photo-autotrophic nutrition. Most producers use this nutritional method.

Chemo-autotrophic nutrition can also supply energy needs to some organisms. Simple inorganic substances are taken in and synthesised into organic molecules. **Chemical energy** is the source for this process.

Here are two examples of chemo-autotrophs:

Did you make the connection? Photo-synthesis is photo-autotrophic nutrition

Nitrosomonas *bacteria*

ammonia + oxygen = nitrite + water + energy

Nitrobacter *bacteria*

nitrite + oxygen = nitrate + energy

The energy released in each of the above reactions is the result of the oxidation of **inorganic** substances. During respiration it is organic chemicals which are oxidised.

The sulphur bacteria oxidise sulphur and release energy.

These bacteria are important in the nitrogen cycle.

The energy released in each reaction supplies the energy input for life for each of these bacteria.

Thiobacillus *bacteria*

sulphur + oxygen = sulphate + energy

Imagine these organisms in an underground cave, with the ability to support a complete food web without the need for light. Remarkable!

The chloroplast

AQA A	M5
AQA B	M4
EDEXCEL	M5
OCR	M4
WJEC	M4
NICCEA	M4

Chloroplasts are organelles in plant cells which photosynthesise. In a leaf they are strategically positioned to harvest the maximum amount of light energy. Most are located in the palisade mesophyll of leaves but they are also found in both spongy mesophyll and guard cells. There is a greater amount of light entering the upper surface of a leaf so the palisade tissues benefit from a greater chloroplast density.

The diagram below shows the structure of a chloroplast.

Remember that not all light reaching a leaf, may hit a chloroplast. Photons of light can be reflected or even absorbed by other parts of the cell. Around 4% of light entering an ecosystem is actually utilised in photosynthesis!

Even when light reaches the green leaf not all energy is fixed in the carbohydrate product. Just one quarter becomes chemical energy in carbohydrate.

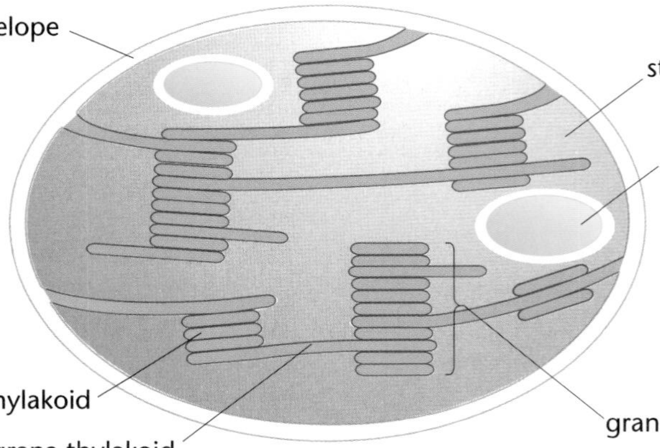

Structure and function

A system of **thylakoid membranes** is located throughout the chloroplast. These are flattened membranous vesicles which are surrounded by a liquid based matrix, the **stroma**.

Along the thylakoid membranes are key substances:

- chlorophyll molecules
- other pigments
- enzymes
- electron acceptor proteins.

Throughout the chloroplasts, circular thylakoid membranes stack on top of each other to form **grana**. Grana are linked by longer **intergrana thylakoids**. Grana thylakoids and intergrana thylakoids have different pigments and proteins. Each type has a different role in photosynthesis!

The key substances in the thylakoids occur in specific groups comprising of pigment, enzyme and electron acceptor proteins. There are two specific groups known as **photosystem I** and **photosystem II**.

Do not be confused by the photosystems. They are groups of chemicals which harness light and pass on energy! Remember the information to understand the biochemistry of photosynthesis.

The photosystems

Each photosystem contains a large number of chlorophyll molecules. As light energy is received at the chlorophyll, electrons from the chlorophyll are boosted to a higher level and energy is passed to pigment molecules known as the **reaction centre**.

KEY POINT

The reaction centre of photosystem I absorbs energy of wavelength 700 nanometres. The reaction centre of photosystem II absorbs energy of wavelength 680–690 nanometres. In this way light of different wavelengths can be harvested.

1.2 The biochemistry of photosynthesis

After studying this section you should be able to:

LEARNING SUMMARY

- *recall and explain the biochemical processes of photosynthesis*
- *understand that glucose can be converted into a number of useful chemicals*
- *relate the properties of chlorophyll to the absorption and action spectra*
- *understand how the law of limiting factors is linked to productivity*

The process of photosynthesis

AQA A	M5
AQA B	M4
EDEXCEL	M5
OCR	M4, M6
WJEC	M4
NICCEA	M4

The process of photosynthesis is summarised by the flow diagram below.

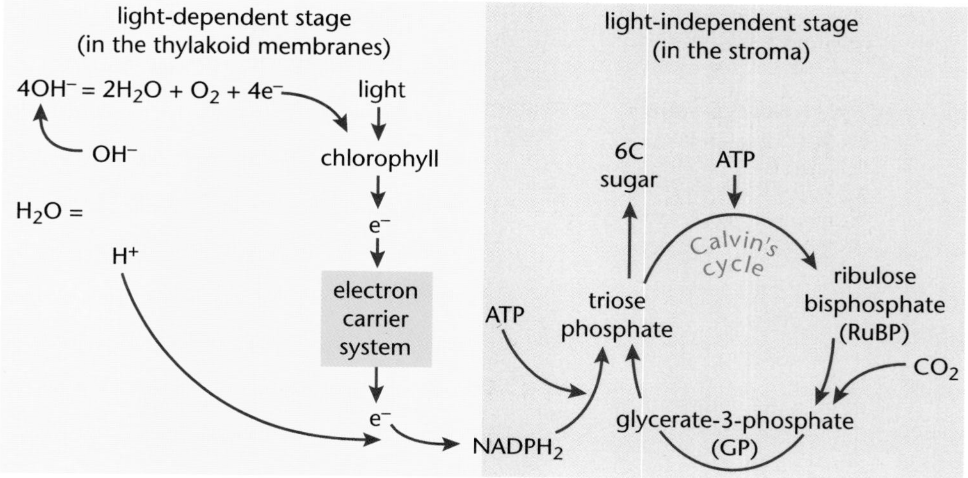

In examinations look out for parts of this diagram. There may be a few empty boxes where a key substance is missing. Will you be able to recall it?

- photosynthesis harnesses solar energy
- photosynthesis involves a light-dependent and light-independent reactions
- photosynthesis results in the flow of energy through an ecosystem.

Light-dependent reaction

- Light energy results in the excitation of electrons in the **chlorophyll**.
- These electrons are passed along a series of electron acceptors in the thylakoid membranes, collectively known as the **electron carrier system**.
- Energy from excited electrons funds the production of **ATP** (adenosine triphosphate).
- The final electron acceptor forms **$NADP^+$**.
- Electron loss from chlorophyll causes the splitting of water (photolysis)

$$H_2O = H^+ + OH^- \quad \text{then} \quad 4OH^- = 2H_2O + O_2 + 4e^-$$

- Oxygen is produced, water to re-use, and electrons stream back to replace those lost in the chlorophyll.
- Hydrogen ions (H^+) from photolysis, together with $NADP^+$ form **$NADPH_2$**.

No ATP and $NADPH_2$ in a chloroplast would result in no glucose being made. Once supplies of ATP and $NADPH_2$ are exhausted then photosynthesis is ended. In exams look out for the 'lights out' questions where the light-independent reaction continues for a while until stores of ATP, $NADPH_2$ and GP are used up. These questions are likely to be graph based.

Light-independent reaction

- Two useful substances are produced by the light-dependent stage, ATP and **$NADPH_2$**. These are needed to drive the light-independent stage.
- They react with glycerate-3-phosphate (GP) to produce a triose sugar – **triose phosphate**.
- Triose phosphate is used *either* to produce a 6C sugar *or* to form **ribulose bisphosphate** (RuBP).
- The conversion of triose phosphate (3C) to RuBP begins Calvin's cycle and utilises ATP, which supplies the energy required.

Key points from AS

- **Gaseous exchange**
  Revise AS page 62
- **Photosynthesis**
  Revise AS pages 109–110.

- A RuBP molecule (5C) together with a carbon dioxide molecule (1C) forms two GP molecules (2 × 3C) to complete Calvin's cycle.
- The GP is then available to react with ATP and $NADPH_2$ to synthesise more triose sugar or RuBP.

How do the photosystems contribute to photosynthesis?

This can be explained in terms of the Z scheme shown below.

The **Z scheme**, so called because the paths of electrons shown in the diagram are in a 'Z' shape.

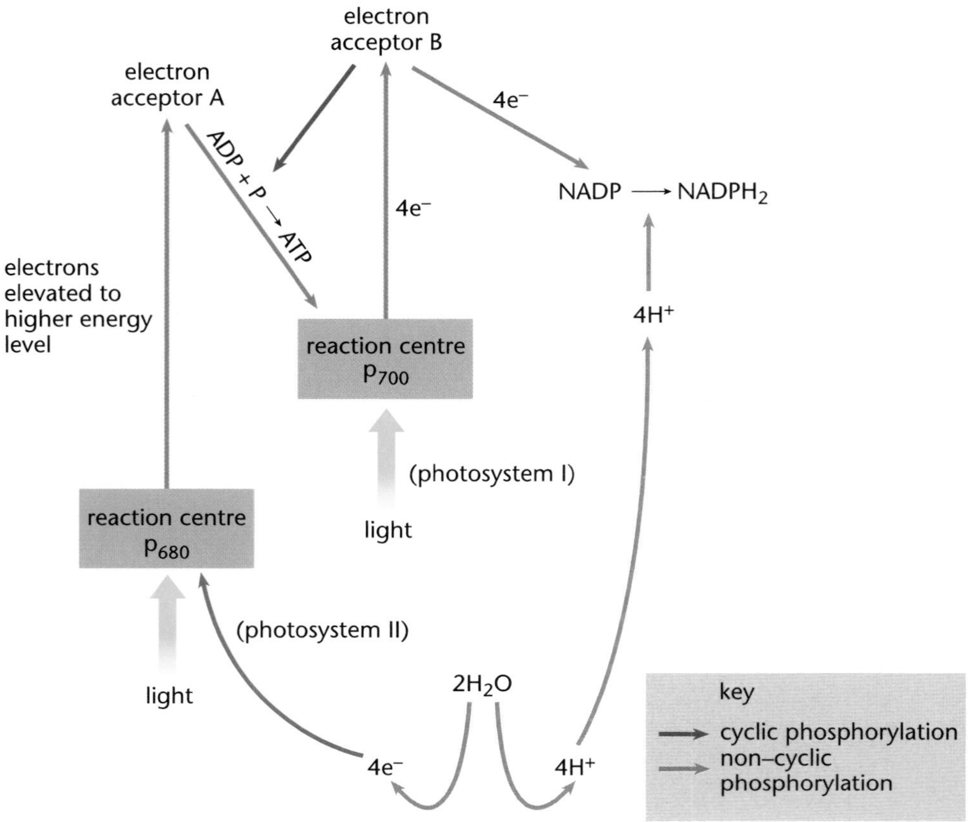

Non-cyclic photophosphorylation

- Light reaches the chlorophyll of both photosystems (P_{680} and P_{700}) which results in the excitation of electrons.
- Electron acceptors receive these electrons (accepting electrons is reduction!).
- P_{680} and P_{700} have become oxidised (loss of electrons is oxidation!).
- P_{680} receives electrons from the lysis (splitting) of water molecules and becomes neutral again.
- Lysis of water molecules releases oxygen which is given off.
- Electrons are elevated to a higher energy level by P_{680} to electron acceptor A and are passed along a series of electron carriers to P_{700}.
- Passage along the electron carrier system funds the production of ATP.
- The electrons pass along a further chain of electron carriers to NADP, which becomes reduced, and at the same time this combines with H^+ ions to form $NADPH_2$.

After analysing this information you will be aware that in cyclic photophosphorylation P_{700} donates electrons then some are recycled back, hence 'cyclic'. In non-cyclic photophosphorylation P_{680} electrons ultimately reach NADP never to return! Neutrality of the chlorophyll of P_{680} is achieved utilising electrons donated from the splitting of water. Different electron sources hence non-cyclic!

Cyclic photophosphorylation

- Electrons from acceptor B move along an electron carrier chain to P_{700}.
- Electron passage along the electron carrier system funds the production of ATP.

Photosynthetic pigments

AQA A	M5
AQA B	M4
EDEXCEL	M5
OCR	M4
WJEC	M4
NICCEA	M4

Chlorophyll **a** is the only photosynthetic pigment found in all green plants!

The role of photosynthetic pigments is to absorb light energy.

Chlorophyll is not just one substance. There are several different chlorophylls, e.g. chlorophyll *a* and chlorophyll *b*.

- Each is a molecule which has a **hydrophilic head** and **hydrophobic tail**.
- The head always contains a **magnesium** ion and plays a key part in the absorbing or harvesting of light.
- The hydrophobic tail anchors to the thylakoid membrane.

As well as the chlorophylls there are other **accessory pigments**, e.g. carotenoids which also absorb light energy. There are a range of photosynthetic pigments found in different species.

The graphs below show the specific wavelengths of light which are absorbed by a range of pigments. The data for the **absorption spectrum** was collected by measuring the absorbance of a range of different wavelengths of light by a solution of each pigment, chlorophyll *a*, chlorophyll *b*, and carotenoids, **separately**. Following this, plants were illuminated at each wavelength of light, in turn, to investigate the amount of photosynthesis achieved at each wavelength. This data is shown in the **action spectrum**.

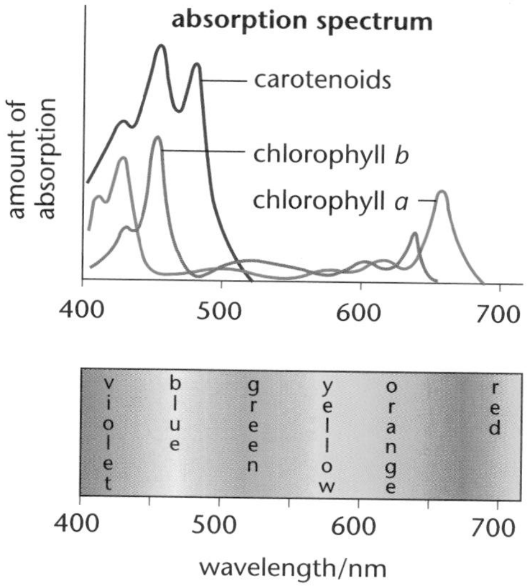

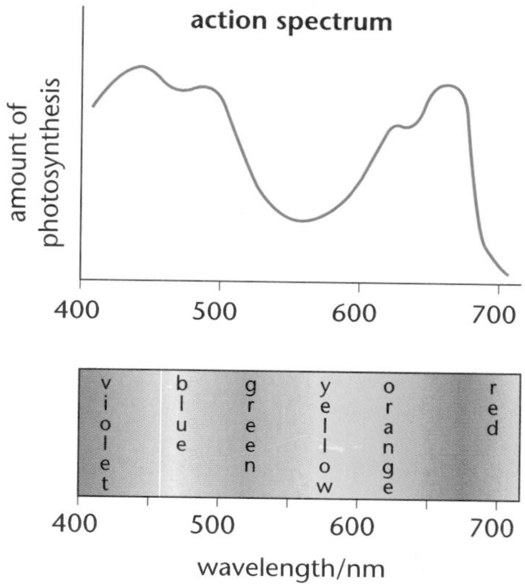

The action spectrum shows the actual wavelengths which are used in photosynthesis.

What can be learned from the graphs?

- Blue and red light are absorbed more, and so are key wavelengths for photosynthesis.
- Different pigments have different light absorptive properties.
- Groups of pigments in a chloroplast are therefore much better than just one as more energy can be harnessed for photosynthesis.
- The green part of the spectrum is not absorbed well; no wonder the plants look green as the light is reflected!

Which factors affect photosynthesis?

AQA A	M5
AQA B	M4
EDEXCEL	M5
OCR	M4
WJEC	M4
NICCEA	M4

If any process is to take place then correct components and conditions are required. In the case of photosynthesis these are:

- light
- water
- carbon dioxide
- suitable temperature.

Additionally, it is most important that the chloroplasts have been able to develop their photosynthetic pigments in the thylakoid membranes. Without an adequate supply of magnesium and iron a plant suffers from **chlorosis** due to chlorophyll not developing. The leaf colour becomes yellow-green and photosynthesis is reduced.

Limiting factors

If a component is in low supply then productivity is prevented from reaching maximum. In photosynthesis carbon dioxide is a key limiting factor. The usual atmospheric level of carbon dioxide is 0.03%. In perfect conditions of water availability, light and temperature this low carbon dioxide level holds back the photosynthetic potential.

Clearly light energy is vital to the process of photosynthesis. It is severely limiting at times of partial light conditions, e.g. dawn or dusk.

Water is vital as a photosynthetic component. It is used in many other processes and has a lesser effect as a limiting factor of photosynthesis. In times of water shortage a plant suffers from a range of problems associated with other processes before a major effect is observed on photosynthesis.

A range of enzymes are involved in photosynthesis, therefore the process has an optimum temperature above and below which the rate reduces (so the temperature of the plant's environment can be limiting!).

Rate of photosynthesis is limited by light intensity from points A to B. After this a maximum rate is achieved – graph levels off.

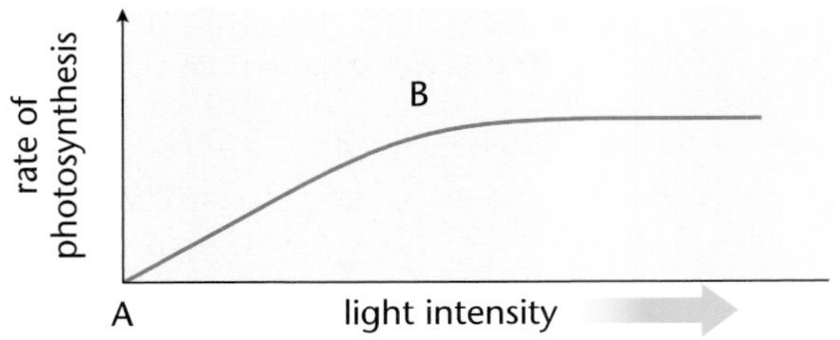

Rate of photosynthesis limited by light intensity until each graph levels off. The 30°C graph shows that at 20°C temperature was also a limiting factor.

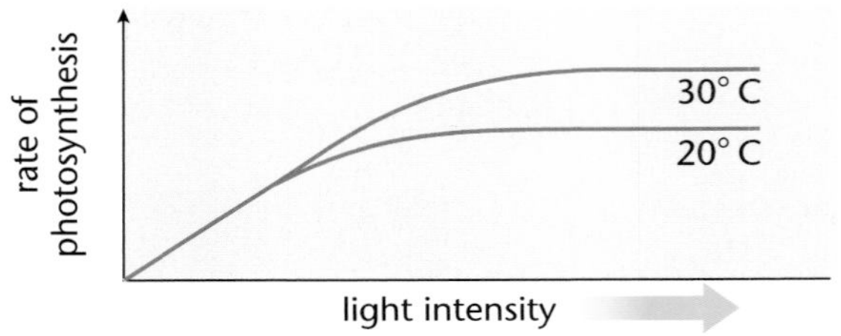

The lower level of CO_2 is also a limiting factor here. The fact that it holds back the process is shown by comparing both graph lines.

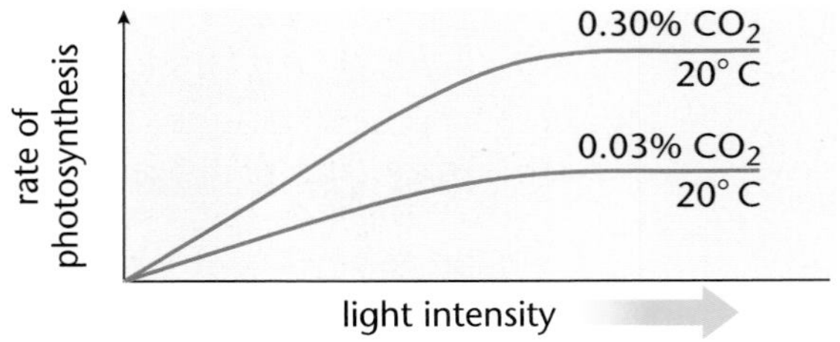

Compensation point

Another way of stating at compensation point is 'when the rate of respiration equals the rate of photosynthesis'.

It is usual for a plant growing outside in warm conditions to have **two** compensation points every day.

Photosynthesis utilises carbon dioxide whereas respiration results in its excretion. At night time during darkness a plant respires and gives out carbon dioxide. Photosynthesis only commences when light becomes available at dawn, if all other conditions are met. At one point the amount of carbon dioxide released by respiration is totally re-used in photosynthesis. This is the compensation point.

Beyond this compensation point the plant may increasingly photosynthesise as conditions of temperature and light improve. The plant at this stage still respires producing carbon dioxide in its cells and all of this carbon dioxide is utilised. However, much more carbon dioxide is needed which diffuses in from the air.

In the evening when dusk arrives a point is reached when the rate of photosynthesis falls due to the decrease in light and the onset of darkness. The amount of carbon dioxide produced at one point is totally utilised in photosynthesis. Another compensation point has arrived!

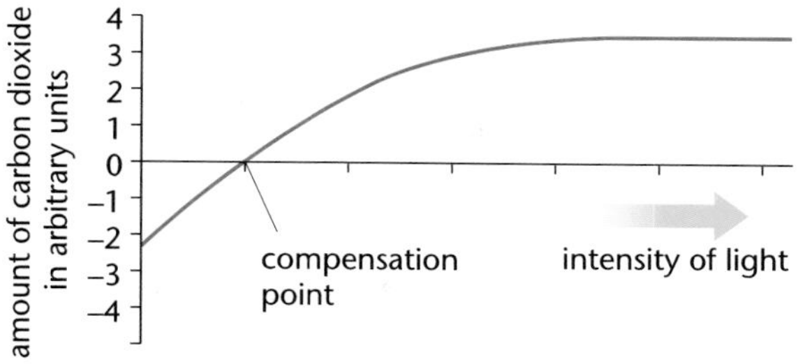

How useful is photosynthesis?

Many more substances are synthesised as a result of photosynthesis. Just a few are highlighted in this section.

Without doubt it is a most important process because it supplies carbohydrates and gives off oxygen. There are many more benefits in that glucose is a 'starter' chemical for the synthesis of many other substances.

Cellulose, **amino acids**, and **lipids** are among the large number of chemicals which can be produced as a result of the initial process of photosynthesis.

The work of the Royal Mint produces the money to run the economy, photosynthesis supplies the **energy currency** for the living world.

The table shows some examples of where and how some carbohydrates are used.

carbohydrate	*use*
deoxyribose (monosaccharide)	DNA 'backbone'
glucose (monosaccharide)	leaves, nectar, blood as energy supply
sucrose (disaccharide)	sugar beet as energy store
lactose (disaccharide)	milk as energy supply
cellulose (disaccharide)	protective cover around all plant cells
starch (polysaccharide)	energy store in plant cells
glycogen (polysaccharide)	energy store in muscle and liver

Progress check

1 In a chloroplast where do the following take place:
(a) light-dependent reaction
(b) light-independent reaction?

2 (a) Which features do photosystems I and II share in a chloroplast?
(b) Which photosystem is responsible for:
(i) the elevation of electrons to their highest level
(ii) acceptance of electrons from the lysis (splitting) of water?

3 (a) Complete the sentence by writing in the correct words.
The compensation point of a plant is when the rate of ....
equals the rate of ....
(b) During a cloudless day in ideal conditions for photosynthesis, how many compensation points does a plant have? Give a reason for your answer.

4 List the three main factors which limit the rate of photosynthesis.

5 During the light-independent stage of photosynthesis which substances are needed to continue the production of RuBP? Underline the substances in your answer which are directly supplied from the light-dependent stage of photosynthesis.

1 (a) thylakoid membranes (b) stroma.
2 (a) Each photosystem contains a large number of chlorophyll molecules. Light energy is received at the chlorophyll where electrons are boosted to a higher level. Energy is passed to pigment molecules known as the **reaction centre**. The reaction centre of each photosystem absorbs energy (but of different wavelengths!).
(b) (i) photosystem I (ii) photosystem II.
3 (a) respiration; photosynthesis (b) Two. Around dawn and dusk there will come a time when the CO_2 produced as a result of respiration is totally used up in photosynthesis.
4 CO_2; light; temperature.
5 $\underline{NADPH_2}$, $\underline{ATP}$ and CO_2.

1.3 Respiration

After studying this section you should be able to:

- *understand the central role of ATP as an energy carrier in cell metabolism*
- *recall the structure of mitochondria and relate structure to function*
- *understand that respiration liberates energy from organic molecules*
- *explain the differences between anaerobic and aerobic respiration*
- *describe different routes which respiratory substrates can take*
- *explain the stages of glycolysis and Krebs cycle*
- *explain the stages in the hydrogen carrier system*
- *understand the term respiratory quotient and how it relates to different substrates*

LEARNING SUMMARY

Adenosine triphosphate (ATP)

AQA A	M4
AQA B	M4
EDEXCEL	M4
OCR	M4
WJEC	M4
NICCEA	M4

A glucose molecule has a high energy content. If all the energy was released at once then there would be severe temperature problems in a cell. It is important that energy liberation is in small bursts. This is achieved by using adenosine triphosphate (ATP) molecules. Substrates such as glucose are broken down in enzyme-catalysed stages to produce a number of ATP molecules.

Remember that in photosynthesis ATP molecules are both synthesised then used to supply energy in the light-independent stage!

ATP synthase

ADP adenosine diphosphate	+	P phosphate	=	ATP adenosine triphosphate

ATP is a molecule which is needed in all energy-requiring processes.

The ATP needs to be broken down to liberate its energy. This is done by an enzyme, **ATPase**.

ATPase is a hydrolysing enzyme so that a water molecule is needed, but this is not normally shown in the equation.

ATPase

ATP adenosine triphosphate	=	ADP adenosine diphosphate	+	P phosphate	+	energy

ATP is a **phosphorylated nucleotide**. Recall DNA structure which consists of nucleotides. Each nucleotide consists of an organic base, ribose sugar and phosphate group. ATP is a nucleotide with two extra phosphate groups! This is the reason for the term 'phosphorylated nucleotide'.

adenine — ribose — phosphate — phosphate — phosphate

ATP is the energy currency of an organism.

The hydrolysis of the terminal phosphate group liberates the energy.

Uses of ATP

- muscle contraction
- active transport
- synthesis of macromolecules
- stimulates the breakdown of substrates to make even more ATP for other uses.

The biochemistry of respiration

Respiration is vital to the activities of every living cell. The flow diagram opposite shows stages in the breakdown of glucose and other substrates to produce a supply of ATP.

The two molecules of ATP are needed to begin the process. Each stage is catalysed by an enzyme, e.g. a decarboxylase removes CO_2 from a molecule.

ALERT! After the production of glycerate-3-phosphate the number of ATP molecules can be doubled. ***Each*** molecule of glycerate-3-phosphate gives rise to **20** molecules of ATP. Do not forget to take away the two ATPs at the start. So the total number of ATPs from one molecule of glucose is **38** (40 – 2). Count the ATPs in the diagram. Account for each ATP in the 38 total. This is a typical examination task!

The production of hydrogen atoms during the process can be monitored using DCPIP (dichlorophenol indophenol). It is a hydrogen acceptor and becomes colourless when fully reduced.

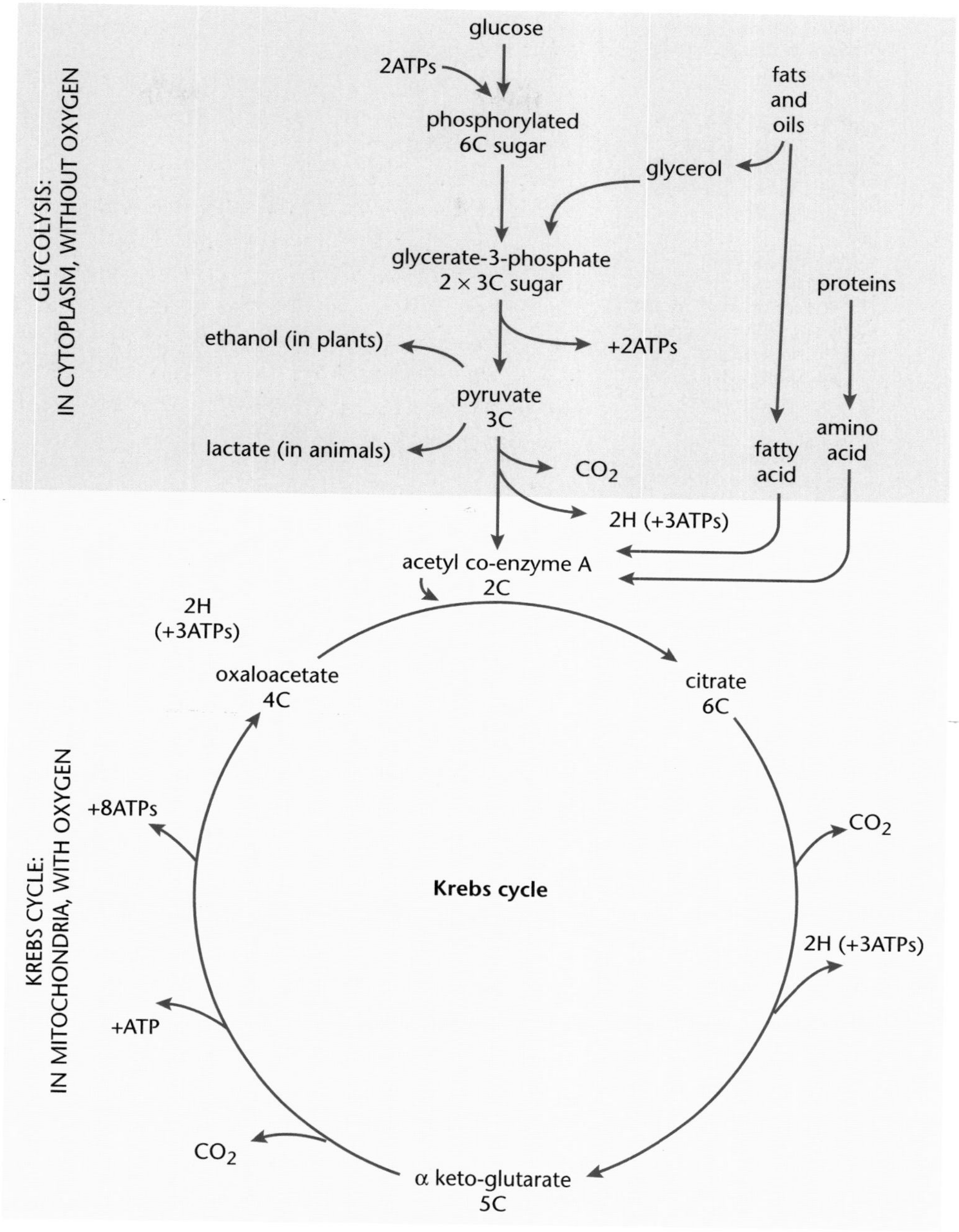

A mitochondrion

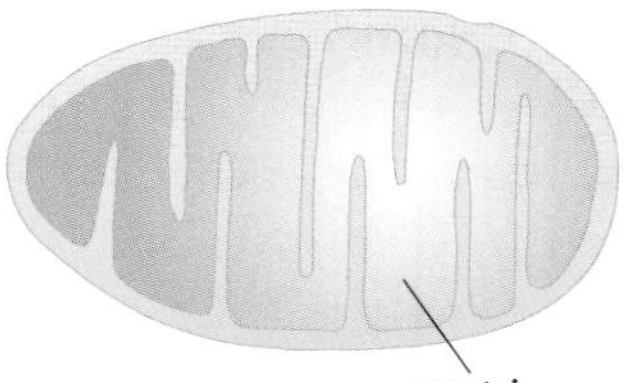

The flow diagram shows only the main stages of each process.

Glycolysis and the Krebs cycle

AQA A	M4
AQA B	M4
EDEXCEL	M4
OCR	M4
WJEC	M4
NICCEA	M4

Both processes produce ATP from substrates but the Krebs cycle produces many more ATP molecules than glycolysis! Every stage in each process is catalysed by a specific enzyme. In aerobic respiration both glycolysis and the Krebs cycle are involved whereas in anaerobic respiration only glycolysis takes place.

The flow diagram shows that every time a stage produces two hydrogen atoms, in the presence of oxygen, three ATP molecules are produced. The role of these hydrogen atoms is shown in the electron carrier system.

Electron carrier system

The main feature of the electron carrier or electron transport system is that three ATPs are produced every time 2H atoms are transported. It takes place in the mitochondria.

This is sometimes known as the hydrogen carrier system.

The carrier, NAD, is nicotinamide adenine dinucleotide. Similarly, FAD is flavine adenine dinucleotide.

Hydrogen is not transferred to cytochrome. Instead, the 2H atoms ionise into $2H^+ + 2e^-$. H is passed via an intermediate co-enzyme Q to cytochrome.

Only the electrons are carried via the cytochromes.

e^- is an electron

H^+ is a hydrogen ion or proton.

Oxygen is needed at the end of the carrier chain as a hydrogen acceptor. This is why we need oxygen to live. Without it the generation of ATP along this route would be stopped.

An enzyme can be both an oxidoreductase and a dehydrogenase at the same time!

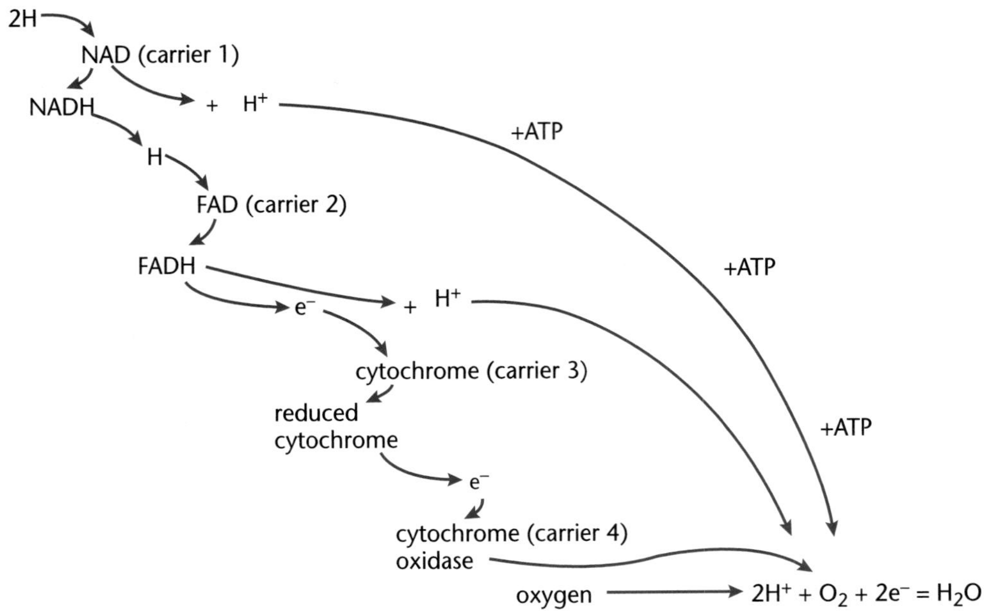

Oxidation	***Reduction***
Gain of oxygen	Loss of oxygen
Loss of hydrogen	Gain of hydrogen
Loss of electrons	Gain of electrons

When oxidation takes place then so does reduction, simultaneously, e.g. $NADH_2$ passes H to FAD. The NAD loses hydrogen and as a result becomes oxidised. FAD gains hydrogen and becomes $FADH_2$, and is therefore reduced. The generic term for an enzyme which catalyses this is **oxidoreductase**. Additionally an enzyme which removes hydrogen from a molecule is a **dehydrogenase**.

Progress check

1 Beginning with starch, write down the substances which could result from its use in glycolysis in an animal cell.

2 Explain how hydrogen atom production in cells during aerobic respiration results in the release of energy for cell activity.

3 Give **three** similarities between respiration and photosynthesis.

4 (a) Name the **four** carriers in the electron transport system in a mitochondrion. Give them in the correct sequence.

(b) Name the waste product which results from the final stage of the electron transport system.

5 For each of the following statements indicate whether a molecule would be oxidised or reduced.

(a) (i) loss of oxygen
(ii) gain of hydrogen
(iii) loss of electrons.

(b) Which type of enzyme enables hydrogen to be transferred from one molecule to another?

1 starch → glucose → glucose phosphate or phosphorylated glucose → glycerate-3-phosphate → pyruvate → lactate

2 used in the electron transport system to produce ATP; 3 ATP molecules produced for every 2H atoms produced; ATP → ADP + P + energy released

3 the stages of each process are catalysed by enzymes; both processes involve ATP; respiration involves GP in glycolysis and photosynthesis involves GP in the light-independent stage

4 (a) NAD → FAD → cytochrome → cytochrome oxidase
(b) water

5 (a) (i) reduced (ii) reduced (iii) oxidised.
(b) Oxidoreductase

Respiratory quotient

AQA A M4
OCR M4

It is sometimes useful to be able to deduce which substrate is being used in a person's metabolism at a specific time. This can be done if the volume of oxygen taken in, and the volume of carbon dioxide given out are measured. From this data the **respiratory quotient** (RQ) can be calculated.

$$RQ = \frac{\text{volume of carbon dioxide given off}}{\text{volume of oxygen taken in}}$$

If the volume of carbon dioxide given off is equal to the volume of oxygen taken in, what is the RQ value?

The RQ values of the following substrates are well documented from previous investigations:

carbohydrate 1.0; protein 0.9; fat 0.7

It is interesting to know which substrate is being metabolised. It is necessary to view such data with caution. If a mixture of substrates is being used then the figure will be different from the above, e.g. an RQ of 0.8 could point to both protein and fat being used.

The graph below shows the different RQ values of a seed during different stages of germination.

Graph to show RQ values of barley through germination

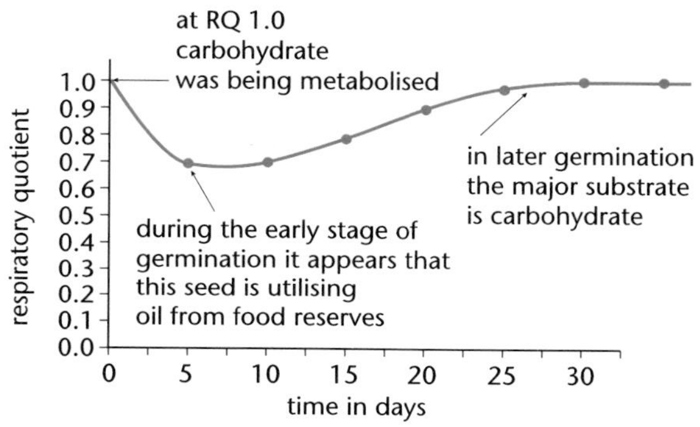

Take great care in interpreting RQ data. This graph suggests that the seed begins with carbohydrate as a metabolite, changes to fat/oil then returns to mainly using carbohydrate. Any RQ which is not of the numbers given suggests a substrate combination is being used.

How is the RQ data collected?

The instrument called a **respirometer**, does this.

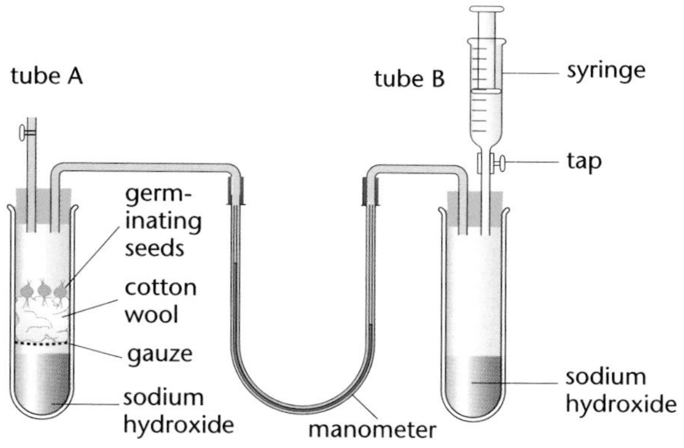

- **Sodium hydroxide** absorbs all CO_2 from the air in the apparatus from the beginning.
- As the germinating seeds use oxygen and the pressure reduces in tube A so the manometer level nearest to the seeds rises.
- Any CO_2 excreted is absorbed by the sodium hydroxide solution.
- The syringe is used to return the manometer fluid levels to normal.
- The volume of oxygen used is calculated by measuring the volume of gas needed from the syringe to return the levels to the original values.

Potassium hydroxide could be used instead of sodium hydroxide. They both absorb CO_2.

If water replaces the sodium hydroxide then the carbon dioxide evolved can be measured.

Sample question and model answer

Radioactivity is used to label molecules. They can then be tracked with a Geiger Müller counter.

In an experiment pondweed was immersed in water which was saturated with radioactive carbon dioxide ($^{14}CO_2$). It was illuminated for a time so that photosynthesis took place, the light was then switched off. The graph below shows the relative levels of some substances.

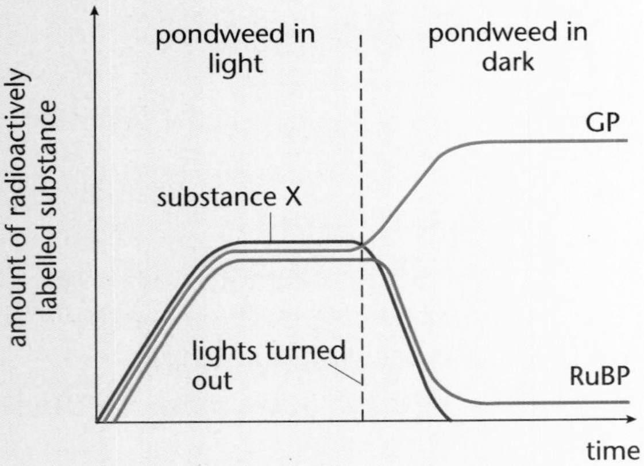

Always be ready to link the rise in one graph line with the dip of another. The relationship holds true here as substance X and RuBP are used up in the production of GP via the Calvin cycle. It is likely that some GP would have been used with substance X to make triose sugar. This is not shown on this graph.

Use the graph and your knowledge to answer the following questions.

(a) (i) Substance X is produced after a substance becomes reduced during the light-dependent stage of photosynthesis. Name substance X. [1]

$NADPH_2$, reduced nicotinamide adenine dinucleotide phosphate

(ii) Explain why substance X cannot be produced without light energy. [3]

- Light energy removes electrons from chlorophyll;
- the electrons are passed along the electron carrier chain;
- the electrons are needed to reduce NADP.

(b) Explain the levels of substance X, GP and RuBP after the lights were turned off. [6]

- It seems that substance X is used to make the other two substances because it becomes used up.
- Supply of substance X cannot be produced without light energy.
- GP is made from RuBP.
- GP levels out because more $NADPH_2$ is needed to make triose sugar or RuBP, the supply being exhausted.
- RuBP levels out at a low level because more $NADPH_2$ is needed to make GP.
- ATP is needed to make RuBP, ATP is needed to make GP.

ATP is not shown on the graph. Always be ready to consider substances involved in a process but not shown. Here it is worth a mark to remember that ATP is needed to continue the light-independent system of photosynthesis.

(c) After the lights were switched off glucose was found to decrease rapidly. Explain this decrease. [1]

- Glucose is used up in respiration to release energy for the cell.

(d) Give the specific sites of each of the following stages of photosynthesis in a chloroplast: [2]

(i) light-dependent stage thylakoid membranes
(ii) light-independent stage. stroma

Practice examination questions

1 The flow diagram below shows stages in the process of glycolysis.

2ATPs
glucose → phosphorylated → GP → substance X → lactate
6C sugar   6C sugar   glycerate-3-phosphate (2 × 3C)   3C
2ATPs

Use the information in the diagram and your knowledge to answer the questions below.

(a) Where in a cell does the above process take place? [1]

(b) Name substance X. [1]

(c) How many ATPs are *produced* during the above process? [1]

(d) Is the above process from an animal or plant?
Give a reason for your answer. [1]

(e) Under which condition could lactate be metabolised? [1]

[Total: 5]

2 The graph shows the relative amount of carbon dioxide taken in or evolved by a plant at different times during a day when the sun rose at 5.50 a.m.

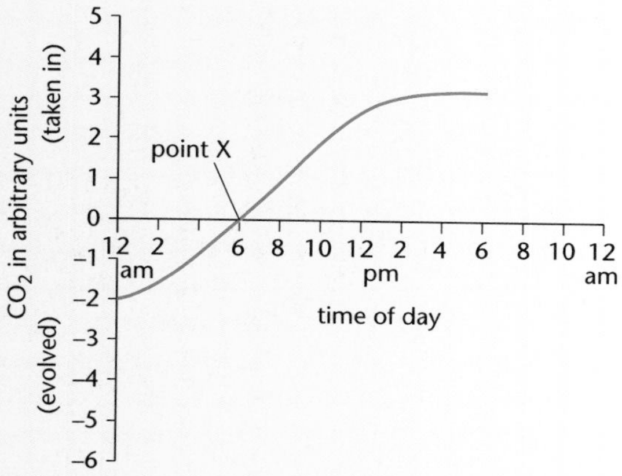

(a) Explain the significance of point X. [2]

(b) What name is given to point X? [1]

(c) Complete the graph between 6.00 p.m. and 12.00 a.m. [2]

[Total: 5]

3 An equation for the aerobic respiration of a lipid molecule included the production of 102 units of carbon dioxide.

The respiratory quotient was calculated as 0.7.

(a) Calculate the number (to nearest whole number) of oxygen units needed in the aerobic respiration of the lipid molecule. Show your working. [2]

(b) State the RQ value of:

(i) protein
(ii) carbohydrate. [2]

[Total: 4]

Practice examination questions (continued)

4 The diagram shows a respirometer set up to measure the amount of carbon dioxide produced by some insects.

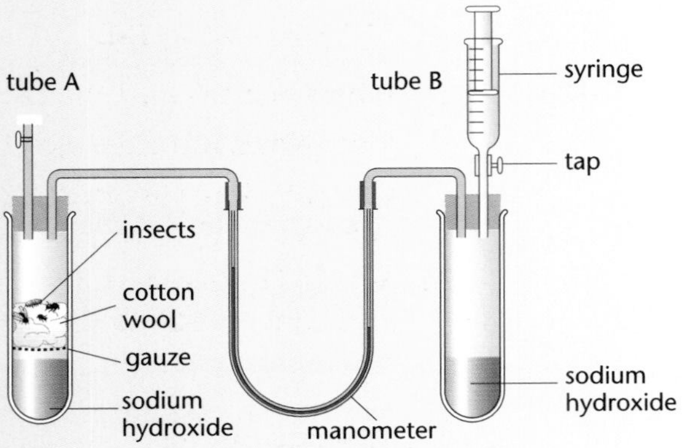

Explain how the apparatus can be used to measure the O_2 taken in by the insects. [4]

[Total: 4]

5 The chlorophyll in a pondweed consisted of several photosynthetic pigments. The graphs below show:

(A) the absorption spectrum of the pondweed's chlorophyll measured in arbitrary units

(B) the action spectrum of the same pondweed measured in cm^3 oxygen evolved.

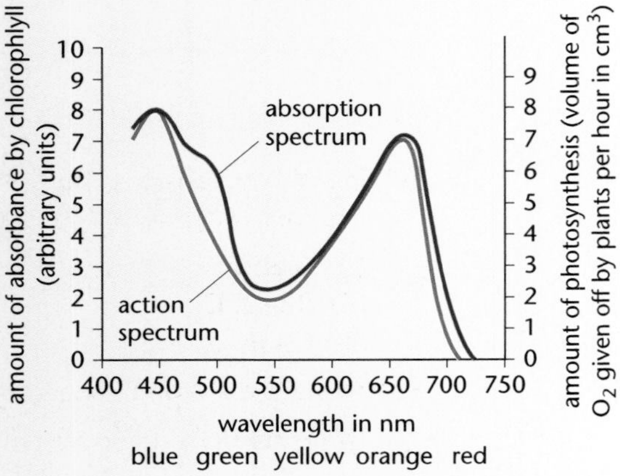

Use the graph and your knowledge to answer the questions.

(a) Explain the difference between the action and absorption spectra. [2]

(b) Explain the effect of a wavelength of 525 nm on the rate of photosynthesis. [1]

(c) How would the data for the action spectrum have been collected using the pondweed? [1]

[Total: 4]

Practice examination questions (continued)

6 The flow diagram below shows part of the electron carrier system in an animal cell.

FADH → FAD + H^+ + e^-

(a) Where in a cell does this process take place? [1]

(b) From which molecule did FAD receive H to become FADH? [1]

(c) Which molecule receives the electron produced by the breakdown of FADH? [1]

(d) As FADH becomes oxidised a useful substance is produced. Name the substance. [1]

[Total: 4]

7 The graph below shows the effect of increasing light intensity on the rate of photosynthesis of a plant where the concentration of carbon dioxide in the atmosphere was 0.03%.

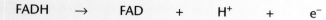

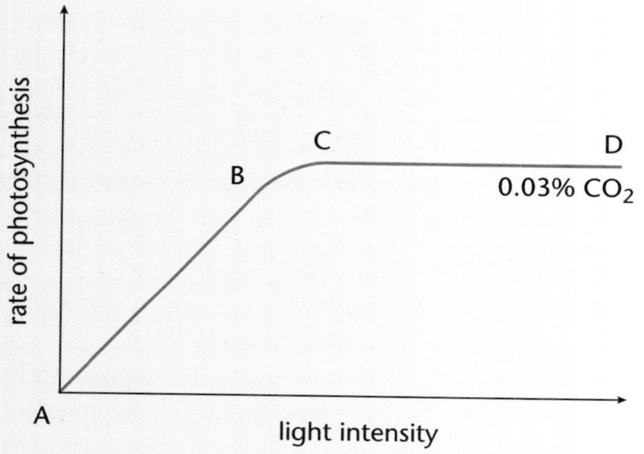

(a) Explain the effect of light intensity on the rate of photosynthesis between the following points on the graph:

(i) A and B
(ii) B and C
(iii) C and D. [3]

(b) Draw the shape of the graph which would result from a CO_2 concentration of 0.3%. [1]

[Total: 4]

Chapter 2

Nutrients

The following topics are covered in this chapter:

- *Heterotrophic nutrition*
- *Digestion*
- *Ruminants and their microbial allies*
- *Dietary changes in moths and butterflies*

2.1 Heterotrophic nutrition

After studying this section you should be able to:

- *understand the principles of heterotrophic nutrition and that it is divisible into holozoic, saprobiotic and parasitic nutrition*
- *understand the structure and function of dentition in herbivores and carnivores*

LEARNING SUMMARY

How do heterotrophic organisms feed?

AQA A	M6
EDEXCEL	M4
OCR	M5
WJEC	M4

Heterotrophic organisms take in **complex organic molecules**. These are made available in ecosystems by autotrophs. The heterotrophs obtain compounds which they use as an **energy source** and as **raw materials** to **build cell structures** and produce components which **assist cell processes**, e.g. assemble enzymes (proteins).

There are three forms of heterotrophic nutrition:

- **parasitic nutrition** where the organism obtains food from another *living* organism, the host
- **saprobiotic nutrition** where certain fungi and bacteria obtain food from dead organic material
- **holozoic nutrition** where solid or liquid food is taken into a 'gut' and digested.

Key points from AS

- **Saprophytic bacteria and fungi**
  Revise AS page 51

Ingestion is the term given to the way animals take in their food. The way in which they do this varies considerably throughout the biosphere. Organisms have adaptations which give them the ability to utilise food in their environment. Each organism has special features:

- **caterpillar** – powerful mandibles to shred leaves
- **butterfly** – coiled proboscis to insert into a nectary and suck up nectar
- **carnivore**, e.g. dog
  - long pointed canine teeth intersect to pierce the prey and prevent escape
  - large pointed molars to crush bone and cut through flesh
- **herbivore**, e.g. sheep
  - sharp incisors to cut plant material with horny pad to cut against
  - diastema (a space) to fit in plant material
  - flattened molars to grind plant material
  - sideways jaw movement to aid grinding.

The sheep is a ruminant. Find out more on p.42.

A caterpillar's head

A butterfly's head

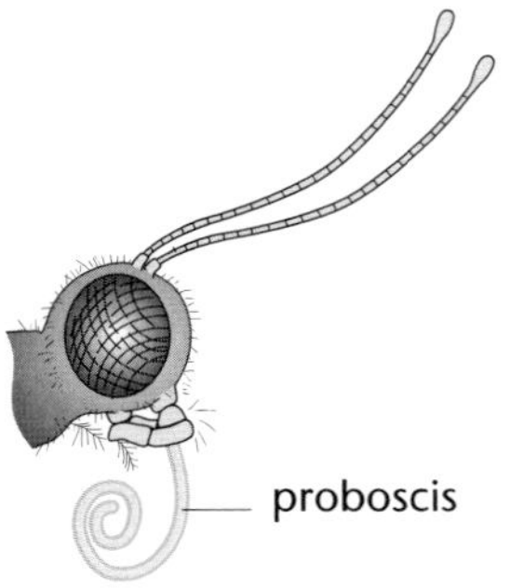

A carnivore's head

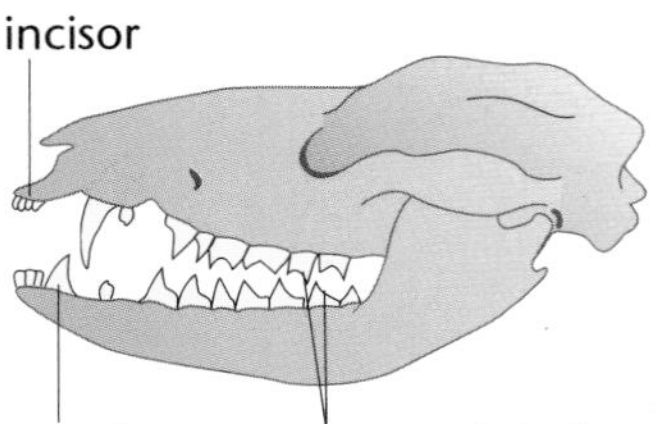

A herbivore's head

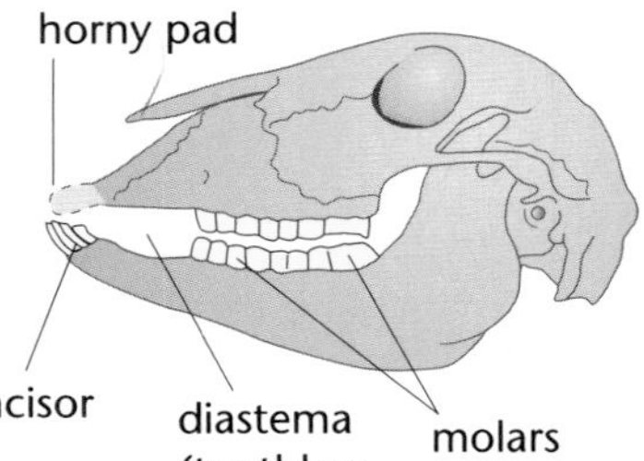

2.2 Digestion

After studying this section you should be able to:

- *understand the process of digestion in a range of organisms*
- *describe the roles of enzymes and hormones in the stages of digestion*
- *understand the absorption of nutrients in a mammalian gut*

LEARNING SUMMARY

How is food digested?

AQA A	M6
EDEXCEL	M4
OCR	M5
WJEC	M4

Food consists mainly of insoluble molecules which must be broken down into smaller soluble ones to enable entry into the blood stream. In this way they can enter cells and be used by the organism. This is **assimilation**.

In the mouth the teeth **mechanically digest** food by breaking it up into smaller pieces. The **higher surface area** of these pieces enables the digestive enzymes to act efficiently. The greater the surface area of food molecules the greater the chance of these substrate molecules binding with the active sites of the digestive enzymes. The role of these enzymes is known as **chemical digestion**.

Key points from AS

- **Human digestive enzymes.** *Revise AS page 51*

From the mouth to the anus the food passes through a tubular structure, the **alimentary canal**.

The diagram shows the arrangement of muscle tissue for the automatic movement of food through the alimentary canal. Smooth muscle cells lie in two different orientations, i.e. around the lumen (**circular**) or along the gut (**longitudinal**). The physical presence of food causes them to push from the oesophagus to the anus. This process transports gut contents and allows the stomach to churn food up to maximise enzyme contact with food substrate.

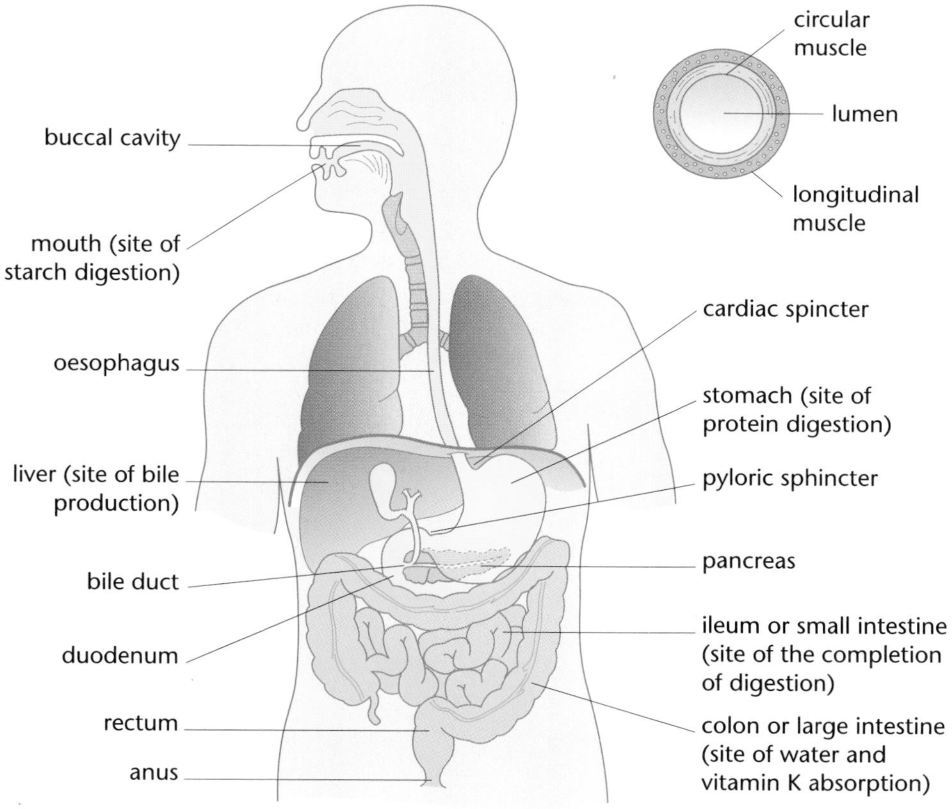

The passage of food through the alimentary canal requires assistance of both nervous and endocrine systems.

Digestion and the stomach

Additionally babies secrete the enzyme rennin. This clots milk protein (caseinogen) so that it remains in the stomach long enough to be digested.

soluble caseinogen → insoluble casein

This is the site where protein digestion begins. The enzyme produced is pepsin and proteins are broken down into polypeptides.

$$\text{protein} \xrightarrow{\text{pepsin}} \text{polypeptides}$$

Pepsin is an **endopeptidase** which breaks down the inner peptide links rather than the ends. In this way chains of amino acids (polypeptides) are formed.

Proteins are digested with the aid of cells in the **gastric glands** of the **stomach mucosa**.

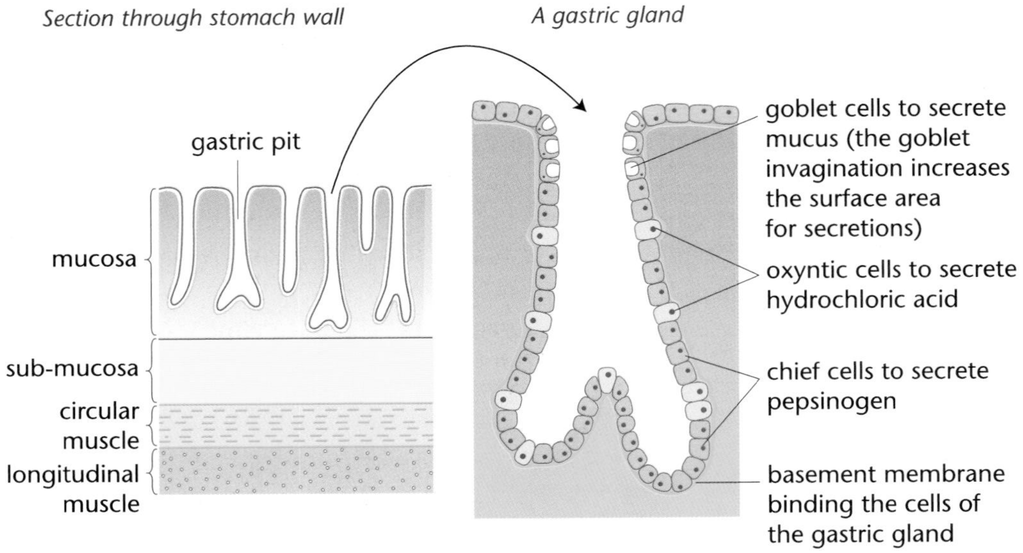

The inside of the stomach wall is the **mucosa** where the important gastric pits are located. Lining each gastric pit is a lining of columnar epithelium. The cells of this lining tissue have a secretive role. Pepsin is produced in the stomach which creates a potential problem. Our cells are made of protein! Cells lining the gastric pit enable protein digestion without the danger of 'self' digestion. Mucus secreted by goblet cells across the stomach mucosa surface protects the stomach cell from its enzymes and from HCl.

An inactive enzyme is a **precursor**. This is how the body prevents a potentially dangerous reaction taking place. The precursor is only activated when food is present! Look out for other precursors.

Cells of the gastric pit:

- secrete **pepsinogen** from the **chief cells**
- secrete HCl from the **oxyntic** cells
- HCl activates the pepsinogen by hydrolysis
- **pepsin** is formed from the action of HCl on pepsinogen
- protein → polypeptides.

Peristalsis churns the food up for a period of around two to four hours. After this time the food will be ejected by peristaltic action via the pyloric sphincter. Sphincters are rings of muscle which hold substances in position for some time.

The partially digested food called chyme is at a low pH (around pH 2). This acidity can create problems because:

- other digestive enzymes do not work efficiently at low pH
- the small intestine does not secrete enough mucus to protect against harmful acid.

Again the body solves the problem by carefully controlled alkaline secretions which take effect in the first part of the small intestine, the **duodenum**.

When you revise for your exams put the enzymes into learning sequences. Begin with pepsin in the stomach then follow the break down of all proteins → polypeptides → amino acids. The final small soluble molecules are ideal for absorption.

Can you work out a sequence for carbohydrates?

Can you spot **two** precursors (inactive enzymes) in the table?

Do you remember pepsinogen in the stomach being activated by HCl? There is your clue.

Digestion in the duodenum and small intestine (ileum)

What a lot of enzymes! A number of enzymic secretions by the pancreas, duodenum and small intestine change the food molecules significantly. The table shows the major changes which take place in the duodenum and ileum.

PANCREATIC JUICE *Acts on food in duodenum and in ileum*	*INTESTINAL JUICE* *Acts on food in ileum*
enteropeptidase or enterokinase trypsinogen → trypsin	*amylase* starch → maltose
trypsin protein → polypeptides	*maltase* maltose → **glucose**
peptidase polypeptides → **amino acids**	*peptidase* polypeptides → **amino acids**
chymotrypsin chymotrypsinogen → chymotrypsin	*sucrase* sucrose → **glucose** + **fructose**
lipase lipids → **fatty acid** + **glycerol**	*nucleotidase* nucleotides → **pentose sugar** + **phosphate** + **organic bases**
nucleases nucleic acids → nucleotides	*lactase* lactose → **glucose** + **galactose**

Key – the substances in **bold** are small enough to be absorbed into the blood.

The enzymes above (in italics) require a pH around 7–7.5 to hydrolyse the food molecules efficiently.

Stomach acid; the problem solved!

Sometimes we produce so much stomach acid that it cannot be neutralised. Ulcers are the consequence! The drug-based remedy is a proton inhibitor to reduce oxyntic cell action.

HCl from the stomach entering the duodenum and ileum would quickly damage the duodenal and intestinal walls. Secretions are needed to neutralise the dangerous acid. These are supplied as:

- **alkaline** bile secreted by the liver, stored in the gall bladder and passed to the duodenum via the bile duct
- **alkaline** pancreatic juice which enters the duodenum at the same position.

Some people suffer agonising pain when bile cannot reach the duodenum (caused by perhaps gall stones in the bile duct). Accumulations of fats become lodged and stimulate pain receptors. A hospital visit is vital!

Emulsification of lipids

Lipase alone could not break down lipids such as fats successfully unless lumps had been broken up into tiny droplets. This is **emulsification**.

KEY POINT

Increased surface area of food particles always aids enzyme action! Without increased surface area food would either become lodged in the alimentary canal or pass through to the anus with just the outside layer partially digested. This is another function of bile; high surface area of lipids.

Important structures in the small intestine

The small intestine is the place where digestion is completed and the soluble products of digestion can be absorbed. The small intestine, around five metres long, gives the food a suitable period for the final digestive enzymes to be secreted, to take effect and for nutrients to be absorbed.

How do villi aid efficient digestion and absorption?

Try to make a list of all the different ways in which high surface areas are involved in the process of digestion.

Look at the goblet cells around the outer cell layer of each villus. They increase surface area still further!

Peristalsis only takes place when there is a sufficient quantity of food to stimulate receptors in the wall of the alimentary canal. Fibre in food keeps the muscle tone of the gut in prime condition.

- Many villi provide a very high surface area for secretion of enzymes and absorption of nutrients.
- The individual outer layer of epithelium cells have microvilli, which give yet another boost to surface area.
- Near the base of villi the crypts of Lieberkühn are lined with enzyme secreting cells.
- Cells of the crypts of Lieberkühn continually divide mitotically and move to new higher positions up the villi.
- Brunner's glands secrete both mucus to lubricate the passing food and alkaline fluid to ensure neutralisation has been achieved.
- Movements of peristalsis continually push the food through the alimentary canal.
- Smooth muscle in the villi (muscularis mucosa) alternately contract and relax to ensure that a maximum rate of absorption is achieved. (Sluggish movement of the food would stagnate the absorptive processes.)

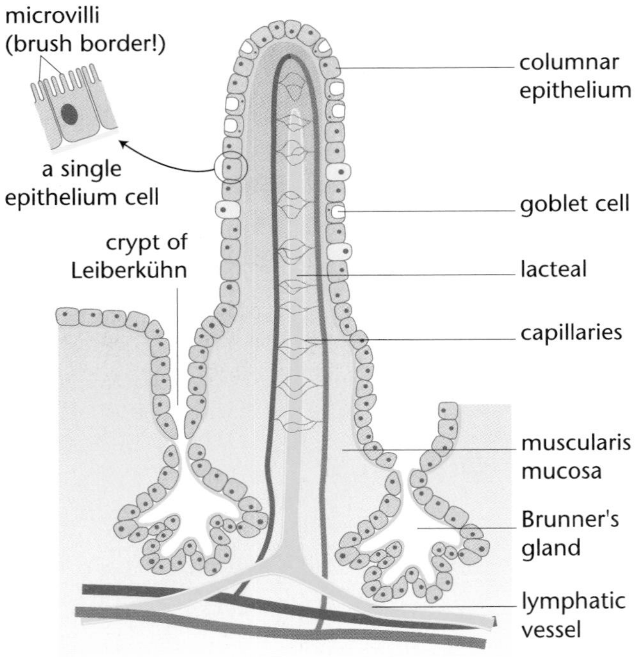

Section through small intestine

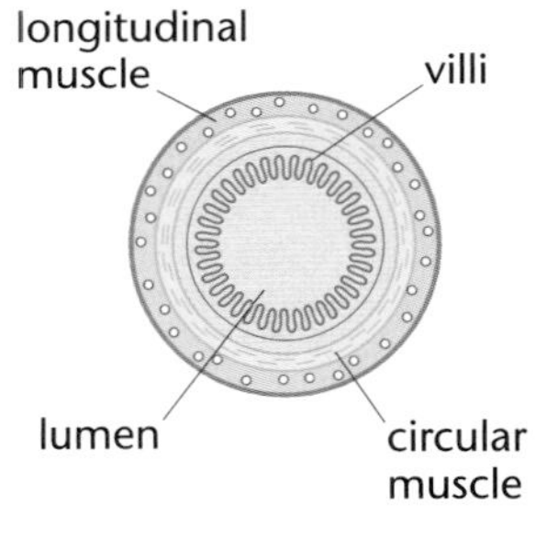

Remember that diffusion takes place down a concentration gradient. Movements of the gut and villi disturb the food contents and maximise the gradient! Concentration gradients between intestine lumen and blood are maximised.

Did you know?
Bacteria in the colon are able to synthesise vitamin K which passes into the blood.

Peristalsis continues the movement of digested food through the ileum. By the end, many of the nutrients (but not all!) will have been absorbed into the bloodstream. Substances such as amino acids and glucose pass into villus capillaries, reach the hepatic portal vein and subsequently enter a route to the body systems. Absorption by the villi is by diffusion and active uptake. Remaining in the intestinal contents are undigested substances such as fibre, water and some nutrients that were not able to contact villi. This mixture enters the colon or large intestine. Here much water is absorbed into the blood. The remains become more solid and are known as faeces. The faeces are stored in the rectum to be egested via the anus at a later stage.

What controls digestion?

AQA A M6
OCR M5

Digestion is coordinated by both the **nervous** and the **endocrine** systems working together. The tables below outline the roles of both systems.

Nervous control

digestive juice	*stimulus and response*
saliva	sight, thought, taste, smell of food causes an autonomic response via vagus nerve
gastric juice	stomach wall is stretched by food causes an autonomic response via vagus nerve
intestinal juice	contact of food with the small intestine wall stimulates Brunner's gland and crypts of Lieberkühn to make secretions

Note that the hormone enterogastrone '**switches off**' gastrin production. This is very useful since there is no food left in the stomach!

Note that secretin and pancreozymin both control the constituents of the pancreatic juice. Which controls the production of enzymes?

Have you ever had a fatty meal that 'lies heavily' on your stomach? It takes a long time to digest the fat because its digestion begins **after** the food has left the stomach. Fat is the last food component to leave. When fat reaches the ileum it stimulates CCK–PZ secretion, which results in bile being ejected from the gall bladder. Do you remember the functions of the bile? (p.39)

Hormonal control

stimulus	*endocrine gland*	*hormone*	*effect*
food in stomach	stomach mucosa	gastrin	causes oxyntic cells to secrete HCl
fat in ileum	intestinal mucosa	enterogastrone	inhibits gastrin production
food in ileum	intestinal mucosa	villikinin	stimulates the muscle in villi (muscularis mucosa) to contract rhythmically (which maximises nutrient absorption and empties lacteals into lymph vessels)
HCl in ileum	intestinal mucosa	secretin	stimulates the pancreas to secrete (i) alkaline ions (ii) watery fluid (but no enzymes!)
peptides and dipeptides in ileum	intestinal mucosa	pancreozymin (PZ)	stimulates the pancreas to produce enzymes
fats and oils	intestinal mucosa	cholecystokinin (CCK)	stimulates the gall bladder to contract

Take care with questions about hormones! The small intestine is very close to the pancreas but **all hormones** enter the general blood circulation. During digestion every blood vessel in the body will contain the hormones above but they only trigger responses to specific organs, e.g. pancreozymin passes through every vessel but only the pancreas responds by secreting enzymes.

Progress check

1 How does the body avoid damage to the duodenum by HCl from the stomach?

2 The diagram shows a gastric pit.
   (a) Name cells A and B.
   (b) In which part of the stomach wall are gastric pits located?
   (c) Explain how pepsinogen is activated in the stomach.

3 What is the effect of the hormone villikinin on digestion?

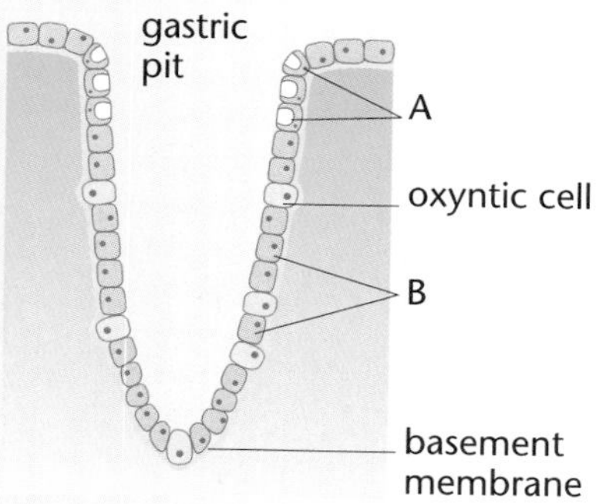

1 Alkaline bile secreted by the liver reaches the duodenum via the bile duct; alkaline pancreatic juice reaches the duodenum; neutralisation takes place; cholecystokinin (CCK) causes the gall bladder to empty; secretin stimulates the pancreas to secrete alkaline fluid.
2 (a) A mucus secreting cells, B chief (peptic) cells
(b) (gastric) mucosa
(c) food in stomach stimulates gastrin secretion; HCl secreted from the oxyntic cells; HCl activates the pepsinogen by hydrolysis; pepsin is formed.
3 Stimulates the muscle in villi (muscularis mucosa) to contract; villus movement maximises nutrient absorption; empties lacteals into lymph vessels; diffusion gradients between intestinal lumen and lumen maximised.

2.3 Ruminants and their microbial allies

After studying this section you should be able to:

LEARNING SUMMARY

- *understand the roles of microorganisms in ruminants*
- *understand the association of partner organisms, ruminants and microorganisms as a mutualistic relationship*

What is a ruminant?

AQA A M6
EDEXCEL M3

A ruminant is a mammal which has a specialised digestive system in which the oesophagus leads to four sacs, the **rumen**, the **reticulum**, the **omasum** and the **abomasum**. In the rumen are **microorganisms** including bacteria and protoctistans. This relationship is an example of mutualism, where both microorganisms and the ruminant benefit from the association. Cows, sheep and antelopes are examples of ruminants.

How do ruminants digest their food?

- Plant material including grass is ingested prior to swallowing.
- Incisor teeth bite grass against the **diastema** or **horny pad** (together they act like a knife and cutting board in a kitchen!).
- Flat molars efficiently grind the plant material by a sideways jaw motion.
- Food boluses reach the **rumen** and **reticulum** where microorganisms commence their role.
- Bacteria produce **cellulase** enzymes which break down **cellulose** which surrounds every plant cell.
- After a time, partially digested boluses are **regurgitated** from the rumen to the mouth where further grinding takes place. (An even higher surface area to volume ratio enhances enzyme efficiency even more.)
- Complete breakdown of cellulose results in **volatile fatty acids** being produced and absorbed.
- Food enters the small intestine via the obomasum, the name for the true stomach, where the ruminant secretes its own enzymes.

Return of boluses to the mouth for further processing is 'chewing the cud!'

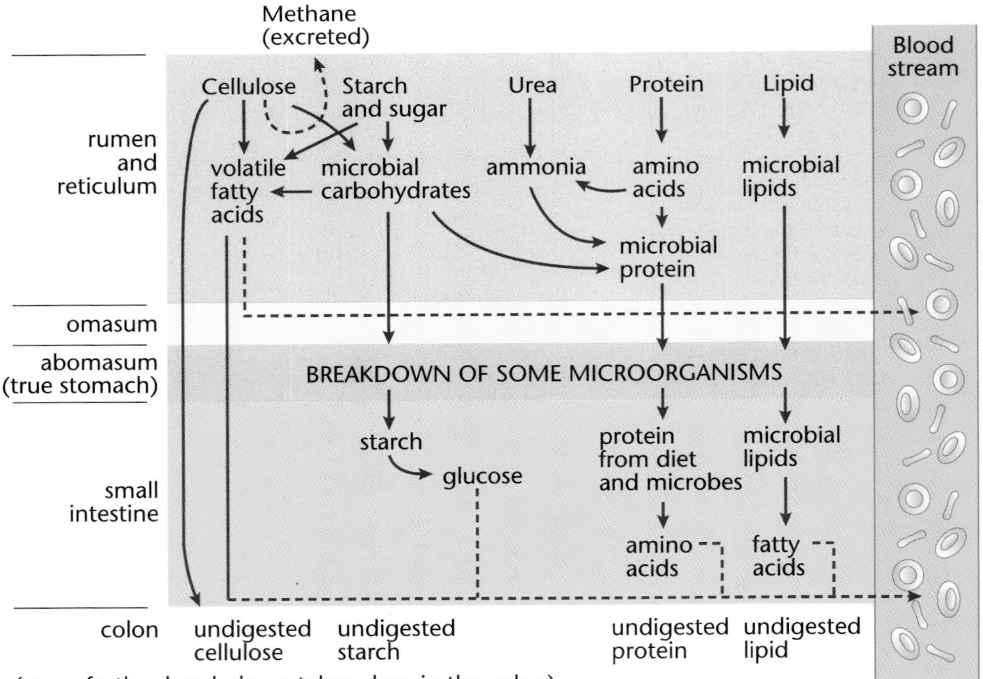

(some further break down takes place in the colon)

Try smelling the breath of a cow! Methane is excreted via the mouth (as well as the anus).

Both urea and protein are sources of nitrogen.

As some microorganisms die they are also digested to form a rich source of useful products including amino acids.

Digestion is never perfect. No wonder the flies have so much to feed on in faeces.

2.4 Dietary changes in moths and butterflies

After studying this section you should be able to:

- *understand the special adaptations of insects to their diet*

LEARNING SUMMARY

Dietary changes through the life cycle of moths and butterflies

AQA A M6

Moths and butterflies are lepidopterous insects (e.g. cabbage white butterfly) and are characterised by a life cycle known as complete metamorphosis.

egg → larva → pupa → adult (imago)

Larva (caterpillar) stage

- Is a specialist feeding stage when vast quantities of protein-rich food are ingested.
- Larvae radiate out colonising new areas, aiding the dispersal of the species.

Pupa (chrysalis) stage

- Signals a period of extreme tissue re-organisation.
- The rich protein supply of the larval stage gives rise to abundant amino acids which are assembled into different proteins, characteristic of the species.
- In time the imago or adult emerges from the pupal case.

Adult (imago) stage

- Is a specialist reproductive stage.
- Needs vast amounts of energy which are supplied by nectar, which the adult obtains by inserting its unwound proboscis into the nectary of a flower.
- Aids the dispersal of the species.

In an examination look out for a table like the one shown. You will have to put the ticks into a blank grid to show appropriate enzymes. Remember the main function of each stage then you will, logically, remember the correct enzymes. No digestive enzymes for the pupa. It does not feed!

Look out for unfamiliar data but, as always with examinations, apply the same principles learned during the course.

	STAGE IN LIFE CYCLE	
	larva	***adult***
food	leaves	nectar (sucrose)
feeding structures	mandibles	proboscis
amylase starch → maltose	✔	
maltase maltose → glucose	✔	
sucrase sucrose → glucose + fructose	✔	✔
protease protein → amino acids	✔	
lipase oils → fatty acids + glycerol	✔	

The table shows the different foods utilised by different stages of the same species. The flying action of the adults is fuelled by sucrose which only requires one enzyme, sucrase. The larva needs a complete range of enzymes.

Sample question and model answer

The contents of an animal's stomach could be removed via an opening known as a fistula. The contents were measured after a meal.

The graph shows the relative levels of pepsinogen, substance X and pH.

Be ready to relate the fall of one graph line to the rise of another!

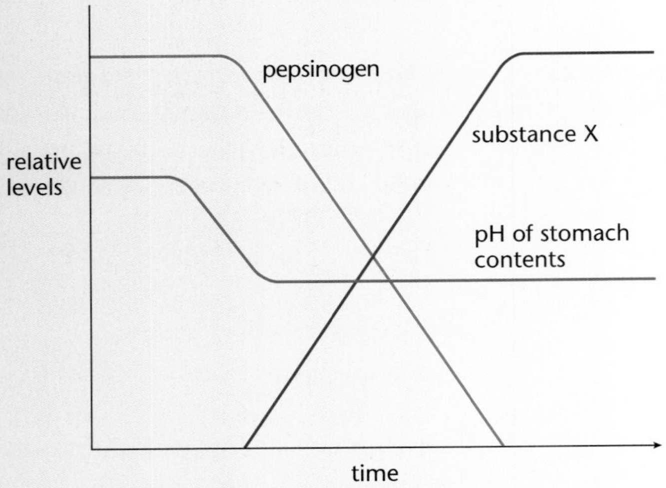

(a) Explain why the pH fell as a result of the meal entering the stomach.

- presence of food stimulates nervous system;
- presence of food in stomach stimulates gastrin production;
- as a result oxyntic cells produce more HCl;
- so the pH fell.

(b) (i) Suggest why the level of pepsinogen fell.

- HCl was used to change the pepsinogen into another substance;
- the fall in pepsinogen seems associated with increase in substance X.

Pepsinogen is a precursor (inactive enzyme) which is activated by HCl in the stomach.

(ii) Name substance X.

- pepsin

(c) The last food components to leave the stomach are fats and oils.

Explain how they are **efficiently** digested and absorbed.

This question may seem a formidable task. Do not worry! The mark scheme of an examiner may require only around 8 of these responses for full marks. This happens regularly on longer response questions.

- These lipids stimulate cholecystokinin to be secreted;
- gall bladder contracts to eject bile;
- bile emulsifies the lipids;
- pancreozymin stimulates pancreas to secrete lipase;
- secretin stimulates pancreas to secrete alkaline fluid
- (fluid environment essential for enzyme-controlled reactions);
- bile/alkali neutralises acid from stomach;
- lipase breaks down lipids into fatty acid + glycerol;
- absorption by villi which have a high surface area;
- absorption through microvilli;
- breakdown products pass into lacteals;
- lacteals emptied by regular contractions of the muscularis mucosa or smooth muscle of the villi.

Practice examination questions

1 (a) **Cellulose**, **starch**, **urea** and **protein** were eaten by a cow.

Complete the table by putting a tick in a box if the statement is true for that substance.

	Food substance			
	cellulose	*starch*	*urea*	*protein*
Can **only** provide a cow with nutrients because bacteria feed on it				
Results in the production of volatile fatty acids				
Contains a source of nitrogen				
Can be digested in the rumen and the small intestine				

[4]

(b) When a ruminant such as a cow chews grass, at first, it is swallowed and **partially** digested.

Describe how a cow makes sure that digestion is completed? [2]

(c) Bacteria live in the rumen of a cow.

Name this type of relationship. [1]

Describe **one** advantage to each partner. [2]

[Total: 9]

2 Complete the table by filling in the gaps.

stimulus	*endocrine gland*	*hormone*	*effect*
food in stomach	stomach mucosa	....	causes oxyntic cells to secrete HCl
fat in ileum	....	enterogastrone	inhibits gastrin production
food in ileum	....	villikinin	stimulates the muscle in villi (muscularis mucosa) to contract
.... in ileum	intestinal mucosa	....	stimulates the pancreas to secrete alkaline ions

[5]

[Total: 5]

Chapter 3

Control in animals and plants

The following topics are covered in this chapter:

- Neurone: structure and function
- Nervous transmission
- The effects of drugs on synapses
- The central nervous system
- Control of skeletal muscle
- The human eye and ear
- Plant sensitivity

3.1 Neurone: structure and function

After studying this section you should be able to:

- describe the structure of a motor neurone and a sensory neurone
- understand the function of sensory, motor, bi-polar and multi-polar neurones

LEARNING SUMMARY

The structure and functions of neurones

AQA A	M6
AQA B	M4
EDEXCEL	M4
OCR	M5
WJEC	M5
NICCEA	M4

Neurones are nerve cells which help to coordinate the activity of an organism by transmitting electrical impulses. In many organisms hormones contribute to this coordination (see next chapter).

Important features of neurones.

1. Each has a **cell body** which contains a nucleus.
2. Each communicates via branched extensions called **dendrites**.
3. Some have long processes known as **axons**.
4. Neurones can transmit **electrical impulses**.

KEY POINT

The nervous system consists of a range of different neurones which work in a network through the organs. The diagrams show two types of neurone.

Note the direction of electrical impulses shown on the diagrams.

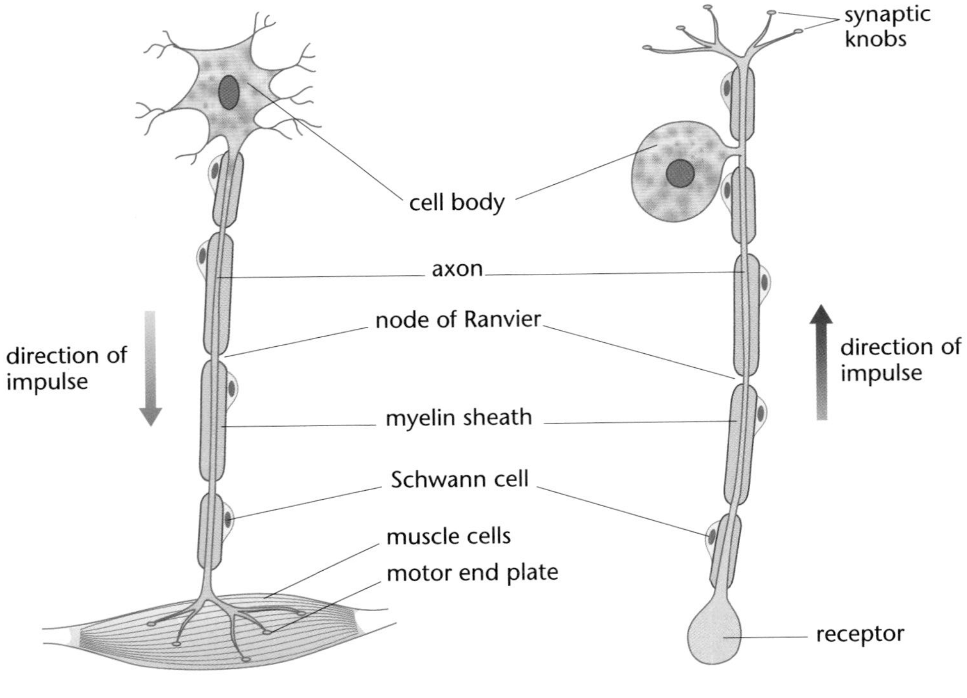

Motor neurone *Sensory neurone*

Key points from AS

- **The cell surface membrane** *Revise AS pages 57–58*
- **The movement of molecules in and out of cells** *Revise AS pages 59–60*
- **The specialisation of cells** *Revise AS pages 41–42*

Structure and function of the motor neurone

The motor neurone controls the contraction of muscle cells and has some important features.

- It has a **cell body** which includes the nucleus and many other cell organelles.
- Many **dendrites** radiate from the cell body to communicate with other neurones.
- A long process, the **axon**, containing many mitochondria, leads from the cell body.
- The axon can transmit a nerve impulse from the central nervous system for a considerable distance.
- The axon is insulated by the **myelin sheath**.
- The myelin sheath consists of a membrane of a **Schwann cell**, wrapped around the axon enclosing a layer of fat, giving the insulation property.
- At intervals there are gaps in the sheath where impulses are regenerated, each being known as a **node of Ranvier**.
- The axon terminates in a number of dendrites which contact muscle tissue via **motor end plates**.

A nervous impulse generated by a motor neurone usually results in the contraction of the muscle. The motor neurone is also known as an **effector** neurone. Some effector neurones control glands which secrete hormones when activated.

What about other neurones?

Multipolar neurones are found in the central nervous system (CNS). Their roles include memory, co-ordination and perception.

Bi-polar neurones link photosensitive cells in the retina to the optic nerve. They act as an intermediary between the two cells.

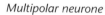

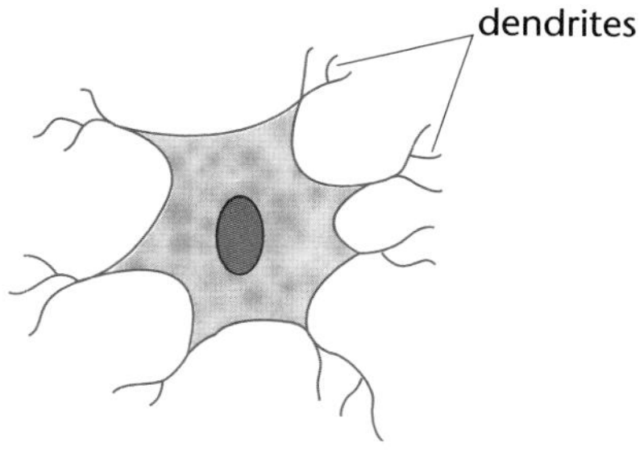

Multipolar neurone

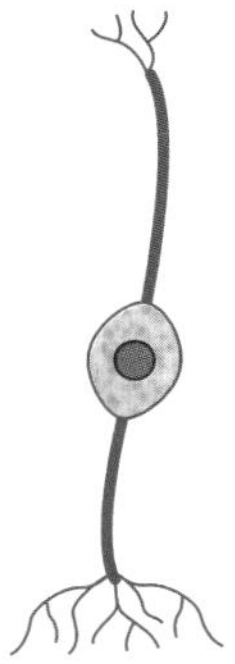
Bi-polar cell

What are the roles of the sensory neurones?

They have many similarities to the motor neurone, e.g. myelin sheath. However, there are important differences.

- The sensory neurones transmit impulses towards the central nervous system.
- Each sensory neurone has a receptor which responds to a specific stimulus, e.g. temperature change.
- The receptor responds to a local change by generating a nervous impulse which can be transmitted along the axon.
- The event at a receptor when a stimulus results in an impulse being generated is known as **transduction**.

Receptors

The more receptors there are in a position, the more sensitive it is, e.g. the fingers have many more touch receptors than the upper arm.

There are a range of different types of sensory cell around the body. Each type responds to different stimuli. Receptors are classified according to these different stimuli.

- **Photoreceptors**, respond to light, e.g. rods and cones in the retina.
- **Chemoreceptors**, respond to chemicals, e.g. taste buds on the tongue.
- **Thermoreceptors**, respond to temperature, e.g. skin thermoreceptors.
- **Mechanoreceptors**, respond to physical deformation, e.g. pressure receptors in the skin or hair cells in the ear.
- **Proprioreceptors**, respond to change in position in some organs, e.g. in muscles.

Did you know?
The umbilical cord has no receptors. It can be cut without any pain.

3.2 Nervous transmission

After studying this section you should be able to:

- *understand nervous transmission by action potential*
- *describe the mechanisms of synaptic transmission*

LEARNING SUMMARY

Transmission of an action potential along a neurone

AQA A	M6
AQA B	M4
EDEXCEL	M4
OCR	M5
WJEC	M5
NICCEA	M4

Neurones can 'transmit an electrical message' along an axon. However you must never write this in your answers. Instead of nerve impulse you must now use the term **action potential**.

The diagrams below show the sequence of events which take place along an axon as an action potential passes.

Resting potential

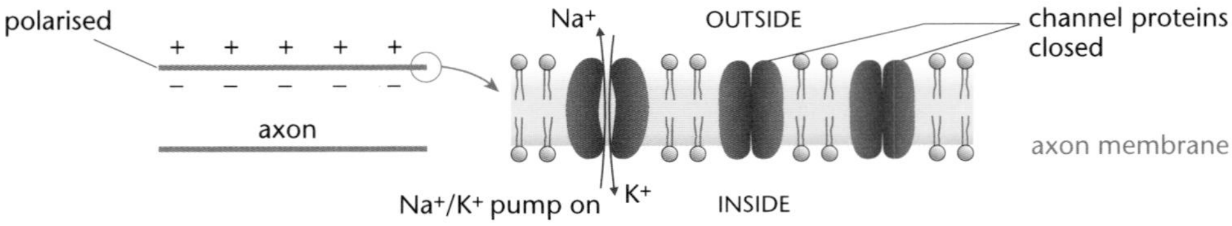

- There are 30 times more Na^+ ions on the outside of an axon during a resting potential.
- If any Na^+ ions diffuse in, then they are expelled by the '**sodium-potassium pump**'.
- The 'sodium-potassium pump' is an active transport mechanism by which a carrier protein, with ATP, expels Na^+ ions against a concentration gradient and allows K^+ ions into the axon.
- This creates a **polarisation**, i.e. there is a +ve charge on the outside of the membrane and a –ve charge on the inside.
- The **potential difference** can be measured at around –60 millivolts.

The Na^+/K^+ pump needs ATP to drive this activity. This is the reason for the large number of mitochondria in an axon.

Action potential

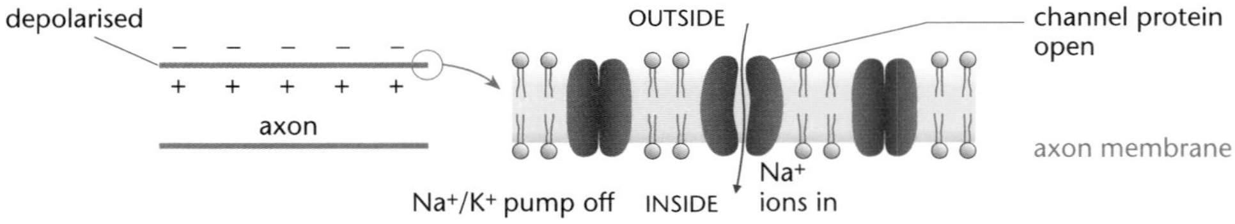

- As the action potential passes the **sodium-potassium pump is turned off**.
- Sodium channel proteins open to allow Na^+ ions into the axon.
- There is now a –ve charge on the outside and a +ve charge on the inside known as **depolarisation**.
- The potential difference changes to around +60 millivolts.
- The profile of the action potential, shown by an oscilloscope, is always the same.

Refractory period

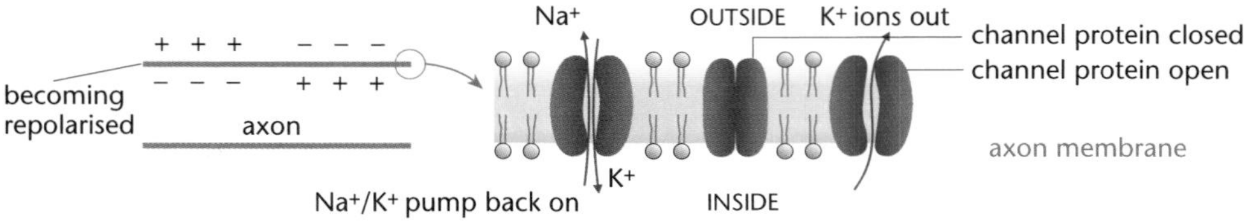

- A K^+ channel opens so K^+ ions leave the axon.
- The resting potential is regained by the 'sodium-potassium pump' being activated again.

KEY POINT

Only when the resting potential has been achieved is the axon ready to allow the passage of another action potential!

Measuring an action potential

- The speed and profile of action potentials can be measured with the help of an oscilloscope and glass electrodes.
- The profile of the action potential for an organism always shows the same pattern, like the one shown.
- The changes in potential difference are tracked via a time base.
- Using the time base you can work out the speed at which action potentials pass along an axon as well as how long one lasts.

If action potentials are the same throughout the nervous system, how can we differentiate different stimuli?

Answer – action potentials are propagated in specific patterns along an axon, e.g. like this. The action potentials are in volleys.

1111 1111 1111 1111

Each 1 represents an action potential on an oscilloscope screen.

The diagram shows the arrangement of the apparatus and the enlarged diagram shows the typical profile of an action potential.

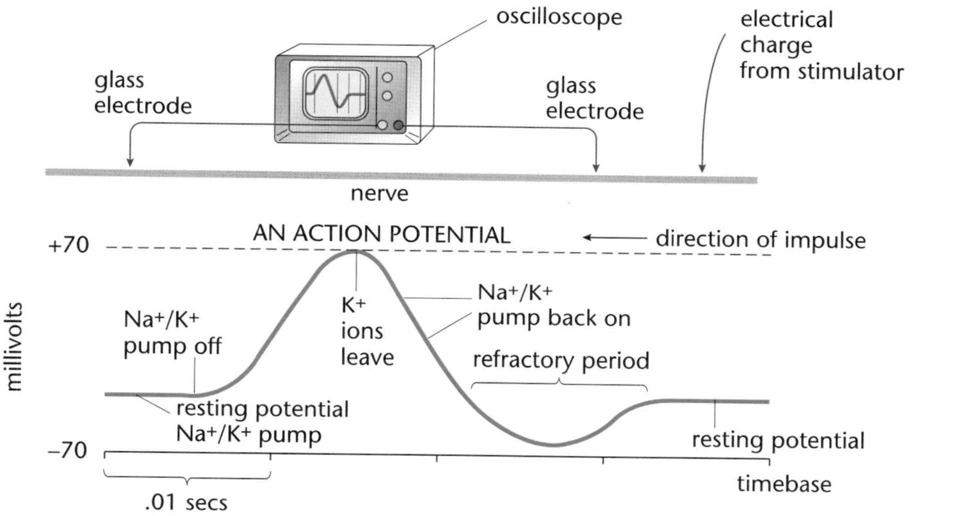

Much of the data about action potentials was collected using neurones from the squid. The reason for this is that this organism has giant axons, suitable for the insertion of glass electrodes. The action potential profile can be applied to transmission along human neurones.

- The front of the action potential is marked by the Na^+/K^+ pump being off.
- The potential difference increases to around +70 millivolts as the Na^+ ions stream into the axon.
- K^+ ions leave the axon.
- The Na^+/K^+ pump re-starts and ultimately polarisation is re-established by the end of the refractory period.
- During the refractory period no other action potential can pass along the axon, which makes each action potential separate or discrete.

The movement of an action potential along an axon is also known as **saltatory conduction.** This is due to the role of Na^+ ions. The impulse is regenerated at every node of Ranvier.

Progress check

What is the function of each of the following?

(a) receptor
(b) axon
(c) myelin sheath
(d) terminal dendrites.

(a) receptors respond to stimulus by producing an action potential
(b) transmit action potential with the help of mitochondria
(c) myelin sheath is a membrane enclosing fat which acts as an insulator
(d) terminal dendrites have motor end plates which can stimulate muscle tissue to contract.

How do neurones communicate with each other?

The key to links between neurones are structures known as synapses. Terminal dendrites branch out from neurones and terminate in synaptic knobs. The diagram below shows a synaptic knob separated from an interlinking neurone by a synapse.

Remember an impulse can 'cross' a synapse by chemical means and the route is in ONE direction only. They cannot go back!

A synapse which conducts using acetylcholine is known as a cholinergic synapse.

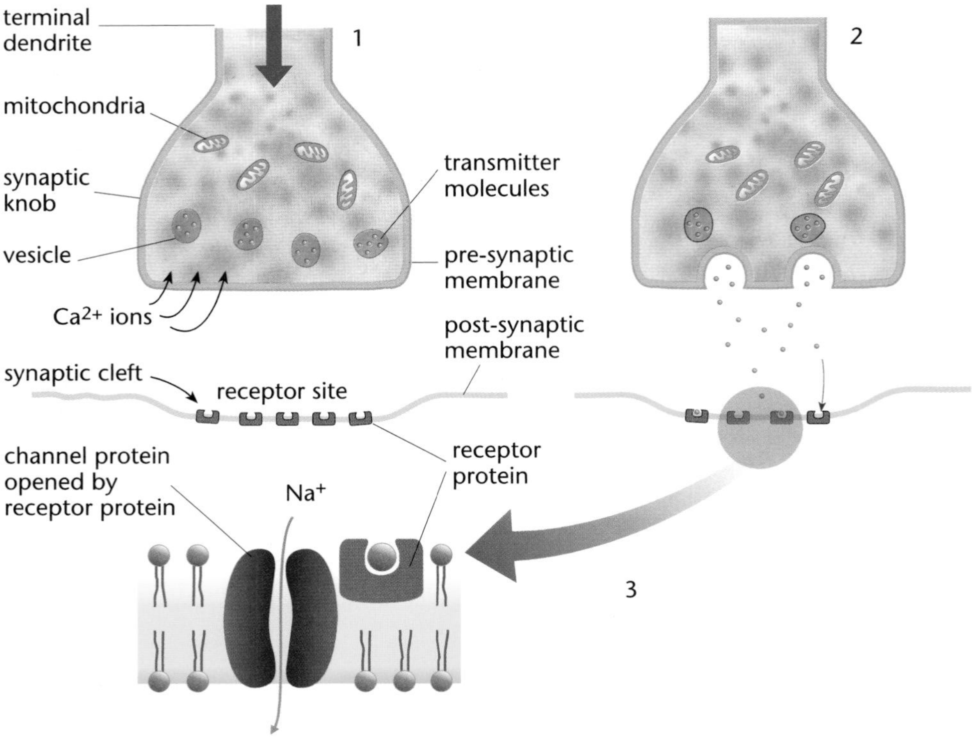

There are **two** types of synapse:

- **excitatory** which can stimulate an action potential in a linked neurone
- **inhibitory** which can prevent an action potential being generated.

Remember that the generation of an action potential is ALL OR NOTHING. Either enough Na^+ ions pass through the post-synaptic membrane and an action potential is generated OR not enough reach the other side, and there is no effect.

As an action potential arrives at a synaptic knob the following sequence takes place.

- Channel proteins in the pre-synaptic membrane open to allow Ca^{2+} ions from the synaptic cleft into the synaptic knob.
- Vesicles then merge with the pre-synaptic membrane, so that transmitter molecules such as acetylcholine are secreted into the gap.
- The transmitter molecules diffuse across the cleft and bind with specific sites in receptor proteins in the post-synaptic membrane.
- Every receptor protein then opens a channel protein so that ions such as Na^+ pass through the post-synaptic membrane into the cell.
- The Na^+ ions depolarise the post-synaptic membrane.
- If enough Na^+ ions enter then depolarisation reaches a threshold level and an action potential is generated in the cell.
- Enzymes in the cleft then remove the transmitter substance from the binding sites, e.g. acetylcholine esterase removes acetylcholine by hydrolysing it into choline and ethanoic acid.
- Breakdown products of transmitter substances are absorbed into the synaptic knob for re-synthesis of transmitter.

Summation

A single action potential may arrive at a synaptic knob and result in some transmitter molecules being secreted into a cleft. However, there may not be enough to cause an action potential to be generated. If a series of action potentials arrive at the synaptic knob then the build up of transmitter substances may reach the threshold and the neurone will now send an action potential. We say that the neurone has 'fired' as the action potential is produced.

KEY POINT

Once you have understood how an excitatory synapse operates then understanding of the neuromuscular junction should pose no problem!

Look out for questions based on how **drugs** act at synapses. Some **drug molecules** mimic **substances in organisms.** Be ready to compare the molecules of both. Spot the parts of the molecules which are similar. These are the active components!

How do motor neurones control muscle tissue?

The link to muscle tissue is by motor end plates which have close proximity to the sarcoplasm of the muscle tissue. The motor end plates have a greater surface area than a synaptic knob, but their action is very similar to the synaptic transmission described on the previous page. Action potentials result in muscle contraction.

Transmitter substances

The synapse described on the previous page used acetylcholine as a transmitter substance. There are others!

- Acetylcholine – the transmitter in the parasympathetic nervous system.
- Noradrenaline – the transmitter in the sympathetic nervous system.
- Dopamine – a transmitter in the brain.
- Serotonin – a transmitter in the brain.

Progress check

1 Explain the importance of summation at a synapse.

2 The diagram shows a synaptic knob.

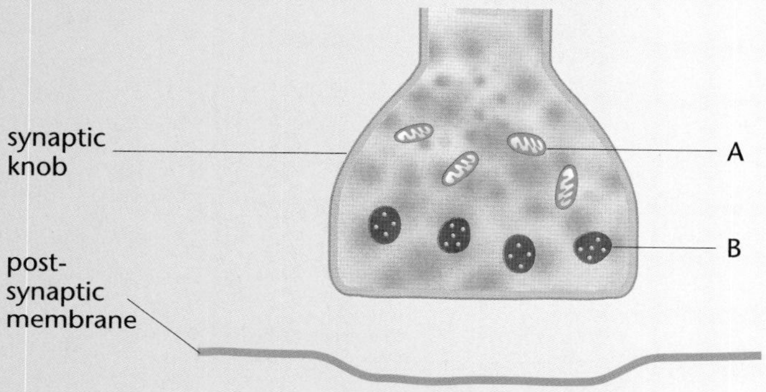

(a) Name A and B

(b) Describe the events which take place after an action potential reaches a synaptic knob and a further action potential is generated as a result.

1 A single action potential may arrive at a synaptic knob; there may not be enough transmitter molecules being secreted into a cleft to cause an action potential to be generated; a series of action potentials arrive at the synapse to build up transmitter substances to reach the threshold; the neurone will now send an action potential.

2 (a) A – mitochondria; B – vesicle

(b) Ca^{2+} ions flow into the synaptic knob; transmitter molecules such as acetylcholine are secreted into the gap; the transmitter molecules bind with sites in receptor proteins in the post-synaptic membrane; this opens channel proteins so that ions such as Na^+ pass through the post-synaptic membrane into the cell; the post-synaptic membrane is depolarised; if *enough* Na^+ ions enter a threshold level is reached and an action potential is generated in the cell.

3.3 The effects of drugs on synapses

After studying this section you should be able to:

- *understand the effects of a range of drugs on synapses*
- *understand the mechanisms of amplification and inhibition*

LEARNING SUMMARY

How do drugs affect synaptic transmission?

AQA A	M6
AQA B	M4
EDEXCEL	M4
OCR	M5
WJEC	M5

Different types of drugs can act on synapses in different ways.

Amplification at synapses

- **Amphetamines** stimulate the increase in secretion of noradrenaline so that transmission across the synapse takes place more quickly. Not surprisingly, in the world of illegal drugs it is known as 'Speed'.
- **Caffeine** or **nicotine** amplify synaptic transmission so that less transmitter molecules are needed to stimulate an action potential. (They work by **reducing the threshold** in the post-synaptic membrane.)

Inhibition at synapses

- **Atropine** binds to receptor proteins on the post-synaptic membrane so that acetylcholine cannot open the Na^+ channels and depolarisation cannot take place. The further conduction of the action potential is stopped.
- **Sarin**, a nerve gas, prevents the breakdown of the transmitter substances, which remain in the receptor sites on the post-synaptic membranes. This has no medical value, being a devastating warfare substance.

Activation of inhibitory synapse

- Tranquillisers stimulate the inhibitory synapses which prevent excitatory synapses from functioning efficiently. Bodily movement slows and perception is less responsive.

A range of drugs have an effect at the synapses.

Some drugs affect the CNS but you will need to remember that a drug is any substance which affects the functioning of the body. The examples in this chapter affect the nervous system but there are many more types.

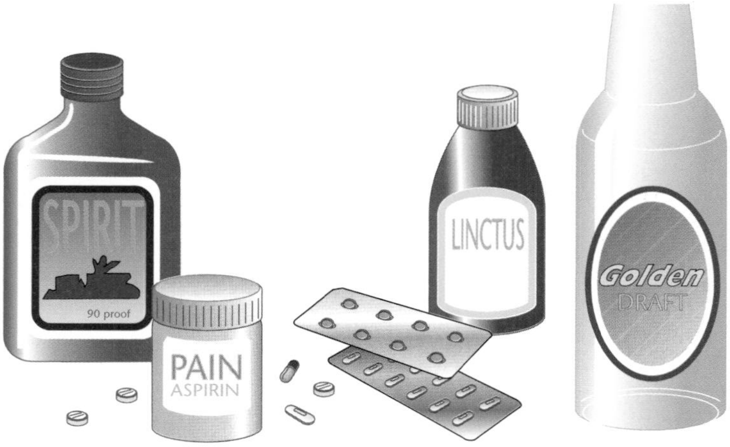

- **Painkillers** stop the conduction of an action potential in the following neurone. Morphine is such a drug so that the feeling of pain is greatly inhibited.
- **Stimulants** like amphetamines speed up synaptic transmission. Increased perception and movements are the result.
- **Depressants** like barbiturates and alcohol slow down conduction across the synapses so that slower reactions and limited perception result.

3.4 The central nervous system

After studying this section you should be able to:

- *outline the structure and functions of the brain and spinal cord*
- *understand the main functions of cerebrum, cerebellum, medulla oblongata and hypothalamus*
- *understand how neurones function together in a reflex arc*
- *describe the structure of skeletal muscle and understand the sliding filament mechanism*
- *outline the features of the autonomic nervous system*
- *describe the structure and function of the eye and ear*

LEARNING SUMMARY

The structure and functions of the CNS

AQA A	M6
AQA B	M4
EDEXCEL	M4
OCR	M5
WJEC	M5
NICCEA	M4

The CNS consists of the brain and spinal cord which work together to aid the coordination of the organism. The human brain has many functions. The spinal cord takes impulses from the brain to effectors and in the opposite direction impulses from receptors are channelled to the brain.

The brain has a complex 3D structure. The diagram below shows part of the brain structure – major components only.

The human brain

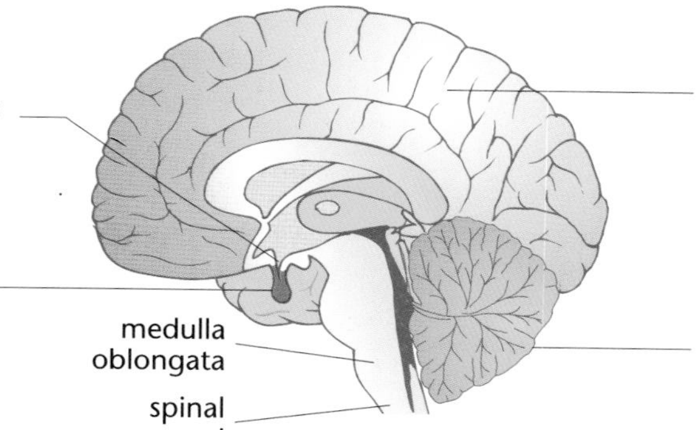

The CNS is like a motorway with impulses going in both directions!

- **Afferent neurones** take impulses **from** organs **to** the **CNS**.
- **Efferent neurones** take impulses **from** the **CNS** **to** an **organ**.

Learn these carefully. There are no marks for reversal!

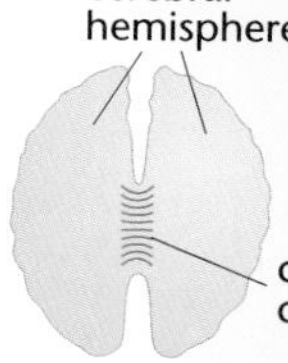

There are two cerebral hemispheres: the left and the right. Note that the right hemisphere controls the left side of the body and vice versa.

Alzheimer's disease

Neurones in the cortex of the cerebrum become progressively less able to produce neurotransmitter substances. Acetylcholine and noradrenaline are usually deficient resulting in major personality changes. The cause is often unknown, but can be genetic.

Functions of parts of the brain

Cerebrum

- Receives sensory information from many organs, e.g. impulses are sent from the eyes to the visual cortex at the back of the cerebrum.
- Controls motor activity of many organs.
- The front of the cerebrum holds the memory and intelligence in a network of multi-polar neurones.

Cerebellum

- Has a key role in the coordination of balance and smooth, controlled muscular movements.
- Initiation of a movement may be by the cerebrum but the smooth, well-coordinated execution of the movement is only possible with the help of the cerebellum.

Medulla oblongata

- Its respiratory centre controls the rhythm of breathing with nerve connections to the intercostal muscles and the diaphragm.
- Its cardiovascular centre controls the cardiac cycle via the sympathetic and vagus nerve.
- Connects to the sino-atrial node of the heart.

The hypothalamus is the key structure in maintaining a homeostatic balance in the body. It is like a thermostat in a house, switching the heating system on or off as internal conditions change. Similarly it is able to control chemical levels in the blood.

Hypothalamus

- Has an exceptional blood supply.
- Many receptors are located in the blood vessel walls which supply it.
- These receptors are highly sensitive detectors which monitor:
  - temperature
  - glucose
  - carbon dioxide
  - ionic concentration of plasma.
- Controls the production of thyroxine via the release factor, thyrotrophic hormone.
- Controls ADH secretion by the pituitary gland and is, therefore, responsible for the water content of both blood plasma and urine.

Pituitary gland

- Secretes a range of hormones and release factors and is the major control agent of the endocrine system.
- Responds to neurosecretion by the hypothalamus.
- Together with the hypothalamus is part of a number of negative feedback loops.
- Is the link between the nervous system and the endocrine system.

The above cover some functions of parts of the brain. There are many more!

KEY POINT

The human brain consists of approximately 10^{12} neurones and all are present at birth. It is no wonder that a baby's head is proportionally large at this stage of our life cycle. During the first three months after birth many synaptic connections are made. This is a most important developmental stage. Neurones cannot be replaced once damaged!

The reflex arc

How can we react quickly without even thinking about making a response?

The answer to this question is that the brain is not involved in the response so the time taken to respond to a stimulus is reduced. This rapid, automatic response is made possible by the reflex arc.

A reflex arc

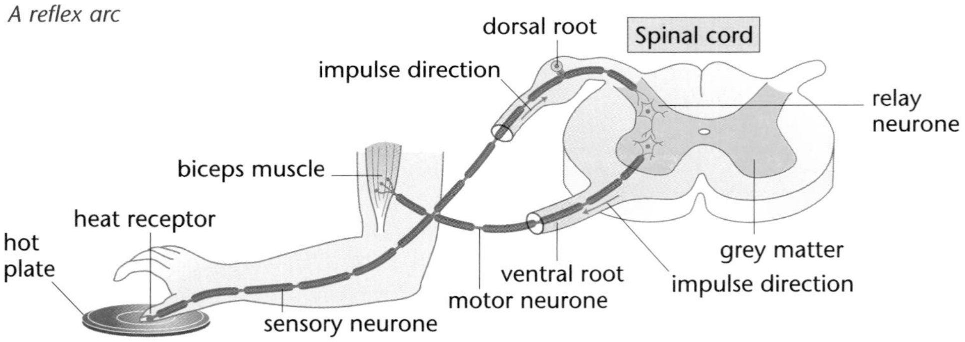

Features of a reflex arc

- The stimulus elicits a response in a receptor of a sensory neurone.
- As a result an action potential is generated along this sensory neurone.
- The sensory neurone, enters the spinal cord via the dorsal root and synapses onto a relay neurone.
- This intermediate neurone synapses onto a motor neurone which in turn conducts the impulse to a muscle via its motor end plates.
- The muscle contracts and the arm instantly withdraws from the stimulus before any harm is done.
- The complete list of events takes place so quickly because the impulses do not, initially, go to the brain! The complete pathway to the muscle conducts the impulse so rapidly, before the brain receives any sensory information.

It is other afferent neurones which *finally* take impulses to the brain which enable us to be aware of the arc which has just taken place. This afferent neurone is NOT part of the reflex arc.

> Reflexes have a high survival value because the organism is able to respond so rapidly. Additionally they are always automatic. There are a range of different reflexes, e.g. iris/pupil reflex, knee-jerk reflex and saliva production.
>
> **KEY POINT**

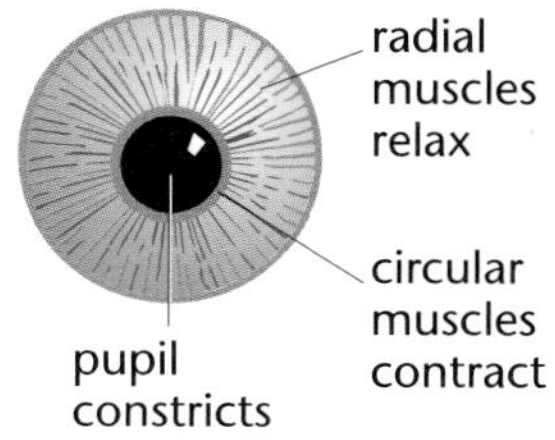

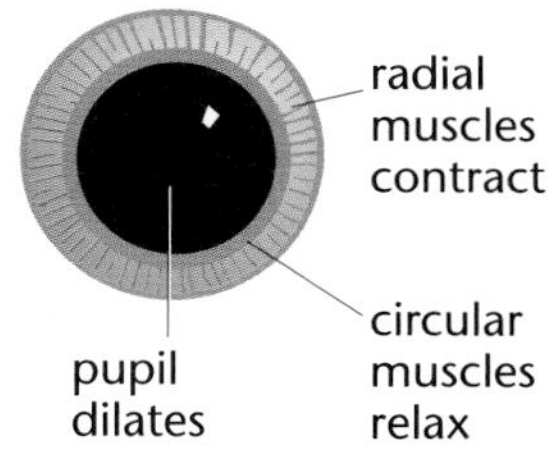

The iris/pupil reflex

The diagrams in the margin show the two extremes of pupil size.

- The amount of light entering the eye is detected by **receptors** in the **retina**.
- Reflex pathways lead to the **circular** and **radial** muscles of the **iris**.
- **High intensity** light activates the **circular muscles** of the iris to **contract**, as the radial muscles relax so the **pupil gets smaller**. (The advantage of this is too much light does not enter which would damage the retina.)
- **Low intensity** light activates the **radial muscles** of the iris to **contract**, as the circular muscles relax so the **pupil gets wider**. (The advantage of this is that the eye allows enough light to see.)
- A balance between the two extremes is achieved across a gradation of light conditions.

Autonomic nervous system

This is the part of the nervous system which controls our involuntary activities, e.g. the control of the heart rate. It is divided into two parts, the **sympathetic system** and the **parasympathetic system**. Each system has a major nerve from which smaller nerves branch out into key organs. In some ways the two systems are **antagonistic** to each other but in other ways they have specific functions not counteracted by the other. The table below shows all of the main facts for each system.

This table of features shows some key points for the autonomic system. ALERT! They are difficult to learn because of the lack of logic in the 'pattern' of functions. Take time to revise this properly because many candidates mix up the features of one system with another.

	Autonomic nervous system	
Feature	***Sympathetic***	***Parasympathetic***
Nerve	sympathetic nerve	vagus nerve
Transmitter substance at synapses	noradrenaline	acetylcholine
Heart rate	speeds up	slows down
Iris control	dilates	constricts
Saliva	———	flow stimulated
Gut movements	slowed down	speeds up
Sweating	sweat production stimulated	———
Erector pili muscles	contracts erector pili muscles	———

> Remember that all of the above functions take place without thought. The system is truly involuntary.
>
> **KEY POINT**

Progress check

State **two** functions of each of the following parts of the human brain:
(a) cerebrum (b) cerebellum (c) medulla oblongata.

(a) (i) receives sensory impulses from the eyes to the visual cortex, enabling sight
(ii) controls voluntary motor activity of the leg muscles.
(b) (i) coordinates balance, e.g. enables upright stance in humans
(ii) enables smooth movement, e.g. hitting a golf ball with a club straight down the fairway. (You could swing the club by voluntary control from the cerebrum but smooth coordination is by the cerebellum.)
(c) (i) controls the rhythm of breathing with nerve connections to the intercostal muscles and the diaphragm
(ii) controls the heart rate via the sympathetic and vagus nerve.

3.5 Control of skeletal muscle

LEARNING SUMMARY

After studying this section you should be able to:

- *understand control via motor end plates*
- *understand the mechanism of sarcomere contraction*

How do motor neurones control skeletal muscle?

AQA A	M6
AQA B	M4
EDEXCEL	M4
OCR	M5
WJEC	M5
NICCEA	M4

No contraction would take place without acetylcholine transmitter being released from the motor end plate. When the sarcolemma (membrane) reaches the threshold level, then the action potential is conducted throughout the sarcoplasm. Contraction is initiated!

Motor neurones control the skeletal muscle via motor end plates.

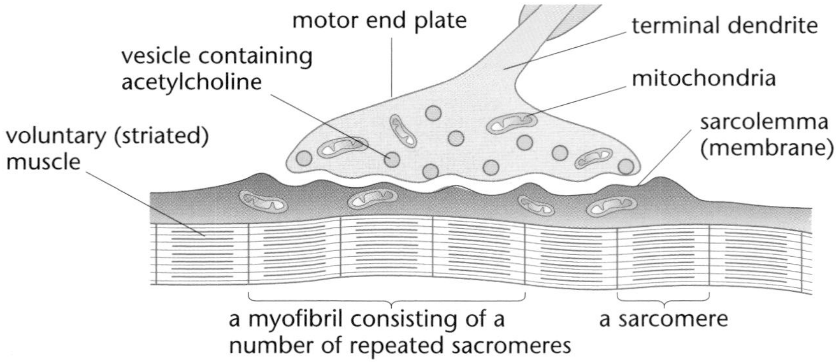

The skeletal muscles move the bones via their tendon attachments. The muscles work in **antagonistic** pairs, i.e. **opposing** each other. In the arm when the biceps contracts the forearm is lifted. At the same time the triceps relaxes. If the forearm is to be lowered then the triceps contracts and the biceps now relaxes.

Skeletal muscle is also known as striated or striped muscle. The structure of a single muscle unit, the sarcomere, shows the striped nature of the muscle.

The sarcomere

A sarcomere showing bands

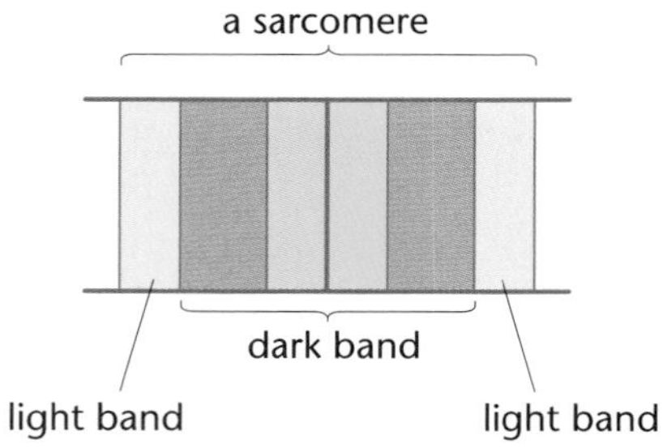

A sarcomere showing filaments

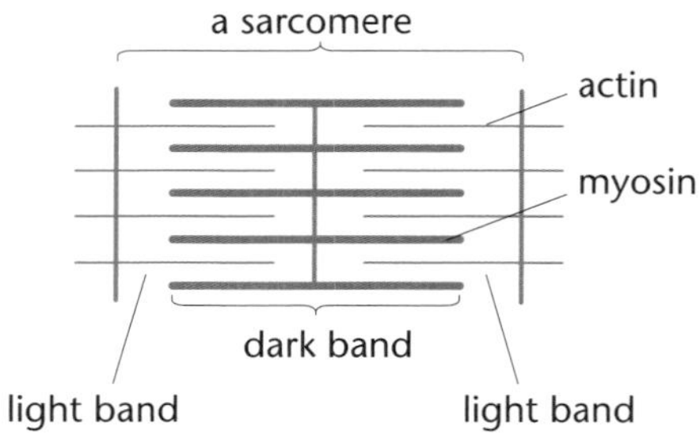

- The sarcomere consists of different filaments, thin ones (**actin**) and thick ones (**myosin**).
- These filaments form bands of different shades:
  – light band – just actin filaments
  – dark band – just myosin filaments or myosin plus actin.
- During contraction the filaments slide together to form a shorter sarcomere.
- As this pattern of contraction is repeated through 1000s of sarcomeres the whole muscle contracts.
- Actin and myosin filaments slide together because of the formation of cross bridges which alternatively build and break during contraction.
- Cross bridge formation is known as the 'ratchet mechanism'.

How does the 'ratchet mechanism' work?

To answer this question the properties of actin and myosin need to be considered. The diagram below represents an actin filament next to a myosin filament. Many 'bulbous heads' are located along the myosin filaments (just one is shown!). Each points towards an actin filament.

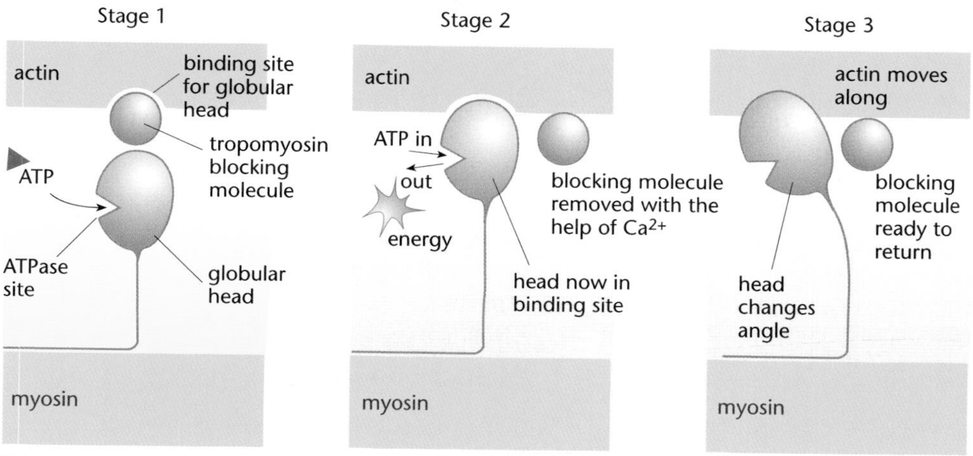

The sequence of the ratchet mechanism

- Once an action potential is generated in the muscle tissue then Ca^{2+} ions are released from the reticulum, a structure in the sarcoplasm.
- Part of the globular head of the myosin has an ATPase (enzyme!) site.
- Ca^{2+} ions activate the myosin head so that this ATPase site hydrolyses an ATP molecule, releasing energy.
- Ca^{2+} ions also bind to troponin in the actin filaments, this in turn removes blocking molecules (tropomyosin) from the actin filament.
- This exposes the binding sites on the actin filaments.
- The globular heads of the myosin then bind to the newly exposed sites forming actin-myosin cross bridges.
- At the stage of energy release the myosin heads change angle.
- This change of angle moves the actin filaments towards the centre of each sarcomere and is termed the power stroke.
- More ATP binds to the myosin head, effectively causing the cross bridge to become straight, the tropomyosin molecules once again block the actin binding sites.
- The myosin is now 'cocked' and ready to repeat the above process.
- Repeated cross bridge formation and breakage results in a rowing action shortening the sarcomere as the filaments slide past each other.

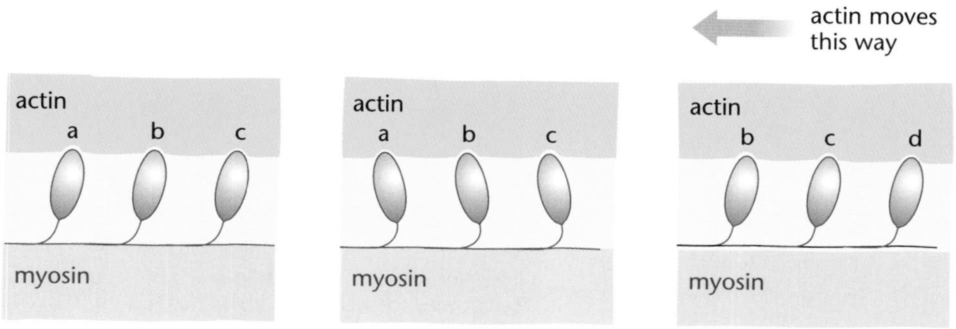

3.6 The human eye and ear

After studying this section you should be able to :

- *describe structures and their functions in the human eye*
- *describe the structures and functions of the cells in the retina*
- *describe the key structures in the human ear and their functions*

LEARNING SUMMARY

Structure of the eye

AQA A	M6
AQA B	M4
EDEXCEL	M4
OCR	M5
NICCEA	M4

The sensory nerve connections of the eyes

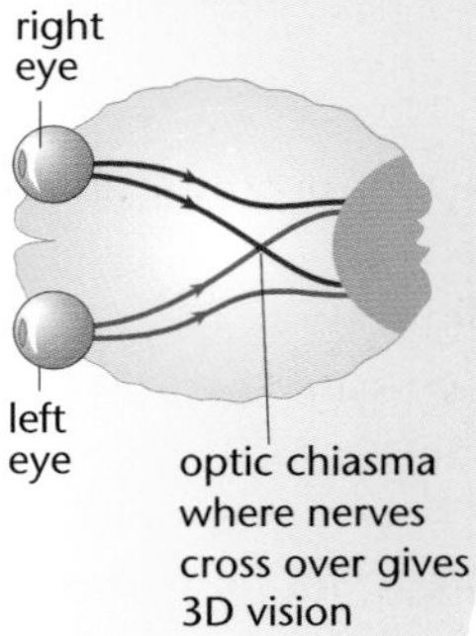

Note that each visual field is slightly different. The routes of the nerves crossing over help to create 'depth' in the image.

The human eye is a typical mammalian eye. The two eyes are located in sockets in the skull. Each eye helps the person to see a slightly different image giving a 3D (stereoscopic) view. Light sensitive cells respond to the light resulting in action potentials being sent along the optic nerves to the visual cortex at the back of the cerebrum.

Section through a human eye

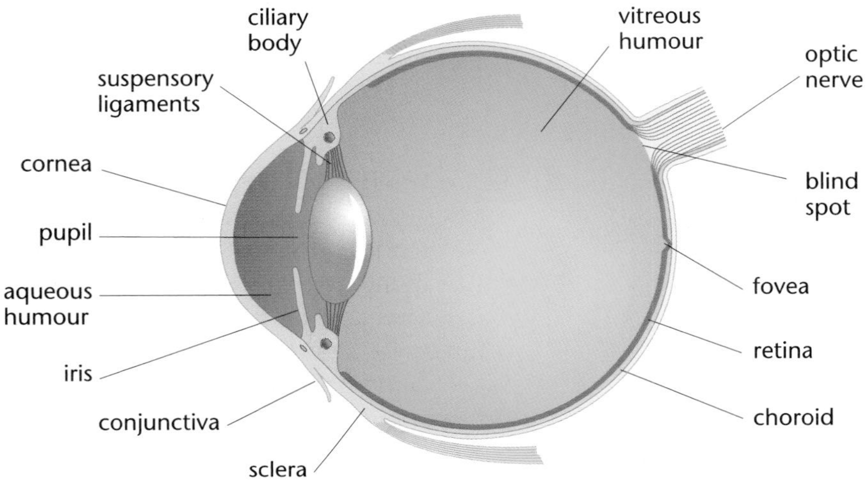

Key structures and their functions

The key parts in the focusing of light are the cornea and lens which changes shape when focusing near or far objects.

Accommodation is the ability to change the focal point of the lens to focus objects at different distances.

Near object focus:
- lens – round
- suspensory ligaments – loose
- ciliary muscle – contracted.

Far object focus:
- lens – long and thin
- suspensory ligament – tight
- ciliary muscle – relaxed

- **Conjunctiva**, is a thin protective covering of epithelial cells.
- **Cornea**, is the transparent, curved front of the eye which helps to converge the light rays which enter the eye.
- **Sclera**, is an opaque, fibrous, protective outer structure.
- **Choroid**, has a network of blood vessels to supply nutrients to cells and remove waste products. It is pigmented to prevent internal reflection.
- **Iris**, is a pigmented muscular structure consisting of an inner ring of **circular muscle** and an outer layer of **radial muscle** (see page 55). Its function is to help control the amount of light entering the eye so that:
  – too much light does not enter which would damage the retina
  – enough light enters to allow the person to see.
- **Pupil**, is a hole in the middle of the iris where light is allowed to continue its passage. In bright light it is constricted and in dim light it is dilated.
- **Vitreous humour**, is a transparent, jelly-like mass located behind the lens. It acts as a 'suspension' for the lens so that the delicate lens is not damaged.
- **Lens**, is a transparent, flexible, curved structure. Its function is to focus incoming light rays onto the retina using its refractive properties.
- **Retina**, is a layer of sensory neurones, the key structures being photoreceptors which respond to light.
- **Blind spot**, is where the bundle of sensory fibres form the optic nerve.

How do the cells of the retina respond to light?

There are two types of cell which are photosensitive, the rod cells and the cone cells. They each have different properties.

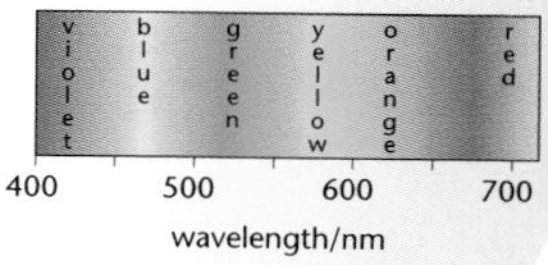

Rod cells – can only do summation

- Are very sensitive to the intensity of light, but are not sensitive to colour.
- Can respond to even dim light.
- Respond by the following reaction:

$$\text{rhodopsin} \xrightarrow{\text{light}} \text{opsin} + \text{retinal}$$

- Low visual acuity in dim conditions.
- Opsin opens ion channels in the cell surface membrane which can result in the generation of an action potential.
- Rhodopsin can be re-generated during an absence of light.

Cone cells

- Require high light intensities to be responsive – high visual acuity.
- Respond by the following reaction:

$$\text{iodopsin} \xrightarrow{\text{light of specific wavelength}} \text{photopsin} + \text{retinal}$$

- Exist in three different types, red, green and blue, each having a different form of iodopsin:
  – red cones are stimulated by wavelengths of red light
  – green cones are stimulated by wavelengths of green light
  – blue cones are stimulated by wavelengths of blue light
  – all three cones when stimulated give white light
  – none of the three types when stimulated gives black.
- Opsin again opens ion channels in the membranes which can lead to the generation of an action potential.

The colour vision mechanism appears to require three types of cone, RED, GREEN, and BLUE and gives the *trichromatic* theory.

Structure of the retina

Remember that red light reaching a cone sensitive to only blue light would not stimulate the generation of an action potential! Cones are only sensitive to light of a specific range of wave-lengths.

Note the direction of light as it reaches the upper retinal surface.

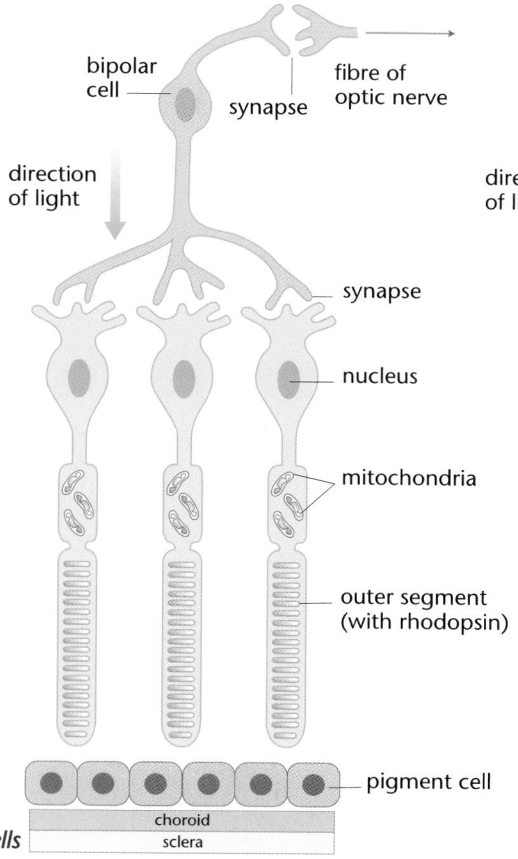

Rod cells

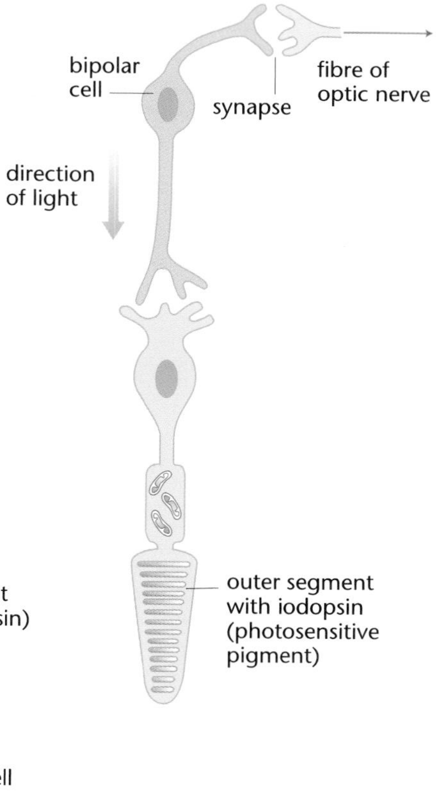

A cone cell – found in forea

Visual acuity

Did you know that the fovea consists of almost totally cones?

What do we see with in dim conditions?

You have guessed it, rods. Their ability to detect dim light is useful but there is no colour!

This is a measure of the detail we can see. The cones are responsible for high visual acuity (high resolution!). Large numbers are packed very close to each other in the fovea. ONE cone cell synapses onto ONE bipolar cell which in turn synapses onto ONE ganglion cell as the information is relayed to the visual cortex. Spatially, much more clarity is perceived than for the rods. The image can be likened to a television picture with high numbers of pixels. High definition!

Compare this with the rods. The rod cells are not packed close together so that visual acuity is low.

Convergence

Many rods can synapse onto one bipolar cell. A ray of light reaching one rod may not be enough to stimulate an action potential along a nerve pathway. Several rods link to one bipolar cell so that enough transmitter molecules at a synapse reach the threshold level. This depolarisation results in an action potential in the bipolar cell. This is summation, as a result of rod cell teamwork!

Structure of an ear

OCR MS
WJEC MS

The human ear responds to sound frequencies within the range 40–20 000 Hz. Outside of this auditory range the sensory neurones do not respond.

Section through a human ear

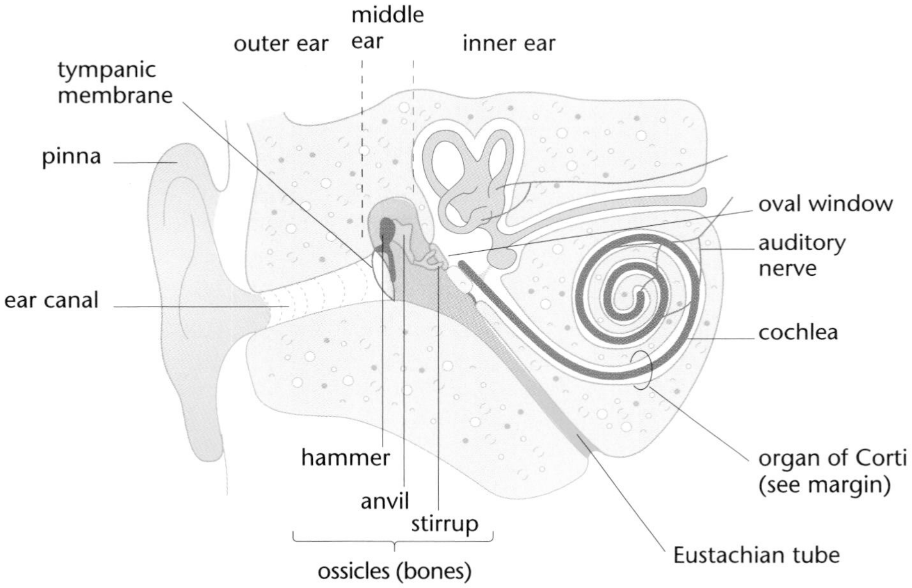

The Eustachian tube allows the pressure at either side of the tympanic membrane to be equalised, i.e. atmospheric pressure = pressure in the inner ear.

Key structures and their functions

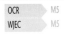

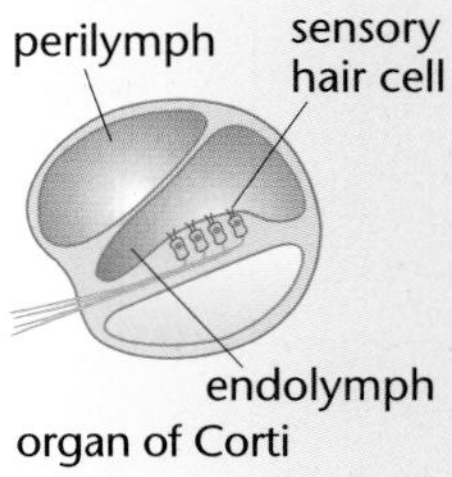

- Sound waves are directed towards the tympanic membrane through the ear canal.
- They reach the tympanic membrane which vibrates as a result.
- The ossicle bones then pass on and amplify these vibrations.
- The membrane of the oval window then vibrates and passes on these vibrations to the perilymph of the cochlea.
- Movements of the fluid perilymph pass through the cochlea and move sensory hair cells on the organ of Corti.
- Physical hair movements result in the generation of action potentials which pass along the auditory nerve (sensory hairs are transducers).

3.7 Plant sensitivity

After studying this section you should be able to:

- understand the range of tropisms which affect plant growth
- understand how auxins, gibberellins and cytokinins control plant growth
- understand how phytochromes control the onset of flowering in plants

LEARNING SUMMARY

Plant growth regulators

EDEXCEL	M5
OCR	M5
WJEC	M5
NICCEA	M4

External stimuli such as light can affect the direction of plant growth. A **tropism** is a **growth response** to an external stimulus. It is important that a plant grows in a direction which will enable it to obtain maximum supplies. Plant regulators are substances produced in minute quantities and tend to interact in their effects.

> Growth response to light is **phototropism**
> Growth response to gravity is **geotropism**
> Growth response to water **hydrotropism**
> Growth response to contact is **thigmotropism**
> Tropisms can be positive (towards) or negative (away from).

KEY POINT

Phototropism

This response is dependent upon the stimulus, light affecting the growth regulator, **auxin** (indoleacetic acid).

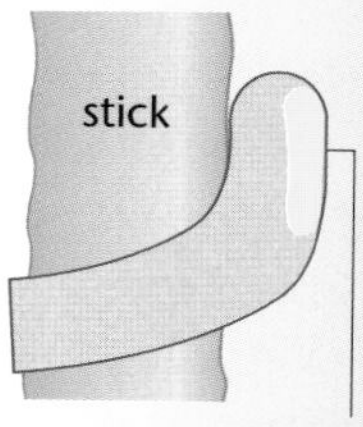

Thigmotropism helps a climbing plant like the runner bean to grow in a twisting pattern around a stick. Auxin is redistributed away from the contact point so the outer cells elongate giving a stronger outer growth.

Auxin and growing shoots

Auxin is produced by cells undergoing mitosis, e.g. growing tips. If a plant shoot is illuminated from one side then the auxin is redistributed to the side furthest from the light. This side grows more strongly, owing to the elongation of the cells, resulting in a bend towards the light. The plant benefits from increased light for photosynthesis. Up to a certain concentration the degree of bending is proportional to auxin concentration.

Tropisms in response to light
light from different directions

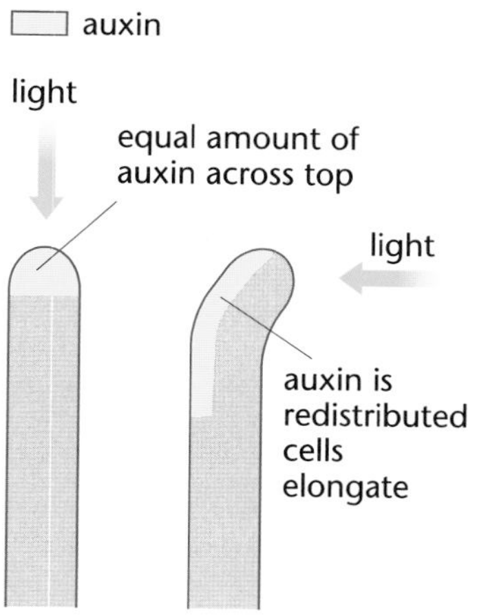

Tropism in response to auxin

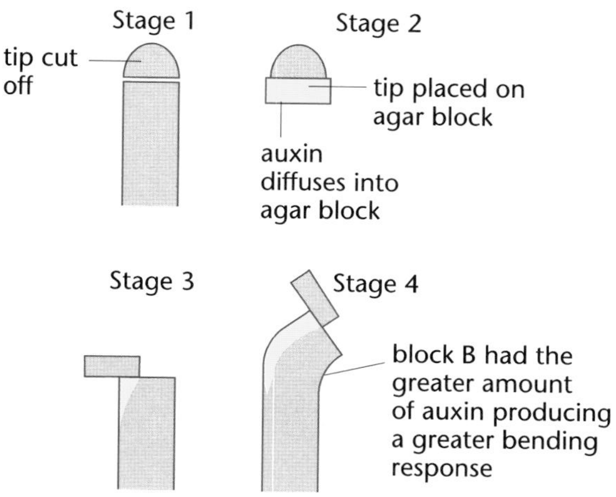

The diagrams show tropic responses to light and auxin.

Auxin research

Many investigations of auxins have taken place using the growing tips (coleoptiles) of grasses. Where a growing tip is removed and placed on an agar block, auxin will diffuse into the agar. Returning the block to the mitotic area stimulates increased cell elongation to the cells receiving a greater supply of auxin.

Is the concentration of auxin important?

It is important to consider the implications of the concentration of auxin in a tissue. The graph below shows that at different concentrations auxin affects the shoot and the root in different ways.

> Analyse this graph carefully. It shows how the same substance can both stimulate or inhibit, depending on concentration.

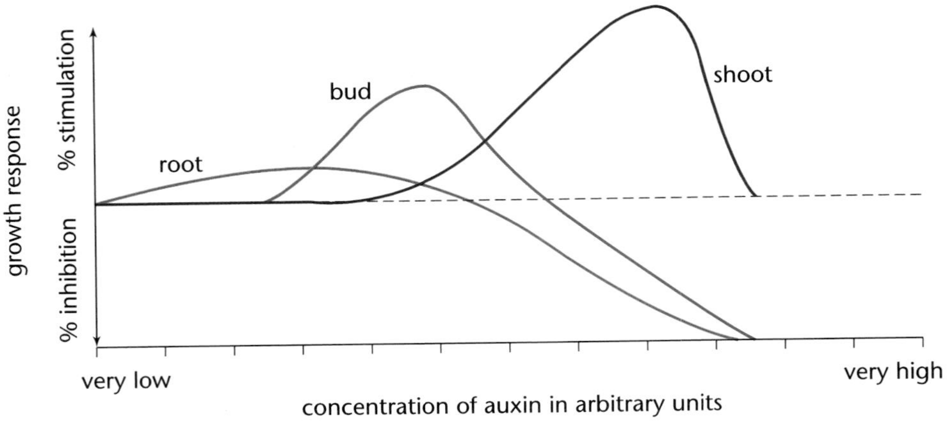

The graph shows:

- auxin has no effect on a shoot at very low concentration
- at these very low concentrations root cell elongation is stimulated
- at higher concentrations the elongation of shoot cells is stimulated
- at these higher concentrations auxin inhibits the elongation of root cells.

Auxin and root growth

The graph shows that auxin affects root cells in a different way at different concentrations. At the root tip auxin accumulates at a lower point because of gravity. This inhibits the lower cells from elongating. However, the higher cells at the tip have a low concentration of auxin and do elongate. The net effect is for the stronger upper cell growth to bend the root downwards. The plant therefore has more chance of obtaining more water and mineral ions.

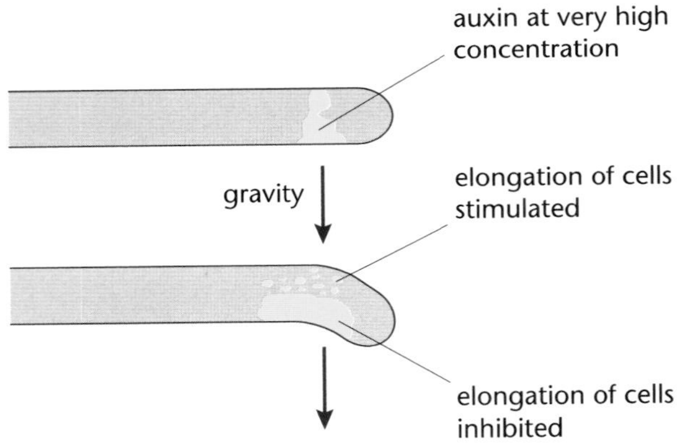

Plant growth regulators

> In your examination look out for data which will be supplied, e.g. the growth regulator gibberellin may be linked to falling starch levels in a seed endosperm and increase in maltose. Gibberellin has stimulated the enzymic activity.

Hormone	*Some key functions*
auxin	increased cell elongation, suppression of lateral bud development
gibberellin	cell elongation, ends dormancy in buds, promotes germination of seeds by activating hydrolytic enzymes such as amylase (food stores are mobilised!)
cytokinin	increased cell division, increased cell enlargement in leaves
ethene	promotes ripening of food

Phytochrome and the onset of flowering in plants

Phytochrome:

- is a regulatory substance
- is photosensitive
- has a number of different roles
- controls the onset of flowering in plants
- exists in two different forms, **phytochrome red** (P_R) and **phytochrome far red** (P_{FR}).

The terms P_R and P_{FR} refer to the peak wavelengths of light, absorbed by each substance:

P_R absorbs a peak of 665 nm

P_{FR} absorbs a peak of 725 nm.

The two forms are inter-convertible as shown below.

very fast in red light
fast in sunlight

$$P_R \rightleftarrows P_{FR}$$

slow conversion in dark
fast in far-red light

The above inter-conversion of the phytochromes is part of the mechanism that controls the onset of flowering. This is known as **photoperiodism**.

Different species of plants respond to different day lengths during the year.

Specific day length triggers the development of the flower buds.

There are three categories of plant:

- long day plants, e.g. petunias (**need P_{FR} to flower**)
- short day plants, e.g. chrysanthemums (**need P_R to flower**)
- day neutral plants, e.g. tomatoes.

The day-length and night-length bars below show the proportion of light and dark and the effect on the flowering.

long day plants in summer

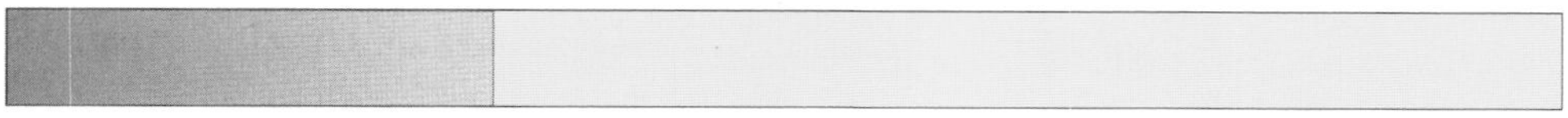

- $P_R \longrightarrow P_{FR}$ (fast conversion in light)
- flowering promoted (long day plants need P_{FR})

short day plants in summer

- $P_R \longrightarrow P_{FR}$
- flowering NOT promoted (short day plants need P_R)

In your examinations look out for data about day length. Particularly look for the short day data where a flash of light occurs during a dark period. This is enough to make P_{FR} which will stimulate long day plants to flower. This is due to the rapid $P_R \rightarrow P_{FR}$ process.

long day plants in winter

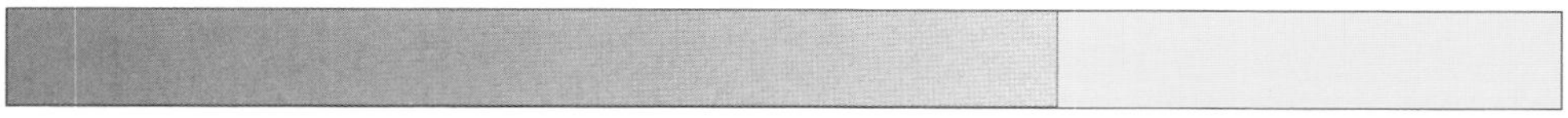

- $P_{FR} \longrightarrow P_R$ (slow process but the night is long enough)
- flowering not promoted (long day plants need P_{FR})

short day plants in summer

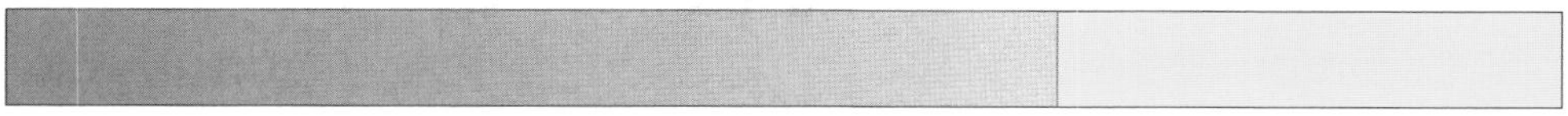

- $P_{FR} \longrightarrow P_R$ (slow process but long enough at night to make P_R)
- flowering promoted (short day plants need P_R)

Key

darkness

sunlight

Sample question and model answer

The diagram below shows a section through a mammalian eye.

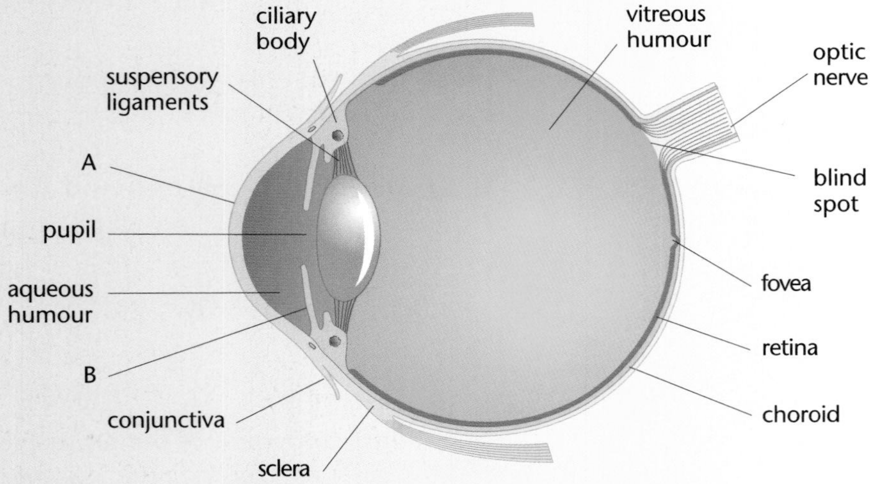

Take care when answering questions like this! Initially it could be a GCSE question but the level of detail required is much greater. Use the key technical terms, i.e. the fact that the cornea is able to begin the focusing of light rays by convergence, possible because of its refractive properties.

Similarly it is important to give detail of the radial and circular muscles of the iris to regulate light entry.

(a) Describe the function of parts A and B. [2]

A (cornea) refracts the light to begin convergence of light rays entering the eye.

B (iris) the radial and circular muscles of the iris change the size of the pupil to regulate light entry.

(b) Complete the table below to show the function of each part in the table.

	lens	***suspensory ligament***	***ciliary body***	
Focusing a near object	round	loose	contracted	[1]
Focusing a far object	longer and thinner	tight	relaxed	[1]

(c) The diagram shows a cone from the retina.

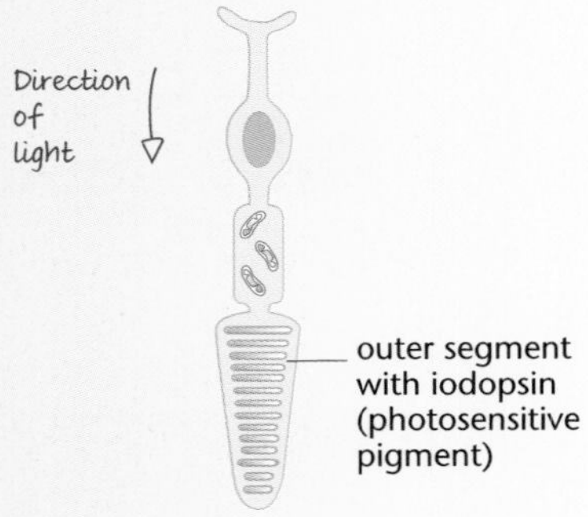

Remember the position of a cone in the retina. This will help you decide that the light comes down towards this cone. Learn this carefully.

(i) Place an arrow on the diagram to show the direction in which light reaches the cone. [1]

(ii) What is the function of the iodopsin in the outer segment? [4]

when stimulated by light <u>of the correct wavelength</u> – breaks down to release opsin; opsin opens ion channels in the membranes; this can lead to the generation of an action potential; in a bipolar cell.

Always look at how many marks per question part. You then know how many points to make.

(iii) How do cones contribute to high visual acuity? [3]

cones are tightly packed giving a high surface area; each cone synapses onto a single bipolar neurone; so the greater detail gives higher resolution.

Practice examination questions

1 The growing tips (coleoptiles) were removed from oat stems. Agar blocks containing different concentrations of synthetic auxin (IAA) replaced the tips on the oat stems. The plants were allowed to grow for a period then the angle of curvature of the stems was measured. The results are shown in the graph below.

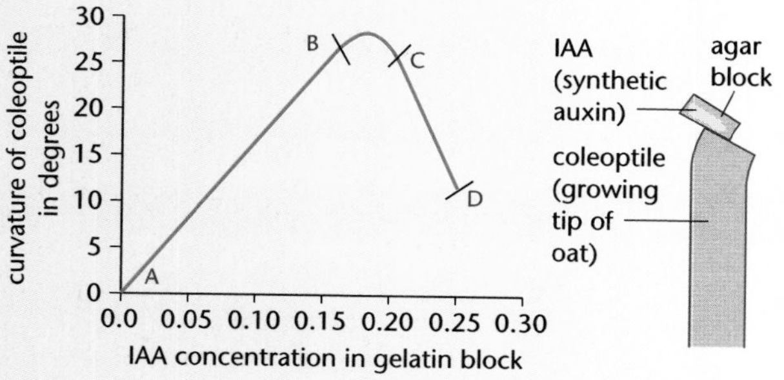

(a) What is the relationship between IAA concentration and curvature of the stem between points:

(i) A and B [1]

(ii) C and D? [1]

(b) Explain how IAA causes a curvature in the oat stems. [2]

(c) Explain the effect a much higher concentration of IAA would have on the curvature of oat stems. [2]

[Total: 6]

2 The diagram below shows a single sarcomere just before contraction.

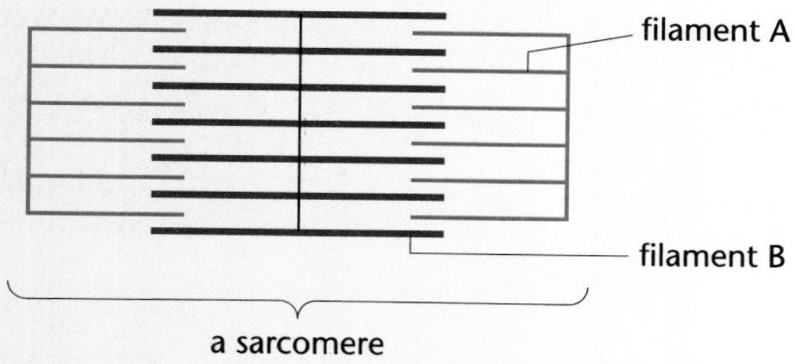

(a) Name filaments A and B. [2]

(b) What stimulus causes the immediate contraction of a sarcomere? [1]

(c) What happens to each type of filament during contraction? [2]

[Total: 5]

3 The diagram below shows the profile of an action potential.

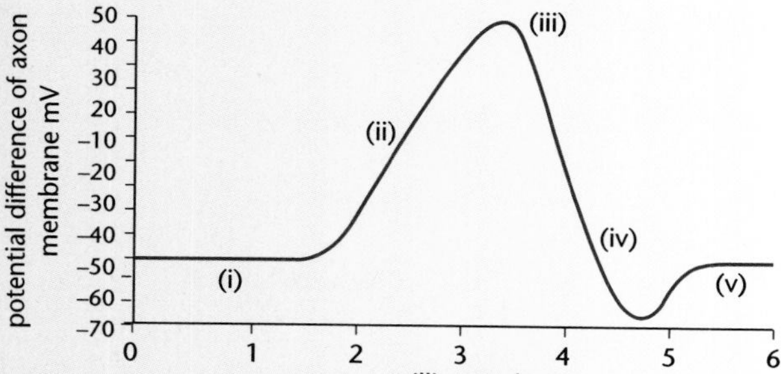

Explain what happens in the axon at each stage shown on the diagram. [10]

[Total: 10]

Chapter 4

Homeostasis

The following topics are covered in this chapter:

- *Hormones*
- *Temperature control in a mammal*
- *Regulation of blood sugar level*
- *The kidneys*
- *Adaptations to desert ecosystems*

4.1 Hormones

LEARNING SUMMARY

After studying this section you should be able to:

- *define homeostasis*
- *describe the route of hormones from source to target organ*
- *understand how hormones contribute to homeostasis*
- *recall the roles of a range of hormones*

The endocrine system

AQA A	M6
AQA B	M4
EDEXCEL	M4
OCR	M4
WJEC	M5
NICCEA	M4

The endocrine system secretes a number of chemicals known as **hormones**. Each hormone is a substance produced by an **endocrine gland**, e.g. adrenal glands produce the hormone adrenalin. Every hormone is **transported in the blood** and has a **target organ**. Once the target organ is reached the hormone **triggers a response** in the organ. Many hormones do this by **activating enzymes**. Others **activate genes**, e.g. steroids.

The great advantage of homeostasis is that the conditions in the environment fluctuate but conditions in the organism remain stable.

KEY POINT

The endocrine and nervous systems both contribute to **coordination** in animals. They help to regulate internal processes. **Homeostasis** is the maintenance of a **constant internal environment**. Nerves and hormones have key roles in the maintenance of this **steady internal state**. Levels of pH, blood glucose, oxygen, carbon dioxide and temperature all need to be controlled.

Parts of the human endocrine system (both male and female organs shown!)

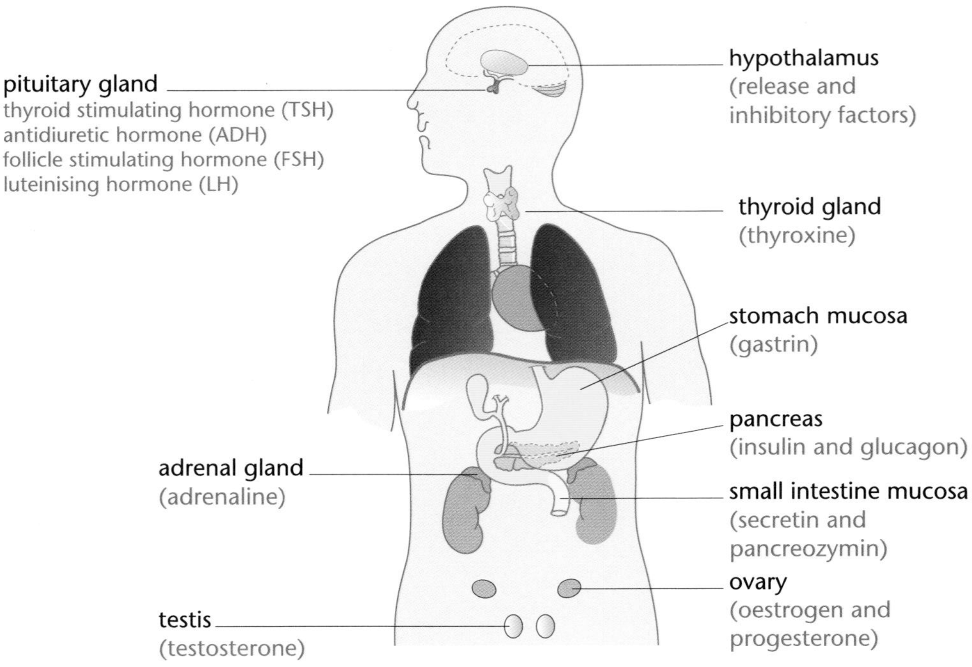

Some important mammalian hormones

The table shows the sources and some functions of a range of mammalian hormones. The pituitary gland is the key control gland. It affects many areas of the body and even stimulates, by the production of tropic hormones, other hormones, e.g. follicle stimulating hormone.

Hormone	*Source*	*Effect*
TSH	pituitary	stimulates the thyroid to secrete thyroxine
thyroxine	thyroid	increases metabolic rate
insulin	pancreas	reduces blood sugar
glucagon	pancreas	stimulates conversion of glycogen to glucose in the liver
ADH	pituitary	increased water reabsorption by kidney
gastrin	stomach mucosa	stimulates HCl production in stomach
secretin	intestinal mucosa	stimulates the pancreas to secrete fluid + alkali
pancreozymin	intestinal mucosa	stimulates the pancreas to secrete enzymes
FSH	pituitary	stimulates primary (Graafian) follicle to develop or testis to make sperms
LH	pituitary	stimulates ovulation or testis to make testosterone
oestrogen	ovary	stimulates development of endometrium stimulates secondary sexual characteristics
progesterone	ovary	maintains endometrium

How does a hormone trigger a cell in a target organ?

Hormones are much slower in eliciting a response than the nervous system. Rather than having an effect in milliseconds like nerves, hormones take longer. However, effects in response to hormones are often long lasting.

The diagram below shows one mechanism by which hormones activate target cells.

Did you know?
Each enzyme shown is constantly re-used as an active site is left free.

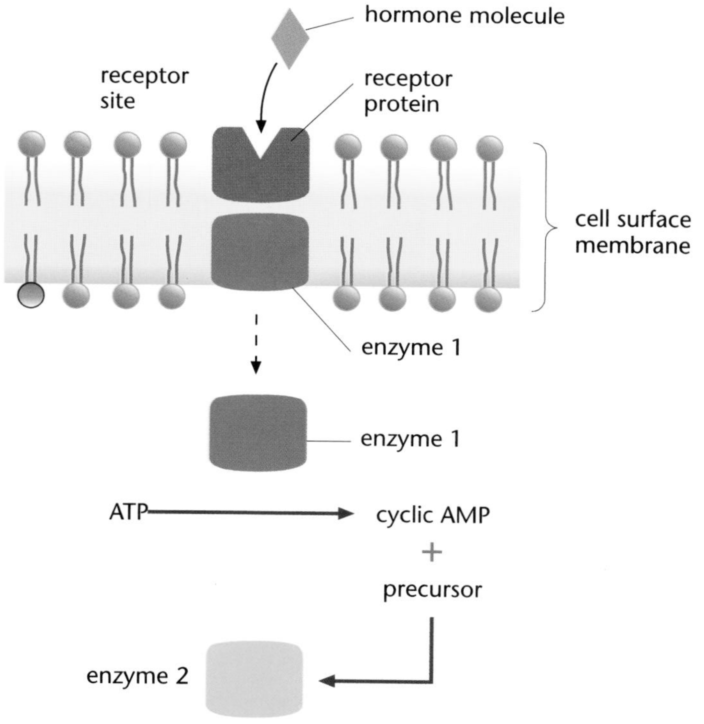

Look carefully at this mechanism! Just **ONE hormone molecule** arriving at the cell releases an enzyme which can be used **many** times. In turn, another enzyme is produced which can be used **many** times. One hormone molecule leads to **amplification**. This is a cascade effect!

4.2 Temperature control in a mammal

After studying this section you should be able to:

- *outline the processes which contribute to temperature regulation in a mammal*
- *understand how nervous and endocrine systems work together to regulate body temperature*
- *understand how internal processes are regulated by negative feedback*

LEARNING SUMMARY

What are the advantages of controlling body temperature?

AQA A	M6
AQA B	M4
EDEXCEL	M4
OCR	M5
NICCEA	M4

It is advantageous to maintain a constant body temperature so that the enzymes which drive the processes of life can function at an optimum level.

- **Endothermic** (warm blooded) animals can maintain their core temperature at an optimal level. This allows internal processes to be consistent. The level of activity of an endotherm is likely to fluctuate less than an ectotherm.
- **Ectothermic** (cold blooded) animals have a body temperature which fluctuates with the environmental temperature. As a result there are times when an animal may be vulnerable due to the enzyme driven reactions being slow. You could approach a crocodile (ectotherm) in cold conditions. Its speed of attack would be slow. If approached in warm conditions the attack would be rapid.

Once the blood temperature decreases, the heat gain centre of the hypothalamus is stimulated. This leads to a rise in blood temperature which, in turn, results in the heat loss centre being stimulated. This is negative feedback! The combination of the two, in both directions, contributes to homeostasis.

How is temperature controlled in a mammal?

The key structure in homeostatic control of all body processes is the **hypothalamus**. The regulation of temperature involves thermoreceptors in the skin, body core and blood vessels supplying the brain, which link to the hypothalamus.

The **hypothalamus** has **many functions**! It controls thirst, hunger, sleep and it stimulates the production of many hormones other than those required for temperature regulation.

The diagram below shows how the peripheral nerves, hypothalamus and pituitary gland integrate nervous and endocrine glands to regulate temperature.

Temperature regulation model

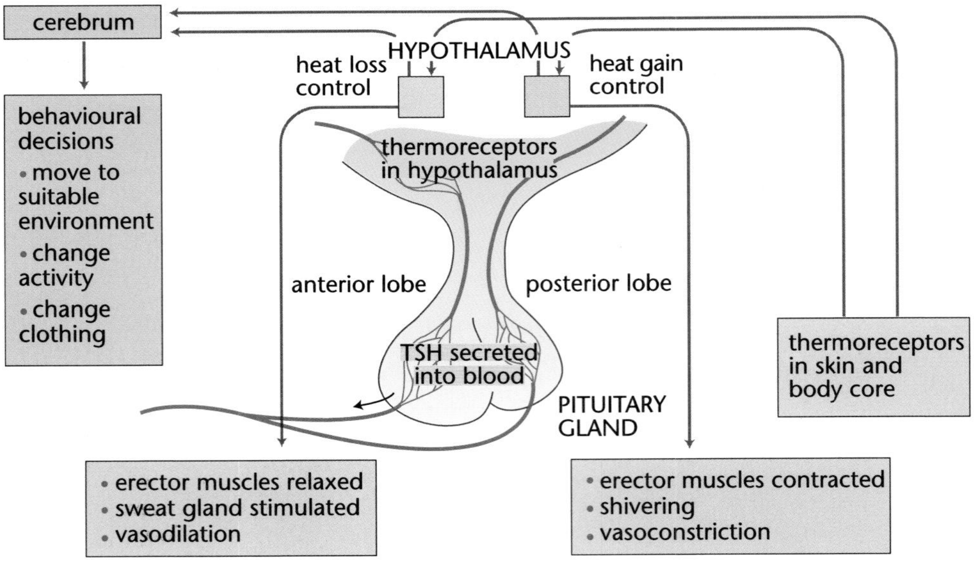

If there is an increase in core temperature then the hypothalamus stimulates greater heat loss by:

- vasodilation (dilation of the skin arterioles)
- erector-pili muscles are relaxed and hairs lie flat
- more sweating
- behavioural response in humans to change to thinner clothing.

When the hypothalamus receives sensory information **heat loss** or **heat gain** control results.

A **fall** in temperature results in the following control responses.

A capillary bed

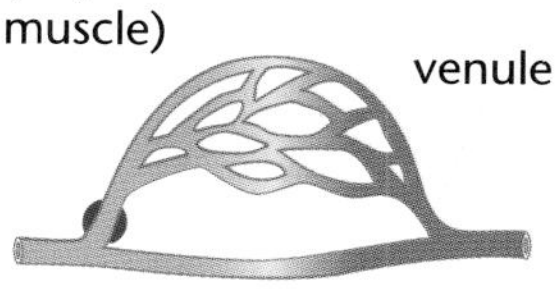

Vasoconstriction

- Arteriole control is initiated by the hypothalamus which results in efferent neurones stimulating constriction of the arteriole sphincters of skin capillary beds.
- This deviates blood to the core of the body, so less heat energy is lost from the skin.

Contraction of the erector-pili muscles

- Erector-pili muscle contraction is initiated in the hypothalamus being controlled via efferent neurones.
- Hairs on skin stand on end and trap an insulating layer of air, so less heat energy is lost from the skin.

Sweat reduction

- The sweat glands control is also initiated in hypothalamus, and is controlled via efferent neurones.
- Less heat energy is lost from the skin by evaporation of sweat.

Shivering

- Increased muscular contraction is accompanied by heat energy release.

Behavioural response

- This could be to switch on the heating, put on warmer clothes, etc.
- A link from the hypothalamus to the cerebrum elicits this voluntary response.

Increased metabolic rate

- The hypothalamus produces a release factor substance.
- This stimulates the anterior part of the pituitary gland to secrete TSH (thyroid stimulating hormone).
- TSH reaches the thyroid via the blood.
- Thyroid gland is stimulated to secrete thyroxine.
- Thyroxine increases respiration in the tissues increasing the body temperature.

Once a higher thyroxine level is detected in the blood the release factor in hypothalamus is inhibited so TSH release by the pituitary gland is prevented. This is **negative feedback**.

An **increase** in body temperature results in almost the **opposite** of each response described for a fall of temperature.

Note:
(a) the outline for heat loss methods does not show the nerve connections. Efferent neurones are again coordinated via the hypothalamus!
(b) heat is lost from the skin via a combination of **conduction, convection** and **radiation.**

Vasodilation

- Arterioles of capillary beds dilate allowing more blood to skin capillary beds.

Relaxation of erector-pili muscles

- Hairs lie flat, no insulating layer of air trapped.
- More heat loss of skin.

Sweat increase

- More sweat excreted so more heat energy from body needed to evaporate the sweat, so we cool down.

Behavioural response

- This could be to move into the shade or consume a cold drink.

Progress check

Hormone X stimulates the production of a substance in a cell of a target organ. The following statements outline events which result in the production of the substance but are in the wrong order. Write the correct order of letters.

A Hormone X is transported in the blood.
B Hormone X binds with a receptor protein in the cell surface membrane.
C The enzyme catalyses a reaction, forming a product.
D Hormone X secreted by gland.
E This releases an enzyme from the cell surface membrane.

D, A, B, E, C.

4.3 Regulation of blood sugar level

After studying this section you should be able to:

- *understand the control of blood glucose levels in a person*
- *describe the sites of insulin and glucagon secretion*
- *explain the functions of insulin and glucagon*

LEARNING SUMMARY

Why is it necessary to control the amount of glucose in the blood?

AQA A	M6
AQA B	M4
EDEXCEL	M4
OCR	M5
NICCEA	M4

Glucose molecules are needed to supply energy for every living cell. The level in the blood must be high enough to meet this need (90 mg per 100 cm^3 blood). This level needs to be maintained at a constant level, even though a person may or may not have eaten. High levels of glucose in the blood would cause great problems. Hypertonic blood plasma would result in water leaving the tissues by osmosis. Dehydration of organs would result in a number of symptoms.

Blood glucose regulation

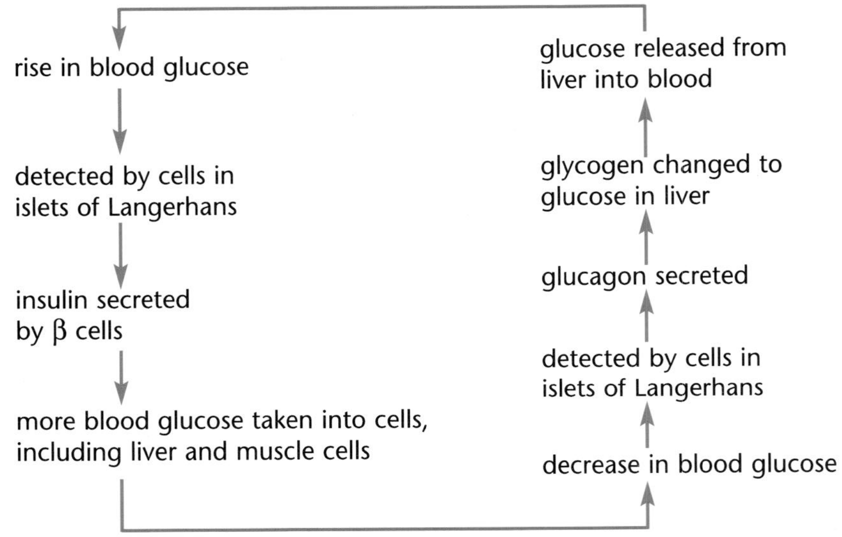

Negative feedback

Blood glucose regulation is an example of negative feedback. Any change in glucose level initiates changes which will result in the return of the original level, **balance is achieved.**

KEY POINT

Insulin

- Is secreted into the blood due to stimulation of pancreatic cells by a high concentration of glucose in the blood.
- Is produced by the β cells of the islets of Langerhans in the pancreas.
- Binds to receptor proteins in cell surface membranes activating carrier proteins to allow glucose entry to cells.
- Allows excess glucose molecules into the liver and muscles where they are converted into glycogen (a storage product), and some fat.

Never state that insulin changes glucose to glycogen. It allows glucose into the liver where glycogen synthase catalyses the conversion!

Glucagon

- Is secreted into the blood due to stimulation of pancreatic cells by a low concentration of glucose in the blood.
- Is produced by the α cells of the islets of Langerhans in the pancreas.
- Stimulates the conversion of glycogen to glucose.

Diabetes

There are two types of this condition.

Type 1

- The pancreas fails to produce enough insulin.
- After a meal when blood glucose level increases dramatically, the level remains high.
- High blood glucose causes hyperglycaemia.
- Kidneys, even though they are healthy, cannot reabsorb the glucose, resulting in glucose being in the urine.
- Symptoms include dehydration, loss of weight and lethargy.

What is the answer?

- Insulin injections and carbohydrate controlled diet.

Type 2

- This form of diabetes usually occurs in later life.
- Insulin is still produced but the receptor proteins on the cell surface membranes may not work correctly.
- Glucose uptake by the cells is erratic.
- Symptoms are similar to those for type 1 but are mild in comparison.

What is the answer?

- Dietary control including low carbohydrate intake.

More liver functions

The role of the liver in its production of bile, as well as the storage and break down of glycogen has been highlighted. The liver does so much more!

Children need 10 essential amino acids (adults need 8). From these they can make different ones by transamination in the liver!

Transamination

This is the way an R group of a keto acid is transferred to an amino acid. It replaces the existing R group with another, a new amino acid has been formed.

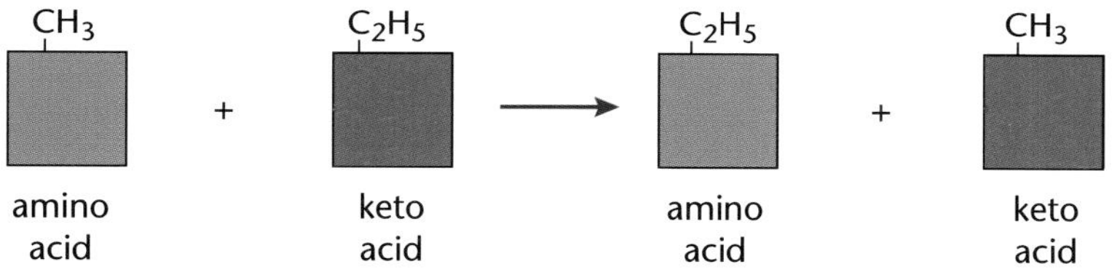

note the changes in the 'R' group of each acid.

The liver has many functions including:

- detoxification of poisonous substances
- heat production
- formation of red cells.

Deamination

This process is necessary to lower the level of **excess amino acids**. They are produced when proteins are digested. Nitrogenous materials have a high degree of toxicity, so the level in the blood must be limited.

$$2NH_2-\underset{\displaystyle H}{\overset{\displaystyle R}{\underset{|}{\overset{|}{C}}}}-COOH + O_2 \rightarrow 2\underset{\displaystyle O}{\overset{\displaystyle R}{\underset{||}{\overset{|}{C}}}}-COOH + 2NH_3$$

amino acid + oxygen → keto acid + ammonia

Both deamination and the ornithine cycle are needed to process excess amino acids. Remember that urea is a less toxic substance. The **liver makes** it but the **kidneys** help to **excrete** it.

Ornithine cycle

Ammonia is immediately taken up by ornithine to help make a less toxic substance, urea.

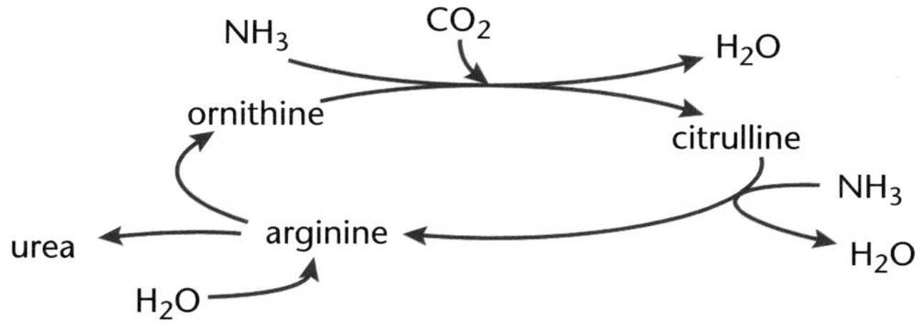

4.4 The kidneys

LEARNING SUMMARY

After studying this section you should be able to:

- *describe the structure and functions of a nephron*
- *understand the processes of ultrafiltration and reabsorption*
- *understand the countercurrent multiplier*

Kidney structure and function

AQA A	M6
AQA B	M4
EDEXCEL	M4
OCR	M5
WJEC	M5
NICCEA	M4

Each kidney has three major regions: the **cortex**, **medulla** and **pelvis**. The renal artery takes blood into a kidney where it is filtered to remove potentially toxic material. Useful substances leave the blood as well as toxic ones but are reabsorbed back into the blood. Toxic substances such as urea leave the kidneys and enter the bladder, via the ureters.

The diagram shows one nephron of the many thousands in each kidney.

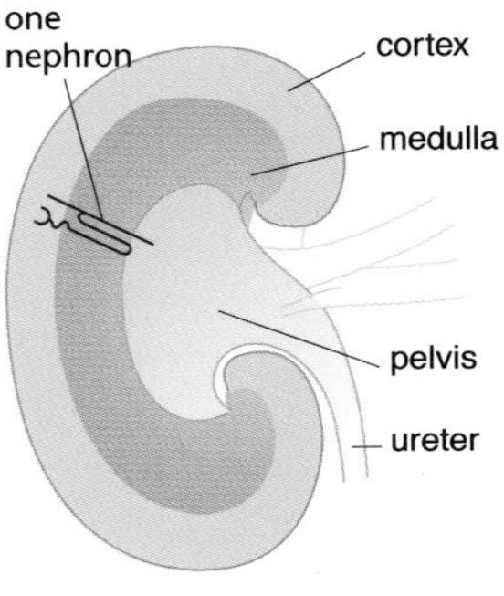

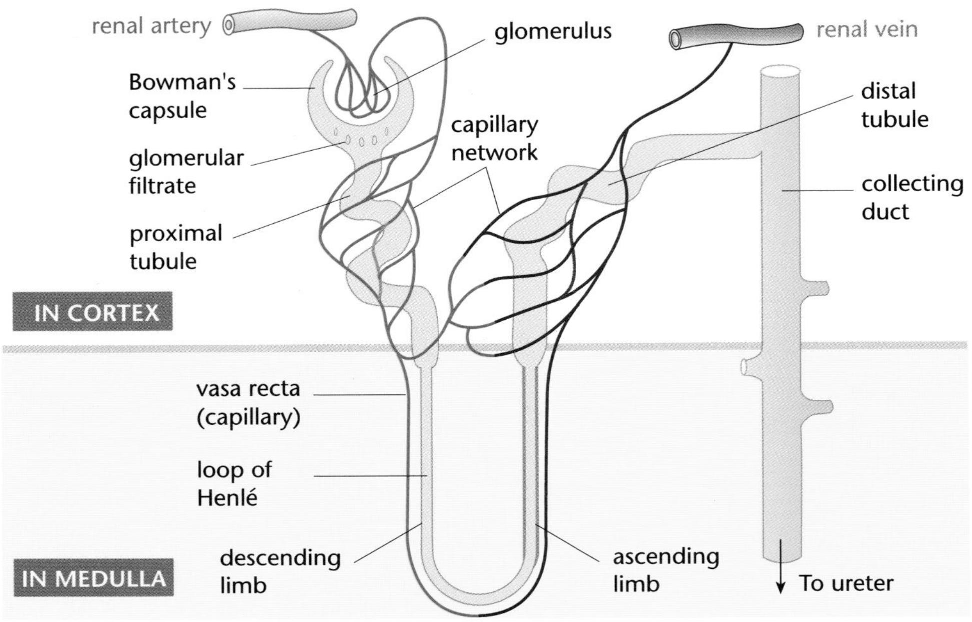

How does a nephron function?

- Blood arrives at the **glomerulus** from the renal artery.
- The **blood pressure is very high** as a result of:
  - contraction of the left ventricle of the heart
  - contraction of aorta and renal artery
  - the arteriole leading to glomerular capillaries is wider than venule leaving them
  - high resistance of the interface between glomerular capillaries and inner wall of the renal (Bowman's) capsule.
- **Glomerular filtrate** is forced into the nephron, this is known as **ultrafiltration**.
- Glomerular filtrate includes **urea**, **glucose**, **water**, **amino acids** and **mineral ions**.
- Selective reabsorption takes place in the **proximal tubule** resulting in substances such as glucose being returned to the blood.
- 100% of glucose and 80% of water are reabsorbed at the proximal tubule.
- Urea continues through the tubule to the collecting duct and finally down a ureter to be excreted from the bladder.
- Further reabsorption of substances can take place at the distal tubule.

The selective property of the renal membrane.

What do not leave the blood due to being too large?

Most proteins, red and white blood cells.

Ultrafiltration

Also known as pressure filtration it relies on the properties of the capillaries and the inner wall of the renal (Bowman's) capsule.

In your examination you may be requested to label a diagram. Test yourself!

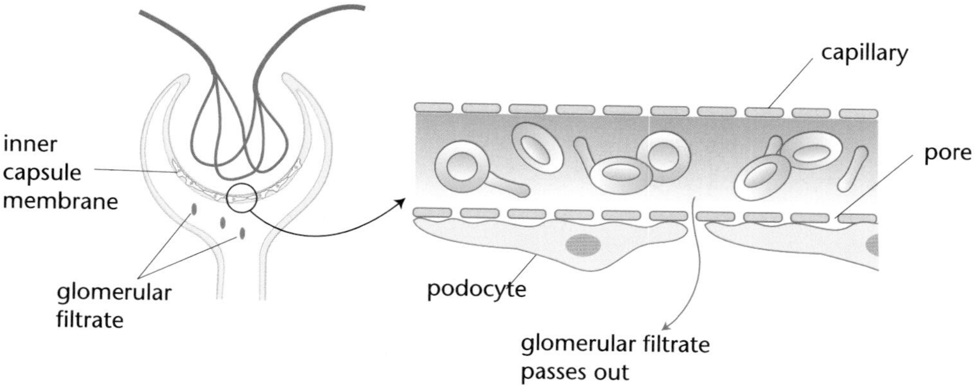

Learn explanations in bullet points. Bullet points in this book may resemble the examiner's mark scheme.

- Capillaries lie very close to the **inner capsular membrane** (see above).
- The capillaries have many tiny pores.
- The capsular membrane consists of **podocytes**.
- **Podocytes** are shaped so that many tiny gaps exist between the capsular membrane and capillaries.
- Together these form a high pressure sieve.
- Only molecules which are small enough can pass through.

Reabsorption

Capillaries from the glomerulus extend to a network across both proximal and distal tubules. The close contact between capillary and tubule is important.

Section through proximal tubule

Remember what reabsorption is! The return of substances into the blood which have just left.

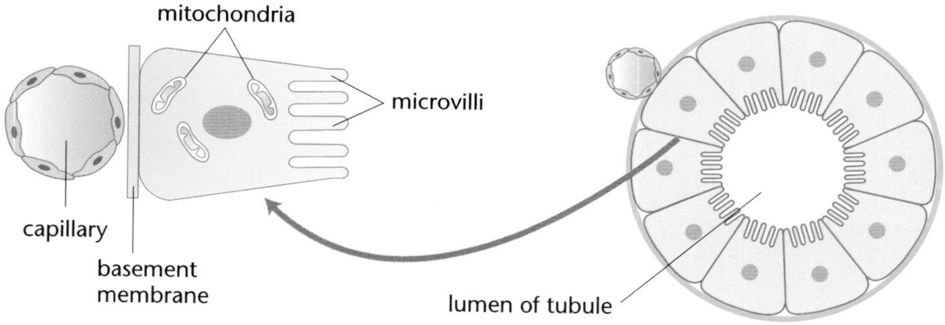

- Substances such as **glucose**, **urea**, and **water** travel along the tubule.
- Each tubule is one cell thick, consisting of epithelial cells with **microvilli** on the outer membrane.
- Microvilli give a **high surface area** to allow the efficient transport of substances to cross to the capillaries.
- **Carrier proteins** on the microvilli, aided by mitochondria, **actively reabsorb** glucose from the filtrate into the tubules.
- Glucose molecules are then actively transported into the fluids surrounding the capillaries.
- Glucose molecules finally enter the capillaries and so have re-entered the blood.
- By the end of the proximal tubule **all glucose** has been **returned to the blood.**

The distal tubule is also in close contact with the capillary network. Even more reabsorption can take place here.

How do the kidneys conserve water?

Water molecules which pass into the tubule and reach the kidney pelvis continue down a ureter and are lost in urine. Such water loss is carefully controlled, some is always reabsorbed. This control involves both the nervous system, the endocrine system and structures along a nephron. The diagram below outlines the role of the **countercurrent multiplier** in the control of water content in the body.

Countercurrent multiplier

The vasa recta capillaries follow the path of the loop of Henlé to:

(a) supply oxygen to the cells so that active transport of Na^+, Cl^- can take place efficiently (the process needs energy!)
(b) remove CO_2
(c) reabsorb water.

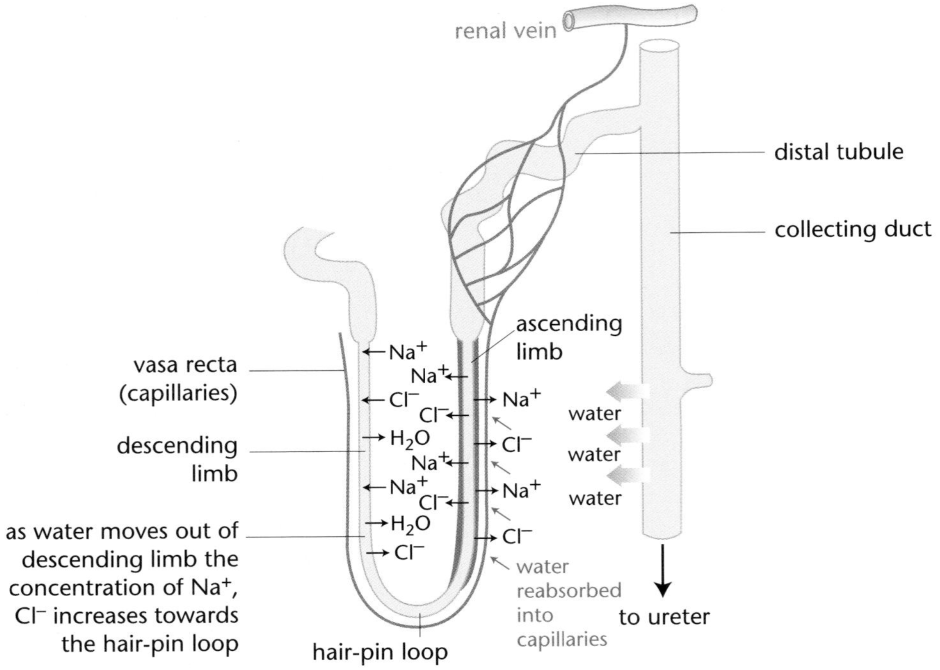

The role of the loop of Henlé

- Na^+ and Cl^- ions are actively transported into the medulla from the ascending limb of the loop of Henlé.
- The ascending limb is thicker than the descending one, and impermeable to the outward movement of water so only the ions leave.
- The Na^+ and Cl^- ions slowly diffuse into the descending limb resulting in their greater concentration towards the base of the loop.
- A high concentration of Na^+ and Cl^- ions in the medulla causes water to leave the collecting duct by osmosis.
- Additionally water leaves the descending limb by osmosis due to the ions in the medulla.
- Water molecules pass into the capillary network and have been successfully reabsorbed.

The distal tubule is also a site of more reabsorption. Even more substances are returned to the blood here.

The role of the distal tubule

The structure of the distal tubule is similar to the proximal tubule, however its specific roles are:

- maintenance of a constant blood plasma pH at around 7.4
- if blood plasma falls **below** a pH of 7.4 then ionic movements take place
  - (**H^+** ions) plasma → filtrate
  - (**HCO_3^-** ions) filtrate → plasma
- if blood plasma **rises** above a pH of 7.4 then more ion movements take place
  - (**OH^-** ions) plasma → filtrate
  - (**HCO_3^-** ions) plasma → filtrate

The control of water balance

It is necessary to control the amount of water in the blood. The kidneys can help to achieve this with their ability to intercept water before it can reach the ureters. There are, however, problems to overcome.

Here the consequences of the two extremes of hot and cold are explained. Do remember that there are a range of conditions **between** these extremes. ADH level changes in response to osmoreceptor sensory input to the hypothalamus.

> **KEY POINT**
>
> In hot conditions we lose a lot of water by sweating, too much loss would lead to dehydration problems.
>
> In cold conditions much less water is lost by sweating, giving a potential problem of too much water being retained in the blood.
>
> A balance must be achieved!

Hormonal control of the kidneys – the role of ADH

Control is achieved with the help of antidiuretic hormone (ADH), produced by the posterior lobe of the pituitary gland.

Examination tip!

Look out for graphs in questions about kidneys.

- Levels of key substances may be shown.
- If water content down a collecting duct decreases as water content in the medullary region increases
  - then water molecules are crossing the collecting duct
  - sodium and chloride ions have drawn this water from the collecting duct into the medulla by osmosis.

Scenario 1: warm environmental conditions

- **Osmoreceptors** in the hypothalamus detect an **increase** in the solute concentration of the blood plasma.
- The **hypothalamus** then produces, by neurosecretion, the hormone **ADH**.
- The ADH is secreted into the posterior lobe of the **pituitary gland**.
- From here it passes into the blood and finally reaches the target organs, the **kidneys**.
- Here it **increases** permeability of:
  (i) the collecting ducts
  (ii) the distal tubules.
- The effect is that more water can be **reabsorbed** back into blood.

The events outlined above give a maximum effect of the countercurrent multiplier. Too much water would be lost by sweating so the water component of the urine must be drastically limited. The resulting urine is therefore low in water content and high in solutes.

Scenario 2: cold environmental conditions

- **Osmoreceptors** in the hypothalamus detect a **decrease** in the solute concentration of the blood plasma.
- The hypothalamus then produces **less ADH**.
- Less ADH leaves the posterior lobe of the pituitary gland.
- Less ADH reaches the target organs, the kidneys.
- The collecting ducts and the distal tubules are **not so permeable**.
- **Less water** can be **reabsorbed** back.

The urine is of greater volume due to greater water content. No wonder we urinate more in cold weather!

Diuresis

Diuresis is a condition in which excessive amounts of watery urine are produced. In a healthy person this is avoided with the secretion of ADH.

Sometimes people are prescribed a drug equivalent to ADH to cure the symptoms. Reabsorption can take place efficiently so urine at a correct solute concentration is excreted.

4.5 Adaptations to desert ecosystems

LEARNING SUMMARY

After studying this section you should be able to:

- *describe how water loss is limited in desert organisms*

How do desert organisms limit water loss?

AQA A	M6
AQA B	M6
EDEXCEL	M4
OCR	M5
NICCEA	M4

Organisms which successfully live in deserts have structural, physiological and behavioural adaptations. The following organisms display a range of water conserving features.

Kangaroo rat

- Inhaled air accepts heat energy from nasal passages.
- Water vapour from exhaled air condenses on the **cooler** nasal passages and so less water vapour is breathed out.
- It eats plant material, does not drink, but obtains useful **metabolic water** from respiration.
- Remains underground in its burrow for a high proportion of the day, where the humidity is high.
- Less moisture is lost by evaporation from the animal because the **diffusion gradient is reduced**.

In an examination question you may be given another animal, not the kangaroo rat! Analyse the data, and you will find the principles are similar!

A kangaroo rat

A camel

Camel

- During a period of water deprivation, can routinely have a core temperature from 35°C in the morning to around 42°C in early evening.
- Toleration to the increased temperature gives a period for the camel to cool down slowly by **conduction**, **convection** and **radiation**.
- If cooling was by water evaporation from the animal, then an excessive amount of water would be needed (not possible in desert journeys!).
- The respiration of fat also supplies metabolites, useful to the camel in other processes.
  - Have very long loops of Henlé so that much more water reabsorption can take place.
- The reason for this is that a greater length allows for more Na^+ and Cl^- to be actively transported out of the loop of Henlé, hence greater water retention.

This list of points may be useful in your examination. The temperature range in a day is only applicable in times of water shortage. At an oasis with a plentiful supply of water, camel temperature range in the day is 36°C to 38°C.

Sample question and model answer

Note the close proximity of cell A to the capillary. This gives a clue as to their function.

The diagram shows a cell of the inner wall of a renal (Bowman's) capsule. These two structures shown in the diagram are very important in the passage of substances out of the blood into the proximal tubule.

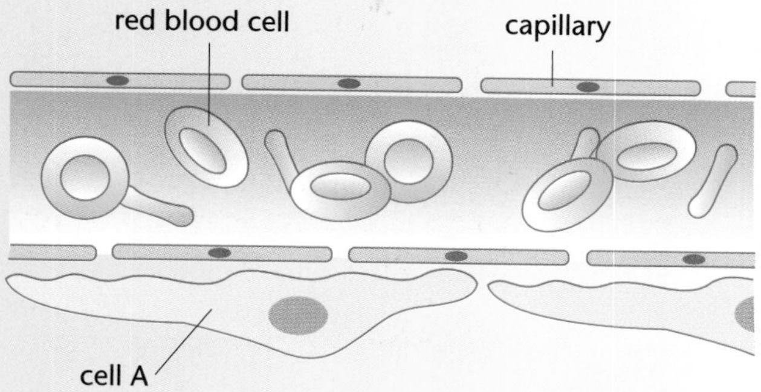

(a) Name cell A. [1]

podocyte

The question shows that five marks are available. Make sure that you give at least five points to gain you marks. Superficial answers fall short of the total.

(b) Explain how the cells of the inner capsule wall and the capillaries of the glomerulus help in the process of ultrafiltration. [5]

capillaries lie very close to the inner capsular wall; the capillaries have pores; the podocytes are shaped so that many gaps exist between the capsular wall and capillaries; the resistance to flow caused by tiny pores and gaps contributes to high pressure; only molecules which are small enough are forced through pores so the process is selective.

(c) As glomerular filtrate leaves the renal (Bowman's) capsule it enters the proximal convoluted tubule. The graph below shows the ratio of glucose and urea in the blood plasma and the filtrate through the proximal tubule. A ratio of 1.0 means that the concentration in both plasma and filtrate are the same.

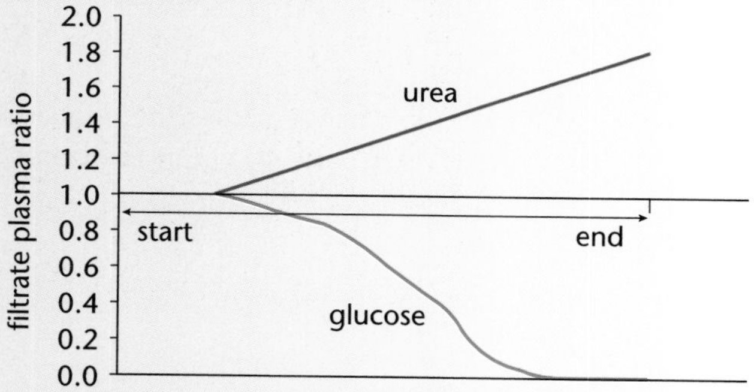

You may find this difficult. However, you can link the fact that the kidney nephron does reabsorb useful substances but not the waste, urea. Relate this to the graph then your task is possible!

Explain the changes in plasma–filtrate from the beginning to the end of the proximal tubule for:

(i) glucose [3]

As the fluid moves along the tubule there is increasingly more glucose in the plasma than the filtrate; this is because glucose is reabsorbed into blood; all glucose is returned to blood before end of proximal tubule.

(ii) urea. [3]

As the fluid moves along the tubule there is increasingly more urea in the filtrate than in the blood plasma; no urea is reabsorbed so it remains in tubule; water is reabsorbed which has the effect of increasing the relative concentration of urea.

Practice examination questions

1 (a) Complete the table below to compare the nervous and endocrine systems. Put a tick in each correct box for the features shown.

	Nervous system	*Endocrine system*
Usually have longer lasting effects		
Have cells which secrete transmitter molecules		
Cells communicate by substances in the blood plasma		
Use chemicals which bind to receptor sites in cell surface proteins		
Involve the use of Na^+ and K^+ pumps		

[2]

(b) Name the process which keeps the human body temperature and water content of blood regulated. [1]

[Total: 3]

2 A mammal is in hot environmental conditions. Explain the effect of a high quantity of ADH entering the blood from the pituitary gland. [6]

3 (a) The products of transamination have been represented below. Complete the equation

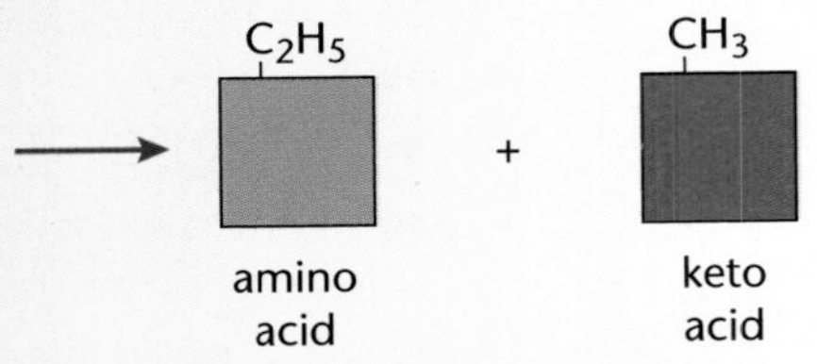

[2]

(b) (i) Where in the human body does transamination take place? [1]

(ii) Why is transamination necessary in the human body? [2]

[Total: 5]

4 The graph below shows the relative levels of glucose in the blood of two people A and B. One is healthy and the other one is diabetic.

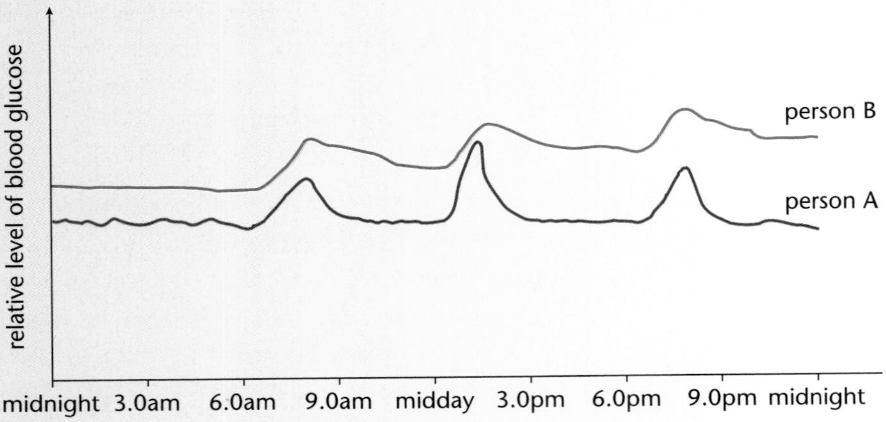

(a) Which person is diabetic? Give evidence from the graph for your answer. [1]

(b) What is the evidence that both of the people do produce insulin? [1]

(c) Where in the body is insulin produced? [2]

[Total: 4]

Chapter 5

Further genetics

The following topics are covered in this chapter:

- Genes, alleles and chromosomes
- Cell division
- Inheritance
- Applications of genetics

5.1 Genes, alleles and chromosomes

After studying this section you should be able to:

- define a range of important genetic terms
- understand the origin and range of mutations

LEARNING SUMMARY

Essential genetic terms

AQA A	M5
AQA B	M4
EDEXCEL	M5
OCR	M5
WJEC	M5
NICCEA	M5

Check out all of these genetic terms.

- Look carefully at the technique of giving an example with each definition. Often examples help to clarify your answer and are usually accepted by the examiners.
- In examination papers you will need to apply your understanding to **new** situations.
- Genetics has a specialist language which you will need to use.

A gene is a section of DNA which controls the production of a protein in an organism. The total effects of all of the genes of an organism are responsible for the characteristics of that organism. Each protein contributes to these characteristics whatever its role, e.g. structural, enzymic or hormonal.

It is necessary to understand the following specialist range of terms used in genetics.

Allele – an alternative form of a gene, always located on the same position along a chromosome.

E.g. white colour of petals

Dominant allele – if an organism has two different alleles then this is the one which is expressed, often represented by a capital letter.

E.g. red colour pigment of petals, **R**

Recessive allele – if an organism has two different alleles then this is the one which is **not** expressed, often represented by a lower case letter. Recessive alleles are only expressed when they are not masked by the presence of a dominant allele.

E.g. white colour pigment of petals, **r**

Homozygous – refers to the fact that in a diploid organism both alleles are the same.

E.g. **R R** or **r r**

Heterozygous – refers to the fact that in a diploid organism both alleles are different.

E.g. **R r** (petal colour would be expressed as red)

Key points from AS

- **The genetic code**
  Revise AS pages 82–84

Co-dominance – refers to the fact that occasionally two alleles are equally expressed in the organism.

E.g. A, B alleles = AB (blood group with antigens A and B)

> A number of inherited alleles of a range of genes often exhibit continuous variation, e.g. height. Each allele contributes small incremental differences. That is why there are smooth changes in height across a population.

Polygenic inheritance – where an inherited feature is controlled by two or more genes, along different loci along a chromosome. Results in continuous variation.

E.g. height of a person is controlled by a number of different genes.

> Remember that both sperms and ova are haploid.

Haploid – refers to a cell which has a single set of chromosomes.
E.g. a nucleus in a human sperm has 23 single chromosomes.

Diploid – refers to a cell which has two sets of chromosomes.
E.g. a nucleus in a human liver cell has 23 pairs of chromosomes.

> In diploid cells one set of chromosomes is from the male parent and one from the female.

Homologous chromosomes – refers to the pairs of chromosomes seen during cell division. These chromosomes lie side by side, each gene at each locus being the same.

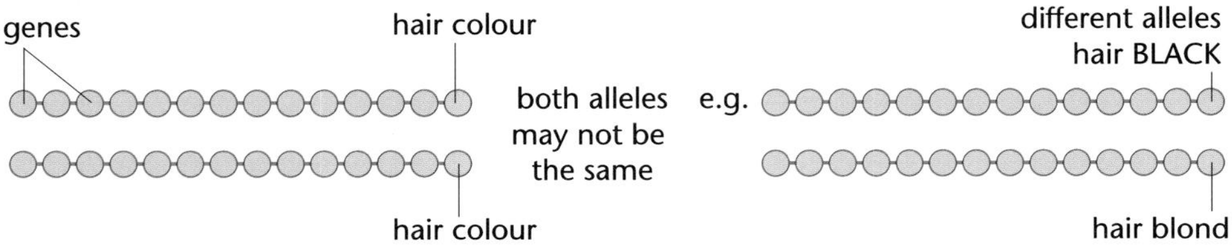

> Often polyploid organisms cannot reproduce sexually but asexually they are successful.

Polyploid – refers to the fact that a cell has three or more sets of chromosomes. This can increase yield.

E.g. cultivated potato plants are **tetraploid**, that is four sets of chromosomes in a cell. (*Tetraploidy is a form of polyploidy*.)

> **phenotype = genotype + environment**
> Phenotype includes all alleles which are expressed in an organism. The environment supplies resources and conditions for development. Varying conditions result in an organism developing differently. Identical twins fed different diets will show some differences, e.g. weight.
> Environment has considerable effect.

Genotype – refers to all of the genes found in the nuclei of an organism, including both dominant and recessive alleles.

dominant

E.g. A B c d E F g H i (all alleles are included in a genotype)
a B C D e f g h I

recessive

Phenotype – refers to only the alleles of an organism which are expressed (the appearance of an organism).

E.g. **A B** c d **E F g H** i only alleles in bold included in a phenotype
a **B C D** e f **g** h **I**

Linkage – refers to two or more genes which are located on the same chromosome.

E.g. linked X-------------------Y-- (same chromosomes) not linked X-------------------- / --------------------Y-- (different chromosomes)

Somatic cell – refers to any cell which is not involved in reproduction.
E.g. liver cell

Autosome – refers to every chromosome apart from the sex chromosomes, X and Y.

Bases can change along DNA and this may cause mutation. One changed base along the coding strand of DNA may have a sequential effect of changing most amino acids along a polypeptide.

before mutation
TTA CCG GCC ATC
after mutation
ATT ACC GGC CAT C
This is addition!

More mutations shown below. Each section of DNA along the chromosomes is shown by organic bases.

Addition
before
TTA CCG GCC ATC
after
CCG TTA CCG GCC ATC
A new triplet has been added. If a triplet is repeated it is also duplication.

Deletion
before
TTA CCG GCC ATC
after
TTA CCG GCC

Inversion
before
TTA CCG GCC ATC
after
TTA CCG GCC **CTA**
CTA codes for new amino acid.

Translocation
before
TTA CCG GCC ATC
after
TTA CCG GCC ATC **CAT**
CAT broke away from another chromosome.

Gene therapy – where the function of defective genes of an organism is rectified by supplying correct DNA material.

E.g. symptoms of the genetic disease, cystic fibrosis, are relieved by applying a 'blast' of corrected genes into alveoli in the lungs. (This is experimental, symptom relief is currently very limited.)

Mutation

Mutation is a change in the DNA of a cell. If the cell affected by mutation is a somatic cell, then its effect is restricted to the organism itself. If, however, the mutation affects gametes, then the genetic change will be inherited by the future population.

KEY POINT

DNA codes for the sequence of amino acids along polypeptides and ultimately the characteristics of an organism. Each amino acid is coded for by a triplet of bases along the coding strand of DNA, e.g. TTA codes for threonine. The change in a triplet base code can result in a new amino acid, e.g. ATT codes for serine. This type of DNA change along a chromosome is known as a **point mutation**. A point mutation involves a change in a small section along a chromosome by **addition**, **deletion** or **inversion**.

If a complete chromosome is added or deleted, this is a **chromosomal mutation**, such as Down's syndrome where a person has an additional chromosome, totalling 47 in each nucleus rather than the usual 46.

What causes mutations?

All organisms tend to mutate randomly, so different sections of DNA can appear to alter by chance. The appearance of such a random mutation is usually very rare, typically one mutation in many thousands of individuals in a population. The rate can be increased by mutagens such as:

- ionising radiation – including ultra violet light, X rays and α, β and γ (gamma) rays and neutrons. These forms of radiation tend to dislodge the electrons of atoms and so disrupt the bonding of the DNA which may re-bond in different combinations.
- chemicals – including asbestos, tobacco, nitrous oxide, mustard gas and many substances used in industrial processes such as vinyl chloride. Many pesticides are suspected mutagens. Dichlorvos, an insecticide, is a proven mutagen.

  Additionally colchicine is a chemical derived from the Autumn crocus, *Colchicium*, which stimulates the development of extra sets of chromosomes.

Are mutations harmful or helpful?

An individual mutation may be either harmful or helpful. When tobacco is smoked this can increase the rate of mutation in some somatic cells. The DNA disruption can result in the formation of a cell which divides uncontrollably and causes the disruption of normal body processes. This is cancer, and can be lethal.

Chrysanthemum plants have a high rate of mutation. A chrysanthemum grower will often see a new colour flower on a plant, e.g. a plant with red flowers could develop a side shoot which has a different colour, such as bronze. Most modern chrysanthemums appeared in this way, production being by asexual techniques.

Some mutated human genes have through evolution been successful. Many successful mutations contributed to the greater size of cerebrum, proportionally than other primates.

5.2 Cell division

After studying this section you should be able to:

- *compare the main features of mitosis and meiosis*
- *describe and explain the process of meiosis*
- *understand the consequences of chiasmata (crossing over)*

LEARNING SUMMARY

Why are there two types of cell division?

AQA A	M5
AQA B	M4
EDEXCEL	M5
OCR	M5
WJEC	M5
NICCEA	M5

Each type of cell division has a different purpose.

Mitosis

There are occasions when it is necessary to replicate cells, e.g. in growth and repair. This is the role of mitosis. It produces a clonal line of cells. Each cell divides to form 2 diploid, daughter cells, identical in every way.

Meiosis

This is needed in gamete formation. In human cells a body (somatic) cell has 46 chromosomes. If each gamete contained 46 chromosomes then the zygote produced at fertilisation would have 92 chromosomes. This would be lethal! Meiosis is also called reduction division because the gametes produced are haploid. In human gametes the haploid chromosome number is 23. Each cell divides to form 4 haploid, daughter cells. Every daughter cell is different to the parent cell and each other.

Examiner's tip

At AS Level you learned the names of the stages in sequence. The stages of meiosis use the same names, in the same order but there are two nuclear divisions this time!

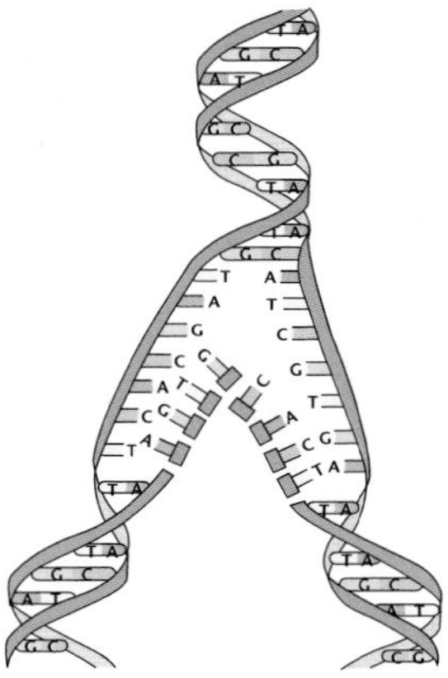

Meiosis: the process explained

The preparation of a cell prior to meiotic division is during interphase. During this pre-stage each double strand of DNA replicates to produce two exact copies of itself. This also takes place in exactly the same way before mitosis takes place. After interphase, when the cell division commences, major differences occur.

In meiosis during the first stage, prophase 1, a fundamentally important event takes place, where chromatids cross over. Each crossover is termed a chiasma.

The mechanism of cross overs (chiasmata)

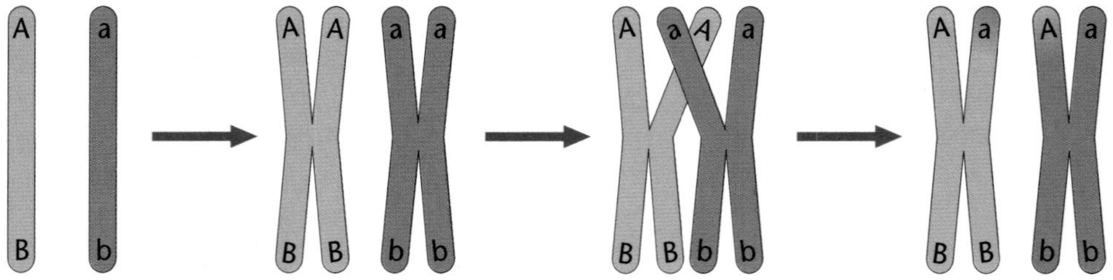

A represents an allele dominant to a, a recessive allele.

B represents an allele dominant to b, a recessive allele.

In humans, with many chiasmata taking place along all 23 pairs of chromosomes every cell at the completion of meiosis is genetically different.

Chiasmata result in **different allele combinations**!

KEY POINT

Key points from AS

- **Cell division**
  Revise AS pages 85–86

In the division of a human cell by meiosis there are 23 pairs of chromosomes in the parent cell. If all 46 chromosomes were represented in diagrams then there would be confusion. In these diagrams only 2 pairs of chromosomes are shown, but remember there are 21 other pairs! One homologous pair is shown in two colours to show the consequence of crossovers.

The process of meiosis

early prophase I

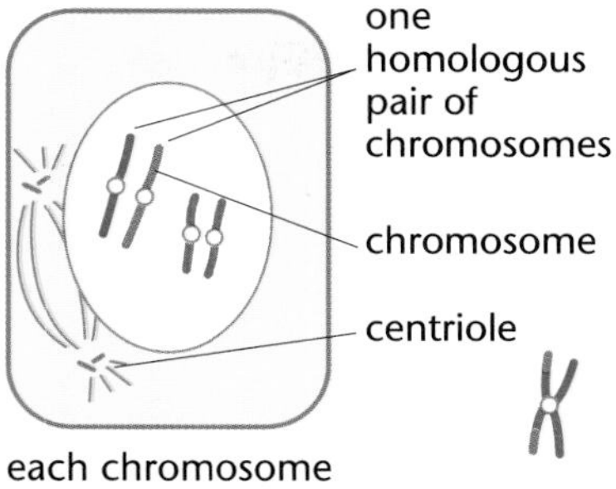

each chromosome forms 2 chromatids 2 centrioles begin to move forming a spindle

late prophase I

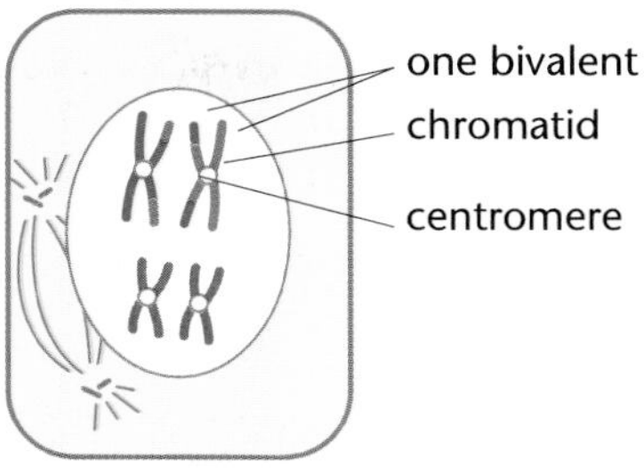

the chromatids have crossed over and exchanged DNA at 2 positions

metaphase I

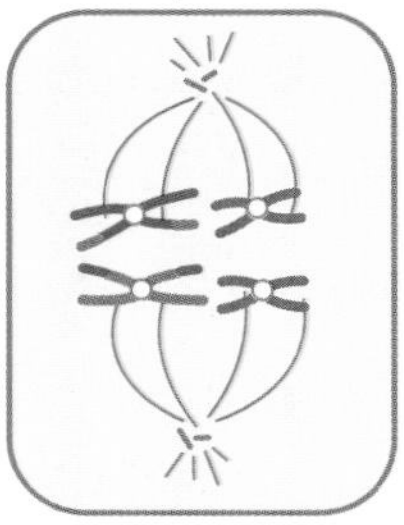

bivalents form homologous chromosomes lie parallel to each other along the equator

anaphase I

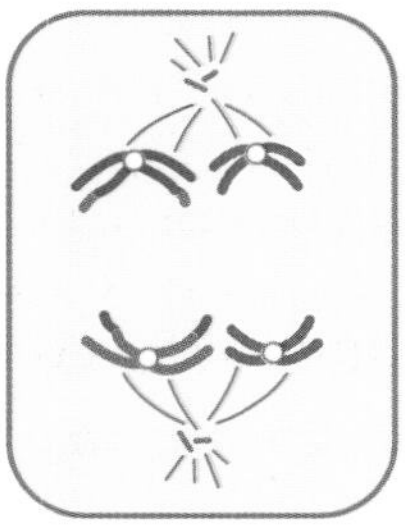

corresponding bivalents are pulled by spindle fibres towards poles

telophase I

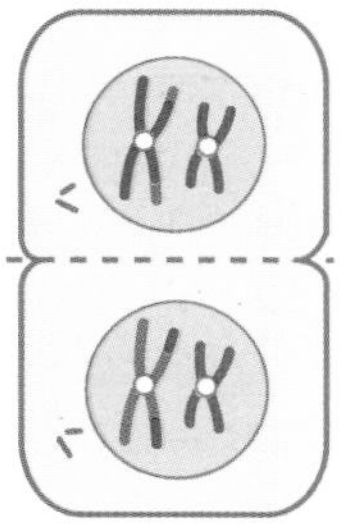

cell constricts at equator to form daughter cells

prophase II

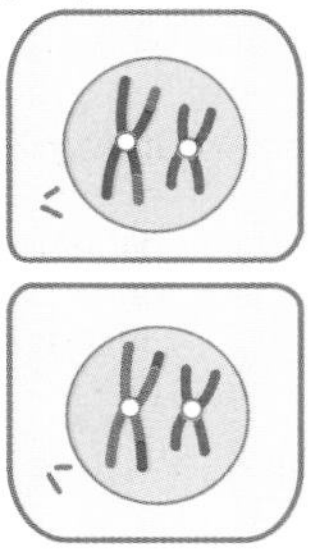

EACH of these cells will divide to form 2 daughter cells

metaphase II

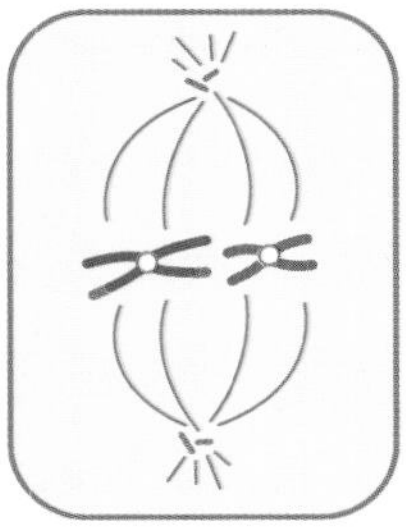

single bivalents lie across the equator

anaphase II

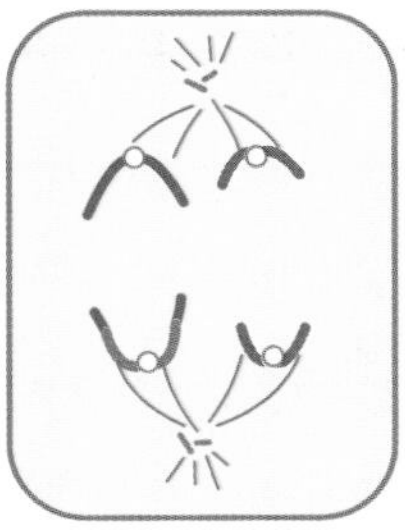

spindle fibres contract to pull centromere apart. Single chromosomes dragged to the poles

early telophase II

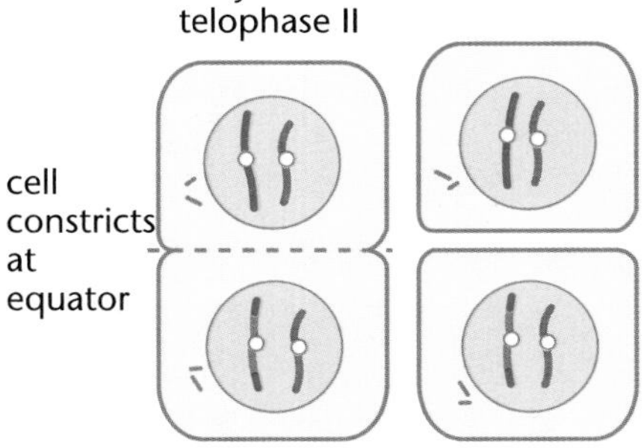

2 daughter cells produced for each cell form first division = 4 daughter cells

The significance of meiosis

Diagram to show the single chromosomes produced as a result of two crossovers.

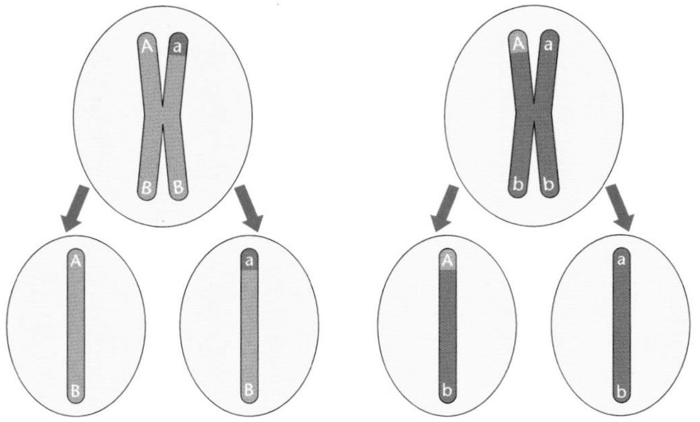

The combination of each of these chromosomes with others, results in further genetic variation

In an examination you will need to understand the consequence of many crossovers. Crossovers are a source of genetic variation.

A represents an allele dominant to a, a recessive allele.

B represents an allele dominant to b, a recessive allele.

- Many more than two crossovers can take place between each homologous pair! The presence of 23 homologous pairs of chromosomes in a diploid human cell result in a lot of crossovers.
- Once the chromatids finally separate in anaphase II, each moves with 22 others to a pole to produce a daughter cell.
- After division, four different chromatids are produced from each homologous pair (see above).

1 from 4 chromatids combine with 1 from another 4 chromatids. These combinations give **16 possibilities.** Add the combination of another 1 from 4 chromatids and there are **64 possibilities**. Another 1 from 4 is added .... and another .... to include all 23 pairs. This gives millions of combinations. No wonder we all look different!

KEY POINT

What determines which chromatid from the four of one homologous pair is grouped with chromatids from the other homologous pairs?

The answer is **'chance'** and the combination of the 23 single chromosomes dragged through the cytoplasm by the spindle fibres, is known as **independent assortment**.

Every gamete produced by meiosis is genetically different. However, there are two sexes. This means that in sexual reproduction, the fact that there are two different gametes which combine their alleles in the zygote, this gives another major source of variation.

Progress check

The diagram below shows a stage in cell division.

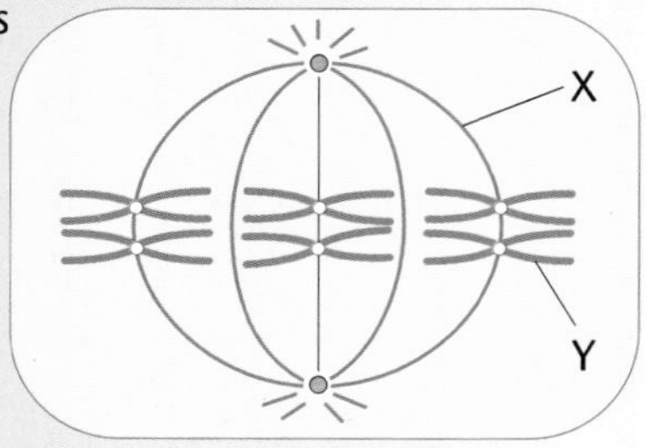

(a) Name parts X and Y.

(b) Which type of cell division is shown? Give a reason for your answer.

(a) X = spindle fibre Y = chromatid or bivalent

(b) Metaphase I of meiosis. Bivalents line up in twos along the equator whereas in mitosis they lie singly.

5.3 Inheritance

After studying this section you should be able to:

LEARNING SUMMARY

- *understand Mendel's laws of inheritance*
- *understand the principles of monohybrid inheritance and dihybrid inheritance*
- *understand the terms parental DNA, recombinant DNA and co-dominance*
- *describe the principle of sex determination*
- *use the Hardy–Weinberg Principle to predict the numbers of future genotypes*

Mendel and the laws of inheritance

AQA A	M5
AQA B	M4
EDEXCEL	M5
OCR	M5
WJEC	M5
NICCEA	M5

Gregor Mendel was the monk who gave us our understanding of genetics. He worked with organisms such as pea plants to work out genetic relationships.

KEY POINT

Mendel's first law indicates that:
- each character of a diploid organism is controlled by a pair of alleles
- from this pair of alleles only one can be represented in a gamete.

Always show your working out of a genetical relationship in a logical way, just like solving a mathematics problem.

Monohybrid inheritance

Mendel found that when homozygous pea plants were crossed, a predictable ratio resulted. The cross below shows Mendel's principle.

pea plants
T = TALL (dominant)

pea plants
t = dwarf (recessive)

TOP TIP ALERT!
If you have to choose the symbols to explain genetics, then use something like **N** and **n**. Here the upper and lower cases are very different. **S** and **s** are corrupted as you write quickly and may be confused by the examiner awarding your marks.

A homozygous TALL plant was crossed with a homozygous recessive plant

TT x tt

gametes (T) (T) (t) (t)

F_1 generation Tt

All offspring 100% TALL, and heterozygous.

Heterozygous plants were crossed

Tt x Tt

gametes (T) (t) (T) (t)

	(T)	(t)
(T)	TT	Tt
(t)	Tt	tt

2 × 2 punnet square to work out different genotypes

F_2 generation 3 TALL : 1 DWARF

In examinations you may have to work out a probability. 3 : 1 is the same as a 1 in 4 chance. Remember only large numbers would confirm the ratio.

In making this cross Mendel investigated one gene only. The height differences of the plants was due to the different alleles. Mendel kept all environmental conditions the same for all seedlings as they developed. The 3:1 ratio of tall to short plants only holds true for large numbers of offspring.

Dihybrid Inheritance

Mendel again investigated using pea plants to work out the genetic relationship between plants for genes at different loci (positions) on chromosomes.

KEY POINT

Mendel's second law of independent assortment indicates that:
- either of a pair of alleles, say **A** and **a**
- can combine with either of another pair, say **B** and **b**.

> **Examiner's tip**
> You probably will not be given the example of pea plants in your examinations. Coloured petals or fruit fly features are often given. Make sure that you clearly show the symbols and apply the principles learned from this example. The key part in a genetics question is that you give correct gametes.
> For a heterozygous genotype of AaBb the gametes are
> **AB Ab aB ab**
> NOT
> ~~AA~~ ~~aa~~ ~~BB~~ ~~bb~~

The cross below shows Mendel's dihybrid principle.

pea plants	*pea plants*
R = round seeds (dominant)	r = wrinkled seeds (recessive)
Y = yellow seeds (dominant)	y = green seeds (recessive)

A homozygous dominant plant with yellow, round seeds was crossed with a homozygous recessive plant with green, wrinkled seeds.

RRYY x rryy

gametes (RY) (ry)

F_1 generation RrYy

seeds 100% round, yellow, and heterozygous

Heterozygous plants from F_1 generation were crossed.

RrYy x RrYy

gametes (RY) (Ry) (rY) (ry) (RY) (Ry) (rY) (ry)

F_1 generation

> Be ready to cross two organisms from a punnet square, e.g.
> RrYY x rrYy
> Do not expect a 9:3:3:1 ratio!

	RY	Ry	rY	ry
RY	RRYY	RRYy	RrYY	RrYy
Ry	RRYy	RRyy	RrYy	Rryy
rY	RrYY	RrYy	rrYY	rrYy
ry	RrYy	RRyy	rrYy	rryy

4 × 4 punnet square to work out genotypes

F_1 generation 9 : 3 : 3 : 1 ratio

9	3	3	1
round yellow	round green	wrinkled yellow	wrinkled green

The 9 : 3 : 3 : 1 ratio only holds true for large numbers of offspring.

The principles above can be applied to any dihybrid example. The F_1 generation is so predictable that many varieties of commercial crop are grown from F_1 generation seeds, known as F_1 hybrids, e.g. Brussels sprout, variety 'Peer Gynt'. A uniform crop of high yield.

Linkage

> Linkage can occur on autosomes and sex chromosomes.

Each chromosome consists of a sequence of genes. All genes along a chromosome are **linked** because they are part of the same chromosome. Most chromosomes have between 500 and 1000 genes in a linear sequence. These genes are linked.

What is the significance of linkage?

We are able to make predictions about the proportion of future offspring when we know the genotype of parents, like the 9:3:3:1 ratio for dihybrid inheritance. This is only true if the pair of contrasting genes are **on different chromosomes**. Consider these two alternatives:

A dominant, **a** recessive; **B** dominant, **b** recessive

loci (positions) of genes

AaBb x AaBb

Not linked. This cross would produce 9:3:3:1 proportion in offspring

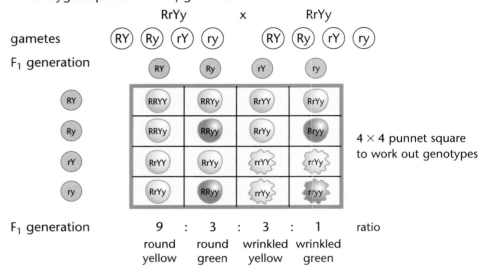

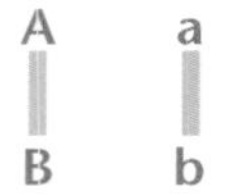

AaBb x AaBb

Linked. This cross would be unlikely to produce a 9:3:3:1 proportion in offspring

> The more crossovers there are, the greater the chance that the four different gene combinations will be produced in each parental genotype. They could produce a 9:3:3:1 proportion in cross 1. However, if the genes are closer along the chromosome then the proportions deviate significantly from this pattern. Genes **adjacent** to each other tend to be **inherited together**, because the chance of them being parted is very low.

When two genes, e.g. A,a and B,b are on **different chromosomes** then their inheritance together is **not affected by crossovers**. Either of one pair **can** be inherited with either of the other pair. The relationship changes when the genes are along the same chromosome. Crossovers are affected! Alleles along the same gene locus can be swapped from one chromatid to another.

Consider these alternatives for linked genes, where a homozygous dominant genotype is crossed with a homozygous recessive.

Crossover 1 (AABB x aabb)

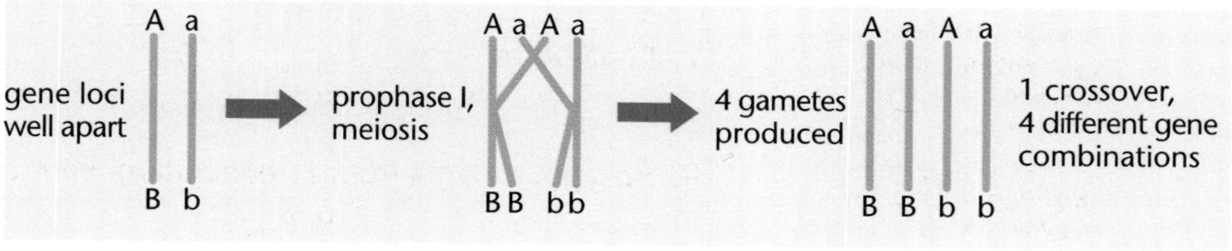

Crossover 2 (AABB x aabb)

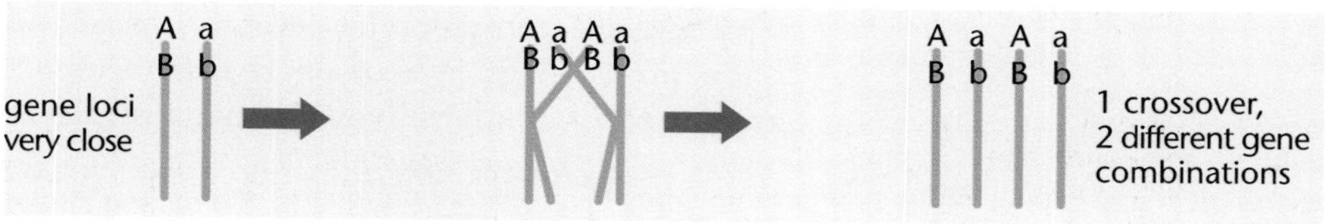

Linkage and probability

Consider these crosses

Cross one

R = red petals (dominant) r = blue (recessive)
L = long stems (dominant) l = short stems (recessive)

homozygous red petals long stemmed — homozygous blue petals short stemmed

> The young organisms are often termed progeny or offspring.

RRLL x rrll

gametes: **R L**, **R L** — **r l**, **r l**

F_1 generation: RrLl — 100% heterozygous red petals, long stemmed

Cross two

Heterozygous red petals long stemmed — Heterozygous red petals long stemmed

RrLl x RrLl

gametes: **R L**, **r l** — **R L**, **r l**

F_2 generation

	(RL)	(rl)
(RL)	RRLL red long	RrLl red long
(rl)	RrLl red long	rrll blue short

probability is: red petals long stems 3 : 1 blue petals short stems

actual numbers: 610 202

(That is almost the one in four chance!)

> **Examiner's tip**
> Do not fall into the 'linkage' trap. Here the 9:3:3:1 ratio is replaced by a 3:1 ratio due to genes being adjacent on the chromosome. The net result is that **RL** and **rl** tend to be inherited together as a package. Do not dive into questions like this. Keep alert!

This example shows the consequence of very close linkage. In this genuine example the genes were so close that the RL and rl combinations were never parted by crossovers. No Rl or rL allele combinations were evident. So the classic RrLl x RrLl ratio of 9 : 3 : 3 : 1 was not possible. Instead a 3 : 1 ratio was produced. This is not monohybrid inheritance!

Progress check

(a) List the gametes for the following dihybrid cross. (The genes are not linked.)

Ddee x DDEe

(b) Show the genotypes of the progeny.

(a) De de DE De
(b) DDEe, DdEe, DDee, Ddee

Sex determination

The genetic information for gender is carried on specific chromosomes. In humans there are 22 pairs of autosomes plus the special sex determining pair, either XY (male) or XX (female). In some organisms such as birds this is reversed.

Some genes for sex determination are on autosomes but are activated by genes on the sex chromosomes.

Sperms can carry an X or Y chromosome, whereas an egg carries only an X chromosome.

The genetic cross shown should not give you any problems at A2 Level. However, look out for the combination of another factor which will increase difficulty.

genotype: XX (female) x XY (male)

gametes: (X) (X) (X) (Y)

offspring:

	(X)	(X)
(X)	XX	XX
(Y)	XY	XY

probability: 1 male : 1 female

This shows how 50 : 50 males to females are produced.

Sex linkage

Look more closely at the structure of the X and Y chromosomes.

Why do they not look like X and Y? Only when the cells are dividing, do they take the X,Y shape, after chromatid formation.

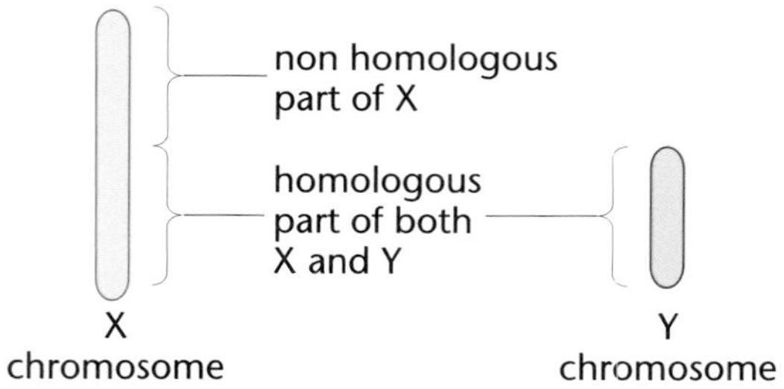

Homologous part of the sex chromosomes

- Has the same genes in both sexes.
- Each gene can be represented by the same or different alleles at each locus.

Non-homologous part of the sex chromosomes

- This means that the X chromosome has genes in this area, whereas the Y chromosome, being shorter, has no corresponding genes.
- Genes in this area of the X chromosome are always expressed, because there is no potential of a dominant allele to mask them.
- There are some notable genes found on the non-homologous part, e.g. haemophilia trait, and colour blindness trait.

The sex chromosomes, X and Y, carry genes other than those involved in sex determination. Examples of such genes are:

- a gene which controls the ability to detect red and green colours
- a gene which controls blood clotting; i.e. responsible for the production of factor VIII vital in the clotting process.

The loci of both genes are on the non-homologous part of chromosome X.

gene for normal blood clotting

gene for normal colour detection of red and green

X chromosome

Y chromosome

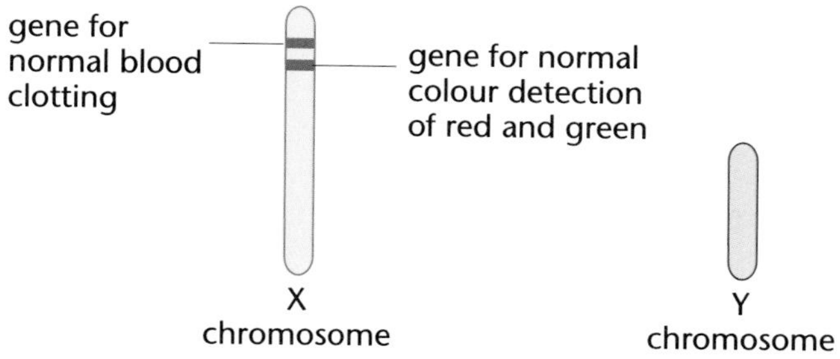

What is the effect of sex linked genes?

The fact that these genes are linked to the X chromosome has no significant effect when the genes perform their functions correctly. There are consequences, however, if the genes fail. This can be illustrated by a consideration of red-green colour blindness. When a gene is carried on a sex chromosome, the usual way to show this is by X^R.

R = normal colour vision (dominant) r = red-green colour blindness (recessive)

male	male	female	female	female
R	r	R r	R R	r r
X Y	X Y	X X	X X	X X
normal colour vision	red-green colour blind	normal colour vision (carrier)	normal colour vision	red-green colour blind

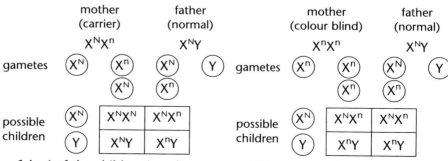

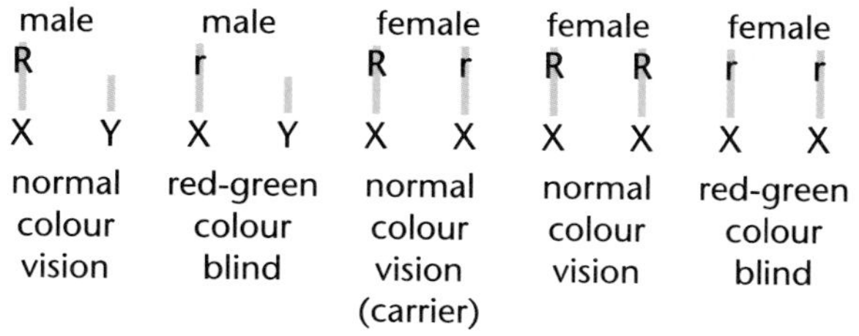

The genetic diagram shows that a female needs two recessive alleles (one from each parent!) to be colour blind. A male has only one gene at this locus, so one recessive allele is enough to give colour blindness.

The colour blindness gene is rare, so the chances of being a colour blind female are very low. Consider these crosses.

mother (carrier)	father (normal)	mother (colour blind)	father (normal)
$X^N X^n$	$X^N Y$	$X^n X^n$	$X^N Y$

gametes X^N X^n X^N Y gametes X^n X^n X^N Y

possible children

	X^N	X^n
X^N	$X^N X^N$	$X^N X^n$
Y	$X^N Y$	$X^n Y$

possible children

	X^n	X^n
X^N	$X^N X^n$	$X^N X^n$
Y	$X^n Y$	$X^n Y$

1 in 4 of the children is red-green colour blind. 50% of boys are colour blind, but no girls.

All boys are red-green colour blind No girls are colour blind.

> You can see the four possible genotypes. A female needs two r alleles, a male just need one!

Co-dominance

Remember that for co-dominance there is no dominance. Both alleles are equally expressed.

This term is given when each of two *different* alleles of a gene are expressed in the phenotype of an organism. In humans there are two co-dominant alleles. These alleles produce the antigens in blood which are responsible for our blood groups.

Consider these crosses

Blood group	*Genotypes*
A	I^AI^A, I^AI^O
B	I^BI^B, I^BI^O
AB	I^AI^B
O	I^OI^O

The allele for production of:

A antigen in blood = I^A
B antigen in blood = I^B
No antigen in blood = I^O

Examiner's tip

Look out for more examples of co-dominance in examination questions, e.g. in shorthorn cattle, R = red and W = white.

Where they occur in the phenotype together they produce a dappled intermediary colour known as roan.

Mother x Father
$I^B I^O$ $I^A I^O$

gametes I^B I^O I^A I^O

children

	I^B	I^O
I^A	I^AI^B	I^AI^O
I^O	I^BI^O	I^OI^O

All blood groups produced by this cross.

Mother x Father
$I^A I^B$ $I^A I^O$

gametes I^A I^B I^A I^O

children

	I^A	I^B
I^A	I^AI^A	I^AI^B
I^O	I^AI^O	I^BI^O

There must be a I^O from both parents to produce an O blood group.

In this instance there are two co-dominant alleles, I^A and I^B. When inherited together they are both expressed in the phenotype. Group O blood does not have any antigen.

Hardy–Weinberg Principle

The application of this principle allows us to **predict numbers of expected genotypes** in a population in the future. The principle tracks the proportion of two different alleles in the population.

Before applying the Hardy–Weinberg principle the following criteria must be satisfied.

- There must be no immigration and no emigration.
- There must be no mutations.
- There must be no selection (natural or artificial).
- There must be true random mating.
- All genotypes must be equally fertile.

Once the above criteria are satisfied then **gene frequencies remain constant**.

A **gene pool** consists of all genes and their alleles, which are part of the reproductive cells of an organism. Only genes that are in cells that **can be passed on** are part of the gene pool.

Hardy–Weinberg Principle: the terms identified

p = the frequency of the dominant allele in the population
q = the frequency of the recessive allele in the population
p^2 = the frequency of homozygous dominant individuals
q^2 = the frequency of homozygous recessive individuals
$2pq$ = the frequency of heterozygous individuals

KEY POINT

The principle is based on two equations:

(i) $p + q = 1$ (gene pool)
(ii) $p^2 + 2pq + q^2 = 1$ (total population)

Applying the Hardy–Weinberg Principle

A population of *Cepaea nemoralis* (land snail) lived in a field. In a survey there were 1400 pink-shelled snails and 600 were yellow. There were two alleles for shell colour.

y = yellow shell (recessive) Y = pink shell (dominant). Snails with pink shells can be YY or Yy. Snails with yellow shells can be yy only

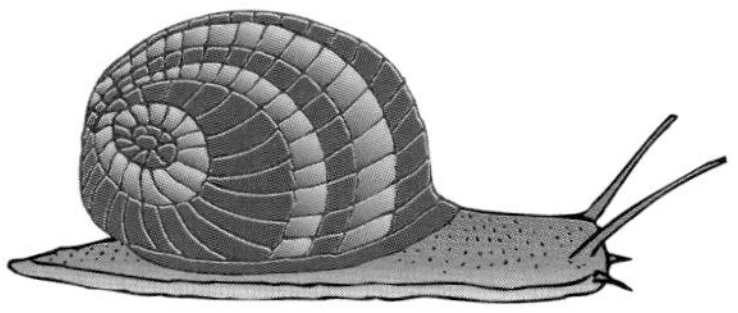

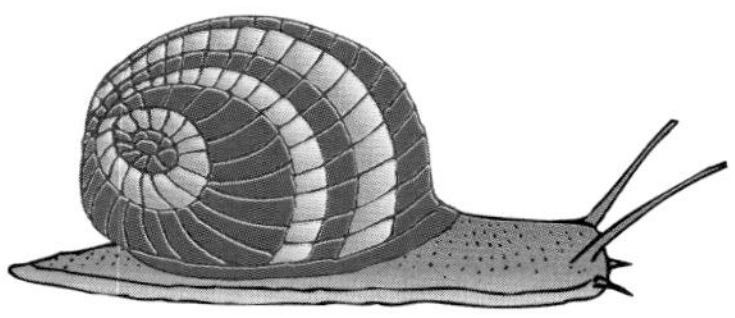

phenotype	pink	yellow
genotype	YY Yy	yy

This part of the calculation is to find the frequency of the recessive and dominant alleles in the population.

$$q^2 = \frac{600}{2000}$$

$$= 0.3$$

$$q = \sqrt{0.3} = 0.55$$

But $p + q = 1$

$$p = 1 - 0.55$$

$$= 0.45$$

So $p^2 = 0.20$

This part of the calculation is to find the frequency of homozygous and heterozygous snails in the population.

But $p^2 + 2pq + q^2 = 1$

$$0.20 + 0.5 + 0.3 = 1$$

YY Yy yy

Points to note

- These proportions can be applied to the snail populations say, 10 years in the future.
- If there were 24 000 snails in the population then the relative numbers would be:
  - YY $0.2 \times 24\,000 = 4800$
  - Yy $0.5 \times 24\,000 = 12\,000$
  - yy $0.3 \times 24\,000 = 7200$
- Remember that the five criteria must be satisfied if the relationship is to hold true.
- It is not possible to see which snails are homozygous dominant and which are heterozygous. They all look the same, pink! Hardy–Weinberg informs us, statistically, of those proportions.

It is also possible to apply the Hardy–Weinberg principle to a co-dominant pair of alleles. P and q are calculated by exactly the same method.

Examiner's tip

Always use the p + q = 1 equation to calculate the frequency of alleles if you are given suitable data, e.g. 'out of 400 diploid organisms in a population there were 40 homozygous recessive individuals.' 40 organisms have 80 recessive alleles.

$$q = \frac{80}{800}$$

$$= 0.1$$

From this figure you can calculate the others.

Progress check

What is the probability of a colour blind male and carrier female producing:

(a) a boy with normal colour vision

(b) a colour blind girl? Show your working.

mother (carrier) X^NX^n father (colour blind) X^nY

	X^N	X^n
X^n	X^NX^n	X^nX^n
Y	X^NY	X^nY

(a) 1 in 4 (b) 1 in 4

Epistasis

This involves two different genes which affect each other. A form of epistasis can be explained by referring to the sweet pea plant. *Lathyrus odoratus* is a white flowered sweet pea. When crossed, two white parent plants can produce white and purple flowers. This can be explained as follows:

Dominant epistasis also exists. In this instance a dominant allele can **inhibit** another, e.g. in the land snail **A** a dominant allele inhibits **B, b** alleles responsible for banding on the shell.

white precursor — white flowers

Allele A → enzyme A →

intermediate substance (white) — white flowers

Allele B → enzyme B →

final pigment — purple flowers

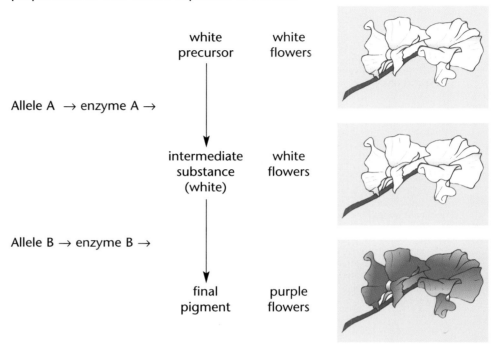

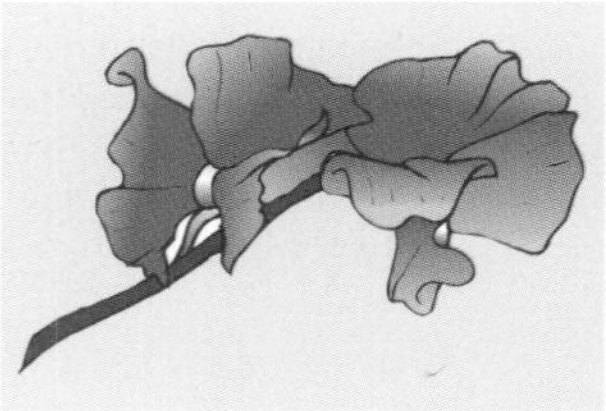

Both alleles A and B are needed to code for their respective enzymes if purple sweet pea flowers are to be produced. The alleles to consider are:

A (dominant) a (recessive) B (dominant) b (recessive)

Genotypes	aabb	aaBb	aaBB	Aabb	AaBB	AaBb	AAbb	AABb	AABB
Phenotypes	white	white	white	white	purple	purple	white	purple	purple

Without the combined effects of both A and B alleles then the flowers are white. The reliance of one gene on another is an example of epistasis.

How is it possible for two white flowered plants to be crossed to give purple offspring?

Questions about epistasis usually give some data which you will need to analyse. The organisms may not be sweet pea plants but the principles remain the same.

	white		white
genotype	AAbb	x	aaBB
gametes	Ab Ab		aB aB
F_1 generation		AaBb	

100% purple flowered plants from white flowered parents.

Check out the above genotypes to find two more genotypes of white flowered plants which could be crossed to give purple offspring.

Chi-squared: a statistical test

When doing scientific investigations we need to know if our results are significant or due to chance. We should not, for example, conclude that a new genetic ratio we have found represents a significant pattern for a particular cross. The χ^2 (chi-squared) test helps us to check out the difference between expected results and actual results. We can then state the probability that any differences between expected and actual results are due to chance or have significance.

Remember in **co-dominance** both alleles are expressed in the phenotype.

$\chi^2 = \sum \frac{d^2}{x}$ d = difference between actual and expected results

x = expected results

Σ = the sum of

Consider this example

Dianthus (campion) has flowers of three different colours, red, pink and white. Two pink flowered plants were crossed and the collected seeds grown to the flowering stage.

R = red r = white (both alleles are co-dominant)

genotypes Rr x Rr

gametes R r R r

F_1 generation

	R	r
R	RR	Rr
r	Rr	rr

white 0.25
pink 0.5
red 0.25

In an examination you may be given another term for 'actual'. It may be observed, but it means the same!

numbers	RR = red flowers	Rr = pink flowers	rr = white flowers
actual	34	84	42
expected	40	80	40

$$\chi^2 = \frac{(40-34)^2}{40} + \frac{(80-84)^2}{80} + \frac{(40-42)^2}{40}$$
$$= 0.9 + 0.2 + 0.1$$
$$= 1.2$$

The next stage is to assess the degrees of freedom for this investigation. This value is always one less than the number of classes of results. In this case there are three classes, i.e. red, pink and white.

Degrees of freedom = (3 – 1) = 2

Now check the χ^2 value against the table.

Degrees of freedom	*No of classes*	χ^2							
1	2	0.00	0.10	0.45	1.32	2.71	3.84	5.41	6.64
2	3	0.02	0.58	1.39	2.77	4.61	5.99	7.82	9.21
Probability that deviation is due to chance alone		0.99 (99%)	0.75 (75%)	0.50 (50%)	0.25 (25%)	0.10 (10%)	0.05 (5%)	0.02 (2%)	0.01 (1%)

What do you do with the χ^2 value?

- Go to the 2 degrees of freedom line (highlighted).
- Find the nearest figures to 1.2, which comes between the 70% and 50% columns.
- A χ^2 value of 1.2 shows that it is at least 70% probable that the result is by chance alone.
- The difference of this result against the expected is not significant.

For a significant difference the value should fall between (1–5)% columns.

If you are given a χ^2 question in an examination you will be given a data table. A mark may be given for degrees of freedom. Remember, **10** classes of results would give **9** degrees of freedom.

5.4 Applications of genetics

After studying this section you should be able to:

- *understand the principles of artificial selection*
- *describe the technique of micropropagation*
- *outline the inheritance and symptoms of cystic fibrosis, Huntington's chorea and Down's syndrome*
- *understand the need for genetic screening and counselling*
- *understand the need for genetic compatibility in transplant surgery*
- *understand potential applications which may result from the human genome project*

LEARNING SUMMARY

Artificial selection

AQA A	M5
AQA B	M4
EDEXCEL	M5
OCR	M5
WJEC	M5
NICCEA	M5

Compare artificial selection with natural selection (see p.102). The two processes have similarities but in natural selection it is change of the environment which is the selective agent.

Artificial selection is not the only way to improve animals and plants. Genetic modification is another method. A variety of soya bean plants now have resistance to selective herbicide.

Can you suggest four excellent features offered by this new variety?

This is *selective* breeding to improve specific domesticated animals and crop plants. Important points are:

- people are the **selective agents** and choose the parent organisms which will breed
- the organisms are chosen because they have **desired characteristics**
- the aim is to incorporate the desired characteristics from both organisms in their offspring
- the offspring must be **assessed** to find out if they have the desired combination of improvements (there is **no guarantee** that a cross will be successful!)
- offspring which have suitable improvements are used for breeding, the others are deleted from the gene pool (not allowed to breed).

Most modern crops have been produced by artificial selection. The Brussels sprout variety below was produced in this way. Many trials were carried out before the new variety was offered for sale.

Brilliant NEW FOR 2001
F1 Hybrid A brand new early cropping variety which produces dense, dark green buttons of excellent quality in September and October. Suitable for a wide range of soil types it also has a high resistance to powdery mildew and ring spot. Good for freezing. 2152 *pkt* £2.10

All modern racehorses have been artificially selected. Champion thoroughbred horses are selected for breeding on the basis of success in races. Only the best racehorses are actually entered in races. The fastest horses at various distances win races, and the right to breed. Continual improvement results as the gene pool is consistently strengthened.

Key points from AS

- **Genetically modified organisms**
  Revise AS page 90

Genetic disorders

AQA A	M5
AQA B	M4
EDEXCEL	M5
OCR	M5
WJEC	M5
NICCEA	M5

There are many genetic diseases in the human population. Modern medical practices reduce the effects of certain symptoms. Serious diseases which can be life threatening are treated, e.g. haemophiliacs are supplied with factor VIII to allow blood clotting to take place.

Survival of people with a severe genetic deficiency maintains the frequency of defective alleles in the population. Sufferers and carriers who breed, may increase the frequency of the allele in the human gene pool.

Some important genetic disorders

Detection:
- by symptoms shown
- prediction can be made for further children
- e.g. if two people who do not suffer from the condition have a child who is cystic, any further children have a 1 in 4 chance of having the condition.

Cystic fibrosis

- In healthy people a gene codes for a protein which functions as a Cl^- pump in epithelial cells.
- The outward movement of Cl^- ions is accompanied by water, effectively lubricating the outside of these lining cells.
- The **cystic fibrosis trait** is carried by a single, **recessive allele**.
- The disorder is only expressed in the homozygous condition (1 in 2000 people).
- In sufferers the **Cl^- pump protein** does not function correctly.
- The fluid is **more viscous** and moves in a sluggish movement over the epithelial surfaces.
- Adverse effects are evident in the pancreas–duodenum area where there is **inhibited movement** of substances through the alimentary canal.
- Serious effects are found in the lungs where the epithelial cells secrete **thick sticky mucus**.
- The mucus **inhibits breathing** seriously, so must be removed each day to relieve symptoms.

Detection:
- by symptoms shown
- since the allele is dominant even heterozygous people have the disease
- where one person has the disease and the other does not, the chance of a child being born with the condition is 1 in 2.

Huntington's chorea

- The disease is carried by a **dominant allele**.
- Symptoms observed are increasing **involuntary movements** and **mental deterioration**.
- 1 in 100 000 carry the allele and, since it is **dominant**, have the disease.
- Often the symptoms are not shown until the post 40s so that the genes can be passed on before the disease is detected.

Detection:
- before birth by **amniocentesis** or **chorionic villi sampling**
- when detected – in mid-pregnancy, test informs of a certain prediction that child will have Down's syndrome.

Down's syndrome

- This takes place as a consequence of the **chromosomes segregating incorrectly during meiosis**.
- The result is that one gamete carries 22 chromosomes whereas the other carries **24 chromosomes**.
- This is known as **non-disjunction**.
- The gamete carrying 24 chromosomes may then fuse with a normal one carrying 23 to form a zygotic cell with **47 chromosomes**.
- The female gametes can be affected in this way, the incidence increasing above the age of thirty five.
- The chromosome defect can be detected; chromosome numbers are checked out by experienced personnel so that early warning can be given.

Screening

This is checking out the population for a variety of diseases by using screening techniques.

Amniocentesis

The process takes place during mid-pregnancy.

- Some fetal cells detach and become suspended in the amniotic fluid.
- A syringe is inserted through the uterus wall into the amniotic fluid and a sample is removed.
- Some fluid is placed into a Petri dish where the fetal cells grow on a nutrient medium.
- The number of chromosomes in the nuclei is counted.
- 47 chromosomes per nucleus gives an early warning of Down's syndrome.

Chorionic villi sampling

This process also takes place during mid-pregnancy.

- Placental cells arise from the zygote, so the fetus and the placenta have identical nuclei.
- Some chorionic villus cells are removed from the placenta.
- Again the number of chromosomes in the nuclei is counted.

Both of the techniques shown are accompanied by use of an ultrasound scanner. This creates a picture of the fetus in the uterus so that damage can be avoided.

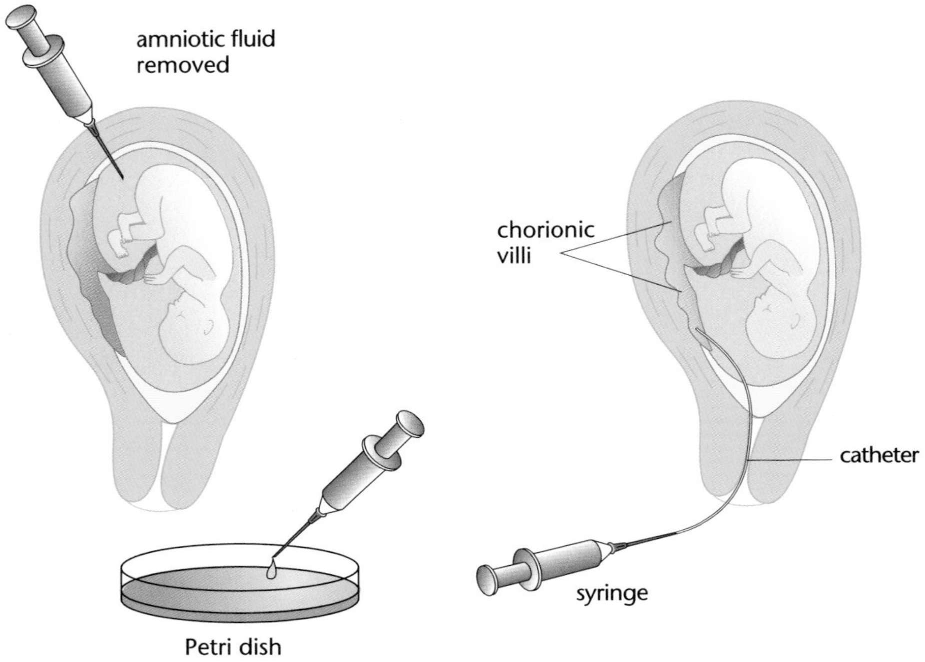

Genetic counselling

It is useful for potential parents to know the probability of a defective allele being expressed in their future children.

If the genetic pattern of a disease is tracked through a family tree then useful information can be given to potential parents. The probability of having healthy or affected children can be considered and a decision made.

Histocompatibility

This is shown by tissues which can be **transplanted** into a person and refers to the fact they are **not rejected** by the immune system. They have histocompatibility!

Cells have a range of protein molecules on their cell surface membranes. In a person these proteins help to identify a cell as 'self' so that the immune system will not be triggered. All of these proteins are coded for by a person's DNA. Different people have different genes for these histocompatible proteins. The best person to donate an organ would be an identical twin to the recipient! This is rarely possible, so tissue-matching histocompatible cell surface proteins is extremely important. The closer the match, the less will be the intensity of the immune response.

Even with the achievement of a reasonable tissue match it is wise to use **immunosuppressive drugs**. These inhibit the action of the white blood cells and enable the transplant to establish.

The human genome project

AQA A	M5
AQA B	M4
EDEXCEL	M5
OCR	M5
WJEC	M5
NICCEA	M5

This is an analysis of the complete human genetic make-up and will ultimately map the organic base sequences of the nucleotides along our DNA.

A brief history

- 1977 Sanger devised DNA base sequencing.
- 1986 Human genome project initiated in USA and UK.
- 1996 30 000 genes mapped.
- 1999 one billion bases mapped including all of chromosome 22.
- 2000 chromosome 21 mapped with the human genome almost complete.
- 2001 human genome mapping complete.

Some important points

- The genome project will sequence the complete set of over 100 000 genes.
- Only around 5% of the base pairs along the DNA actually result in the expression of characteristics. These DNA sequences are known as **exons**.
- 95% of DNA base sequences do not appear to be involved in the expression of characteristics and are known as **introns**.
- Introns do not outwardly seem to be responsible for characteristics. It is likely that they may be regulatory, perhaps in multiple gene role.

Single nucleotide polymorphisms (SNPs)

Effects of single nucleotide polymorphism

Example

5 base sequences from five people →

GTATAGCCGCAT 1
GTATAGCCGCAT 1
GTATAGCCGCAT 1
GTATAGCCGCCT 2
GTATAGCCGCCT 2

Version 1 = ●
Version 2 = ●

Proportion of the SNP in healthy members of population:

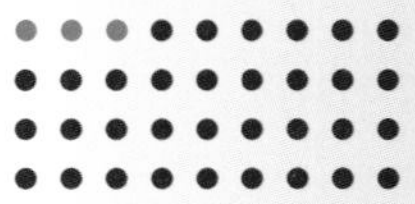

Proportion of the SNP in diseased members of population:

A greater incidence of an SNP in people with a disease may point to a cause.

Around 99.9% of human DNA is the same in all individuals. Merely 0.1% is different! The different sequences in individuals can be the result of **single nucleotide polymorphism**. One base difference from one individual to another at a site may have no difference. Up to a maximum of six different codons can code for one amino acid. An SNP will not necessarily have any effect.

Some SNPs do change a protein significantly. Such changes may result in genetic disease, resistance or susceptibility to disease.

How can the mapping of SNPs be useful?

- The mapping of SNPs along chromosomes signpost where base differences exist.
- Across the gene pool a pattern of SNP positions will be evident.
- There may be a high frequency of common SNPs found in the DNA of people with a specific disease.
- This highlights interesting sites for future research and will help to find answers to genetic problems.

Benefits obtained from the human genome project

Ultimately the human genome data will be instrumental in the development of drugs to treat genetic disease. Additionally, by analysis of parental DNA, it will be possible to give the probability of the development of a specific disease or susceptibility to it, in offspring. Fetal DNA, obtained through amniocentesis or by chorionic villi sampling, will give genetic information about an individual child. Genetic counsellors will have more information about an individual than ever before. Companies will be able to produce 'designer drugs' to alleviate the problems which originate in our DNA molecules. Soon the race will begin to produce the first crop of drugs to treat or even cure serious genetic diseases.

Look to the media for progress updates!

Sample questions and model answers

1

(a) Explain the difference between sex linkage and autosomal linkage. [2]

sex linkage – genes are located on a sex chromosome

autosomal linkage – genes are located on one of the other 44 chromosomes

(b) The diagram below shows part of a family tree where some of the people have haemophilia.

This type of question is a challenge! Note the key for the symbols and then apply them to the family tree. Think logically and work up and down the diagram. In your 'live' examination write on the diagram to help you work out each individual genotype asked in the question. If there are a range of possible genotypes they may be helpful.

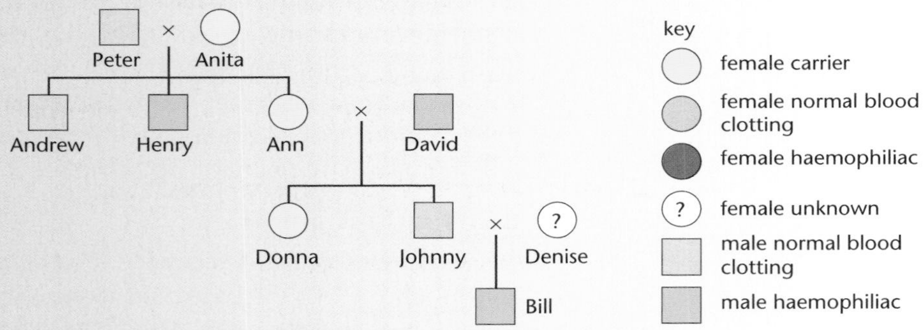

Show the possible genotypes of Denise. Give evidence from the genetic diagram to support your answer. [3]

Let H = *normal* blood clotting

Let h = haemophiliac trait

The genotype can be X^HX^h or X^hX^h

Reason – Johnny is X^HY so he is responsible for Bill's Y chromosome (Y chromosomes do not carry a blood clotting gene)

Working backwards, Bill is haemophiliac so Denise must have at least one X^h

She can, therefore, be X^hX^h or X^HX^h

(c) Peter and Anita had three children. Andrew was born first, then Henry and finally Ann. Use the information in the diagram to answer the questions.

(i) When could genetic counselling have been given to help Peter and Anita? [1]

After the birth of Henry.

(ii) Explain the useful information which they could have been given. [3]

Since Henry is haemophiliac his genotype is X^hY.

His father, Peter, has normal clotting blood so is X^HY and passes on a Y to his son, Henry.

His mother is not haemophiliac but must be a carrier, X^HX^h because mother passes on X^h.

We can predict 2 in 4 children will have normal clotting of blood, 1 in 4 will be female and a carrier 1 in 4 will be haemophiliac male.

2

(a) The symptoms of cystic fibrosis can be reduced by gene therapy. Explain this process. [2]

The correct gene for the secretion of fluid from epithelial cells applied by aerosol (in liposomes) through lungs.

(b) Genetic engineering may help reduce the frequency of the cystic fibrosis gene. Which cell would be genetically modified so that **all** nucleated cells of a person would carry the improved gene? [1]

zygote / fertilised egg

Practice examination questions

1 (a) List the criteria which must be satisfied before applying the Hardy–Weinberg Principle. [4]

(b) In a population of 160 small mammals, some had a dark brown coat and the others had a light brown coat. Dark brown (B) is dominant over light brown (b). In the population there were 48 light brown individuals. Using the Hardy–Weinberg equations calculate:

(i) the frequency of homozygous dominant and heterozygous individuals in the population [3]

(ii) how many of each of the genotypes (BB, Bb, bb) would there be in a future population of 10 000 individuals? [2]

[Total: 9]

2 Match each term with its correct definition.

A co-dominance
B polygenic inheritance
C genotype
D polyploid
E somatic

(i) a cell which is not involved in reproduction [1]

(ii) a nucleus which has three or more sets of chromosomes [1]

(iii) a feature which is controlled by two or more genes, along different loci along a chromosome [1]

(iv) two alleles which are equally expressed in the organism [1]

(v) all of the genes found in a nucleus, including both dominant and recessive alleles. [1]

[Total: 5]

3 The letters below represent the organic bases along the coding strand of a DNA molecule.

CCG ATT CGA TAG

(a) What term is given to each group of three bases? [1]

(b) Give **two** functions of a group of three organic bases. [2]

(c) Using the strand of DNA above show **three** different types of point mutation. [3]

[Total: 6]

4 The cell on the right shows a cell at the beginning of telophase II during meiosis.

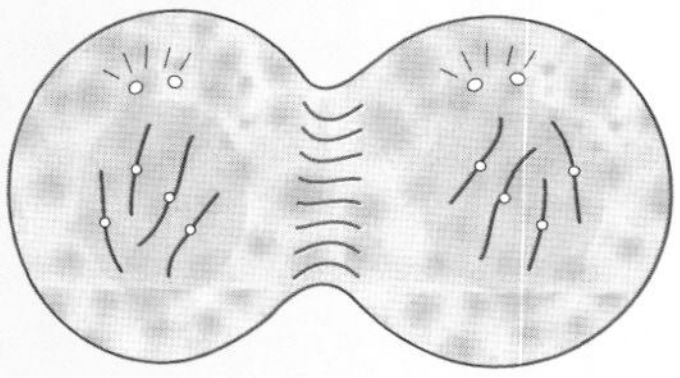

(a) How many chromosomes were there in the parent cell at the beginning of meiosis? [1]

(b) Describe **one** difference between telophase II and

(i) telophase I of meiosis

(ii) telophase of mitosis. [2]

(c) Describe the stage immediately before telophase II. [2]

[Total: 5]

Chapter 6

Biodiversity

The following topics are covered in this chapter:

- *Classification*
- *Evolution*
- *Manipulation of reproduction*

6.1 Classification

After studying this section you should be able to:

- *indicate sources and effects of variation in organisms*
- *outline features of continuous and discontinuous variation*
- *name the five kingdoms and describe the main features of each group*

LEARNING SUMMARY

What is variation?

AQA A	M5
AQA B	M4
EDEXCEL	M5
OCR	M5
WJEC	M5
NICCEA	M5

Species throughout the biosphere differ from each other.

Variation describes the differences which exist in organisms throughout the biosphere. This variation consists of differences **between** species as well as differences **within** the same species. Each individual is influenced by the environment, so this is another source of variation.

genotype + environment = phenotype

The alleles which are expressed in the phenotype can only perform their function efficiently if they have a supply of suitable substances and have appropriate conditions. Ultimately new genes and alleles have appeared by mutation (see page 81). The spontaneous appearance of **advantageous** new mutations is also possible (see page 81). This may lead to formation of new species.

Remember that a species shows continuous variation when there are small incremental differences, e.g. height of people in a town. Beginning with the smallest and ending with the tallest there would probably be at least one person at each height, at 1cm increments. A smooth gradation of differences!

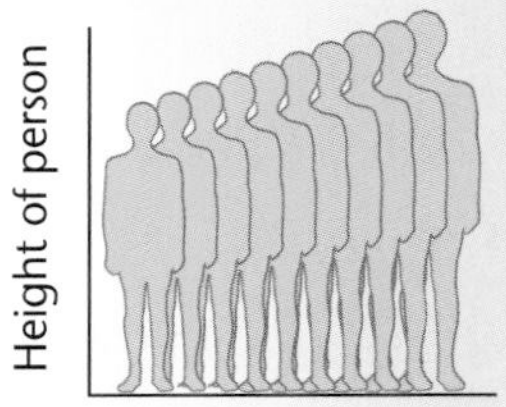

Continuous and discontinuous variation

Continuous variation

This is shown when there is a range of **small incremental differences** in a feature of organisms in a population. An example of this is height in humans. If the height of each pupil in a school is measured then from the shortest pupil to the tallest, there are very small differences across the distribution. This is shown by the graph below which shows smooth changes in height across a population. This type of variation is shown when features are controlled by **polygenic inheritance**. A number of genes **interact** to produce the expressed feature.

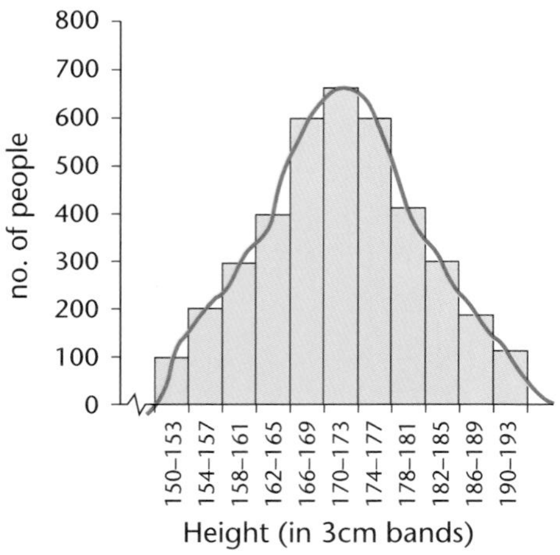

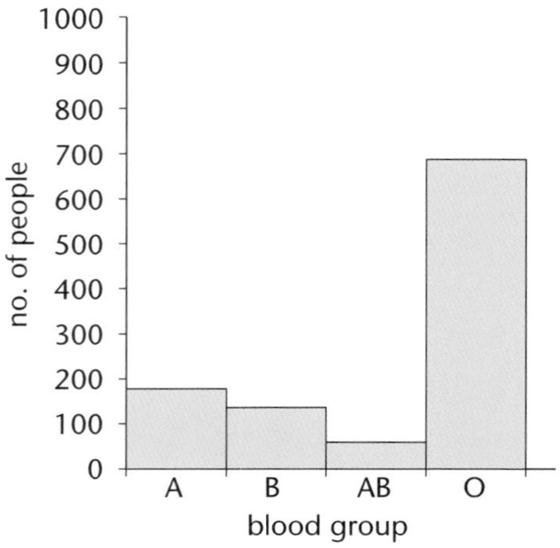

Key points from AS

- **Variation**
  Revise AS pages 94–95

Discontinuous variation

This is shown when a characteristic is expressed in discrete categories. Humans have four discrete blood groups, A, B, AB or O. There are no intermediates, the differences are clear cut!

Classification system

AQA A	M5
AQA B	M4
EDEXCEL	M5
OCR	M5
WJEC	M5
NICCEA	M5

Classification or taxonomy is the way that organisms are divided into groups. The system is based on similarities, differences, and on patterns of evolutionary history (**phylogenetic**). The organisation into groups helps us to identify organisms as we are able to check characteristics against the criteria of a group.

Try this!

Pretty **P**olly **F**inds **P**arrots **A**ttractive.

It will help you to remember the kingdoms!

Most examination boards test knowledge of characteristics across the kingdoms. Information will usually be given for any sub-group tasks.

The table includes some of the main features of each kingdom. Prokaryotae and Protoctista tend to give more of a challenge than some of the other kingdoms, and are examined more often.

Remember that Protoctista, Fungi, Plantae and Animalia are all eukaryotic. They all have membrane-bound organelles, e.g. mitichondria. Flagellae, if present, have a 9 + 2 microtubule structure.

The only similarity with the two examples is that they are in the kingdom Animalia. This is very informative because all Animalia have so common features.

There are five kingdoms

→ *increase in complexity*

Prokaryotae	*Protoctista*	*Fungi*	*Plantae*	*Animalia*
very simple cells with few organelles no membrane-bound organelles if there are flagellae, then not 9 + 2 system of microtubules DNA in strands, no true nucleus e.g. bacteria and cyanobacteria	unicellular cells with membrane-bound organelles some are photo-synthetic, but many have heterotrophic nutrition reproduction usually involves fission e.g. algae, and protozoa	heterotrophic nutrition some saprotro-phic, some parasitic consists of thread-like hyphae, chitin cell walls many nuclei in hyphae, not in one per cell organisation reproduction involves the production of spores	multicellular organisms which are photosynthetic cells have cellulose cell wall, sap vacuole and chloroplasts reproduce by seeds, or by spores, some sexual, some asexual.	multicellular organisms which are heterotrophic no cell walls no sap vacuoles

Taxonomy within a kingdom

Each kingdom can be sub-divided into a number of progressively smaller groups. Ultimately this leads to an individual type of organism, a **species**.

The hierarchy of the groups is shown below.

	Example 1	*Example 2*
Kingdom	Animalia	Animalia
Phylum	Chordata	Arthropoda
Class	Mammalia	Insecta
Order	Primates	Lepidoptera
Family	Hominidae	Pieridae
Genus	Homo	Pieris
Species	sapiens	brassica

The seven groups can be difficult to remember. Try the easy way!

KING **P**ENGUINS **C**LIMB **O**VER **F**ROZEN **G**RASSY **S**LOPES

The first letter of each word will help you remember. It is a **mnemonic**. It is a very successful technique! An excellent strategy to aid recall.

What is a species?

KEY POINT

If two organisms are able to **breed together**, naturally, and **produce fertile offspring**, then they are from the same species.

6.2 Evolution

After studying this section you should be able to:

LEARNING SUMMARY

- *understand the process of natural selection*
- *predict population changes in terms of selective pressures*
- *understand a range of isolating mechanisms and how a new species can be formed*
- *understand the difference between allopatric and sympatric speciation*
- *understand adaptive radiation*

Natural selection

AQA A	M5
AQA B	M4
EDEXCEL	M5
OCR	M5
WJEC	M5
NICCEA	M5

Learn this theory carefully then apply it to the scenarios given in your examination. Candidates often identify that some organisms die and others survive, but few go on to predict the inheritance of advantageous genes and the consequence to the species.

Throughout the biosphere communities of organisms interact in a range of ecosystems. Darwin travelled across the world in his ship, the *Beagle*, observing organisms in their habitats. In 1858 Darwin, in association with Wallace, published *On the Origin of Species*. In this book he gave his theory of **natural selection**.

The key features of this theory are that as organisms interact with their environment:

- individual organisms of populations are not identical, and can **vary in both genotypes and phenotypes**
- **some organisms survive** in their environment other organisms **die**, effectively being **deleted from the gene pool**
- surviving organisms **go on to breed** and **pass on their genes** to their offspring
- this **increases the frequency of the advantageous genes** in the population.

Consider these factors

- Adverse conditions in the environment could make a species extinct, but a range of genotypes increases the chances of the species surviving.
- Different genotypes may be suited to a changing environment, say, as a result of global warming.
- A variant of different genotype, previously low in numbers, may thrive in a changed environment and increase in numbers.
- Where organisms are well suited to their environment they have adaptations which give this advantage.
- If other organisms have been selected against, then more resources are available for survivors.
- Breeding usually produces many more offspring than the mere replacement of parents.
- Resources are limited so that competition for food, shelter and breeding areas takes place. Only the fittest survive!

What is selective pressure?

In this example the fact that the numbers of herbivores decrease is ***another*** selective pressure. This time numbers of predators may decrease.

This is the term given to a factor which has a direct effect on the numbers of individuals in a population of organisms, e.g.

'It is late summer and the days without rainfall have caused the grassland to be parched. There is little food this year.'

Here the **selective pressure** is a **lack of food** for the herbivores. Species which are **best adapted** to this habitat **compete** well for the limited resources and go on to survive. Within a species there is a further application of the selective pressure as weaker organisms perish and the strongest survive.

Variation and natural selection

New genes can appear in a species for the first time, due to a form of mutation. Over 1000s of years repeated natural selection takes place, resulting in superb adaptations to the environment.

- The Venus fly trap with its intricate leaf structures captures insects. The insects decompose, supplying minerals to the mineral deficient soil.
- Crown Imperial lilies (*Fritillaria*) produce colourful flowers, and a scent of stinking, decomposing flesh. Flies are attracted and help pollination.
- The bee orchid flower is so like a queen bee that a male will attempt mating.

Considering the above examples, it is no wonder that candidates seem to consider that the organisms actively adapt to develop in these ways. They suggest that the organisms themselves have control to make active changes. **This is not so! There is no control, no active adaptation.**

KEY POINT

New genes appear by CHANCE!

Selective pressures and populations

To find out more about the effects that selective pressures can have, the **normal distribution** must be considered. The distribution below is illustrated with an example.

The mean value is at the peak. There are fewer tall and short individuals in this example. A taller plant intercepts light better than a shorter one.

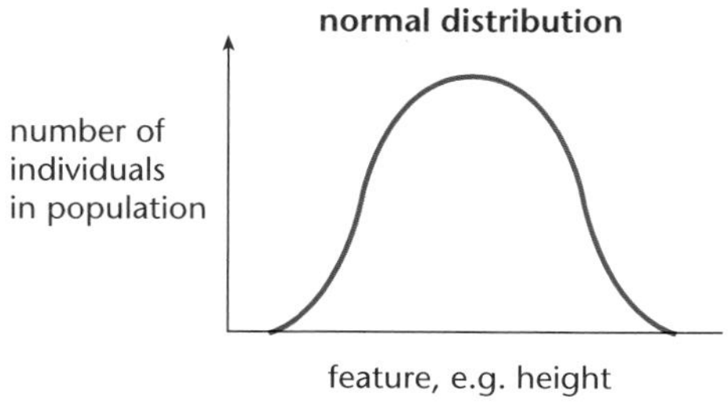

The further distributions below show effects of selective pressures (shown by blue arrow). Each is illustrated with an example.

Selective pressure at both ends of the distribution cause the extreme genotypes to die. This maintains the distribution around the mean value. Mean wing-length better for flight, better for prey capture.

Selective pressure results in death of less fast animals. May die out due to predators. Faster ones (longer legs) pass on advantageous genes. Distribution moves to right as average individual now faster.

Selective pressure results in death of organisms around mean value. In time this can lead to two distributions. Long fur is adapted to a cold temperature and short fur to a warm temperature. Mean suited to neither extreme.

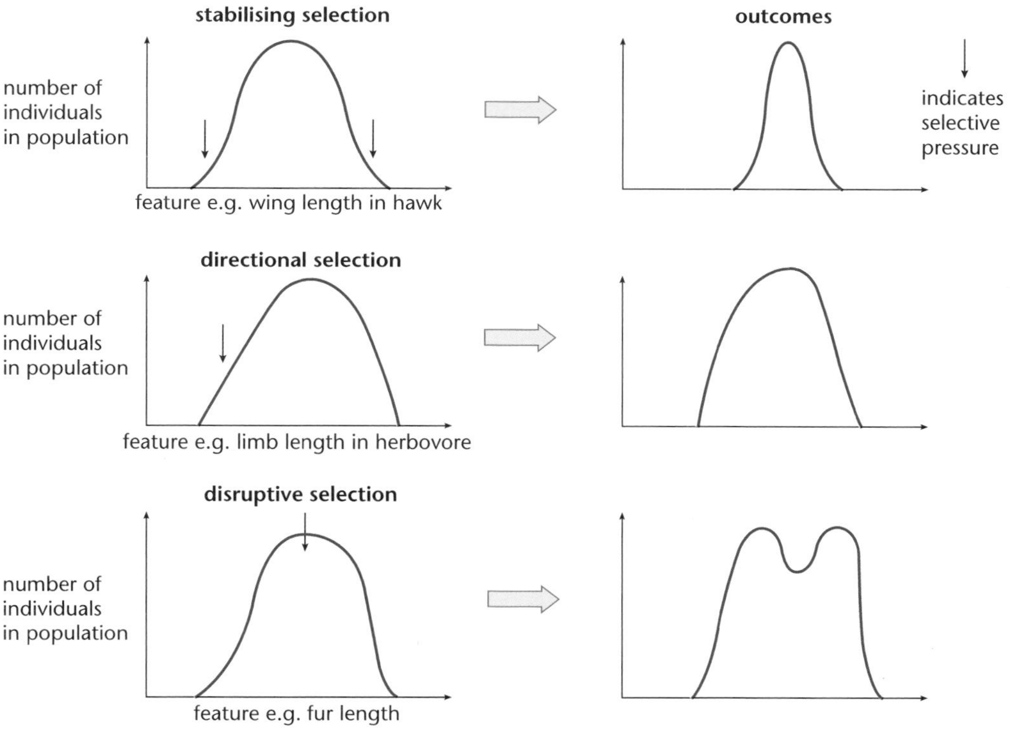

How can a population become isolated?

The previous example of disruptive selection showed how two extreme genotypes can be selected for. Continued selection against individuals around the former mean genotype, finally results in two discrete distributions. This division into two groups may be followed by, say, advantageous mutations. There is a probability that, in time, the two groups will become incompatible, unable to breed successfully. They have become isolated (genetically). Isolation is a key factor in the **development of new species** (**speciation**).

Genetic isolation

There are several different ways in which genetic isolation occurs, from point mutations to polyploidy.

This can occur with a series of mutations over millions of years. The principle of genetic isolation is described above since two groups, with common ancestors cannot breed together. Polyploidy (see page 80) can also give rise to genetic isolation. Here sets of chromosomes increase, conferring advantage to a new variant. An example of this is *Spartina angelica* (cord grass) with 122 chromosomes per cell. This spontaneously arose from the parent species *Spartina townsendii*, which has 61 chromosomes per cell. *Spartina angelica* is unable to breed with the original parent.

Geographical isolation

This will help you. Different finches evolved on different islands, but they did have a common ancestor.

This takes place when a population becomes divided as a result of a physical barrier appearing. For example, a land mass may become divided by a natural disaster like an earthquake or a rise in sea level. Geographical isolation followed by mutations can result in the formation of new species. This can be illustrated with the finches of the Galapagos islands. There are many different species in the Galapagos islands, ultimately from a common ancestral species. Clearly new species do form after many years of geographical isolation. This is **allopatric speciation**.

Reproductive isolation

A new pheromone is produced by several antelopes as a result of a mutation. The mainstream individuals refuse mating as a result of this scent. An isolated few do mate. This is reproductive isolation.

This is a type of genetic isolation. Here the formation of a new species can take place in the same geographical area, e.g. mutation(s) may result in reproductive incompatibility. A new gene producing, say, a hormone, may lead an animal to be rejected from the mainstream group, but breeding may be possible within its own group of variants. When this mechanism results in the production of a new species it is known as **sympatric speciation**.

Progress check

The graph below shows the mean length of roots in *Cirsium arvense*.

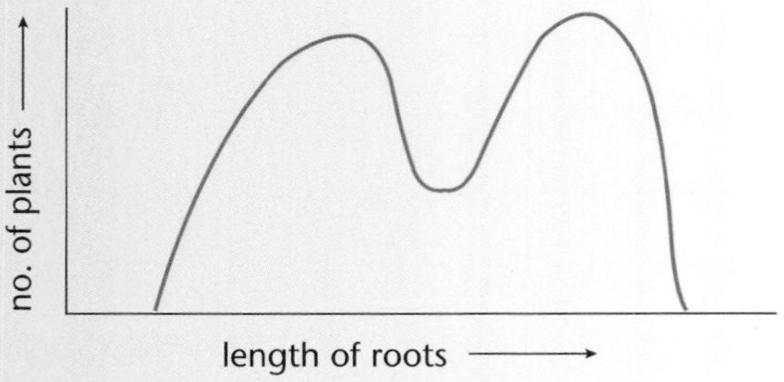

(a) Which type of distribution is shown? Give a reason for your answer.

(b) Name the taxonomic term given to each of the following:

(i) *Cirsium* (ii) *arvense*.

(a) The graph appears to show as disruptive variation, due to two peaks. It also shows as continuous variation since root lengths change in small increments.

(b) (i) genus (ii) species

How does evolution take place?

Existing species are the result of slow, gradual changes in their ancestors over millions of years. This is **evolution**. Evidence for evolution exists because:

- **fossils** have been found and linked to the modern species
- the **fossil time sequence** is laid down in the **sedimentary layers** beneath the Earth's surface
- **mutations appeared spontaneously** resulting in new advantageous features appearing, often visible in the fossil time sequence
- disadvantageous features often resulted in the disappearance of an organism after a certain period; this is **extinction**
- **vestigial features** in modern species no longer have a function; this points to the fact that ancestors *did* have a use for the feature – **change** (a key idea in the theory of evolution) has taken place
- **common DNA** sequences can be traced across the taxonomic groups and back through to the DNA of well preserved ancestors.

Clearly evolution has taken place in the past and is still taking place!

Examiners set questions about genetic conservation. Candidates often give answers which imply that it means the keeping of ***genes*** in some way, as if they are stored, ***detached*** from cells. **WRONG!** Storage methods include freezing semen or embryos, and cold storage of seeds. Whole cell storage is the current mechanism. Safari parks act as gene pool extensions.

Genetic conservation

A supply of genetic material to be used in breeding programmes in future years needs to be retained. Geneticists would benefit from an expanding gene pool to improve domesticated animals and crop plants. The ability to retain old varieties of plants in botanic gardens and keeping 'rare breed' farms is vital so that potentially advantageous genes are always available. We must not lose them! Zoos and safari parks can help. Keeping a breeding line of the organisms active is an option but additionally there are less expensive hi-tech methods available. **Sperm**, **embryo**, and **seed banks** can be used for long-term storage.

Deep-freeze storage is not such a recent invention as we at first thought. Glaciers from a previous Ice-age encapsulate a range of carcasses of extinct organisms. Global warming defrosts outer layers and reveals preserved dead organisms. Immediately on exposure to the air the organic material begins to decompose and flies are attracted. Scientists currently search for pre-historic animals such as the mammoth. Retrieving perfectly preserved DNA is the aim. Insertion of mammoth DNA into a zygote of another animal, e.g. an elephant, may allow the re-emergence of this extinct animal.

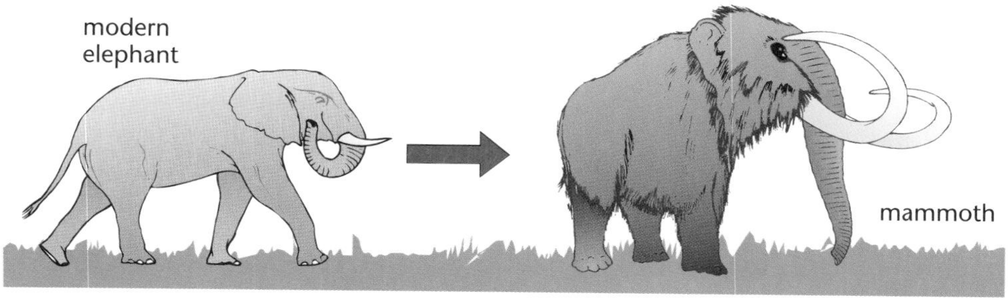

How can we prevent the extinction of organisms?

Wild-life reserves are needed in both terrestrial and aquatic habitats.

The insatiable demand for land to satisfy human requirements is a major problem. Reduced habitat areas means that there is much less land for the organisms to exploit. Modern breeding technology can be employed, e.g. in China the giant panda has problems in that its bamboo habitat is drastically reduced. With numbers very low, and extinction looming, **artificial insemination** has come to the rescue with dramatic success!

6.3 Manipulation of reproduction

After studying this section you should be able to:

- *understand the processes of artificial insemination and embryo transplant*
- *understand the need for progeny testing*
- *understand the problems of inbreeding*

LEARNING SUMMARY

Artificial insemination (AI)

EDEXCEL	M5
OCR	M5
WJEC	M5
NICCEA	M5

AI can be used for a range of different animals. It is even used in humans. Soldiers leaving for action often leave a genetic insurance, their semen!

Important points

- Some domesticated animals have been selectively bred to produce desired features for human needs but which prevent breeding by natural means, e.g. modern turkey breeds. Their breast muscles are so big that the physical act of mating is impossible.
- In many animals a male has limitations as to the number of females he can physically breed with. Males produce millions of sperms, semen dilution allows many more offspring to be produced. Cost effective!
- Top quality, disease-free animals only are used.
- Semen from a variety of males can be used to inseminate a population which avoids inbreeding.
- Even when an animal has died the frozen semen is still viable.

AI in cattle (UK)

Progeny testing

This process allows for the systematic testing of offspring and the comparison of data. Only when a sire (male) has successfully demonstrated that he can transmit suitable features in progeny (offspring) would his semen be used on a wider commercial scale. In the UK a bull is seven years old before his semen becomes available for the national AI programme. His progeny must have performed successfully. Some bulls fail and semen from the seven years would be destroyed. Only genetically superior bulls are used!

Another advantage of AI, easy transport!

Preparation and storage of semen

- Semen from one ejaculation is diluted around ×50 with **milk or egg yolk**.
- **Glycerol** is added as a **cryoprotectant**, preventing damage by ice formation.
- **Sugar** is added as an energy source for sperms.
- The external solution has an **identical water potential** with the sperm contents to prevent osmotic damage.
- **Buffer** is added to prevent damage due to pH changes.
- **Antibiotics** are added to destroy spoilage organisms.
- Storage is in straws, kept at –196 °C, in liquid nitrogen.

How are cows artificially inseminated?

- The cow must be in **oestrous**, having ovulated.
- A straw is thawed out in warm water and inserted into a catheter.
- The catheter is placed in the vagina up to the cervix where the semen is ejected.

A catheter

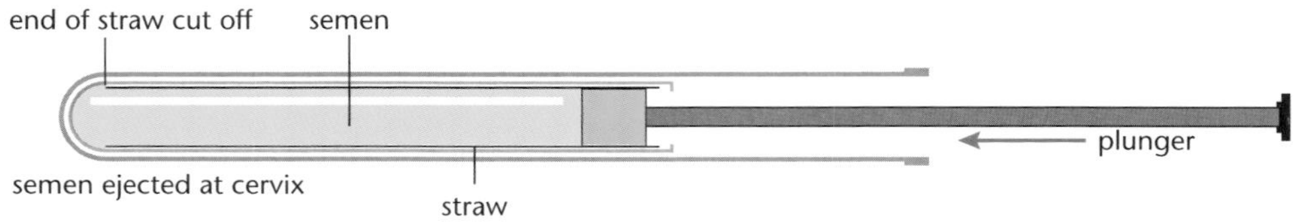

Superovulation techniques are used with other animals. These include humans! Some women have fertility problems. Use of hormones to stimulate ovulation yields a number of ova. After *in vitro* fertilisation (in a test tube) resulting embryos can be immediately implanted or frozen for later.

Superovulation and embryo transfer

These processes can be described with reference to cattle:

- Only genetically superior cows are used in this process.
- Normally a cow produces one ovum at each ovulation.
- Treatment with hormones results in several ova being produced at ovulation.
- Cows would show the signs of oestrous and immediately be artificially inseminated, so that fertilisation takes place.
- This is followed up a week later by the harvesting of embryos.
- This is done with a catheter which does a uterine sweep.
- Embryos are then frozen and kept for later, or artificially implanted into a surrogate cow.
- Transport is very cheap. Formerly a herd of cattle could be exported in a ship at a very expensive cost. Now the same herd is shipped in a liquid nitrogen bucket!
- In this way a Charolais cow can give birth to a pedigree Friesian calf!

Modern reproduction techniques and genetic engineering will continue to hit the headlines during the lifetime of this book. There are many potential uses and refinements. Ethics and morals must always be balanced against potential benefits, and possible problems.

Micropropagation

New plant varieties are produced by artificial selection. After a long, expensive, breeding programme **just one individual plant** may be produced, e.g. a Day lily (*Hemerocallis*) of new petal colour and disease resistance. **Asexual techniques** must be used to **clone** the variety. In the past techniques such as taking cuttings would have been used and it would take a **number of years** to build up enough plants for a commercial launch. It is now possible to replicate plants by another asexual method, **micropropagation**.

The diagrams below outline the process.

Advantages of micopropagation

- Generating new plants from the apical meristem tissue eliminates many plant viruses, so usually, virus free plants are produced.
- If the material is available the process can take place at any time of the year.
- Even a tiny explant or callus can be cut into pieces and sub-cultured.

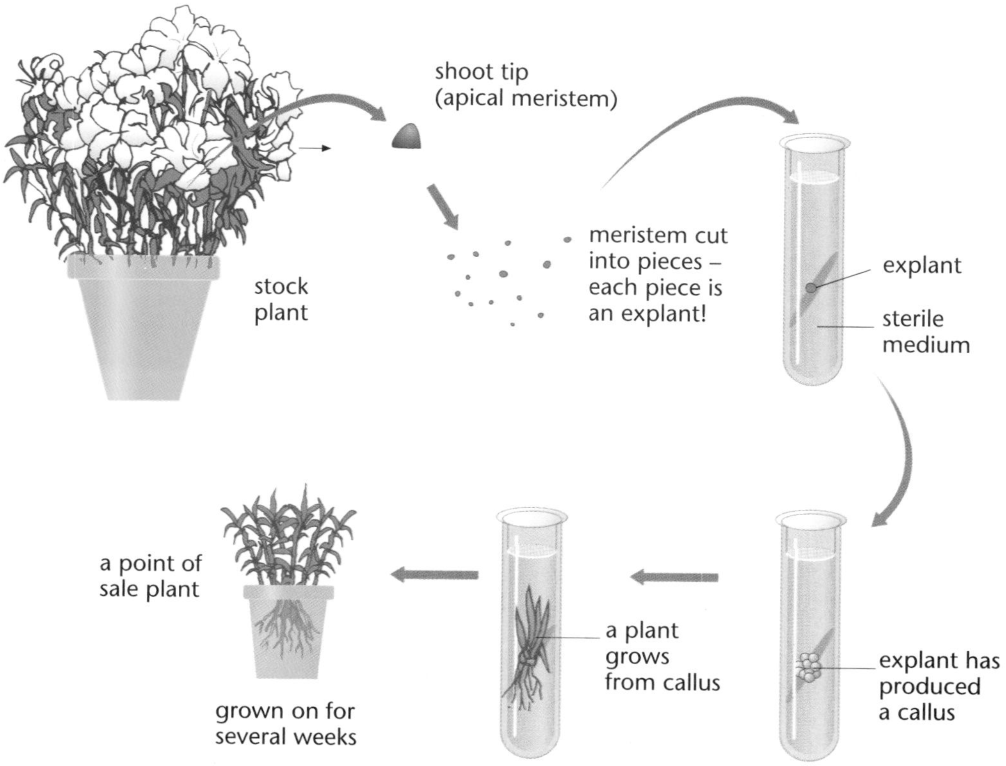

Sample question and model answer

The graphs below show the height of two pure breeding varieties of pea plant, Sutton First and Cava Late.

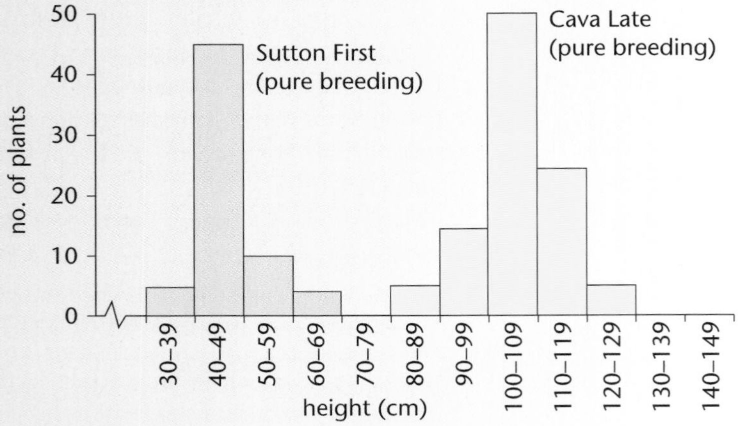

Continuous variation can confuse you sometimes when examiners display the data in categories as histograms. **This is not discontinuous!**

(a) (i) Which types of variation are shown by the pea variety, Sutton First? Give evidence from the bar graph to support your answer. [4]

Continuous variation – this is shown by the increase across the distribution (even though the peas are pure breeding).

Environmental variation – shown by the range of different heights.

(ii) Which type of variation is shown **between** varieties Sutton First and Cava Late? Give evidence from the bar graphs to support your answer. [2]

Discontinuous variation – the two distributions are separate and do not intersect.

(iii) Both Sutton First and Cava Late have compatible pollen for cross-breeding. Suggest why they do **not** cross breed. [1]

As implied by the names, Sutton First flowers before Cava Late, so that flowers are not ready at the same time.

When you are asked to 'suggest' then a range of different plausible answers are usually acceptable.

(b) Plant geneticists considered that many years ago the two varieties of pea had the same ancestor.

(i) Suggest what, in the ancestor, resulted in the difference in height of the two varieties? [1]

mutation

(ii) Suggest what caused this change. [1]

radiation

(c) (i) Define polygenic inheritance. [1]

The inheritance of a feature controlled by a number of genes (not just a gene at one locus!).

(ii) Which type of variation is a consequence of polygenic inheritance? [1]

continuous variation

Practice examination questions

1 The following key distinguishes between the five kingdoms.

	Organisms without membrane bound organelles	A
	Organisms with membrane bound organelles	GOTO 2
2	Organisms have hyphae	B
	Organisms do not have hyphae	GOTO 3
3	Organisms unicellular or colonial	C
	Organisms not unicellular or colonial	GOTO 4
4	Organisms multicellular and have thylakoid membranes in some cells	D
	Organisms multicellular and have no thylakoid membranes in any cells	E

Name kingdoms A, B, C, D and E [5]

2 (a) Explain the difference between allopatric and sympatric speciation. In each instance use an example to illustrate your answer. [6]

(b) How is it possible to find out if two female animals are from the same species? [2]

[Total: 8]

In classification questions always look carefully at the information given. Here *some* of the answers are in the stem of the question.

3 (a) The song-thrush (*Turdus ericetorum*) and mistle-thrush (*Turdus viscivorus*) are in the same family, Turdidae. Large sections of their DNA are common to both species. Complete the table to classify both organisms. [3]

	mistle-thrush	*song-thrush*
Kingdom		
Phylum	Chordata	Chordata
	Aves	
	Passeriformes	Passeriformes
Genus		
Species		

[1] [1] [1]

(b) Assuming that the song-thrush and mistle-thrush evolved from the same ancestry group which type of selection took place to produce the two species? [1]

[Total: 4]

Chapter 7
Ecology and populations

The following topics are covered in this chapter:

- *Investigation of ecosystems*
- *Behaviour*

7.1 Investigation of ecosystems

After studying this section you should be able to:

- *understand how to measure abiotic and biotic factors in the environment*
- *use the capture, mark, recapture technique to assess animal populations*
- *understand suitable techniques to investigate a range of habitats*
- *calculate an index of diversity of the organisms in an ecosystem*
- *use statistical tests to establish confidence levels to experimental results*
- *apply survey conclusions to ecological action*
- *describe conservation techniques and methods of population control*

LEARNING SUMMARY

Measurement in an ecosystem

AQA A	M5
AQA B	M5, M6
EDEXCEL	M5
OCR	M5
NICCEA	M4

The study of ecology investigates the inter-relationships between organisms in an area and their environment. The components of an ecosystem can be measured using a variety of techniques.

Estimating populations

Point quadrat

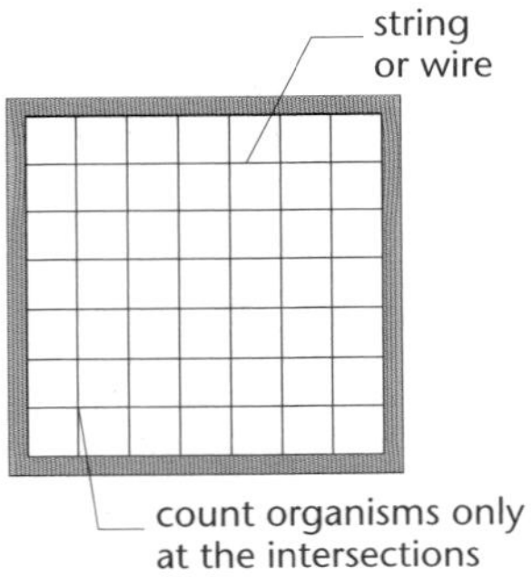

Often a full count of organisms in an ecosystem is not possible because of the size of the ecosystem. A **sampling technique** is used which requires a **quadrat**. This is a small area enclosed by wire or wood, around 0.25 m^2. When placed down in the ecosystem the organisms inside the area can be counted, as well as the **abiotic factors** which influence their distribution. Ecologists use units to measure organisms within the quadrats. Frequency (f) is an indication of the presence of an organism in a quadrat area. This gives no measure of numbers. However the usual unit is that of density, the numbers of the organism per unit area. Sometimes percentage cover is used, an indication of how much of the quadrat area is occupied.

Consider a survey of two species *Taraxacum officinale* (dandelion) and *Plantago major* (Great plantain) of the lawn habitat shown below.

A simplified results table

Quadrat no	Dandelion
1	2
2	12
3	15
4	3
5	4
6	8
7	7
8	10
9	9
10	15

mean = 8.5 per quadrat
Dm^{-2} = 34

Lawn habitat

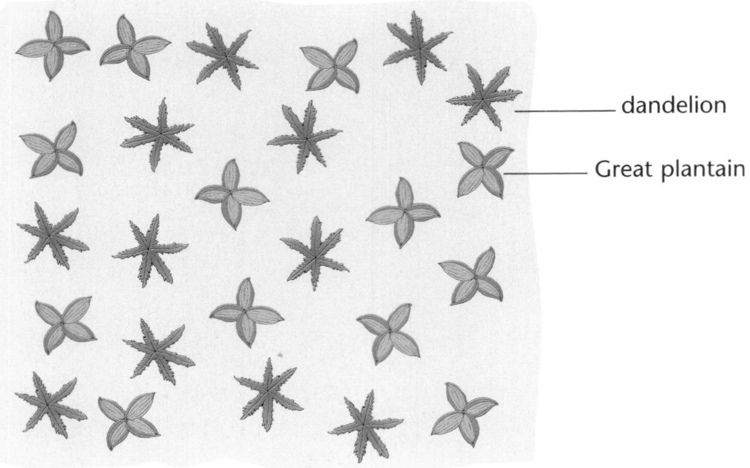

Key points from AS

- **What is an ecosystem?**
  Revise AS page 110

Optimum number of quadrats
The rule which dictates how many quadrats should be used is the point when additional quadrats do not significantly change the average or mean value.

It is important to use a suitable technique when surveying with quadrats. When you observe a habitat which appears **homogeneous** or **uniform**, like a field yellow with buttercups, then you should use **random quadrat placement**. The area should be gridded, numbers given to each sector of the grid, then a random number generator used. The probability of the numbers in one quadrat representing a field would be very low. In practice the **mean** numbers from large numbers of quadrats do represent the true numbers in a habitat.

Belt transects

This term is given to another quadrat technique. This method should be used when there is a **transition** across an area, e.g. across a pond or from high to low tide on the sea shore. Use belt transects where there is **change**. The belt transect is a line of quadrats. In each quadrat a measurement such as density can be made. One transect is not enough! Always do a number of transects then find an average for quadrats in a similar zone.

A simplified results table

Quadrat no	*flag iris*	*water lily*
1	10	0
2	7	0
3	1	0
4	0	5
5	0	4
6	0	0
7	0	5
8	0	3
9	0	0
10	1	0
11	8	0
12	4	0

This is just one belt transect. A number would be used and an average taken for each corresponding quadrat.

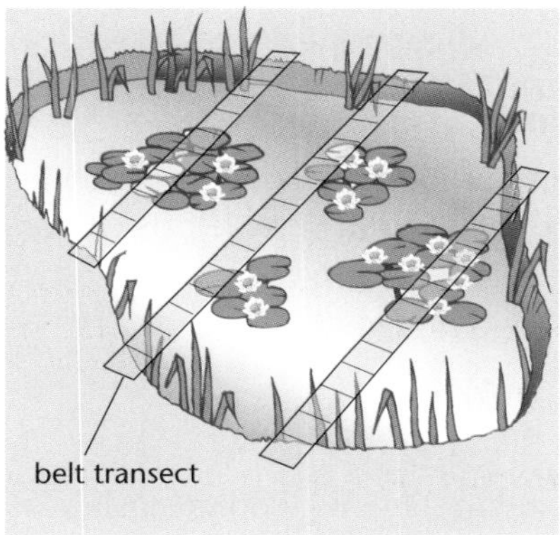

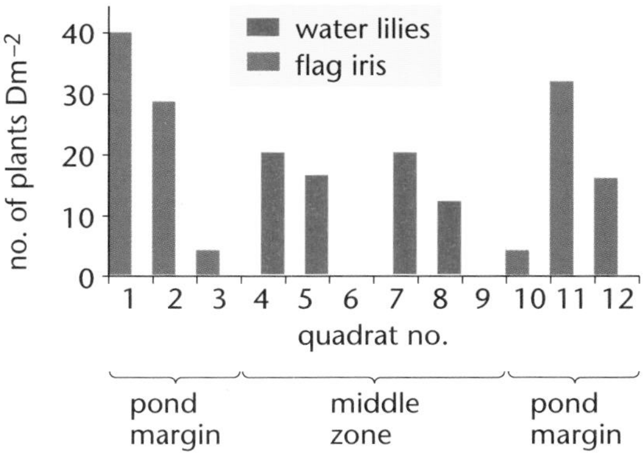

A bar-graph would be used to show the **distribution** of plant species across the pond. Note that there would be more than just two species! The graphs show how you could illustrate the data. Clearly flag irises occupy a different niche to water lilies.

KEY POINT

Other uses of quadrats

They can also be used to survey animal populations. It is made easier if the organisms are **sessile** (*they do not move from place to place*), e.g. barnacles on a rock. In a pond the belt transect could be coupled with a kick sampling technique. Here rocks may be disturbed and escaping animals noted. Adding a further technique can help, such as using a catch net in the quadrat positions. The principle here is that the techniques are **quantitative**.

Measuring factors

Graphical data can show relative numbers and distribution of organisms in a habitat. The ecologist is interested in all factors, **biotic and abiotic**, which influence those organisms. Listed below are some of the factors which may be measured:

- carbon dioxide level
- oxygen level
- pH
- light intensity
- mineral ion concentration
- level of organic material.

There are many more factors. These are just a selection.

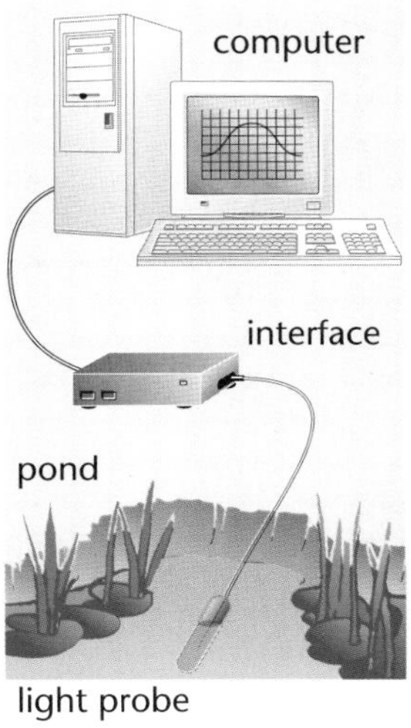

Datalogging

Modern ecology is so much more convenient and accurate than conventional techniques! Datalogging relies on environmental probes, interfaces and computers to measure and display data. Measuring factors over a complete day leaves no data-gaps! Fluctuations in light reaching a plant can be monitored over 24 hours and related to photosynthetic patterns. A light probe would be employed, but there are many more.

Capture, mark, release, recapture

This is a method which is used to estimate animal populations. It is an appropriate method for motile animals such as shrews or woodlice. The ecologist must always ensure minimum disturbance of the organism if results are to be truly representative and that the population will behave as normal.

Before using the technique you must be assured that:

- there is no significant migration
- there are no significant births or deaths
- marking does not have an adverse effect, e.g. the marking paint should not allow predators to see prey more easily (or *vice versa*)
- organisms integrate back into population after capture.

Remember that the method is suitable for large population size only.

The technique

- Organisms are captured, *unharmed*, using a quantitative technique.
- They are counted then discretely marked in some way, e.g. a shrew can be tagged, a woodlouse can be painted (*with non-toxic paint*).
- They are released.
- They are recaptured, and another count is made.
- This gives the number of marked animals and the number unmarked.

The calculation

S = total number of individuals in the total population.
S_1 = number captured in sample one, marked and released, e.g. 8.
S_2 = total number captured in sample two, e.g. 10.
S_3 = total marked individuals captured in sample two, e.g. 2.

$$\frac{S}{S_1} = \frac{S_2}{S_3} \qquad \text{so, } S = \frac{S_1 \times S_2}{S_3}$$

$$S = \frac{8 \times 10}{2} \quad \text{population} = 40 \text{ individuals}$$

Remember the equation carefully. You will **not** be supplied with it in the examination, but you will be given data.

The index of diversity

This is used as a measure of the range and numbers of species in an area.

$$\text{index } d = \frac{N(N-1)}{\Sigma\, n(n-1)}$$

N = total no. of all individuals of all species in the area
n = total no. of individuals of one species in an area
Σ = the sum of

Consider this example of animals in a small pond

crested newt	8
stickleback	20
leech	15
great pond snail	20
dragonfly larva	2
stonefly larva	10
water boatman	6
caddisfly larva	30
	N = 111

$$d = \frac{111 \times 110}{(8\times7) + (20\times19) + (15\times14) + (20\times19) + (2\times1) + (10\times9) + (6\times5) + (30\times29)}$$

$$d = \frac{12\,210}{2018} \qquad \text{so } d = 6.05$$

In another pond there were:

crested newt	45
stickleback	4
leech	18
great pond snail	10

d = 2.6

Look at both indices. 6.05 is an indicator of greater diversity. The higher number indicates greater diversity.

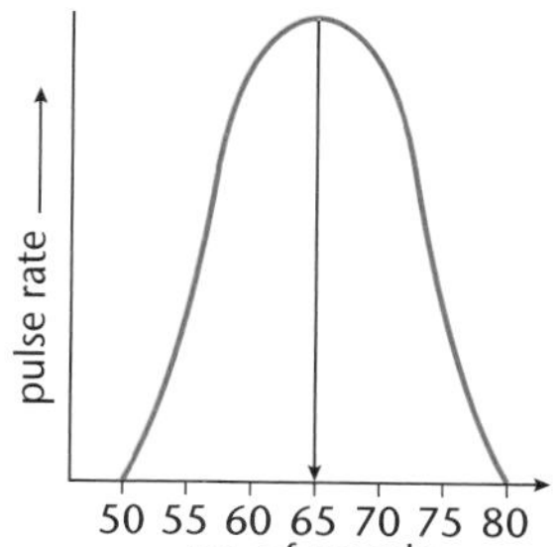

Standard deviation

Standard deviation (SD)

This is a measure of the **spread** of results at **either side of the mean** in an investigation. Consider this example: the pulse is taken from each person at rest, in a group of people. After collecting the results the mean or average is calculated. The mean does not give an indication of the spread of results. For this, standard deviation is needed.

$$\text{Standard deviation} = \sqrt{\frac{\Sigma d^2}{n}}$$

Σ = the sum of

d = difference between each value (e.g. individual pulse) and mean (pulse)

n = total number of readings (e.g. the number of pulses taken)

Statistically it has been shown that 68% of all readings are within + or – one standard deviation and that 95% of all readings are within + or – two standard deviations. Small SDs show that most readings are within a narrow range. Large SDs show that the mainstream of readings have a greater range.

Ecological conservation

In a world where human population increase is responsible for the destruction of so many habitats it is necessary to retain as many habitats as possible. Ecological surveys report to governments and difficult decisions are made. Fragile habitats like the bamboo woodlands of China support a variety of wildlife. Conservation areas need to be kept and maintained to prevent extinction of organisms at risk. In the UK we have **sites of special scientific interest** which are given government protection.

In an examination you may be given data to analyse. Always consider the plant life which is needed to support herbivores, as well as predators further along the food chains.

Conservation requires management

Although the word itself implies to 'keep' something as it is, much effort is needed. An area of climax vegetation, e.g. oak woodland, is less of a problem, since it will not change if merely left to its own devices. However, many of the seral stages, e.g. birch woodland along the route to climax, require much maintenance.

Animal populations need our help, especially when it is often by our own introduction that specific species have colonised an area. Deer introduced into a forest may thrive initially but due to an efficient reproductive rate exceed the carrying capacity of the habitat. **Carrying capacity** is the population of the species which can be adequately supported by the area.

What effect would an increase in mesh size of trawler nets have on the fish catch?

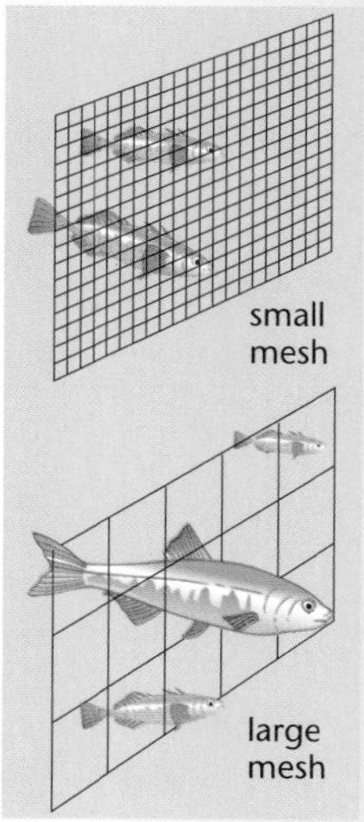

The bigger the mesh the more fish escape.

Sometimes herbivores could cause destruction of their habitat by overgrazing, and so must be **culled**. **Predators** could be introduced to reduce numbers, but they also may need culling at some stage. **Difficult decisions** need to be taken. In the aquatic habitats similar problems exist. Cod in the North Sea is being harmed by over-fishing. Agreements have been made by the EEC to **reduce fishing quotas** and create **exclusion zones** to **allow fish stocks to recover**. Even before this agreement smaller fish had to be returned to the sea after being caught to increase the chances of them growing to maturity and breeding successfully.

Endangered species require protection

All over the world many animals and plants are at the limits of their survival. The World Wide Fund for Nature is a charity organisation which helps. The organisation receives support from the public and artists such as David Shepherd. He gives donations from the sale of all of his wildlife paintings, helping to maintain the profile of animals so that we invest in survival projects like protected reserves.

Interspecific competition takes place when **different** species share the same resources.

Intraspecific competition takes place when the **same** species share the same resources.

7.2 Behaviour

After studying this section you should be able to:

- *describe innate behaviour, kinesis, and taxis*
- *understand habituation and imprinting*
- *describe a range of territorial behaviour*

LEARNING SUMMARY

The behaviour of organisms

AQA A	M6
AQA B	M6
OCR	M5

Organisms respond to the **biotic** and **abiotic factors** of their environment. Biotic factors include response to other species, e.g. the feeding behaviour of grouse from heather on moorlands and the use of the heather to hide from predators. The grouse also respond to each other, e.g. in courtship display. There are different types of behaviour.

Innate behaviour

This behaviour is '**pre-programmed**' by an organism's **genes**. When analysing behaviour it is difficult to determine whether it is innate or learned.

It is safe to say that immediately after the birth of a baby the 'sucking' action to obtain milk from mother's mammary glands is innate. Similarly, the pecking behaviour of a chicken, whilst still in an egg, to break the shell, must be innate. As an animal gets older it may well develop patterns of behaviour learned from its experiences. It becomes more and more **difficult to categorise** the behaviour.

Kinesis

This takes place when the response of an organism is **proportional to the intensity of a stimulus**. Kinesis takes the form of an **increase in movement**, but this is **non-directional**. An example of kinesis is shown by woodlice. Intense heat which would harm the woodlice causes them to increase speed and move in random directions. In this way some of the population have a **greater chance of survival**.

A second example is shown by woodlice. They respond to a dry environment by increasing random movements but slow down if they reach high humidity.

Taxis

This is a **directional response to a stimulus**. It can be a **positive taxis**, towards, or **negative taxis**, away. An example can be seen using a microscope to observe a group of living specimens of *Euglena viridis*. This is a protoctistan which photosynthesises. Individuals swim to an air bubble and cluster around to obtain maximum CO_2 for photosynthesis. This is **positive chemotaxis** because the organism moves towards the CO_2 source.

Progress check

(a) List the abiotic factors you may need to measure in a pond survey.

(b) How could you take measurements most efficiently, over a 24-hour period.

(a) oxygen, carbon dioxide, pH, light, temperature, mineral ions
(b) use of environmental probes, interface and computer

Learning

This takes place when an organism changes behaviour as a result of experience within the environment. As a result of the experience future behaviour becomes modified. For example, a pupil misbehaves and is placed on detention. The pupil learns (hopefully!) that the behaviour should not be repeated. The detention is negative reinforcement. Perhaps positive reinforcement is better to support good behaviour!

Conditioned reflexes

Pavlov experimented with dogs.

- He checked that the group of dogs did not produce saliva when he rang a bell at a time not related to feeding. (**Control**)
- He fed groups of dogs at a specific time each day.
- He measured the amount of saliva produced just before they were fed.
- He then began to ring a bell just before giving the food.
- The dogs began to salivate profusely.
- The bell would elicit exactly the same response as the original stimulus.
- After a while the level of salivation decreased if the food reward was not given.
- Without **positive reinforcement** the level of response would finally disappear completely.

We are conditioned to respond to advertising in a similar way. A cola drink advertisement uses the latest 'rock' song and glamorous models. We go to the supermarket and respond by buying the product, relating it to the pleasurable experience of the advertisement. Repeat purchases will only continue if the taste of the cola elicits a positive taste perception.

Habituation

This takes place when an organism is subjected to a **stimulus which is not harmful or rewarding**. As a result of continued subjection to a stimulus a **response will gradually decrease** and can finally disappear completely. A farmer puts an electronic bird scarer into a field. Birds are frightened off by frequent 'bangs'. They return, gradually more closely and finally have learned that the scarer is non-threatening. Soon they feed close to the scarer which has no effect. This is **habituation**.

Advertisements have a short 'shelf-life'. Continued exposure to the same advertisement results in habituation so that the response decreases. No wonder media advertising is replaced every few weeks!

The Sand Hill Crane and imprinting

This endangered species is reared in incubators and re-introduced into the wild. There is a problem! Young cranes would imprint upon humans, so when re-introduced would move towards people. Dangerous! Each day keepers dress up in 'crane' uniforms. In the wild the birds then move towards groups of adult cranes.

Imprinting

This takes place during the very early life of an organism, e.g. a chick emerges from its egg shell and immediately **bonds** with a close-by object. In nature, this will be the mother hen. The mother hen will impart useful behavioural patterns to the youngster, thus having **survival value**. From an incubator the focus of the imprinting would be a human. The imprinting behaviour is that the chick, in this instance, will follow the human or any object to which it is first exposed.

Examples are given to illustrate **principles**. It is unlikely that you will be given the same examples in your examination. Apply the principles to the given data.

Territorial behaviour

Populations of organisms living in an area can benefit from territorial behaviour. Too many animals of the **same species**, living in an area, **competing** for food would put the whole population in danger. Many species display territorial behaviour which prevents this outcome.

What is the advantage of male aggression to other males in a population?

The fittest organisms need to pass on their advantageous genes to offspring. In deer herds a dominant stag (male) is challenged by a younger male occasionally. Antler to antler fights take place and there is potential damage to both. In time a new dominant stag takes over the family group and now has exclusive mating rights with a group of hinds (females). This behaviour ensures the male reproductive role involves only the strongest males. The gene pool is improved!

Defence of the territory

- Animals are often **aggressive to members of the same species**, outside of the same family group.
- Territory is demarcated in a variety of ways, such as marking with **urine**, **faeces**, or **scent**. Birds use **song**, whereas other animals have characteristic **calls**. Excluding others in these ways **can prevent physical confrontation** which often results in injury.
- It is an advantage to the species to have a **feeding range** which excludes others. This increases the chances of there being **enough food for the family group**.
- The apportioning of territories serves as **density dependent regulation** so that the best use is made of existing resources.
- A further advantage is that a territory marks out a designated **mating area**. Other males will usually remain outside of the zone. Offspring have protection for their early development.

Courtship behaviour

This behaviour is species dependent and courtship display is anchored in the genes (innate behaviour see page 114). Courtship rituals are very important to ensure that:

- the opposite sexes recognise each other
- the animals will mate with organisms from the same species (mating is more likely to produce fertile offspring)
- the act of mating is synchronised with the oestrous cycle. In pigs a boar is always ready to mate but a sow is only receptive to him at ovulation. She produces pheromone attractants to encourage the boar.

Sign–stimulus release factors

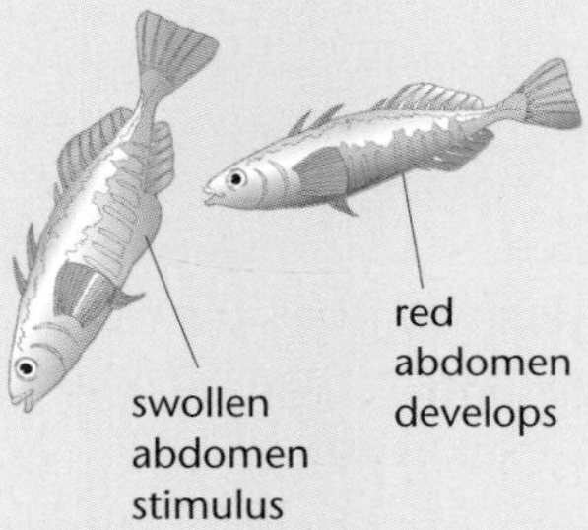

These are environmental cues which trigger patterns of innate behaviour in organisms.

Example 1 – the stickleback

In springtime as the mean temperature and day length increase, a **colour change** in stickleback males takes place. The ventral surface becomes red and they go on to build nests and defend their territory. Clearly the environmental cues stimulate physiological and behavioural changes. A **zig-zag ritual** by the male elicits a female to display her swollen abdomen to the male. The process culminates in fertilisation.

Example 2 – delayed implantation

Animals such as badgers mate at a specific time of year. Environmental cues bring females into season, November in this instance. After fertilisation, implantation into the endometrium is synchronised in all the females regardless of the day of mating. The sychronous timing of implantation ensures that the offspring are born when there is a spring flush of food. Survival is more likely!

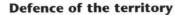

Environmental cues trigger migratory behaviour, e.g. shortening day length elicits preparatory behaviour of swallows, which collectively fly off to South Africa. Similarly, cues stimulate the return journey.

Sample question and model answer

When given a passage, line numbers are often referred to. Try to understand the words in context. Do not rush in with a pre-conceived idea!

Read the passage, then answer the questions below.

Around the UK coast there are two species of barnacle, *Chthamalus stellatus* and *Balanus balanoides*. Both species are sessile, living on rocky sea shores.

The adult barnacles do not move from place to place but do reproduce sexually. They use external fertilisation. Larvae resemble tiny crabs and are able to swim. At a later stage these larvae come to rest on a rock where they become fixed for the remainder of their lives.

The barnacles are only able to feed whilst submerged.

Adult *Chthamalus* are found higher on the rocks than *Balanus* in the adult form as shown in the diagram below. Scientists have shown that the larvae of each species are found at all levels.

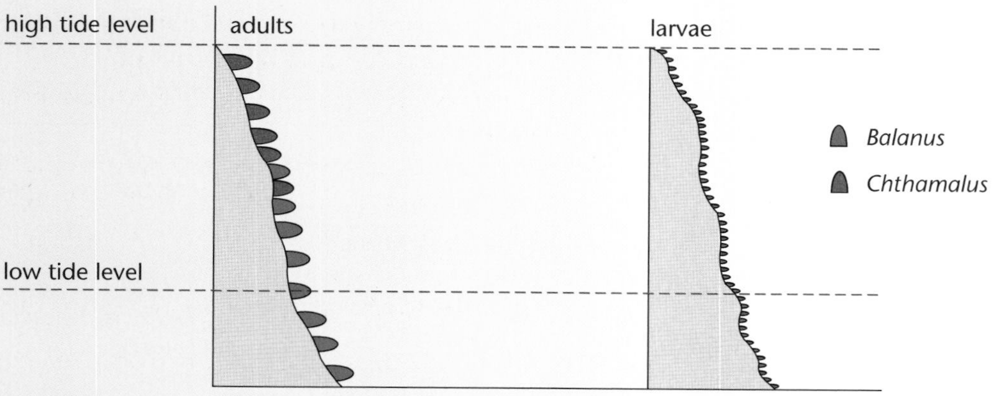

(a) Name the genus for each barnacle. [1]

Chthamalus and Balanus

(b) What does the term sessile mean? (line 2) [1]

is not motile, i.e. does not move from place to place

(c) Suggest how it is possible for neighbouring *Balanus* individuals to breed sexually (line 3) with each other even though they are sessile. [1]

produce sperms which swim through the water

(d) Explain **one** advantage of the larvae being motile. [2]

able to colonise new areas

where there may be more nutrients

(e) Which type of competition exists between *Chthamalus* and *Balanus*? [1]

interspecific competition

(f) Suggest an explanation for the distribution of each species of barnacle. [6]

The larvae are found at all tide levels

at a lower tide level the barnacles are submerged for longer

Balanus may grow at a faster rate can compete for food better than Chthamalus, which dies out at lower levels

near higher tide level the barnacles are exposed to open air for longer Balanus may not be adapted to withstand desiccation, whereas Chthamalus can withstand drying out, and so survives without the competition from Balanus.

In this question are key terms, of which you will need to recall the meaning. This is only possible with effective revision. Did you already know the key terms **genus**, **sessile** and **motile**? Knowledge of these terms would enable access to other marks, only easy when you have key word understanding. Try writing out a glossary of terms to help your long-term memory.

Practice examination questions

1 Ecologists wished to estimate the population of a species of small mammal in a nature reserve.

- They placed humane traps throughout the reserve and made their first trapping on day one, capturing 16 shrews.
- They were tagged then released.
- After day four a second trapping was carried out, capturing 12 shrews.
- Five of these shrews were seen to be tagged.

(a) The ecologists must be satisfied of a number of factors before using the 'capture, mark, release, recapture' method. List three of these factors. [3]

(b) Use the data to estimate the shrew population. Show your working. [2]

(c) Comment on the *level* of reliability of your answer. [1]

[Total: 6]

2 Complete the table below by putting a tick in an appropriate box. You may tick one or more boxes for each example.

	Type of behaviour			
	kinesis	*innate*	*positive taxis*	*negative taxis*
A bolus of food reaches the top of our oesophagus and is swallowed.				
An insect moves from a cold, dry area to a warm, humid one.				
Springtail are subjected to increasingly hot conditions, and react by increasing speed in a number of directions. Some go towards the heat source and die.				
A queen bee accepts the advances of a drone bee and is mated.				
A motile alga swims towards light.				

[5]

3 A Grebe is a water bird which displays a distinctive courtship ritual. Male behaviour is distinctive from that of the female.

State **three** advantages to the species of this behaviour. [3]

Chapter 8

Further effects of pollution

The following topics are covered in this chapter:

- Water pollution
- Air pollution
- Pollution control

8.1 Water pollution

After studying this section you should be able to:

LEARNING SUMMARY

- *describe the sources and effects of a range of aquatic pollutants*
- *understand how the presence of indicator species gives signs of the degree of pollution*
- *determine biochemical oxygen demand (BOD)*
- *understand how water is treated prior to domestic supply*
- *describe a range of methods to reduce, prevent or avoid aquatic pollution*

Sources of water pollution

AQA A	M5
AQA B	M6
EDEXCEL	M5
OCR	M6
NICCEA	M4

A number of domestic, agricultural and industrial processes contribute to water pollution. The following sources result in pollutants reaching habitats such as rivers, and ultimately the sea.

KEY POINT

- **Heavy metal** ions from industrial outflows.
- **Oil spillage** from tanker accidents in the sea.
- **Suspended solids** (e.g. china clay from pottery industry outflows).
- **Excess mineral ions** such as **phosphates** and **nitrates** in sewage, domestic **drainage effluent**, and **fertilisers**.
- **Pesticides**, including **organophosphates**, and **herbicides**, via run-off and leaching.
- **Thermal pollution** as coolant water is returned to rivers from power stations.

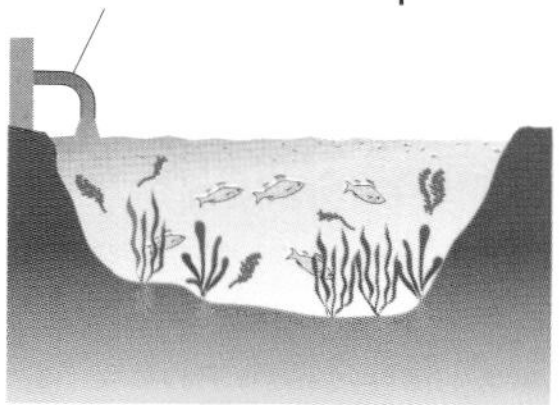

Heavy metal ions

These can enter water accidentally or by discharge of industrial waste. In Minimata, Japan, a mercury compound was discharged into the sea-water. It was absorbed by shell-fish which were not, themselves, killed. However, many shell-fish were consumed by people. The toxic mercury ions were passed through the food chains. Since **many** shell-fish were consumed the **toxin built up**. This is **bio-accumulation**. The human consumers suffered a number of severe problems with their **nervous systems**.

Oil spillage

This takes place as a result of accidents. Sea-going tankers, full of crude oil, occasionally have accidents and spill their oil cargo into the sea. This is potentially catastrophic as **oil floats**. Oxygen diffusion from the air is inhibited by the resultant

Key points from AS

- **Effects of human activities on the environment**
  Revise AS pages 119–121

oil slick. The aquatic organisms often die due to lack of oxygen and plants lack light for photosynthesis. Beneath the oil **putrefaction** can take place. **Bacterial action** leads to the highly toxic gas, **hydrogen sulphide** with its rotten egg smell.

Additionally oil affects the feathers of water birds. Contamination can result in their inability to fly and they lose their buoyancy. Complete food chains are destroyed!

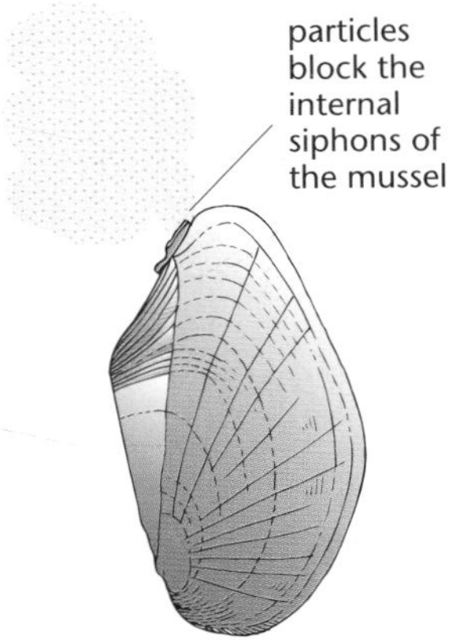

Suspended solids

Whenever there are large amounts of particles in water there are problems for many organisms. Suspended particles intercept light, reducing photosynthetic productivity which has a consequential, adverse effect on consumers in food chains.

The pottery industry has contributed to this problem in the past. Fine particles such as waste china clay are particularly harmful. The particles are so small that they are taken in by bivalves such as mussels. These filter feeders cannot cope with the sheer volume of particles and perish as their feeding and gaseous exchange mechanisms are inhibited.

If particles continue to silt up the bottom of the water habitat then many more organisms are harmed by the continued coverage, e.g. bloodworms (Tubifex).

Excess mineral ions

Low amounts of **nitrates** and **phosphates** would be beneficial to aquatic plants. **In excess** they are harmful and cause **algal blooms** which ultimately result in **eutrophication**. **Phosphates** are in detergents which reach rivers via domestic drainage water. Additionally, together with **nitrates**, they are in fertilisers which reach rivers via leaching and run-off from fields. In most instances, only 50% of fertiliser is actually taken up by plants. Sewage effluent is another contributory factor in eutrophication.

ALERT! Do not confuse herbicides with pesticides. Herbicides are used to destroy weeds and may run-off into rivers. Contact herbicides such as sodium chlorate are highly toxic in the environment. Similarly selective herbicides are used. These kill broad-leaved plants but grasses and cereals are unharmed. They cause uncontrolled growth which results, finally, in death. **Dioxins** are very toxic indeed and are a contaminant of the herbicide production. Entering aquatic food chains is a considerable danger!

Pesticides

These include **insecticides**, **fungicides**, and **molluscicides** (used against snails and slugs). It is important that they are **specific** and kill only the pests. Unfortunately they tend to affect organisms other than the target pests. Run-off and leaching again take them to the rivers. **Persistent** pesticides such as **DDT** (an organochlorine) remain in the ecosystem for long periods. Insects affected by DDT enter food chains. The persistent DDT accumulates as it builds up in fatty tissue. DDT passes through rivers and seas reaching all over the world, even in places where it is not used. Banned in the UK many years ago it still remains in the soil and can be detected in animal tissues. In some countries it is still used!

Accumulation along food chain

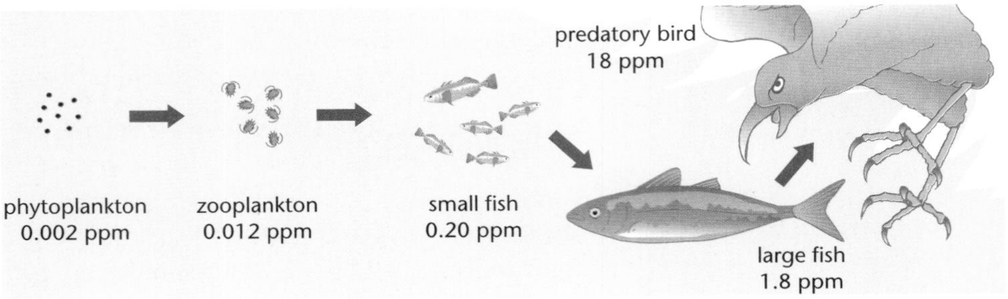

Organophosphates have been used to replace the **organochlorines**, being less persistent. Unfortunately they are toxic to humans as well as insects. In humans they inhibit the action of **acetylcholine esterase** at synapses. Used as sheep dip insecticide they are very dangerous if they contact humans and other organisms.

Most medicated shampoos to destroy head lice, contain organophosphates! It is dangerous to use them regularly.

Typically if these dangerous chemicals reach water habitats they may be accumulated along food chains quickly.

Biochemical oxygen demand (BOD)

OCR M5

This is a quality control method and takes place as follows:

- samples of water or effluent are collected
- each sample is incubated at a temperature of 20 °C for five days
- the amount of dissolved oxygen in mg litre^{-1} or g m^{-3} is the BOD value
- the more microorganisms in the sample the greater is the BOD and the depletion of oxygen is correspondingly high
- the greater the BOD of the effluent the greater is its ability to reduce the dissolved oxygen in a sample.

If investigating BOD of river water, remember:
(a) take samples from different positions – BOD may be variable according to depth
(b) always take an average from each position to ensure that your results are truly representative.

High BOD indicates a low amount of oxygen in the sample!

BOD examples

- Silage effluent seeping into a river = 45 000 g m^{-3}
- Domestic sewage = 348 g m^{-3}
- Non-polluted river water = 2.5 g m^{-3}
- No wonder the fish die when there is a lot of organic pollution around!
- No wonder farmers are fined heavily if sewage effluent seeps into water!
- Legislation helps!

Water treatment

Before being suitable for consumption water needs to be treated. This takes place as follows:

Screening Grids filter out debris such as dislodged weeds.

Sedimentation Water is pumped to a sedimentation tank. Here any heavy particles sink to the bottom. From here the sediment is pumped away.

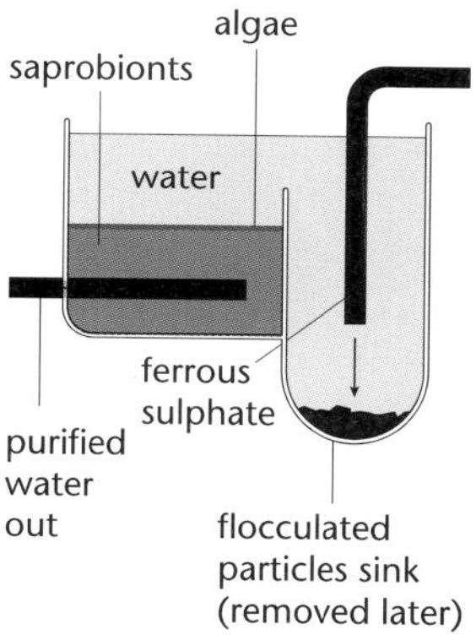

Flocculation Ferrous sulphate is added as a flocculant which allows many of the remaining organic particles and bacteria to stick together.

Ultra-violet light The water is now exposed to ultra-violet light which kills many microorganisms.

Filtration Water is then filtered through layers of graded sand particles (fine particles at the top and more coarse towards the base). Water percolates through this filter bed slowly. Organic debris is held back in the upper layers so that:

- algae in the uppermost layer take up NO_3^- and PO_3^- released by saprobionts.

Under the algae at lower levels are saprobionts which decompose the organic material releasing the NO_3^- and PO_3^- ions.

The algal layer grows and is occasionally removed.

Note that responses to questions at A Level are often expected to be more complex, e.g. consequential effects are needed, not just 'kills filter feeder'.

Sterilisation

During the previous stage the microbial populations increase. During this stage **chlorine** or **ozone** is added to kill many of the **microorganisms**. The process does not destroy all microorganisms and is best described as **partial sterilisation**.

Progress check

The outfall from a pottery works poured suspended particles into a river. Suggest **two** polluting effects.

- Less light reaches aquatic plants, photosynthesis less, less food for consumers along food chains.
- Filter feeders harmed by the volume of particles, which clog up their feeding and gaseous exchange mechanisms.

8.2 Air pollution

After studying this section you should be able to:

- *describe sources and effects of a range of air pollutants*
- *describe the beneficial effects of recycling*

LEARNING SUMMARY

Pollution of the atmosphere

AQA A	M5
AQA B	M6
EDEXCEL	M5
OCR	M6
NICCEA	M4

Gases reach the air in a number of ways including combustion of fossil fuels, industrial emissions and microbial processes. Gases reaching the air include sulphur dioxide, carbon dioxide, carbon monoxide, nitrogen oxides, chlorofluorocarbons (CFCs), methane and smoke particles.

Key points from AS

- **Effects of human activities on the environment**
  Revise AS pages 119–121

Polluting effects

Large amounts of the above gases can have very serious effects. The greenhouse effect is caused by a number of gases but water vapour and carbon dioxide have the greatest effect due to their high volume in the troposphere. CFCs have a stronger potential contribution to the greenhouse effect but are found in smaller quantities.

Industrial emissions

Industries have traditionally been very defensive about admitting to the production of harmful waste gases. Good examples of known dangerous emissions are **polychlorinated biphenyls** (**PCBs**). These are used in plastics manufacture. Limited release of these gases occur during manufacture but much more is given off during incineration of plastics waste.

These persistent chemicals build up in animal tissues and have been found in fat cells in seals. PCBs are considered to be carcinogenic.

What about the hole in the ozone layer?

ALERT!
The 'hole in the ozone layer' is completely different to the 'greenhouse effect!' Students are often confused. The reason for this is that ozone and CFCs are both greenhouse gases.
When answering a question about either topic clarify which topic is being examined. There are no marks if you are wrong!

High up in the stratosphere at around 20–30 km is a layer of ozone (O_3). It is very important because when radiation from the sun passes through this layer much of the UV radiation is absorbed.

What effect does UV radiation have on people?

If skin is exposed to UV radiation then skin cancer, cataracts and problems with the immune system can result.

Which pollutants damage the ozone layer?

Chlorine, nitrogen oxides and CFCs are all responsible. Each reacts to break down the ozone, by a variety of mechanisms. Oxygen is a product of these reactions.

Progress check

Outline the processes by which water is purified before being supplied to the public.

Screening to filter out debris. Sedimentation – heavy particles sink to the bottom.
Flocculation – ferrous sulphate is added, particles stick together.
Ultra-violet light – kills many microorganisms.
Filter – water moves through sand particles slowly.
Organic material is decomposed by saprobionts.
Algae use NO_3^- and PO_3^- released by decay.
Chlorination to kill microorganisms.

8.3 Pollution control

After studying this section you should be able to:

LEARNING SUMMARY

- *describe methods of controlling pollution*
- *understand the benefits of recycling and use of renewable energy resources*
- *understand the importance of legislation and personal responsibility*

What can we do about the pollution problem?

AQA A	M5
AQA B	M6
EDEXCEL	M5
OCR	M5, M6
NICCEA	M4

It is easy to state that many potentially harmful chemicals should not be allowed to enter the environment. However, the human population is increasing at a phenomenal rate and resources are needed to support this growth including housing, food and other products. We need to keep pollution under control. Lifestyle and personal responsibility are key factors to consider if we are to control pollution.

- Legislation and international agreement to limit or ban toxic emissions, e.g. SO_2 reduction.
- Car sharing, using low sulphur fuel, use of catalytic converters.
- Buying organic products rather than those which have been sprayed with pesticides.
- Use of biological control which targets specific pests, rather than using pesticides.
- Breeding programmes to reintroduce endangered species in some areas.
- Set up sites of special scientific interest so that the fragile habitats almost destroyed by previous pollution can be conserved.
- Recycling of products such as aluminium cans requires much less energy input than the processing of bauxite ore, and less of the environment is spoiled at mines.
- Composting of organic waste reduces the use of inorganic fertilisers. Slow release of ions and better holding capacity ensures that less ions reach the rivers by run-off and leaching.
- Use of renewable energy sources including solar power, wind power, wave power, tidal power, hydro-electric power. Gasohol, a derivative of photo-synthetic products, produces H_2O and CO_2 as waste. Methane gas produced from decomposing organic waste is an excellent alternative to fossil fuels.
- 'Scrubbing' of waste gases at coal-fired power stations reduces SO_2 emission. Emission gases are mixed with alkaline fluids.

  $$CaCO_3 + SO_2 \rightarrow CaSO_3 + CO_2$$

  Calcium sulphite produced in the process is dumped. CO_2 is a lesser problem! There could be an additional charge. Perhaps we should be prepared to pay more to safeguard our environment.

Lethal dose 50 (LD_{50})

These are toxicity tests for chemicals such as insecticides used in the environment. LD_{50} is the amount of substance, given orally, which kills 50% of a population in the laboratory.

The LD_{50} value for DDT in male mice is $500\,mg\,kg^{-1}$ and for females is $550\,mg\,kg^{-1}$. This proves that scientists showed some responsibility. DDT is now a banned persistent *insecticide*. It was not used on mice, but we need data on toxicity to organisms other than the target because they encounter chemicals in their environment.

Some people have ethical objections to LD_{50} testing. Alternative tests using laboratory cultured tissues are also used.

Sample question and model answer

Do not become confused with multiple graph lines! Follow each along and try to think why each one changes. A fall in one line, followed by a rise in another may suggest that a substance is being used up or converted into another!

The graphs below show the levels of some key substances and the relative numbers of organisms.

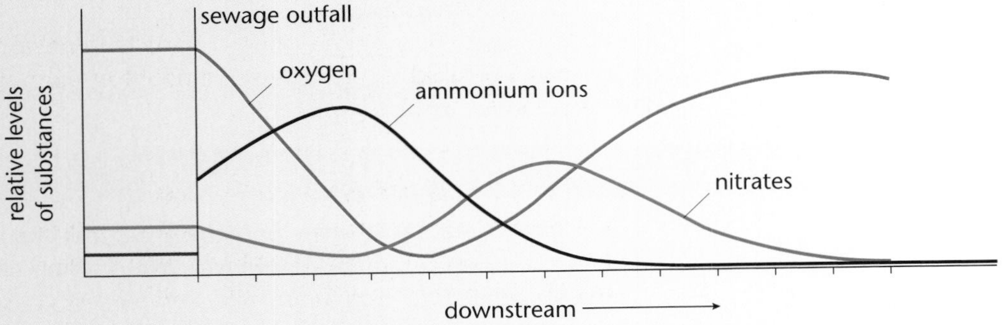

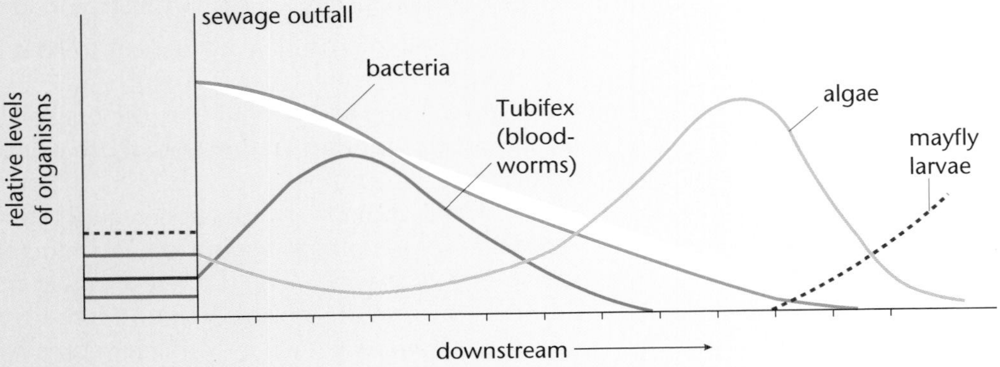

Use the graphs above and your own knowledge to answer the questions below.

(a) Explain the increase of nitrate ions after the sewage outfall. [4]

Sewage is decomposed by saprobiotic bacteria and saprobiotic fungi, this produces ammonium ions.
These are used by nitrosomonas bacteria to produce nitrite (not measured).
Nitrite converted to nitrate by nitrobacter bacteria.

(b) Account for the increase in Tubifex (bloodworm) numbers after the sewage entered the river even though oxygen levels decreased. [3]

Tubifex worms contain haemoglobin.
They absorb oxygen even when it is at low concentration.
Other organisms which normally feed on the Tubifex cannot live with the pollutants.

(c) Which organisms utilise the nitrates? Give reasons for your answer. [3]

Algae.
They need the nitrates to produce proteins.
Peak of algae follows the decrease of nitrates.

(d) Why did the oxygen decrease after the sewage outfall? [1]

Used in aerobic respiration by the saprobiotic bacteria.

Indicator species show the pollution level of an area because of the presence or absence of key species. Mayfly larvae survive in pollution-free water whereas bloodworms in large numbers indicate high sewage levels.

(e) Name **three** indicator species and in each instance suggest an environmental factor associated with their numbers.

Mayfly larvae only present where oxygen is high = low pollution.
Algae are in large numbers where there are nitrates.
Bacteria are in large numbers where organic material (sewage) is high.

Practice examination questions

1 The swan mussel (*Anodonta cygnia*) is a filter feeder. River water is taken into their mantle cavities and past gills before being ejected. Organic particles are moved to the mouth by cilia.

Students investigated the efficiency of particle removal by swan mussels. A colorimeter was used to measure the amount of light absorbed by the water at different stages.

Four tanks were used:

Tank A – 10 litres non-polluted river water
Tank B – 10 litres non-polluted river water + 20 swan mussels
Tank C – 10 litres river water polluted with china clay particles
Tank D – 10 litres river water polluted with china clay particles + 20 swan mussels.

The graph below shows the mean rate of particle removal from water at a temperature of 20°C.

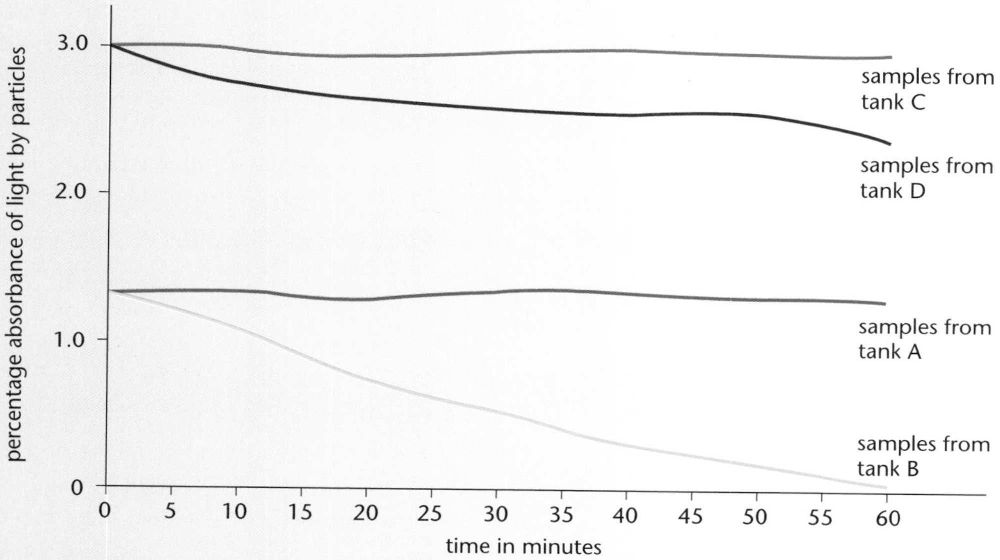

(a) Each tank had a magnetic stirrer. What is the advantage of using a stirrer? [1]

(b) Explain how the units of percentage absorbance can be used to measure the efficiency of filter feeding. [2]

(c) Explain the effect of china clay particles on the efficiency of filter feeding by the mussels. [3]

(d) Suggest **one** effect the swan mussels may have on the plant life of a river. [1]

[Total: 7]

2 Sewage effluent entered a river at two points, A and B, causing eutrophication.

BOD of sewage effluent at A = 350 g m^{-3}
BOD of sewage effluent at B = 389 g m^{-3}

(a) (i) What do the letters BOD represent? [1]

(ii) Explain what the BOD value, 350 g m^{-3} means. [2]

(b) Which effluent, A or B would contribute more to eutrophication? Give a reason for your answer. [2]

[Total: 5]

Chapter 9

Microbiology

The following topics are covered in this chapter:

- *Diversity of microorganisms*
- *Microbial culture and measurement*

9.1 Diversity of microorganisms

LEARNING SUMMARY

After studying this section you should be able to:

- *describe the general characteristics of a range of important microorganisms*
- *understand how to use Gram staining to help identify bacteria*

Some important microorganisms

AQA B	M7
EDEXCEL	M4
OCR	M5
WJEC	M4
NICCEA	M5

The microorganisms are members of kingdoms Prokaryotae, Protoctista and Fungi. Each type of organism has important structural differences.

Viruses

These are so simple in structure, that they are not considered members of any kingdom. They do not breathe, feed, excrete. They can however replicate.

The diagrams below show typical viral characteristics.

Many viruses are disease causing agents, e.g. the polio causing virus. Some viruses, e.g. the T2 bacteriophage can be helpful.

Rod shaped virus

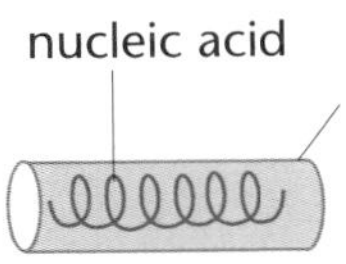

A bacteriophage virus

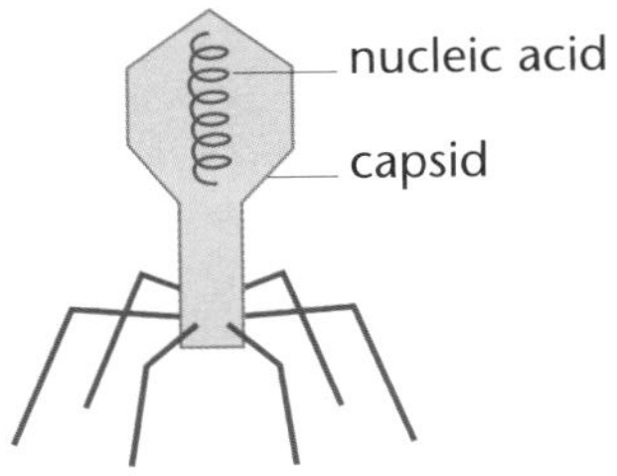

Top view of bacteriophage virus

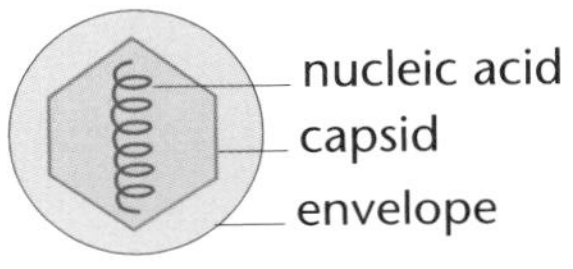

KEY POINT

Shape is variable but they do have some common features:
- an outer coat (**capsid**) consisting of protein units (**capsomeres**)
- an internal core of **RNA** or **DNA**
- they all **reproduce** by using the DNA of a **host cell**, so in this respect they are **parasitic**
- some viruses have an additional outer cover known as an **envelope**.

The diagram shows the stages of viral attack on a host cell.

The bacteriophage can be used in genetic engineering to incorporate a gene into a host cell. On this occasion lysis would not take place. Instead a virus can be in **provirus** form. It is inactive and the host cell is **lysogenic**, in this state.

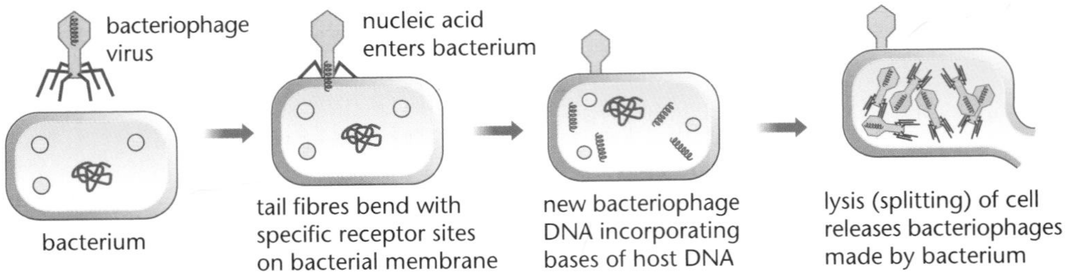

Once they have replicated the viruses are ready to attack new host cells.

Key points from AS

- AIDS
  Revise AS pages 133–134

Retroviruses: useful or deadly?

Special consideration should be given to these viruses. They can be useful and they can be deadly! Here are the important features.

- They all have an RNA core.
- They all produce a special enzyme called **reverse transcriptase**.
- They are able to **synthesise a strand of DNA from a strand of RNA**.
- This is followed by the synthesis of the complementary DNA strand, so that a full **double stranded DNA can be formed**.
- The **DNA** forms a circular shape then **enters the host cell** and incorporates into the host DNA.
- Here it exists as a **provirus**, able to lie inactive for a number of years.
- However, the **host-viral DNA** is able to make **viral proteins**.
- Every time the host cell divides then so does the provirus, therefore the number of infected cells can replicate dramatically.

First the bad news. The above bullet points outline the action of the human immunodeficiency virus (HIV) which causes AIDS. The lymphocytes are attacked and the consequences, in time, are fatal.

Now the good news! Reverse transcriptase is used in genetic engineering. Imagine a genetic engineer is trying to locate a specific gene responsible for a particular protein, e.g. glucagon, along a chromosome. There may be a 1000 genes along the chromosome. Where does he or she begin to find the correct bases along a coding strand of DNA? Finding a needle in a haystack might be easier. Reverse transcriptase is an excellent tool for this process. The example below shows the principle.

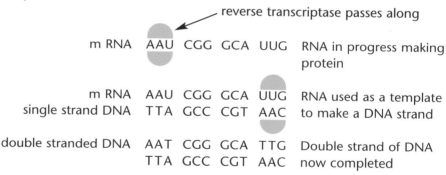

reverse transcriptase passes along

m RNA	AAU	CGG	GCA	UUG	RNA in progress making protein
m RNA	AAU	CGG	GCA	UUG	RNA used as a template
single strand DNA	TTA	GCC	CGT	AAC	to make a DNA strand
double stranded DNA	AAT	CGG	GCA	TTG	Double strand of DNA
	TTA	GCC	CGT	AAC	now completed

Escherichia coli (E. coli) has the typical bacterial structures shown. Note

- it is Gram negative (see next page.)
- it has pili.

Bacteria

These are members of the kingdom Prokaryotae, and include saprobiotic and parasitic species. They exist in a number of different shapes. A selection is shown in the margin, together with a generalised structure.

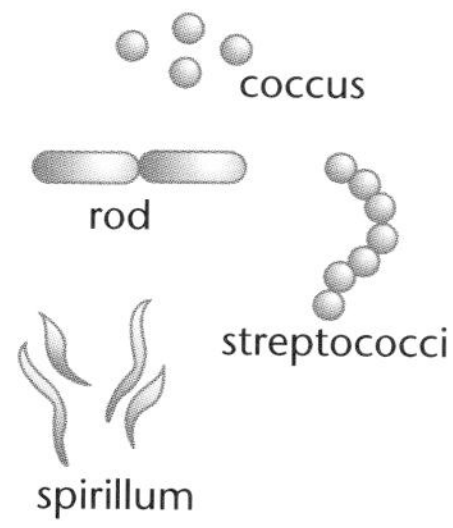

Typical bacterial features

- Cell wall which is not made of cellulose.
- No true nucleus, but the DNA is in nucleiod form, a single chromosome of coiled DNA, and in circular plasmids (in some bacteria).
- If flagellae are present there is not a 9 + 2 filament structure.
- Ribosomes are present but they are small.
- Usual reproduction by binary fission, a form of asexual reproduction.
- No membrane bound organelles.

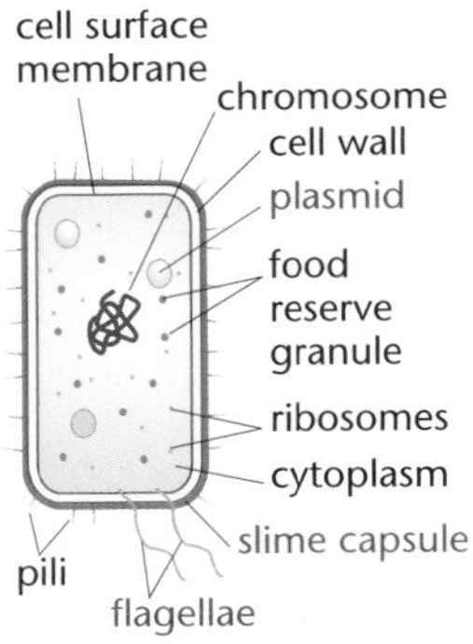

Key structures labelled in red not always present.

Gram positive and Gram negative

Christian Gram devised his staining technique in 1884. It depends upon two different surface structures.

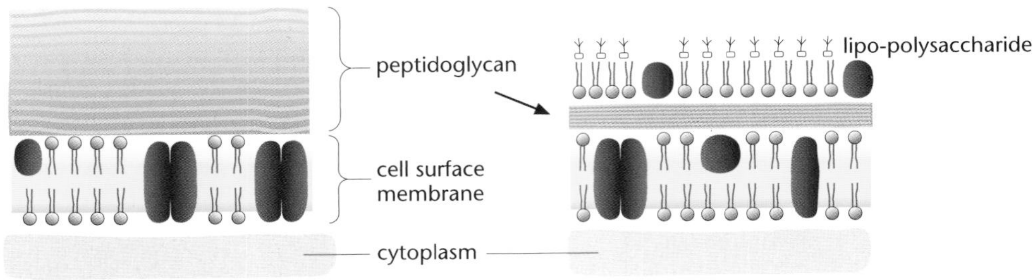

> **KEY POINT**
>
> Bacteria have either of two types of cell wall structure:
>
> - **Gram positive bacteria** – outside the cell surface membrane is a thick (around 8 nm) rigid layer of peptidoglycan.
> - **Gram negative bacteria** – outside the cell surface membrane is a thin (around 2 nm) layer of peptidoglycan, and additionally an extra outer membrane which includes lipopolysaccharides.

How can bacteria receive new DNA?

Conjugation – bacteria join by pili and can donate plasmid from one bacterium to another. Can be replicated each time bacterium divides.

Transformation – one bacterium donates DNA to another, which has now acquired new properties.

Transduction – a bacteriophage introduces DNA into a bacterium, which develops new properties.

What is the procedure for Gram's staining technique?

- Smear actively growing bacteria on a slide.
- Heat fix, then stain with crystal violet and dilute iodine.
- Wash slide off with ethanol or propanone.
- Gram positive bacteria retain the stain and show up as purple (the colour of the violet-iodine complex).
- Gram negative bacteria lose the stain as it is washed away with the ethanol or propanone.
- These Gram negative bacteria can be counterstained with a stain such as safranin O (red in colour).

Reproduction of bacteria

In optimum conditions reproduction can take place in around 20 minutes for some species. Usually by binary fission the following stages take place:

- the single chromosome replicates
- the chromosome at this time attaches to the cell surface membrane or a mesosome, which helps to part the two chromosomes
- a cross membrane and cross wall form in a central position, dividing off the two chromosomes, so that two daughter cells are produced.

Fungi

Organisms of this kingdom are eukaryotic and heterotrophic. In obtaining their complex organic substances they can be classified into parasitic, saprobiotic and mutualistic groups.

The diagrams below show typical fungal structure.

An aseptate fungus

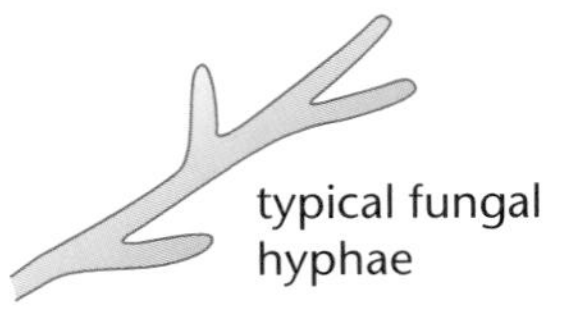

A septate fungus

A single hypha

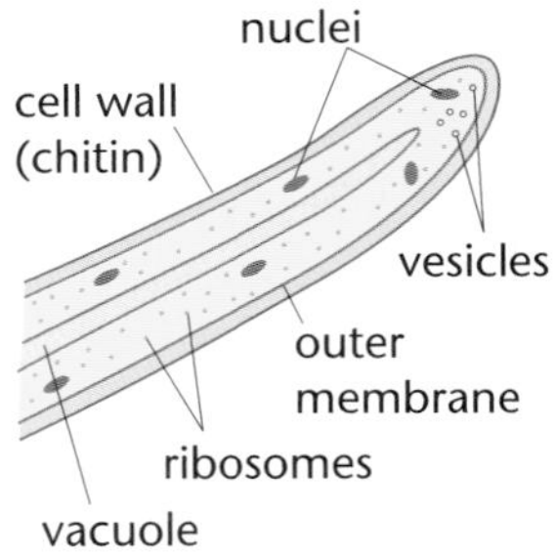

Typical features of fungi

- Many have a thread-like basic unit known as a hypha.
- These hyphae are multinucleate.
- They have a cell wall of chitin, not cellulose.
- Nutrients are absorbed directly through the outer wall and membrane.
- They produce spores, either asexually or sexually.
- Bread mould (*Mucor hiemalis*) exemplifies all of the listed features.

Saccharomyces cerevisiae

This species of fungus is structurally different.

- This fungus is unicellular and is not multinucleate.
- It reproduces sexually or asexually by budding.

A single yeast cell

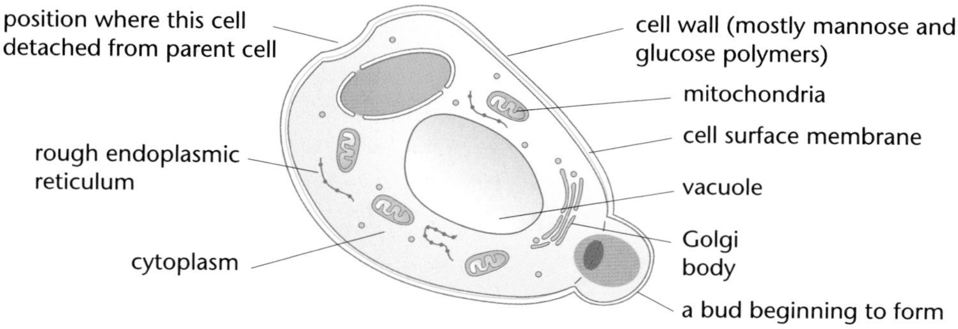

Progress check

(a) Outline the procedure for the Gram staining technique.

(b) After staining how is it possible to identify Gram positive from Gram negative bacteria?

(a) Smear (actively growing) bacteria on a microscope slide, heat fix, then stain with crystal violet and dilute iodine, wash slide off with ethanol or propanone.

(b) Gram positive bacteria show up as purple but Gram negative do not.

9.2 Microbial culture and measurement

After studying this section you should be able to:

- *describe suitable conditions and nutrients for the growth of microorganisms*
- *describe techniques to culture microorganisms*
- *describe a number of techniques to measure microbial populations*

LEARNING SUMMARY

Nutritional needs

AQA B M7
EDEXCEL M4
OCR M5
WJEC M4

Before attempting to grow populations of microorganisms we need to know their nutritional requirements. These are needed as an energy source and for synthesis of cell components.

Key elements	*Example of use*
carbon, hydrogen, oxygen	a constituent of all organic molecules and structures
nitrogen	a constituent of all proteins
sulphur	a constituent of some proteins and co-enzymes
phosphorus	a constituent of phospholipids and ATP

- They also require potassium, magnesium, calcium and iron.
- All of the above elements are present in some form in culture media.
- Additionally, certain microorganisms need other specific substances.
- They do need growth factors, which are substances needed by the microorganisms because they cannot make them themselves.
- All substances must be present in balanced quantities to support the growth of the microorganisms.

Conditions for growth

Individual microorganisms have specific requirements. Some important requirements are listed below.

- Suitable temperature (Psychrophilic bacteria optimum usually below 0 °C
  Mesophilic bacteria optimum around 30 °C
  Thermophilic bacteria optimum above 45 °C)
- Oxygen – some microorganisms are aerobic and some anaerobic. Yeast is a facultative anaerobe, having the ability to respire aerobically if oxygen is present.
- pH – most bacteria grow best at around pH 6.5 but will tolerate pH 4.0 – 9.0. *Thiobacillus thiooxidans* can grow at pH 3!

How can we prepare sterile agar plates?

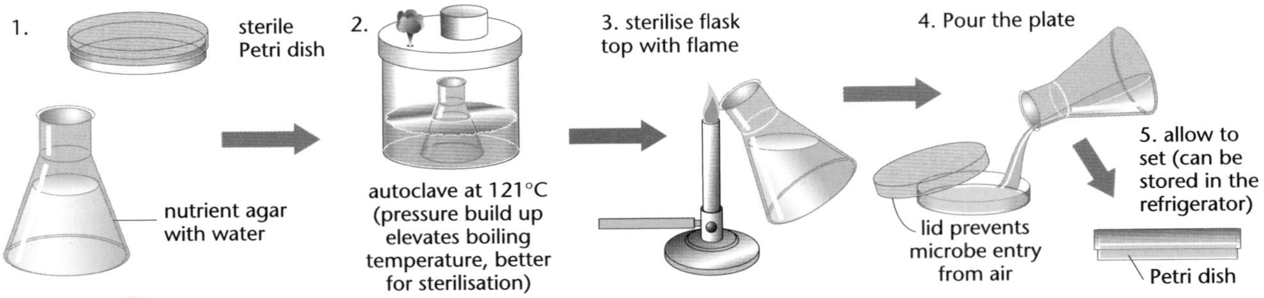

1.
sterile Petri dish
nutrient agar with water
2.
autoclave at 121 °C (pressure build up elevates boiling temperature, better for sterilisation)
3. sterilise flask top with flame
4. Pour the plate
lid prevents microbe entry from air
5. allow to set (can be stored in the refrigerator)
Petri dish

Nutrient broth (a liquid medium) is also used to culture microorganisms. Both agar and broth are examples of nutrient media. Often a broad spectrum medium is used, suitable for a wide range of microorganisms. Usually a buffer is present in the medium, to maintain the pH.

The conditions in which a plate is incubated are selective. In school, the incubation temperature for plates is normally 25°C. This is to avoid pathogens which attack humans. They would be encouraged to grow if a temperature of 37°C was used.

Can nutrient media be selective?

> **KEY POINT**
> It is possible to use a highly selective growth medium, suitable for only a specific organism. This medium will not support the growth of other microorganisms even if they are present. They are inhibited.

Example 1

Culture of *Azotobacter* (nitrogen fixing bacteria found in soil).

- The medium used should contain sugar and essential minerals.
- No ammonium ions would be added because *Azotobacter* obtain their nitrogen from atmospheric nitrogen.
- Initially the only bacteria growing would be *Azotobacter* with other bacteria suppressed.
- Later, as *Azotobacter* die, they release NH_4^+, so that other microorganisms can develop.

Example 2

Culture of *Salmonella* (pathogenic bacteria found in human gut).

- MacConkey agar includes sodium taurocholate (a bile salt which prevents growth of Gram positive bacteria) and lactose.
- It contains a pH indicator which changes to red if the pH drops to less than 6.8.
- Other bacteria, e.g. *E. coli,* use lactose and as a result produce an acidic waste product, so with the indicator present, these bacteria show up as red.

- *Salmonella* bacteria do not use the lactose and remain colourless.

So the red colonies are other bacteria, Gram positive bacteria do not grow, and the colourless colonies are the dangerous *Salmonella*. This would be excellent diagnostic information for doctors!

Streaking a plate

The term plate refers to a Petri dish. The diagrams below show how a sterile inoculating loop is used to pick up and transfer microorganisms.

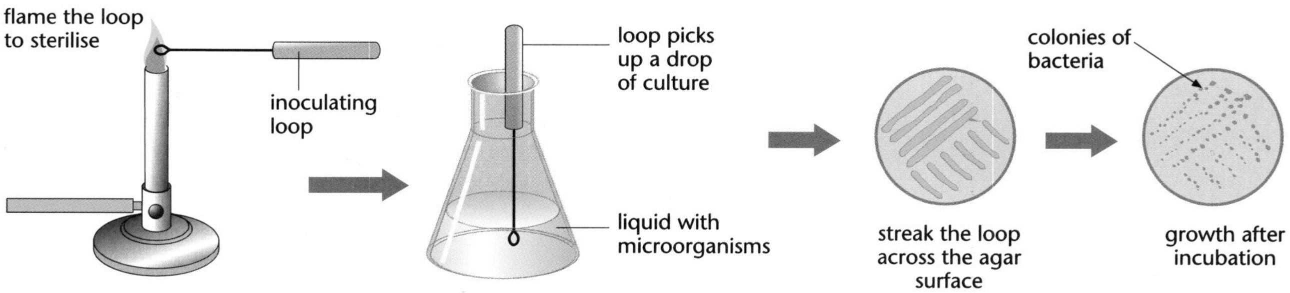

Other techniques can be used but all parts of the process must be aseptic. Any transfer instrument must be sterilised in some way.

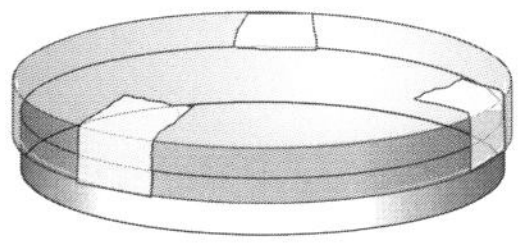

Taping a Petri dish ready for incubation

Taping is important. The lid should be kept on at all times but air is still allowed into the dish. This encourages aerobes and discourages dangerous anaerobes from developing.

Dilution plating

In one Petri dish there can be millions of bacteria which are impossible to count accurately. A dilution technique must be employed.

> **KEY POINT**
>
> **Remember this principle**. One **viable**, bacterium, when transferred to a suitable medium, will reproduce to form a circular colony. One bacterium is invisible to the naked eye but we work backwards. If there are 20 colonies which have grown then we know that we began with 20 individual bacteria on day 1.

Pond water and milk contain too many bacteria to be directly counted. When plated the colonies of bacteria would merge together. Any count would be inaccurate!

The dilution technique

The principle of dilution plating.

- Take a 1 cm^3 sample of say, pond water, then add 9 cm^3 sterilised water.
- The population of microorganisms is now at 1 in 10 cm^3 of the initial sample.
- Mix thoroughly then take 1 cm^3 of the diluted population and add 9 cm^3 sterilised water.
- The population of microorganisms is now at 1 in 100 or 10^{-2} of the initial sample.
- The above dilution process can be continued down to 1 in 10 000.
- The 1 in 10 000 (10^{-4}), 1 in 1000 (10^{-3}), 1 in 100 (10^{-2}), samples are used and for each, 1 cm^3 is transferred to molten agar which is added to Petri dishes, which are incubated for 48 hours.
- Counts are then made, colony numbers in a plate from 30 – 300 are counted.
- If there are less than 30 colonies, the number is considered not reliable.
- If there are more than 300 colonies, the colonies merge with each other so that reliable counting is not possible.
- Remember that every circular colony can be tracked back to a single bacterium!

A worked example

If you found that the plates for a 1 in 10000 dilution were below 30 then they would be immediately discounted.

At a dilution of 1 in 1000 (10^{-3}) a sample of $0.2\,cm^3$ is plated and the average plate count is 96.5 colonies.

Number of colonies in $1\,cm^3$ of 10^{-3} dilution pond water $= \frac{96.5 \times 1}{0.2} = 482.5$

Number of bacteria in $1\,cm^3$ original pond water $= \frac{482.5 \times 1}{10^{-3}} = 482\,500$

Turbidimetry is not as accurate as dilution plating as:

- the cloudiness or opacity of the culture is measured – dead microorganisms as well as the viable ones
- it does not give numbers of microorganisms.

Turbidimetry

This is another way to estimate the growth in a microbial population. The technique is based on the culture becoming increasingly cloudy as the population increases. Turbidity is the cloudiness of the culture. It can be measured using a spectrophotometer or colorimeter.

- A sample of the culture is poured into a cuvette and inserted into the spectrophotometer or colorimeter.
- Light is passed through each sample.
- The amount of light received by a sensor after being passed through the sample is indicated via a meter.
- The less light reaching the sensor, the greater the growth of the microbial population.
- The more light absorbed by the culture, the greater the growth of the microbial population.

Sample question and model answer

This question illustrates an interesting point. Bacteria Y appeared after 14 days but they must have been present at the beginning. They were just too small to see!

(a) The diagram below shows a Petri dish containing a **selective** agar medium for **nitrogen fixing bacteria**. The agar had all the essential nutrients but ammonium ions were excluded. The diagrams show the growth of bacteria after 2 days, 8 days and 14 days. Colonies of species X were visible after two days and an additional species,Y, appeared after 14 days.

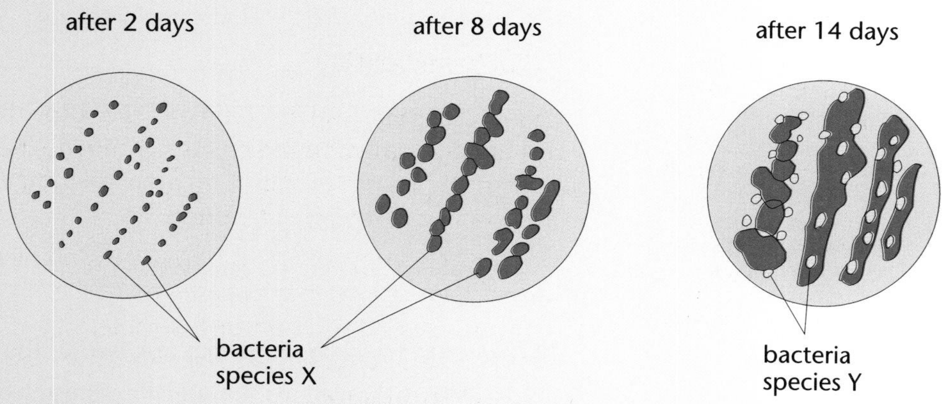

(i) Why did **only** species X grow during the first few days of the investigation? [4]

No ammonium ions added so species Y could not grow.

Species X bacteria obtain their nitrogen from atmospheric nitrogen, so can make their proteins, having all requirements for growth.

Species X releases ammonium (NH_4^+), so that species Y can now grow.

(ii) How was the agar medium inoculated with the bacteria? Give evidence from the diagrams to support your answer. [1]

Streaking, because the colonies are growing in lines.

(iii) Why were circular colonies of bacteria not visible after 14 days? [1]

The colonies had grown together or merged together.

There are often mathematics questions in biology papers. Always practise before you take your 'live' examination. This Guide will help you.

(b) After two days there were 39 colonies of species X. Assuming,

(i) the original sample containing the bacteria was diluted to 1 in 10 000

(ii) $0.1\,cm^3$ of the diluted sample was plated to produce the 39 colonies, how many **viable** bacteria were there in $1\,cm^3$ of the original sample?

Show your working. [2]

In $1\,cm^3$ of the 1 in 10 000 dilution there were $\frac{39 \times 1}{0.1} = 390$

But the dilution factor is 1 in 10 000 or 10^{-4}

so number of viable cells is $\frac{390}{10^{-4}} = 3\,900\,000$ in $1\,cm^3$ of the original sample.

(c) If you wished to measure population growth and include dead bacteria as well as the living ones which method would you use? [1]

Turbidimetry, using a spectrophotometer or colorimeter.

Practice examination questions

1 (a) The table below includes features shown by viruses, bacteria and fungi. Complete the table below by putting a tick in each correct box, for a feature shown by the group of organisms.

	Virus	*Bacterium*	*Fungus*
has membrane bound organelles			
has an outer protein coat of capsomeres			
has ribosomes			
is prokaryotic			
is multinucleate			
cannot respire			
has plasmids			
has an outer wall of chitin			
has nucleic acid but no cytoplasm			

[9]

(b) The term bacteriophage can link two of the above groups of organisms.

Describe the relationship which links the two groups together. [2]

[Total: 11]

2 A retrovirus made double stranded DNA from mRNA which was in the process of protein synthesis. The base sequence below shows part of the first single strand of DNA which the virus was able to synthesise.

GGC TTA ATC GCT AAG TAC single strand DNA

(a) (i) What sequence of bases on the mRNA strand would have coded for the production of the first single strand of DNA? [1]

(ii) What is the complementary strand to the first single strand of DNA? [1]

(b) Which type of enzyme would the virus use to synthesise the double stranded DNA form the mRNA? [1]

[Total: 3]

3 A patient submits a sample of faeces to the pathology department of a hospital.

(a) Outline how the laboratory technician would test for the presence of suspected *Salmonella* bacteria, using MacConkey agar. [2]

(b) Explain how the MacConkey agar allows *Salmonella* to be differentiated from other Gram negative bacteria. [4]

(c) Explain what happens to Gram positive bacteria if they are present in the sample transferred to the plate. [2]

[Total: 8]

Chapter 10

Biotechnology

The following topics are covered in this chapter:

- *Large scale production*
- *Medical applications*
- *Further gene transfer*

10.1 Large scale production

After studying this section you should be able to:

LEARNING SUMMARY

- *describe the main features of batch and continuous culture*
- *outline fermentation processes which yield substances useful to human requirements*
- *describe the production of mycoprotein using a commercial fermenter*
- *describe the production of yoghurt and yeast extract*

An introduction to biotechnology

AQA B M7
EDEXCEL M4
OCR M5
WJEC M4

Before describing how substances are commercially produced it is necessary to consider the meaning of the term, **biotechnology**.

KEY POINT

Biotechnology is the use of organisms and biological processes to supply nutrients, other substances and services to meet human needs. **Fermentation** is a key process in biotechnology as microorganisms are used to produce traditional products such as ethanol and the more recent production of substances such as pharmaceutical chemicals and the enzymes for biological washing powder.

Batch fermentation

In commercial fermentation large scale fermenters are used in production. Batch fermentation takes place in a **closed** vessel.

KEY POINT

- The fermenter is steam sterilised, then sterile nutrients are added.
- Fermentation commences and optimal conditions are maintained throughout the process.
- Fermentation continues until a maximum level of product is reached, when the process is stopped and the yield of product harvested.
- Harvesting time is critical because waste substances can result in a decrease of the product.
- So harvesting must be implemented before this takes place.

Advantages

- If the culture becomes contaminated in any way, just one batch is spoiled.
- The fermenter can be used for a variety of fermentation processes, e.g. different antibiotics.

Disadvantages

- At the end of every production period **shut down** takes place. The vessel needs to be cleaned and re-sterilised. This lost time can be expensive to the company.
- Often the product, waste substances and unused nutrients are mixed together, e.g. in penicillin production. Product removal is made more difficult by these contaminants.

Key points from AS

- **Modern industrial fermenters**
Revise AS page 88

Continuous fermentation

Continuous fermentation takes place in an open fermenter.

- The fermenter is steam sterilised.
- Regular amounts of sterile nutrients are added.
- At the same time regular amounts of product are removed.
- Optimum levels of pH, oxygen, nutrients and temperature are maintained.

Advantages

- The rate of growth of the microbial population is kept at a maximum level: this is known as the **exponential rate**.
- There is **no** regular pattern of **shut down**.

Disadvantage

- Maintaining the levels at **optimal levels** is difficult.
- **Regular** sampling is necessary for quality control, ensuring that chemicals are in equilibrium, and contaminants are absent.
- There is more chance of contaminants entering due to regular input and output.

The continuous production of mycoprotein in an air-lift fermenter

No stirrer required! Mixing is by the air bubbles produced from the sparger. A stirrer would break the hyphae which are needed to give a meat-like texture to the product.

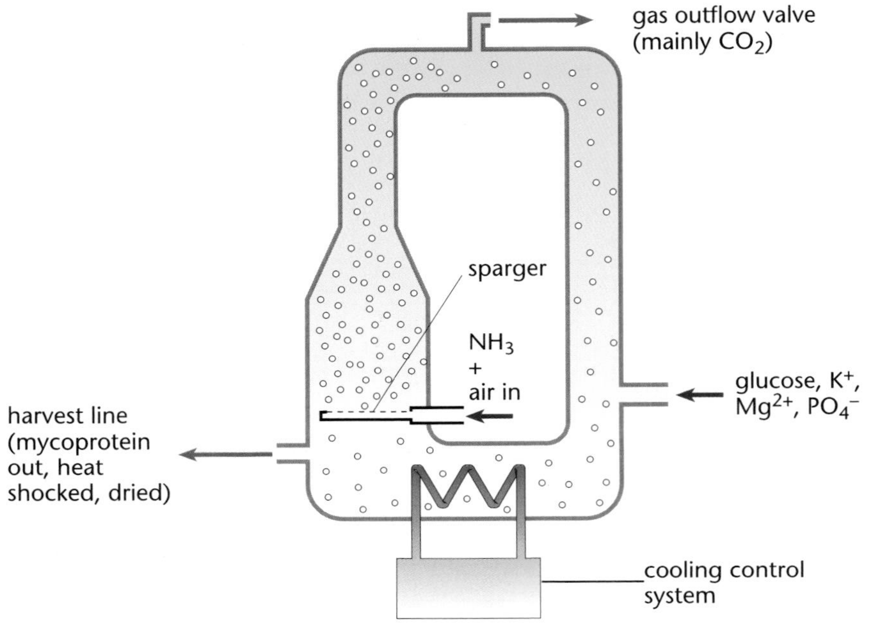

KEY POINT

- *Fusarium graminearum* is the fungus which is cultured to produce mycoprotein.
- The fermenter is operated continuously for six weeks during which there is a steady input of nutrients and an equal output of product.
- Air pumped into the fermenter supplies the required oxygen for the aerobic fungus and agitates (mixes!) the culture.
- Gas outlet of carbon dioxide takes place at the top of the fermenter.
- Probes monitor internal conditions by interfacing with a computer so that modifications to the internal environment can be made during fermentation (optimum temperature is at 30°C).
- Fungal hyphae can be filtered out during the harvesting process.
- The harvested fungus is then heat shocked at 65°C which denatures the fungal nuclei.
- Addition of flavours converts the very healthy, low fat food into a popular food sold in all major supermarkets as Quorn™.

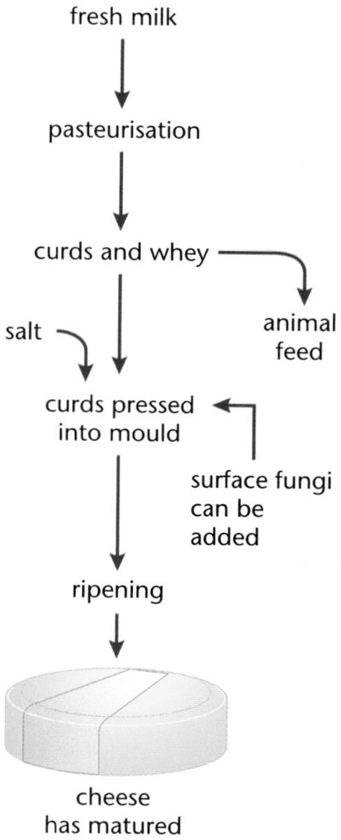

Commercial production of cheese

The process

- Milk is first **pasteurised** to destroy unwanted microorganisms.
- Selected bacteria are added such as:
  - *Leuconostoc lactis* which **produces CO_2** and has a major role in the determination of cheese **texture**
  - *Streptococcus lactis* which produces **lactic acid** from the milk sugar, lactose, and has a major role in the determination of **flavour**.
- Lactic acid **coagulates** (clots) the milk protein (casein) to form solid curds in a liquid component, the whey.
- **Rennet** is added which also coagulates the milk protein. (The rennet is usually artificially produced from genetically modified bacteria in fermenters.)
- The whey is removed and used in pig food.
- The curds have salt added as an osmotic preservative and they are pressed into a mould.
- In the coming weeks and months the bacteria and often fungi continue to grow on the surface and through the cheese.
- Enzymically driven changes take place such as protein breakdown to amino acids, until finally a characteristic cheese taste is achieved after this **ripening**.

Commercial production of beer

Beer is produced by the fermentation of a barley/hop mixture using a strain of *Saccharomyces cerevisiae* (yeast).

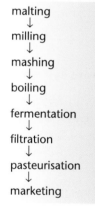

malting
↓
milling
↓
mashing
↓
boiling
↓
fermentation
↓
filtration
↓
pasteurisation
↓
marketing

The process

- **Malting** – germinating the barley so that amylase is produced.
- **Heating** to 80 °C to **kill the seed embryos** but **not denature amylase**.
- **Milling** – the malted barley is ground into a powder called grist (increase in surface area!).
- **Mashing** – hot water addition plus amylase, hydrolyses starch into wort.
- **Boiling** – hops added to wort at high temperature which imparts flavour.
- **Fermentation** – the addition of *S. cerevisiae* results in ethanol production.
- **Finings** – are added to clear the beer.
- **Filtration** – this follows the addition of finings to clear the beer, removes any yeast cell debris.
- **Pasteurisation** – to prevent any further fermentation in the marketed container.

Meat tenderisation

Traditionally a carcass of a meat animal such as a bullock is hung for several days, before the beef is sold to the public, during which proteolytic enzymes hydrolyse the proteins. This tenderises the meat.

The modern technique is to use enzymes which make the meat tender, e.g. papain from the papaya plant.

The process is helpful to the people selling the product rather than the consumer!

Advantages

- Storage time of meat is reduced since tenderisation is fast.
- Older animals with tough meat, not normally marketed as a prime product, can yield a better profit due to the tenderisation treatment.

Commercial production of yoghurt

Yoghurt is made by fermentation using a range of bacteria as the active microorganisms and milk as a food substrate. An important component of the milk is lactose, milk sugar.

Key points of the process

- Milk is heat treated at 90 °C for 30 minutes then cooled to the incubation temperature.
- The milk is homogenised so that components are equally distributed throughout.
- The fermenter is inoculated with a starter culture (e.g. *Lactobacillus bulgaricus* and *Streptococcus thermophilus*).
- Incubated at around 40 °C for about 6 hours.
- *L. bulgaricus* breaks down milk protein into peptides.
- *S. thermophilus* uses the peptides and produces formic acid.
- *L. bulgaricus* uses the formic acid and breaks down lactose into lactic acid, so the pH falls to about 4.3.
- Lactic acid also causes the coagulation of milk protein so that the characteristic thickening of the yoghurt takes place.
- Ethanal (acetaldehyde) is produced by each bacterial species giving the buttery taste, whereas lactic acid gives a 'tangy' taste.

Microbial processes

Note that there are common parts to each process involving microorganisms. Pre-process sterilisation is always carried out with steam. Disinfectant would contaminate the product. A suitable temperature is always required so that the microbial enzymes function at an optimum rate. The pH level is always monitored carefully.

KEY POINT

Yeast extract: a by-product of 'spent' brewers' yeast

Yeast is produced during the production of ethanol. During fermentation as the ethanol increases then so does the yeast population, yielding large quantities of a potentially useful by-product. Yeast contains the full range of B complex vitamins.

How is the yeast processed?

- Yeast is warmed to 50°C which results in self-digestion known as autolysis.
- Carbohydrates, proteins and lipids are hydrolysed by enzymes within the yeast cells.
- Breakdown products such as amino acids and glycerol form in the organic mixture.
- These substances are known as the autolysate.
- Separation of these useful substances is by filtration and centrifugation.
- After dehydration it can be used as a food additive to impart a meaty flavour.

Additionally a **hydrolysate** can be produced:

- heat yeast with HCl to change proteins to amino acids
- neutralise with NaOH
- tastes meaty and salty.

Salt is produced as the HCl is neutralised by NaOH.

Progress check

State **two** differences between continuous and batch production.

- Batch production is shut down on a more regular basis.
- In continuous production nutrients are added on a regular basis, and products are removed in similar quantities. In batch production product retrieval is at the end rather than during the process.

10.2 Medical applications

After studying this section you should be able to:

- *outline the production of antibiotics*
- *describe the production and applications of monoclonal antibodies*

LEARNING SUMMARY

Antibiotic production

AQA B M7
EDEXCEL M4
OCR M5
WJEC M4

Antibiotics are substances produced by microorganisms which kill or inhibit further growth of other microorganisms. There are a number of different antibiotics, including penicillin.

- Discovery of penicillin was by Sir Alexander Fleming in 1928.
- He grew the bacterium *Staphylococcus* on agar.
- *Penicillium notatum* spores had reached the agar and had begun to grow.
- Next to the fungal mycelium a gap remained where no bacteria would grow.
- He found that a substance had been secreted by the fungus which he named penicillin.
- He followed this up with further research to show that the penicillin killed a number of pathogenic organisms.

Note that the fermenter on p.88 in the AS guide would be used for penicillin production.

KEY POINT

Antibiotics can be either bactericidal or bacteriostatic in action.

Bactericidal is the term used when they kill the microbe which they attack, e.g. penicillin is bactericidal.

Bacteriostatic is the term used when antibiotics halt further microbial growth.

Penicillin production

Penicillin is able to destroy a narrow range of bacteria so is classified as a **narrow spectrum antibiotic**.

Chloramphenicol can destroy a wide range of bacteria and so is classified as a **broad spectrum antibiotic.**

- Large scale production takes place in a fermenter.
- The nutrient medium usually contains glucose and lactose.
- The *Penicillium* fungus is usually cultured in a fermenter for about 6–8 days.
- Production is by batch culture so that harvesting comes when the penicillin yield is considered to be at a maximum (see graph below).
- The fungal hyphae can be removed by filtration.
- The remaining liquid contains the antibiotic.
- K^+ ions are added to this liquid component forming a compound with the penicillin.
- This compound precipitates so that it can readily be removed.
- After drying, the product is removed at over 99% purity.

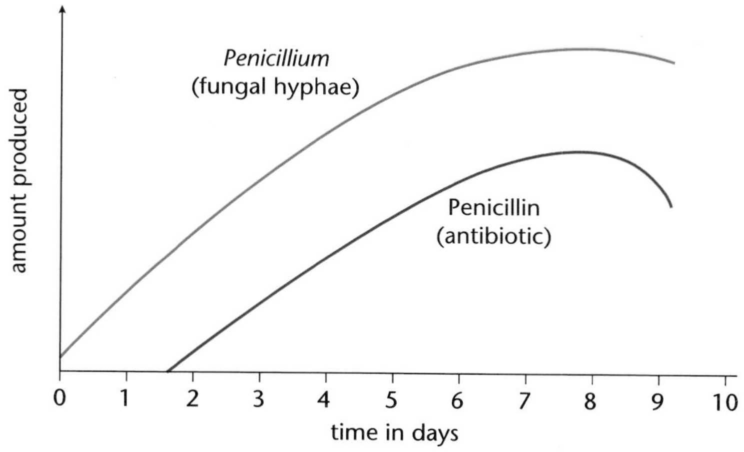

Monoclonal antibodies

AQA B	M8
EDEXCEL	M5
OCR	M5
WJEC	M4

Antibodies are produced by B-lymphocytes in response to specific antigens. We have many different lines of B-lymphocyte, each being so specific in action that it will only bind with a highly specific antigen. Many researchers looked towards production of antibodies, targeted at cancer cells.

It is hoped that these will be the answer: **monoclonal antibodies**.

Key points from AS

- **How do antibodies destroy pathogens** *Revise AS page 136*

The problems

- Isolated lymphocytes die quickly outside an organism.
- More robust cells are needed to exist in production vessels outside the organism if commercial antibody production is to be possible.

Principles of production

- An organism, e.g. mouse is injected with antigen, e.g. red blood cells of a sheep.
- Antigens on the red cells stimulate B-lymphocytes to produce antibodies.
- The B lymphocytes produce plasma cells which are removed from the spleen of the mouse.
- Tumour cells from the bone marrow of another mouse are collected.
- Plasma cells are fused with tumour cells forming a **hybridoma**, a very robust cell.
- The resulting cells are incubated on a special medium; only cells which have successfully fused and become hybridomas can survive.
- Hybridoma cells are then cloned on media in a laboratory.
- The hybridoma cells are assayed quantitatively for antibody secretion and only the best line of hybridoma cells is selected.
- Large scale production is in an air-lift fermenter to prevent damage to the cells.

Do not get confused! At the end of this process the antibodies could **only** be targeted at the antigens on the red blood cells.

Whichever antigen is injected into the first animal is the one which the antibody will successfully bind to.

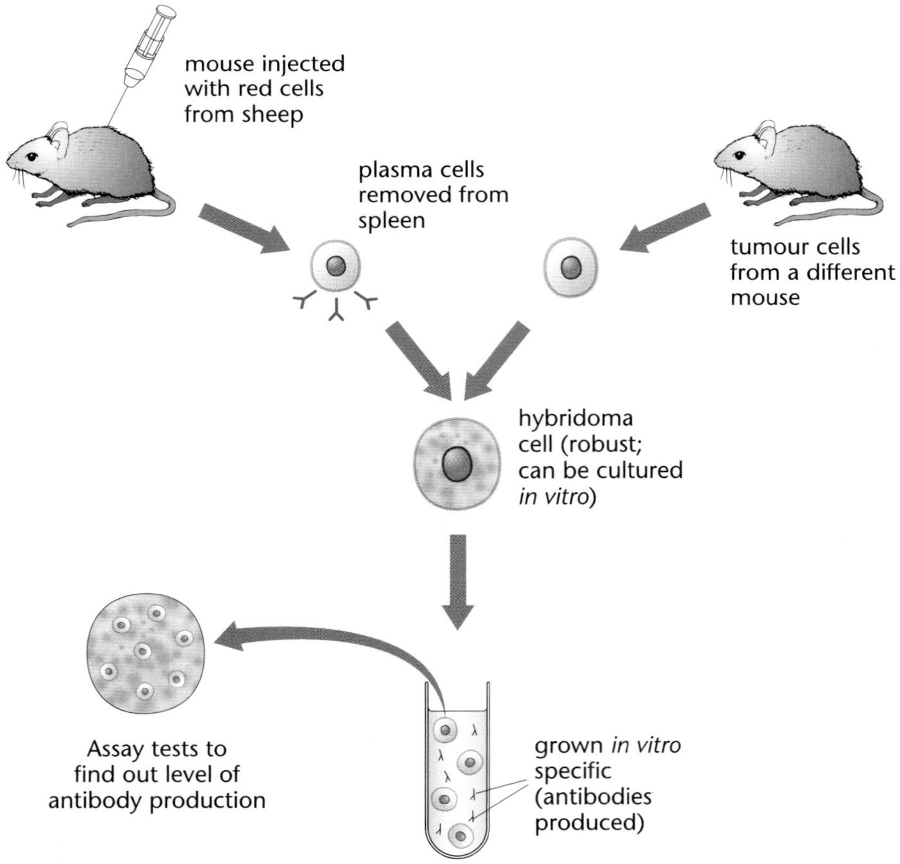

What can monoclonal antibodies be used for?

Treatment of tetanus – the tetanus antigen is injected into a mouse, as seen in the process above. The antibodies produced are reasonably successful but, owing to their 'mouse' origin they are recognised as antigenic themselves and eventually attacked by the immune system.

Monoclonal antibodies and pregnancy testing

The principles

- The hormone human chorionic gonadotrophin (HCG) is present in the urine of a pregnant woman.
- The base of the pregnancy testing strip is put into urine.
- At the base are coloured mobile monoclonal antibodies which have been produced against HCG.
- If HCG is present in the urine then these antibodies bind to the HCG and move up the test strip by capillary action.
- Midway up the strip is a line of immobilised antibodies capable of binding to HCG.
- Resulting along this mid-line is a complex of three molecules:

  mobile antibodies + HCG + immobilised antibodies

  which show up as a blue line, a positive pregnancy test.
- In a negative test, HCG would not be bound to the mobile antibodies.
- The mobile antibodies then rise to the top of the testing strip where they bind to an immobilised line of complementary antibodies.
- The antibodies bind together to give a blue line at the top to show that the woman is not pregnant.

Not all of the mobile antibodies bind with HCG, even though it is present in the urine sample. The result is that some mobile antibodies rise to the top of the strip, bind with the immobilised antibodies there producing another blue line. TWO blue lines show up for a pregnant woman!

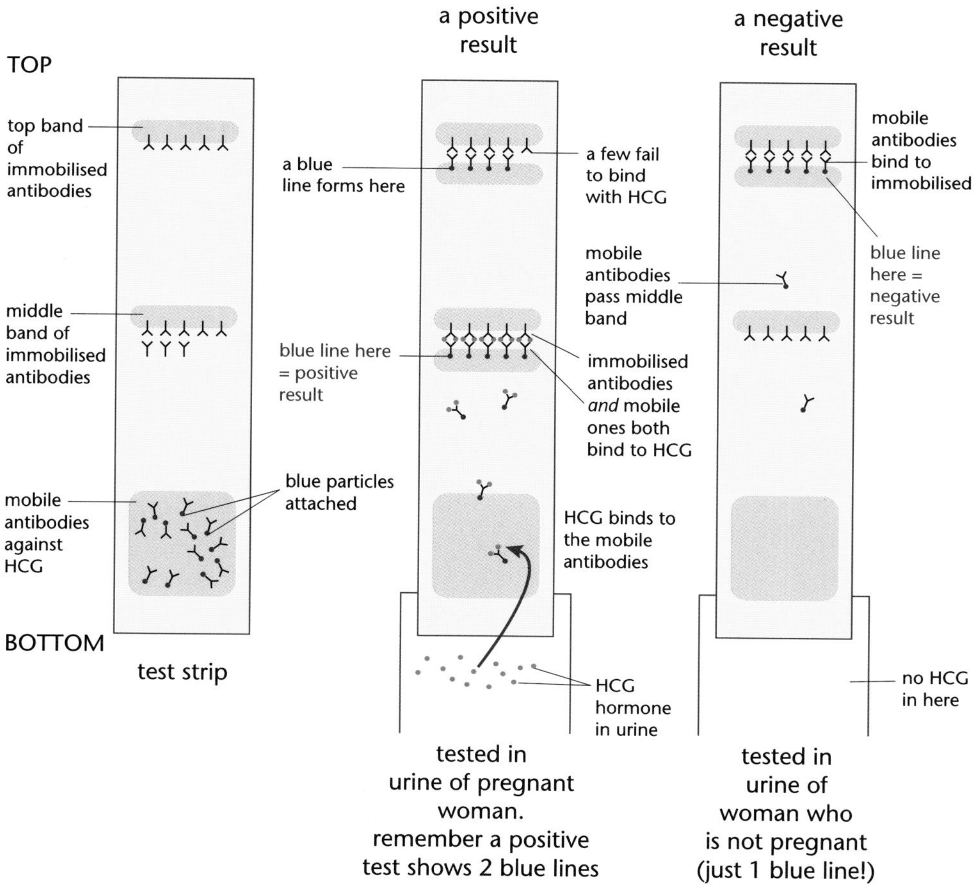

How can monoclonal antibodies be used to purify drugs?

It is vital to produce drugs such as interferon at a very high level of purity. This can be achieved with monoclonal antibodies in a resin-based column.

Addition of acid removes the drug which is collected then the mixture is neutralised.

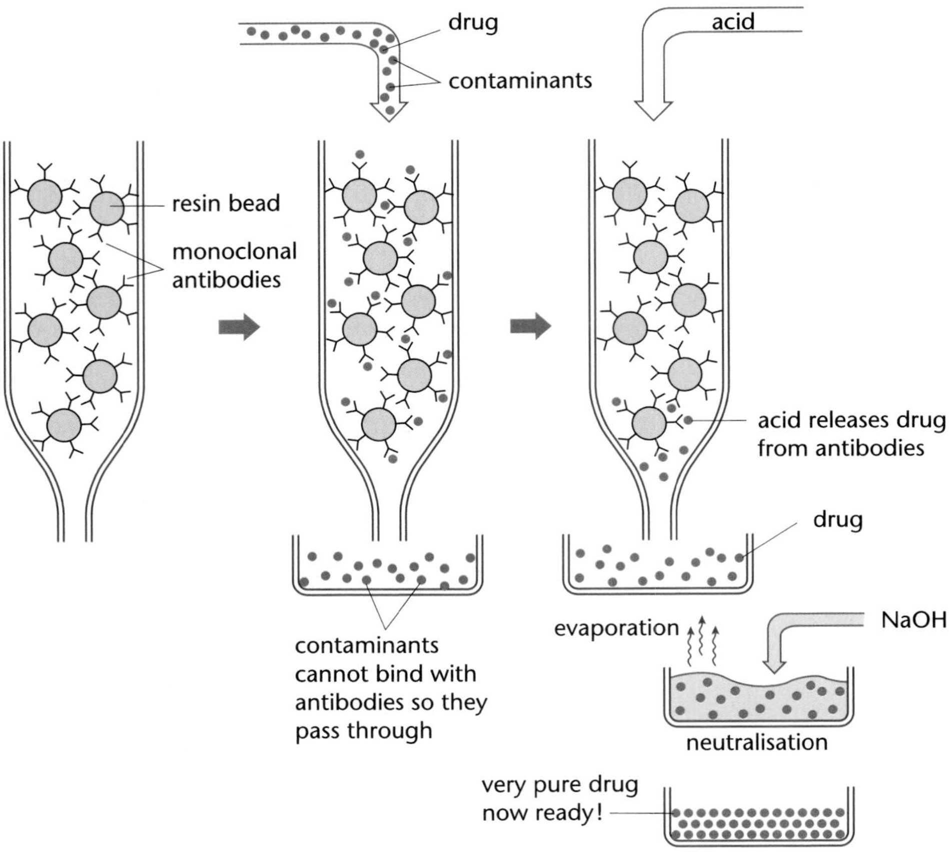

The principles

- Specific monoclonal antibodies adhere to resin beads in a glass column.
- Impure mixtures containing the drug are trickled through the column.
- The drug binds to the antibodies which are immobilised on the beads. (Immobilised means the antibodies are stuck on to the beads!)
- The impurities trickle down beneath the column and are removed.

10.3 Further gene transfer

After studying this section you should be able to:

- *describe a range of transgenic applications*
- *describe advantages and potential disadvantages of genetic modification*

LEARNING SUMMARY

Transgenic organisms

EDEXCEL	M5
OCR	M5
WJEC	M4

Modern gene technology will result in huge advances during the shelf-life of this book. Moving genes from one species to another may have great benefits.

It will be necessary to balance these benefits against the potential dangers and the ethics of interfering with the genome of a species.

Transgenic organisms have very useful genes, acquired by **gene transfer from other organisms.** The stage at which the gene transfer is made is critical. This is usually when the gene(s) insertion takes place into the **nucleus of a zygote**, before the first mitotic division. Every subsequent cell division passes on this gene to every somatic cell of the organism. Additionally the new gene will be passed on to offspring; the gene has been incorporated into the genome of the species.

KEY POINT

Transgenic crop plants

Inserting genes into crop plants is becoming increasingly important in meeting the needs of a rising world population. A range of techniques is used to engineer new genes into a species.

In plants there is an important technique which uses a vector to insert a novel gene, the bacterium *Agrobacterium tumefaciens*.

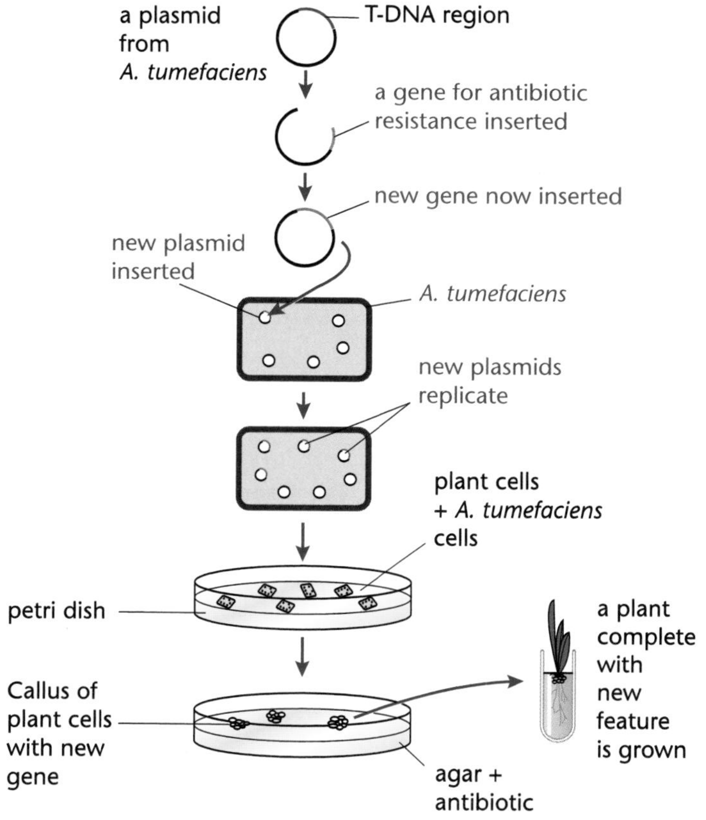

Key points from AS

- **Genetically modified organisms**
  Revise AS page 90
- **Gene technology**
  Revise AS page 87

Agrobacterium tumefaciens

- This is a **pathogenic bacterium** which **invades** plants forming a gall (abnormal growth).
- The bacterium contains **plasmids** (circles of DNA) which carry a gene that stimulates tumour formation in the plants it attacks.
- The part of the plasmid which does this is known as the **T-DNA region** and can insert into any of the chromosomes of a host plant cell.
- Part of the T-DNA controls the production of two growth hormones, auxin and cytokinin.
- The extra quantities of these hormones stimulate rapid cell division, the cause of the tumour.

KEY POINT

How can *Agrobacterium tumefaciens* be used in gene transfer?

The principle of using *A. tumefaciens* can be used in gene transfer to many different plants. Applications are in an early stage of development. Look to the media!

- Firstly, the DNA section controlling auxin and cytokinin was deleted, tumours were not formed, and cells of the plant retained their normal characteristics.
- A gene which gave the bacterial cell **resistance to a specific antibiotic** was inserted into the T-DNA position.
- The **useful gene** was **inserted into a plasmid**.
- Plant cells, minus cell walls, were removed and put into a Petri dish with nutrients and *A. tumefaciens*, which contained the engineered plasmids.
- The cells were **incubated** for several days then transferred to another Petri dish containing nutrients plus the specific antibiotic.
- **Only plant cells with antibiotic resistance and the desired gene grew**.
- Any surviving cells grew into a callus, from which an adult plant formed, complete with the transferred gene.

KEY POINT

Genetically modified soya bean plants – case study 1

Growing soya beans in the USA was big business and a big problem! Inefficient, physical methods of killing weeds had to be used because the crop plant was sensitive to herbicide (weedkiller).

The transgenic answer

- A gene from a plant resistant to herbicide was transferred into a soya bean plant.
- A new line was bred from this first resistant variant.
- This enabled the herbicide, **glyphosate**, to be used in the soya fields.
- Without weeds in the field there is no competition from weeds, so more light, more water, and more mineral ions are available to the crop.
- The result: a great increase in yield!

Concerns

- The new soya plants may interbreed with weeds around the fields and pass on resistance to herbicides. What effect would the herbicide have on weeds if this was to take place?
- With so much herbicide being sprayed in the field, what would happen if some of the chemicals remained in the food so that it passed to the humans in the food chain?
- Most soya protein entering the UK is of this genetically modified type.

Bovine somatotrophin (BST) – case study 2

Cattle produce a growth hormone known as bovine somatotrophin (BST) from their pituitary gland. The use of BST can improve the rate of meat production so that the animals are ready for the market earlier and have very lean meat, owing to their younger age. Additionally an increased milk yield, around 20%, is possible.

Scientists attempted to find a source of BST to inject into cows.

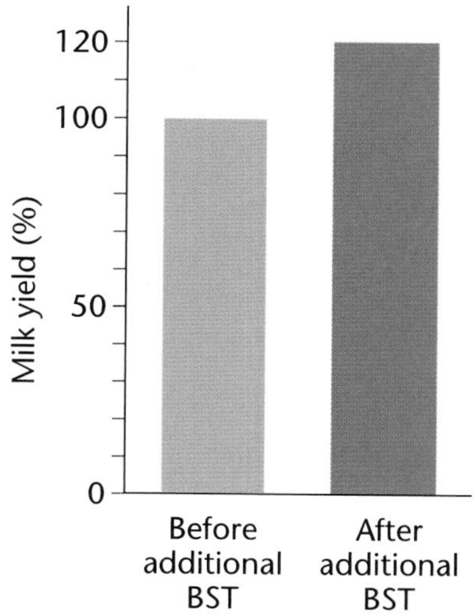

The transgenic answer

- The gene for BST production was transferred from cow cells into bacteria.
- The usual technique of gene transfer using restriction endonuclease was followed and the gene inserted into bacteria.
- The transgenic bacteria are grown in industrial fermenters where they secrete BST.
- After injection with BST cows produce more milk.

BST in milk will be consumed by people, but it has no effect because BST, as a protein, is digested in the stomach.

Concerns

- Injecting a healthy cow on a regular basis may be considered cruel.
- The number of cows becoming infertile is greater in those being injected with BST.

The Flavr Savr™ Tomato – case study 3

As tomatoes mature they change from green to red and become softer. Often they are picked green and turn red during transit. The taste is not good after this treatment. They can go soft very quickly and have a short shelf-life.

Flavr Savr™

The transgenic answer

- The tomatoes ripen due to the conversion of amino acids into ethene.
- Ethene stimulates the production of pectinase enzymes which break down the middle lamellae between tomato cells, softening them.
- Two genes have been transferred into a tomato which inhibit both changes.
- This results in the Flavr Savr™ tomato staying firmer for longer; the shelf- life has improved!

Sample question and model answer

The diagrams below show the transfer of a useful gene from a donor plant cell to the production of a transgenic crop plant. The numbers on the diagram show the stages in the process.

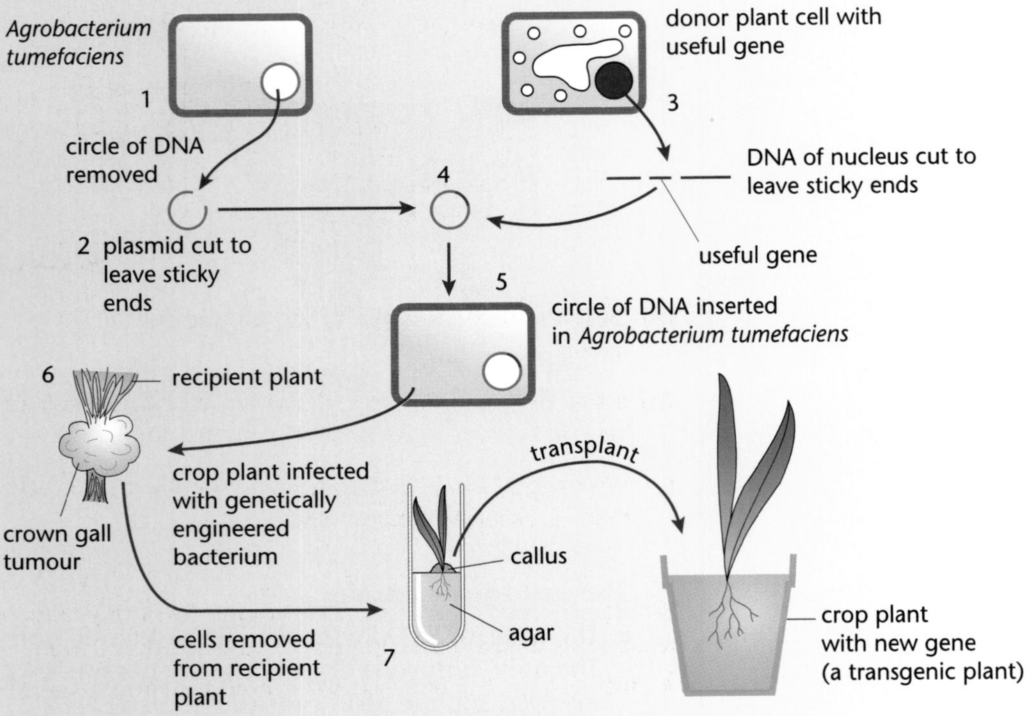

Look out for transgenic stories in the media. The principles are often the same. This will prepare you for potentially new ideas in your 'live' examinations. You could encounter the same account!

(a) Give the correct name for the circle of DNA found in the bacterium, *A. tumefaciens*. [1]

plasmid

(b) The same enzyme was used to cut the DNA of the bacterium and of the plant cell.

(i) Name the type of enzyme used to cut the DNA. [1]

restriction endonuclease

(ii) Explain why it is important to use exactly the same enzyme at this stage. [2]

The same enzyme produces the same sticky ends.

Complementary sticky ends on donor gene bind with the sticky ends of the plasmid.

(iii) Which type of enzyme would be used to splice the new gene into the circle of DNA? [1]

ligase

This question covers key techniques in gene transfer. Be prepared for your examination.

(c) How was the new gene incorporated into the DNA of the crop plant cells? [2]

Crop plant infected by genetically engineered bacterium.

The DNA of bacterium causes a change in the DNA of crop plant to produce the gall or tumour cells.

(d) How would you know if the gene had been transferred successfully? [1]

The feature would be expressed in the transgenic plants.

Practice examination questions

1 The diagram below shows an industrial fermenter used to produce the antibiotic, penicillin.

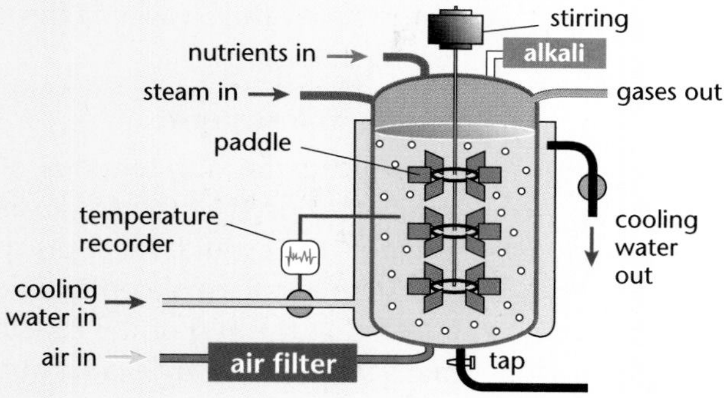

(a) Describe **three** ways in which aseptic conditions are achieved in the fermenter. [3]

(b) If the air filter failed, explain what would be the likely effect inside the fermenter. [3]

(c) Which type of culture, batch or continuous, is used to produce penicillin? Give a reason for your answer. [2]

[Total: 8]

2 The statements below describe the principles of production of monoclonal antibodies. Place the statements in the correct sequence.

A Antigens on the red cells stimulated B-lymphocytes to produce antibodies

B Hybridoma cells are assessed for antibody secretion and only the best line of hybridoma cells is selected

C Plasma cells are fused with tumour cells forming hybridoma cells

D The resulting cells are incubated on a special medium, on which only hybridomas can survive

E B-lymphocytes produce plasma cells which were removed from the spleen of the mouse

F Hybridoma cells are cloned on media in a laboratory

G Tumour cells from the bone marrow of a different mouse are collected

H A mouse was injected with red blood cells [8]

3 The graph below shows the level of product secreted by microorganisms in a commercial fermenter.

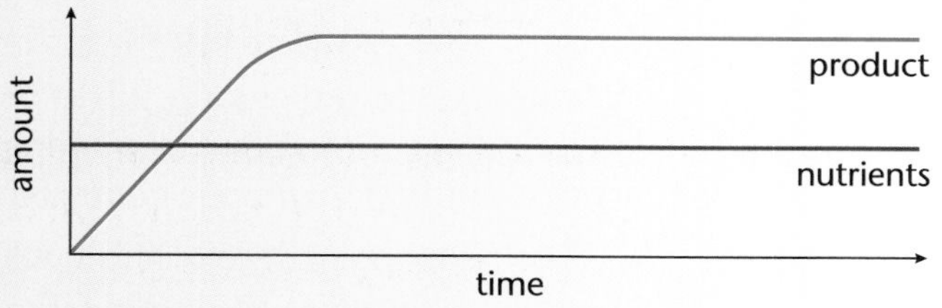

(a) Account for the shape of the graph. [1]

(b) Which type of culture, batch or continuous, took place in this fermenter? Give **two** reasons for your choice. [2]

[Total: 3]

Chapter 11

Synoptic assessment

What is synoptic assessment?

You must know the answer to this question if you are to be fully prepared for your A2 examinations!

Synoptic assessment:

- involves the drawing together of knowledge, understanding and skills learned in different parts of the AS/A2 Biology courses
- requires that candidates apply their knowledge of a number of areas of the course to a variety of contexts
- is tested at the end of the A2 course by both assessment of investigative/ practical skills and by examinations
- is valued at 20% of the marks of the course total.

Each Examination Group identifies which parts of its specification will be tested in the end-assessed synoptic questions. (Synoptically assessed content is highlighted in the specification grids for each Examination group in the specification list section of this book.)

Practical investigations

You will need to apply knowledge and understanding of the concepts and principles, learned throughout the course, in the **planning**, **execution**, **analysis** and **evaluation** of each investigation.

How can I prepare for the synoptic questions?

Why are synoptic skills examined?

Once studying at a higher level or in employment, having a narrow view, or superficial knowledge of a problem, limits your ability to contribute. Having discrete knowledge is not sufficient. You need to have confidence in applying your skills and knowledge.

- **Check out the modules** which will be examined for your specification's synoptic questions.
- Expect **new contexts** which draw together lots of different ideas.
- Get ready to **apply** your knowledge to a new situation; contexts change but the **principles remain the same**.
- In modular courses there is sometimes a tendency for candidates to learn for a module, achieve success, then forget the concepts. Do not allow this to happen! **Transfer concepts** from one lesson to another and from one module to another. Make those connections!
- Improve your powers of analysis – **take a range of different factors into consideration** when making conclusions; synoptic questions often involve both graphical data and comprehension passages.
- Less able candidates make limited conclusions; high ability candidates are able to consider several factors at the same time, then make a **number of sound conclusions** (not guesses!).
- You need to do **Regular Revision** through the course; this keeps the concepts 'hot' in your memory, 'simmering and distilling', ready to be **retrieved** and **applied** in the synoptic contexts.
- The bullet point style of this book will help a lot; back this up by summarising points yourself as you make notes.

Synoptic favourites

The final modules, specified by the Examination Group for synoptic assessment, include targeted synoptic questions. Concepts and principles from earlier modules will be tested together with those of the final modules. You can easily identify these questions, as they will be longer and span wide-ranging ideas.

> **Can we predict what may be regularly examined in synoptic questions?**
>
> 'Yes we can!' Below are the top five concepts. Look out for common processes which permeate through the other modules. An earlier module will include centrally important concepts which are important to your understanding of the rest.
>
> KEY POINT

Check out the synoptic charts!

1 Energy release

Both aerobic and anaerobic respiration release energy for many cell processes. Any process which harnesses this energy makes a link.

Synoptic links

Try this yourself! Think logically. Write down an important biological term such as 'cell division'. Link related words to it in a 'flow diagram' or 'mind map'. The links will become evident and could form the framework of a synoptic question.

Examples

- Reabsorption of glucose involves active transport in the proximal tubule of a kidney nephron. If you are given a diagram of tubule cells which show both mitochondria and cell surface membrane with transporter proteins, then this is a cue that active transport will probably be required in your answer.
- Contraction of striated (skeletal) muscle requires energy input. This is another link with energy release by mitochondria and could be integrated into a synoptic question.
- The role of the molecule ATP as an energy carrier and its use in the liberation of energy in a range of cellular activity may be regularly linked into synoptic questions. The liberation of energy by ATP hydrolysis to fund the sodium pump action in the axon of a neurone.
- The maintenance of proton gradients by proton pumps are driven by electron energy. Any process involving a proton pump can be integrated into a synoptic question.

Energy: input and output

This has to be a favourite for many synoptic questions. Energy is involved in so many processes that the frequency of examination will be high.

2 Energy capture

Photosynthesis is responsible for availability of most organic substances entering ecosystems. It is not surprising that examiners may explore knowledge of this process and your ability to apply it to ecological scenarios.

Examples

- Given the data of the interacting species in an ecosystem you may be given a short question about the mechanism of photosynthesis then have to follow the energy transfer routes through food webs.
- Often both photosynthesis and respiration are examined in a synoptic type question. There are similarities in both the thylakoid membranes in chloroplasts and cristae of mitochondria.
- Many graphs in ecologically based questions show the increase in herbivore numbers, followed by a corresponding carnivore increase. Missed off the graph, your knowledge of a photosynthetic flush which stimulates herbivore numbers may be expected.

3 The structure and role of DNA

It is important to know the structure of DNA because it is fundamentally important to the maintenance of life processes and the transfer of characteristics from one generation of a species to the next generation. DNA links into many environmentally and evolutionally based questions.

- The ultimate source of variation is the mutation of DNA. Questions may involve the mechanism of a mutation in terms of DNA change and be followed by natural selection. This can lead to extinction or the formation of a new species. Clearly there are many potential synoptic variations.
- DNA molecules carry the genetic code by which proteins are produced in cells. This links into the production of important proteins. The structure of a protein into primary, secondary, tertiary and quaternary structure may be tested. All enzymes are proteins, so a range of enzymically based question components can be expected in synoptic questions.
- The human genome project is a high profile project. The uses of this human gene 'atlas' will lead to many developments in the coming years. The reporting of developments, radiating from the human genome project, could be the basis of many comprehension type questions, spanning diverse areas of biology courses. Save newspaper cuttings, search the internet, watch documentaries. Note links with genetic diseases, ethics, drugs, etc.

DNA: fundamental to life

A high profile molecule involved in many biochemical and biotechnological processes. It must figure regularly in synoptic questions. Genetic engineering, the process, and how it can be harnessed to solve problems may be regularly tested.

4 Structure and function of the cell surface membrane

There are a range of different mechanisms by which substances can cross the cell surface membrane. These include diffusion, facilitated diffusion, osmosis, active transport, exocytosis and pinocytosis. Additionally glycoproteins have a cell recognition function and some proteins are enzymic in function. Knowledge of these concepts and processes can be tested in cross module questions.

- In an ecologically based question the increasing salinity of a rock pool in sunny conditions could be linked to water potential changes in an aquatic plant or animal. Inter-relationships of organisms within a related food web could follow, identifying such a question as synoptic.
- In cystic fibrosis a transmembrane regulator protein is defective. A mutant gene responsible for the condition codes for a protein with a missing amino acid. This can link to both the correct functioning of the protein, the mechanism of the mutation, and the functioning of the DNA.

5 Transport mechanisms

This theme may unify the following into a synoptic question, transport across membranes, transport mechanisms in animal and plant organs. Additionally they may be linked to homeostatic processes.

- The route of a substance from production in a cell, through a vessel to the consequences of a tissue which receives the substance, could expand into a synoptic question. Homeostasis and negative feedback could well be linked into these ideas.

Synoptic predictions

The list is given as an attempted prediction. There may be other links not listed in this chapter! Look at the specification for your Examination Group. You will be given more detailed information. Check out past papers for your Examination Group as the pattern is created. Do not be phased by new ideas and unknown organisms. Simply apply the concepts and principles learned in the course to new situations to be successful.

Sample questions and model answers

A short question which cuts across the course. It refers back to AS. Do not forget those modules! See the *Letts AS Guide* for additional advice and those concepts not found in this volume.

Question 1 *(a short structured question)*

Answer the following questions (a) to (f) in the spaces provided.

(a) Name the kingdom to which all bacteria belong. [1]

Prokaryotae

(b) What is the name given to embryonic plant seed leaves? [1]

cotyledons

(c) In which part of the kidney would you expect to find the glomerulus? [1]

cortex

(d) What is the term used to describe hormone secreting glands? [1]

endocrine

(e) During gametogenesis, name the process which results in the formation of haploid cells? [1]

meiosis

(f) Name the structure which provides the link between nervous and endocrine regulation. [1]

hypothalamus

[Total: 6]

WJEC specimen

This is an open-ended synoptic question. The examples you would refer to, to illustrate principles of exchange, depend upon which modules you have studied. Alveoli and tracheoles, as well as the structure of cell surface membranes are key aspects in your answer.

Question 2 *(a longer, more open-ended question)*

Living organisms exchange materials with their environment. These exchanges occur across surfaces which have special features. With reference to named examples, discuss how these surfaces are adapted for efficient exchange. [10]

(Quality of written communication assessed in this answer.)

- large surface area;
- maintenance of diffusion gradients;
- way(s) in which this is achieved;
- ref. to uptake of organic molecules;
- layer(s) of cells, e.g. squamous epithelium;
- ref. to uptake of ions;
- internal surface of leaf mesophyll;
- channel proteins;
- root hairs; carrier proteins;
  active uptake;
- any structural detail of surfaces;
- gills/alveoli;
- selectively permeable; permeable/thin;
- ref. to gaseous exchange;
- well ventilated;
- well supplied with blood;
- any detail;
- credit given for other examples such as tracheoles in insects, surface of protoctists, fungi, bacteria – any examples taken from optional modules

Note, there is one mark available for legible text with accurate spelling, punctuation and grammar. [1]

[Total: 10]

OCR specimen

Sample questions and model answers (continued)

Prepare yourself for this type of synoptic question. It cuts across a large part of the specification. Make the links with different ideas. This fact is very important; concepts from AS are needed. Check out your AS Biology Guide!

Question 3 *(a longer question of higher mark tariff)*

Different concentrations of maltose were placed in the small intestine of a mammal. The amount of glucose appearing in the blood and the small intestine were measured. The results are shown in the graph.

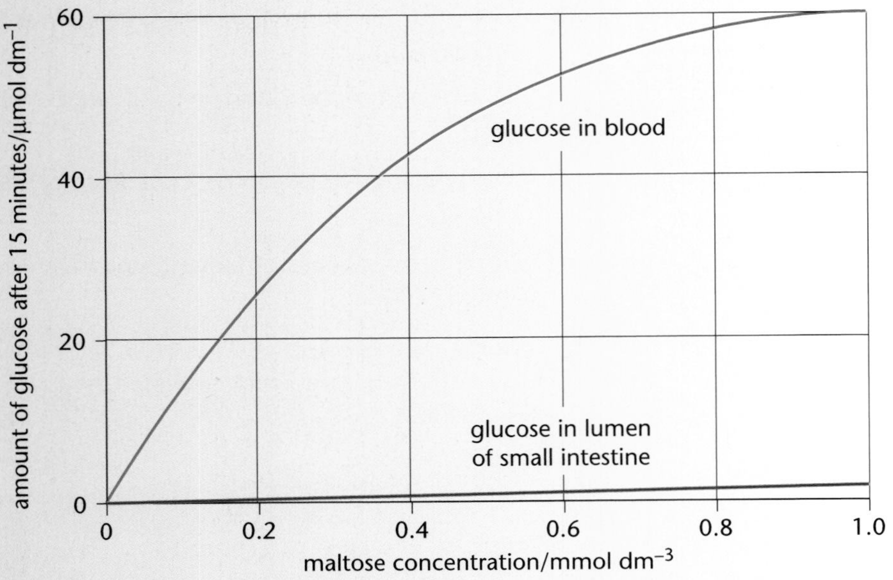

(a) (i) Give the name of the blood vessel most likely to be sampled for glucose. [1]

hepatic portal vein

(ii) By what chemical process is a molecule of maltose converted into two molecules of glucose? [1]

hydrolysis

(b) The enzyme maltase converts maltose into glucose. This enzyme is found in the cell surface membrane of the epithelial cells of the small intestine.

(i) Explain the evidence from the graph which supports the view that the breakdown of maltose does not occur in the lumen of the small intestine. [2]

Very little/no increase in the amount of glucose in the lumen;
if breakdown took place in the lumen then it would increase here/
would take some time to diffuse through the wall. [max 2]

Note this is a more challenging part of the question. You had to switch your mind to enzyme action. The graph is a classic enzyme curve but you may not have been aware of this in the context of epithelial cells. Be alert!

(ii) Suggest an explanation for the shape of the curve showing the change in the amount of glucose in the blood. [3]

More glucose, more active sites occupied;
curve flattens as enzyme becomes limiting;
at any one time, all active sites are occupied. [max 3]

[Total: 7]

Assessment and Qualifications Alliance A specimen

Sample questions and model answers (continued)

This flow diagram is complex. Follow the input of nutrients and note the reactions which take place. Clearly the microorganisms aid the digestive process of the cow. There are no enzymes shown but you would be aware that enzymes of both the cow and microorganisms would be active in these processes.

Question 4

A cow obtains most of its nutritional requirements from mutualistic microorganisms in its rumen. The diagram summarises the biochemical processes carried out by these microorganisms.

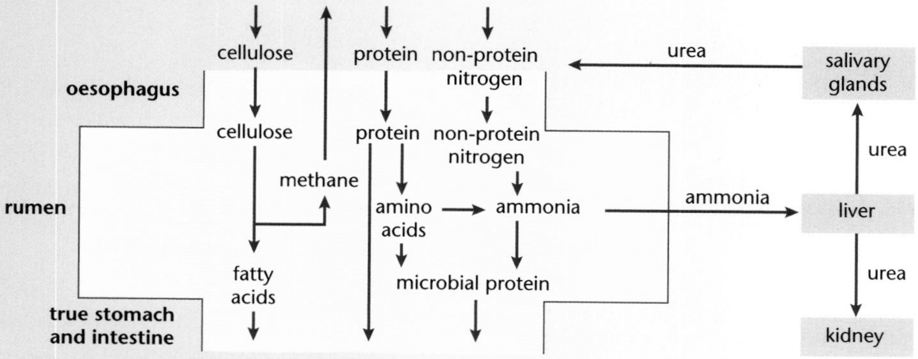

(a) Use the information in the diagram to explain why:

(i) the relation between the cow and the microorganisms which live in its rumen may be described as mutualistic [2]

Both organisms have a nutritional advantage;
cow gains fatty acids/cow gains proteins;
microorganisms gain cellulose/protein/urea. [max 2]

(ii) it is possible for a cow to survive on a diet which is poor in protein [2]

Obtain non-protein nitrogen;
microorganisms convert this to protein;
which cow can digest.

(iii) ruminant animals such as cows are less efficient than non-ruminant animals in converting energy in food into energy in their tissues. [2]

Some food energy is used by microorganisms;
some lost in methane.

This confirms the synoptic nature of this question! It switches to nitrogenous compounds in plants and nitrogen compound uptake by parasitic aphids.

(b) Aphids are small insects which feed on plant sap. The table shows the relationship between the amount of soluble nitrogen in plant sap and the body mass and reproductive rate of one species of aphid.

Soluble nitrogen in plant sap as percentage of dry mass	*Mean adult body mass (mg)*	*Reproductive rate (number of young produced per day per aphid)*
2.0	1.8	1.3
2.5	1.6	1.0
3.0	1.3	0.7
3.5	1.0	0.4
4.0	0.7	0.1

Explain how the amount of soluble nitrogen in plant sap affects the body mass and reproductive rate of aphids.

Growth and reproduction requires the production of new tissue;
which has a high protein requirement;
nitrogen is an essential part of protein. [max 2]

[Total: 8]

Assessment and Qualifications Alliance A specimen

Practice examination answers

Chapter 1 Energy for life

1

(a) in cytoplasm [1]

(b) pyruvate [1]

(c) 2 ATPs begin process;
2ATPs are produced from each of the two GP molecules, so –2 + 4 = +2 ATPs net [1]

(d) animal; animal cells produce lactate [1]

(e) oxygen or aerobic [1]

[Total: 5]

2

(a) At this point the amount of carbon dioxide given off by the plant in *respiration*, is totally used by the plant in *photosynthesis*. [2]

(b) compensation point [1]

(c) The continued graph line falls (as light dims); line ends below the horizontal axis (when its dark!). [2]

[Total: 5]

3

(a) $RQ = \frac{\text{units of } CO_2}{\text{units of } O_2}$

$0.7 = \frac{102}{x}$

$x = \frac{102}{0.7}$

$x = 145.7$

$= 146$ [2]

(b) (i) 0.9

(ii) 1.0 [2]

[Total: 4]

4

NaOH absorbs CO_2; as O_2 is taken in, any CO_2 replacing it is absorbed by the NaOH;

liquid in manometer moves;

use the syringe to equalise levels;
volume of oxygen shown by the volume change in the syringe. [max 4]

[Total: 4]

5

(a) Absorption spectrum is obtained from the amount of each wavelength absorbed by the pigments which made up the chlorophyll of the plant.

Action spectrum produced by measuring the amount of photosynthesis by the plant for each separate wavelength. [2]

(b) Low amount of photosynthesis because not much light energy absorbed, most is reflected. [1]

(c) Evolution of oxygen, collected by water displacement. [1]

6

(a) mitochondrion [1]

(b) NADH [1]

(c) cytochrome [1]

(d) ATP [1]

[Total: 4]

7

(a) (i) rate of photosynthesis is proportional to light intensity; rate limited by amount of light available

(ii) as light intensity increases it results in significantly less increase on the rate of photosynthesis

(iii) rate of photosynthesis has levelled off, no longer limited by light (but other conditions could be limiting!). [3]

(b) Similar shape of graph, begins at origin, but graph line above the given plotted curve. [1]

[Total: 4]

Chapter 2 Nutrients

1

(a) cellulose and urea ticked
cellulose and starch ticked
urea and protein ticked
cellulose, starch, urea and protein ticked [4]

(b) bolus is regurgitated;
it is then ground up again by the molars;
(thus increased surface area)
bolus is passed to the omasum then abomasum (true stomach) to be digested further [2]

(c) mutualism (symbiosis would be accepted) [1]
Microorganisms have a habitat at suitable temperature, microorganisms have a supply of food obtained by cow. [1]
Cow obtains a supply of protein; microorganisms breakdown cellulose into substances which are useful to the cow, e.g. (volatile) fatty acids. [1]

[Total: 9]

2

Fill in the gaps in this order

gastrin; intestinal mucosa; intestinal mucosa; lipids; cholecystokinin. [5]

[Total: 5]

Chapter 3 Control in animals and plants

1

(a) (i) IAA (at these lower) concentrations is *proportional* to the angle of curvature of the stem. [1]

(ii) IAA (at these higher) concentrations is *inversely proportional* to the angle of curvature. [1]

(b) *More* IAA causes the cells at side of stem in contact with agar block to elongate more than other side.

So this side grows more strongly bending stem towards the weaker side. [2]

(c) Growth is only stimulated up to a certain high IAA concentration, after this curvature would be inhibited. [2]

[Total: 6]

2

(a) A = actin
B = myosin [2]

(b) action potential reaches sarcomere [1]

(c) both filaments slide alongside each other;
they form cross bridges;
during contraction the filaments slide together to form a shorter sarcomere [2]

[Total: 5]

3

(i) resting potential achieved; [2]
Na^+ / K^+ pump is on

(ii) Na+ / K^+ pump is off;
so Na^+ ions enter axon [2]

(iii) maximum depolarisation achieved; K^+ ions leave [2]

(iv) Na^+ ions leave due to Na^+/ K^+ pump being back on;
this is during the refractory period;
at end of this resting potential re-established;
axon membrane re-polarised [4]

[Total: 10]

Chapter 4 Homeostasis

1 (a)

	Nervous system	*Endocrine system*
Usually have longer lasting effects		✓
Have cells which secrete transmitter molecules	✓	
Cells communicate by substances in the blood plasma		✓
Use chemicals which bind to receptor sites in cell surface proteins	✓	✓
Involve the use of Na^+ and K^+ pumps	✓	

[2]

(b) homeostasis [1]

[Total: 3]

2

It increases permeability of; the collecting ducts, and the distal convoluted tubules of the nephron;

- more water drawn out of the collecting ducts;
- by the sodium and chloride ions;
- in medulla of kidney;
- so more water can be reabsorbed back into blood;
- through capillary network. (max 6) [6]

[Total: 6]

3

(a)

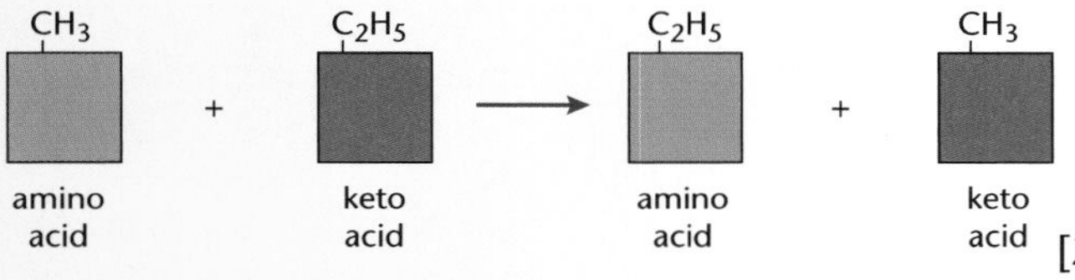

[2]

(b) (i) liver [1]

(ii) To make different amino acids with the help of the essential amino acids. [2]

[Total: 5]

4

(a) **B**, because as glucose levels rose after meals they did not decrease enough (this kept the blood glucose level too high) [1]

(b) glucose levels fell after every meal, so glucose must have entered the cells and liver [1]

(c) in pancreas;
in the β cells of islets of Langerhans (max 2) [2]

[Total: 4]

Chapter 5 Further genetics

1

(a) no immigration and no emigration; no mutations; no natural selection; true random mating; all genotypes must be equally fertile [4]

(b) (i) $q^2 = \frac{48}{160}$

$= 0.3$

$q = 0.55$

but $p + q = 1$

so $p = 1 - 0.55$

$= 0.45$

but $p^2 + 2pq + q^2 = 1$

so $0.45^2 + 2 \times 0.45 \times 0.55 + 0.55^2 = 1$

$0.2 + 0.5 + 0.3 = 1$

BB = 0.2 Bb = 0.5 bb = 0.3 [3]

(ii) BB 2000 Bb 5000 bb 3000 [2]

[Total: 9]

2

A (iv), B (iii), C (v), D, (ii), E (i). [Total: 5]

3

(a) triplet [1]

(b) codes for an amino acid, codes for stop or start [2]

(c) Addition CCG ATT CGA TAG <u>CAT</u>
Deletion CCG ATT CGA
Inversion CCG ATT CGA <u>GAT</u> [3]

[Total: 6]

4

(a) 8 or 4 pairs

(b) (i) During telophase I of meiosis the chromosomes are bivalent/ the centromeres are still intact, whereas in telophase II the chromosomes are single [1]

(ii) During telophase of mitosis the chromosomes are in pairs, whereas in telophase II of meiosis they are single (haploid) [2]

(c) the spindle contracts; pulls the centromeres apart; chromosomes begin to be pulled to both poles. [2]

[Total: 5]

Chapter 6 Biodiversity

1

A = Prokaryotae C = Protoctista E = Animalia
B = Fungi D = Plantae [5]

[Total: 5]

2

(a) **Allopatric speciation** takes place after geographical isolation;

- the rising of sea level splits a population of animals; formerly connected by land creating two islands;
- mutations take place so that two groups result in different species.

Sympatric speciation takes place through genetic variation;

- in the same geographical area;
- mutation may result in reproductive incompatibility;
- perhaps a structure in birds may lead to a different song being produced by the new variant;
- this may lead to the new variant being rejected from the mainstream group;
- breeding may be possible within its own group of variants. [6]

(b) Mate them both with a similar male, to give them a chance to produce fertile offspring.

- If they both produce offspring, take a male and female from the offspring, mate them,
- if they produce fertile offspring then original females **are** from the same species. [2]

[Total: 8]

3

(a)

	mistle-thrush	*song-thrush*
Kingdom	**Animalia**	**Animalia**
Phylum	Chordata	Chordata
Class	Aves	**Aves**
Order	Passeriformes	Passeriformes
Family	**Turdidae**	**Turdidae**
Genus	**Turdus**	**Turdus**
Species	**viscivorus**	**ericetorum**

[3]

(b) disruptive selection [1]

[Total: 4]

Chapter 7 Ecology and populations

1

(a) no significant migration;
no significant births or deaths;
marking does not have an adverse effect. [3]

(b) S = total number of individuals in the total population
S_1 = number captured in sample one, marked and released, i.e. 16
S_2 = total number captured in sample two, i.e. 12
S_3 = total marked individuals captured in sample two, i.e. 5

$\frac{S}{S_1} = \frac{S_2}{S_3}$ so, $S = \frac{S_1 \times S_2}{S_3}$

$S = \frac{16 \times 12}{5}$ Estimated no. of shrews is 38.4 [2]

(c) Not be very reliable because the numbers are quite low. High population numbers are more reliable. [1]

[Total: 6]

2

	Type of behaviour			
	kinesis	***innate***	***positive taxis***	***negative taxis***
A bolus of food reaches the top of our oesophagus and is swallowed.		✓		
Insects move from a cold dry area to a warm humid one.			✓	✓
Spring tails (insects) are subjected to increasingly hot conditions, and react by increasing speed in a number of directions. Some go towards the heat source and die.	✓			
A queen bee accepts the advances of a drone bee and is mated.		✓		
A motile alga swims towards light.			✓	

[Total:5]

3

The opposite sexes recognise each other;
the grebes will only mate with other grebes so are more likely to produce fertile offspring;
mating is synchronised, to coincide with ovulation. [3]

[Total: 3]

Chapter 8 Further effects of human pollution

1

(a) Make sure that water is **homogeneous** when taking the sample for the colorimeter. [1]

(b) Light is passed through the water sample;
the more particles there are the more light is absorbed;
so the smaller the absorbance the more the particles removed by the mussels. [2]

(c) Rate of removal of particles is higher in non-polluted water, shown by steeper gradient of graph.
Rate of particle removal decreased in polluted water, shown by the less steep gradient.
So the china clay particles seem to impede removal of some of the particles;
suggests that the organic molecules cannot be taken out as efficiently. [3]

(d) increase photosynthesis; more light able to reach plants because some particles are removed ***or*** excreta of mussels decomposed to release mineral ions e.g. NO_3^- taken in by plants. [1]

[Total: 7]

2

(a) (i) Biochemical oxygen demand [1]

(ii) the amount of **dissolved oxygen** (350g) in a cubic metres of effluent. Oxygen has depleted to this level owing to microbial organisms in the sewage. [2]

(b) B, indicates a greater bacterial presence;
which would add more minerals. [2]

[Total: 5]

Chapter 9 Microbiology

1

(a)

	Virus	*Bacterium*	*Fungus*
has membrane-bound organelles			✓
has an outer protein coat of capsomeres	✓		
has ribosomes		✓	✓
is prokaryotic		✓	
is multinucleate			✓
cannot respire	✓		
has plasmids		✓	
has an outer wall of chitin			✓
has nucleic acid but no cytoplasm	✓		

[9]

(b) Bacteriophage is a virus;
which attacks a bacterium;
in order to replicate new viruses. [2]

[Total: 11]

2

(a) (i) CCG AAU UAG CGA UUC AUG mRNA strand [1]

(ii) CCG AAT TAG CGA TTC ATG complementary DNA strand [1]

(b) reverse transcriptase [1]

[Total: 3]

3

(a) Aseptic transfer of sample from faeces to plate / use of a sterile loop; incubate at optimum temperature / 37°C. [2]

(b) Other Gram negative bacteria use lactose in agar;
which results in acid waste;

acid (below pH 6.8) causes the indicator to show these bacteria as red;

Salmonella bacteria do not use the lactose and remain colourless. [4]

(c) Bile salts (in MacConkey agar) prevent growth of Gram positive bacteria. [2]

[Total: 8]

Chapter 10 Biotechnology

1

(a) Steam sterilisation;
microorganisms cannot enter through air filter;
nutrients are pre-sterilised before entry into fermenter. [3]

(b) Contaminant microorganisms enter the fermenter;
compete with the *Penicillium*; fungus;
penicillin yield reduced. [3]

(c) Batch culture: gives best yield; less chance of contamination. [2]

[Total: 8]

2

H, A, E, G, C, D, F, B. [8]

[Total: 8]

3

(a) Beginning of fermentation process shown.
The microorganisms took time to reach maximum production but kept at this level.
Nutrients constantly added. [1]

(b) continuous
product amount reaches a constant level;
nutrients at constant level. [2]

[Total: 3]

Index